# SETS AND CLASSES

# STUDIES IN LOGIC

## AND

## THE FOUNDATIONS OF MATHEMATICS

VOLUME 84

NORTH-HOLLAND PUBLISHING COMPANY – AMSTERDAM · NEW YORK · OXFORD

# SETS AND CLASSES

## ON THE WORK BY PAUL BERNAYS

*Edited by*

GERT H. MÜLLER

*Professor of Mathematics, University of Heidelberg*

1976

NORTH-HOLLAND PUBLISHING COMPANY – AMSTERDAM · NEW YORK · OXFORD

Library of Congress Catalog Card Number 76-16791

North-Holland ISBN S 0 7204 2200 0

0 7204 2284 1

*Published by:*

North-Holland Publishing Company – Amsterdam · New York · Oxford

*Sole distributors for the U.S.A. and Canada:*

Elsevier/North-Holland Inc.
52 Vanderbilt Avenue
New York, N.Y. 10017

**Library of Congress Cataloging in Publication Data**
Main entry under title:

Sets and classes.

(Studies in logic and the foundations of mathematics; v. 84.)
Bibliography: p. 341.
Includes index.
1. Axiomatic set theory – Addresses, essays, lectures.
2. Bernays, Paul, 1888– . I. Bernays, Paul, 1888– .
II. Müller, Gert Heinz, 1923– . III. Series.
QA248.S415      511′.32      76-16791
ISBN 0-7204-2284-1

PRINTED IN THE NETHERLANDS

# PREFACE

The suggestion of republishing the main papers of Paul Bernays on set theory in one volume in the series *Studies in Logic* originated several years ago and is due to the late Professor A. Mostowski. Many plans were discussed how, in this volume, Bernays' work could be linked with the history of the concepts of set and class as well as with the present state of knowledge of class-theory. On the one hand the main lines of the history of the development of the theories of sets and classes are widely known, so that it did not seem worth while repeating them here. On the other hand the present state of knowledge is described in a well-organized way in the excellent study by Professor A. Lévy contained in *Foundations of Set Theory* by A. A. Fraenkel, Y. Bar-Hillel and A. Lévy (with collaboration of D. van Dalen), pp. 119–153, and in this volume pp. 173–215. I therefore decided to make a mental division of this volume into two parts, the *first* containing the papers of Paul Bernays in the *Journal of Symbolic Logic* and his contribution to the Fraenkel anniversary volume together with a republication of the study of A. Lévy mentioned above, and the *second* containing four original contributions on various themes connected with the role of classes in Set Theory. I am most grateful to Professor Lévy for agreeing to the inclusion of his study in this volume.

In the second part, Dr. U. Felgner's paper contains an extensive treatment of independence questions concerning various choice principles for sets and classes. Dr. T. Flannagan gives a new proof of the Novak–Mostowski theorem that the extension of ZF by predicative classes is a conservative one, including Shoenfield's result that there is a primitive recursive translation of proofs for ZF-formulae. Dr. K. Gloede takes up the question of the axiomatic use of class variables in higher reflection principles and the theory of indescribable cardinals (introduced by W. Hanf and D. S. Scott). Prof. A. Mostowski proves (using a method of Felgner) that for any given transitive denumerable model $M$ of GBC (Gödel–Bernays set theory with a set form of the axiom of choice) there exist $2^{\aleph_1}$ many transitive denumerable "class-extensions" of $M$ which are again models of GBC. Here by a class-extension $M_2$ of $M_1$ we mean an extension $M_1 \leq M_2$ such that the respective classes of sets $V_{M_1}$ and $V_{M_2}$ are equal.

Although most of the themes which are relevant to the role of classes in set theory are treated in Lévy's contribution to this volume, there are some which should have been elaborated to a greater extent in this book. The only excuse I have for such omissions is the lack of time and space; but let me at least mention some of them:

(i) *Non-finitizability.* The late Professor R. Montague was supposed to report on non-finitizability results concerning ZF and its extensions in the same language. Unfortunately his manuscript (already written up, as he told me) could not be found in what he left. (The results in question are reviewed in Lévy's paper.)

(ii) *Iterating the operation "class of . . . ".* Let $T(ZF)$ resp. $T(ZFC)$ be a form of transfinite impredicative type theory over ZF resp. ZFC, assuming class variables for any ordinal $\alpha \in On$. As is well known, assuming consistency, a theorem in the ZF-language expressing the existence of an inaccessible cardinal is not derivable in $T(ZF)$ or $T(ZFC)$, although many "new" theorems (in the ZF-language) are. The "new" theorems which are known are of "metamathematical" character (Lévy, p. 199). Is there any way of pinning down this impression in a precise way? One could look at $T(ZF(C))$ as a *conceptual hull of* ZF. How could

$$\{\phi \text{ in ZF-language} | T(ZF(C)) \vdash \phi\}$$

be characterized by some closure properties, or better completeness properties, which ZF does not enjoy?—Of course analogous considerations apply to the more familiar system of ZF without the infinity axiom, i.e. essentially number theory.

(iii) *Takeuti's approach* (cf. TAKEUTI (1969)). Extending $T(ZFC)$ by reflection principles using bound class variables of higher type, the existence of many large cardinals becomes provable (cf. K. Gloede's paper in this volume). One could even strengthen the Takeuti approach by forming a tower $T$ of systems $T_\alpha$, such that in $T_\alpha$ class variables, appropriate axiom schemata and reflection principles for all $\beta \geq \alpha$, $\beta \in On$, are available. Compared with extensions of ZF by infinity axioms (for instance by assuming the existence of ineffable cardinals), the tower of systems $T$ could be viewed as a way of extending ZF as far as possible from below. As is well known, assuming consistency, there are upper bounds for $T$ in the sense of the existence of large cardinals, which, by the way, are still compatible with $V = L$. Questions similar to those in (ii) arise and, in particular, an elegant and workable axiomatization of $T$ or of a theory a bit stronger than $T$ (using predicative "superclasses") would be valuable.

(iv) *Ultimate classes* are used by W. N. Reinhardt for axiom schemata of "projection"; here a new primitive concept (in addition to the $\epsilon$-relation) is introduced corresponding to embeddings from V into V.

Assuming consistency, these schemata provide for many very large cardinals viz. "extendable" cardinals of high degree. As is well known from Kunen's result, we are here demonstrably near to an outer limit of extensions of ZF.

(v) *Semisets.* P. Hájek and P. Vopenka are using classes in quite a different way, defining semisets as subclasses of sets in such a way that semisets which are not sets are exactly the non-comprehensive subclasses of sets. Although the motivation for this step arose from Vopenka's way of introducing forcing into Gödel–Bernays set theory, semisets are of interest in their own right. (I regret very much that it was not possible to include at least a survey paper on this subject in this book.)

(vi) *Model theoretic considerations.* In distinction to the use of classes for setting up various axiomatic extensions of ZF($C$), there is a great deal of work in progress on modelling set theoretic systems with classes (predicative or impredicative) in the presence or absence of the axiom of foundation.

(vii) *Category theory.* Looking at this theory as a theory of second order logic over the ZF-hereditarily accessible sets (like, for example, analysis over the ZF-hereditarily finite sets), the class concept comes in as in any applied type theory and no new foundational problems arise (occasionally some metamathematical schemata replacing third order logic may be necessary for this approach). However, if we do not restrict ourselves to a certain collection of sets described in advance but like to be able to bring *any* set under "the blessings of category theory" (cf. Lévy loc. cit. p. 203), or if we insist that category theory should be closed under any desired diagonalisation (self application), we have to pay some price for this, e.g. inconsistency, some sort of type raising, some restriction to partially defined objects or some artificial devices.

As far as I have understood from many discussions, Paul Bernays did not consider classes as real mathematical objects (in this respect his attitude differs from von Neumann's). In describing the *use* of the set concept (via some axiomatisation) in its *frame theoretic role for mathematics* (i.e. its outermost use), classes (as extensions of conditions) are considered as a *useful element* of our language with which we describe such an axiomatization. In addition the distinction between mathematical objects as elements of something vs. classes which are not objects (in the formal sense) becomes transparent. For this purpose the axiomatic arrangement of sets and classes as given in BERNAYS (1958) and described in Lévy's article p. 205 ff. seems to be the best adaptation. The fact that the fruitfulness of the concept of class vs. set extends far beyond its role in serving the said purpose is witnessed by the examples given above.

I wish to take this opportunity to add a final personal note: It was

Professor Paul Bernays' noble character and his deep scientific impetus to search for truth in the unknown which essentially influenced my way of thinking. I am deeply thankful to him.

## Acknowledgments

The article by P. Bernays "Zur Frage der Unendlichkeitsschemata in der axiomatischen Mengenlehre", in: *Essays on the Foundations of Mathematics*, dedicated to Prof. A. A. Fraenkel (Magnes Press, Jerusalem, 1966) pp. 3–49, was translated into English by J. Bell (Oxford) and M. Plänitz (Southampton).

Prof. Bernays was so good as to provide a list of publications and a "Kurze Biographie" which was kindly translated into English by Dr. Diana Schmidt (Heidelberg).

I am grateful to Dr. U. Felgner (Tübingen) and Dr. T. Flannagan (Louvain) for their kind help in preparing this volume. It was the continuous and unselfish readiness and help of my friend Dr. K. Gloede (Heidelberg) which enabled me to overcome many difficulties; in addition he prepared the Index and looked after the coordination of the Bibliography. I wish to express my warmest personal thanks to him.

## Postscript

After the manuscript for this volume had gone to press, we received the sad news of the untimely death of Professor Andrzej Mostowski, one of the editors of the series *Studies in Logic* and the main promoter of this volume. Having known Andrzej Mostowski for many years and cooperated with him in several organizational matters, I am filled with deep personal regret that he did not live to see the completion of the book he suggested to honor Paul Bernays.

Gert H. Müller

# CONTENTS

Paul Bernays

# PAUL BERNAYS – A SHORT BIOGRAPHY

Paul Bernays was born on October 17th, 1888 in London, the son of Julius and Sara Bernays, and spent a happy childhood in Berlin.

He attended school at the Köllnisches Gymnasium from 1895 to 1907. After that he studied at the Technische Hochschule Charlottenburg for six months and then transferred to the University of Berlin. He studied there for four semesters, then for six more in Göttingen, majoring in mathematics with philosophy and theoretical physics as subsidiaries. At the University in Berlin he studied mainly under Issai Schur, Landau, Frobenius and Schottky in mathematics, Riehl, Stumpf and Cassirer in philosophy and Max Planck in physics; in Göttingen he attended lectures on mathematics chiefly by Hilbert, Landau, Weyl and Klein, on physics by Voigt and Born, and on philosophy mainly by Leonard Nelson. It was through Nelson that he took up closer acquaintance with the Neu-Fries'sche Schule, and his first philosophical papers were published in this setting.

In the Spring of 1912 he received his doctorate under Edmund Landau with a dissertation on the analytic number theory of binary quadratic forms. At the end of the same year he obtained his Habilitation in Zürich, where Zermelo was professor; his Habilitationsschrift was on function theory and had to do with Picard's theorem.

From the end of 1912 till Autumn 1917 he was a Privatdozent at the University of Zürich. During this period he got to know Georg Pólya, both as a friend and intellectually; visited Einstein a few times; and enjoyed stimulating social occasions at Hermann Weyl's.

At the beginning of the First World War he worked on a reply to a critique by Alfred Kastil of the Fries philosophy. This reply was not published (by the time there was an opportunity to have it published he no longer agreed with all of it).

In the Autumn of 1917, on the occasion of his lecture in Zürich on "Axiomatisches Denken", Hilbert invited Bernays to work with him as his assistant on his investigations of the foundations of arithmetic, which he was then resuming. This brought him back to Göttingen. His work with Hilbert consisted on the one hand of helping him to prepare his lectures and making notes of some of them, and on the other hand of talking over his research, which gave rise to a lot of discussions.

xi

Alongside this work for Hilbert he was soon also giving lectures on various general areas of mathematics at the University of Göttingen, at which he obtained the venia legendi in 1919, with a Habilitationsschrift on the axiomatics of the propositional calculus of "Principia Mathematica"; this, however, was not published until 1926, and then only in abridged form.

From 1922 on he was extraordinary professor without tenure at Göttingen. He himself also went to lectures, among others to those of Emmy Noether, van der Waerden and Herglotz, preferring to learn by listening to a lecture delivered personally rather than by reading. During term-time he enjoyed the intellectually stimulating company of his colleagues; the vacations were spent with the family in Berlin, now diminished by the loss of his father in 1916.

In 1933 Bernays, as a "non-Aryan", was deprived of the venia legendi of the University of Göttingen. Hilbert employed him privately as his assistant for six months, then the family moved to Switzerland, whose nationality they had inherited from Bernays' father.

For the summer semester of 1934, and several times after that, Bernays received a temporary teaching post at the ETH (Eidgenössische Technische Hochschule) Zürich. For the academic year 1935/36 he was invited to the Institute for Advanced Study in Princeton, where he gave lectures on mathematical logic and axiomatic set theory. In set theory he lectured on his own axiomatisation, thought out a few years before on the basis of von Neumann's axiom system. He had presented this axiomatisation in Göttingen, at the end of a lecture on set theory in 1931, and also, before that, in a talk given to the Mathematical Society of Göttingen, but had hesitated to publish it because he felt that axiomatisation was, to a certain extent, artificial. He expressed this feeling to Alonzo Church, who replied with a consoling smile: "That cannot be otherwise"; this persuaded him to publish. Before publication he made certain changes in the terminology and in the definitions. In particular, he altered his original definition of ordered pair in favour of Kuratowski's, and adopted Raphael Robinson's definition of ordinal number instead of the one he had had before.

In the Autumn of 1939 Bernays was awarded the venia legendi of the ETH Zürich, and in the Autumn of 1945 he became extraordinary professor there. His lectures at the ETH were on: Algebraic number fields, set theory, elliptic functions, geometrical constructions and the concept of number, elements of analysis, mathematical logic, theory of the Lebesgue integral, introduction of proof theory, lattice theory, constitution of the continuum. Here too he went to lectures given by various colleagues, among others to those of Michel Plancherel, Beno

Eckmann and Eduard Stiefel; and he participated in the seminars of Heinz Hopf, whom he knew from his Göttingen days and with whom he was friendly.

In Bernays' study of Kant, Fries and Nelson, he had become acquainted with Ferdinand Gonseth and discovered much in common between their points of view. This led him to a closer association and participation in several symposia ("Entretiens") organized by Gonseth and to join the editorial board of the philosophical review "Dialectica", which Gonseth had founded. He also became a member of the International Society for the Philosophy of Science founded by Père S. Dockx, and was its president for two years.

During the period from 1956 to 1965 Bernays was invited to the University of Pennsylvania in Philadelphia as visiting professor three times, and to the Institute for Advanced Study in Princeton in 1959/60.

Paul Bernays, who now lives in Zürich, still maintains close contact with many of the friends he has made during his long academic life.

# KURZE BIOGRAPHIE

Am 17. Oktober 1888 bin ich in London geboren als Sohn von Julius Bernays und Sara Bernays geb. Brecher. In Berlin bin ich aufgewachsen. Wir hatten ein schönes Familienleben.

Ich besuchte das Köllnische Gymnasium (mit Vorschule) 1895–1907. Das Studium begann ich an der Technischen Hochschule Charlottenburg, wechselte aber nach einem halben Jahr zur Berliner Universität. Dort studierte ich vier Semester und weitere sechs in Göttingen, und zwar im Hauptfach Mathematik, daneben Philosophie und theoretische Physik. Meine hauptsächlichsten Lehrer an der Berliner Universität waren in Mathematik Issai Schur, Landau, Frobenius, Schottky, in Philosophie Riehl, Stumpf, Cassirer, in Physik Planck.

In Göttingen hörte ich mathematische Vorlesungen hauptsächlich bei Hilbert, Landau, Weyl und Klein, Vorlesungen über Physik bei Voigt und Born, und philosophische Vorlesungen vornehmlich bei Leonard Nelson.

Durch Nelson kam ich in den Kreis der Neu-Fries'schen Schule, in deren Rahmen auch meine ersten philosophischen Publikationen erfolgten.

Im Frühjahr 1912 promovierte ich bei Edmund Landau mit einer Dissertation über die analytische Zahlentheorie der binären quadratischen Formen. Schon am Ende des gleichen Jahres hatte ich die Gelegenheit zur Habilitation in Zürich, wo Zermelo Ordinarius für Mathematik war. Meine Habilitationsschrift war eine funktionentheoretische Arbeit aus dem Gebiet des Picard'schen Satzes.

Von Ende 1912 bis zum Herbst 1917 war ich Privatdozent an der Universität Zürich.

In dieser Zeit wurde ich mit Georg Pólya bekannt, mit dem ich mich befreundete und von dem ich viel geistige Anregung erhielt.—1913 war ich ein paarmal bei Einstein zu Besuch.—Bei Hermann Weyl gab es anregende Geselligkeiten.

In der Anfangszeit des ersten Weltkrieges arbeitete ich an einer Erwiderung auf eine von Alfred Kastil verfasste Kritik an der Fries'schen Philosophie. Diese Erwiderung ist jedoch nicht publiziert worden. (Zu der Zeit, als sie hätte veröffentlicht werden können, war ich mit Etlichem nicht mehr einverstanden.)

Im Herbst 1917 wurde ich von Hilbert anlässlich seines in Zürich gehaltenen Vortrages "Axiomatisches Denken" aufgefordert, an seinen wieder aufgenommenen Untersuchungen über die Grundlagen der Arithmetik als sein Assistent mitzuwirken. So kam ich 1917 zum zweiten Mal nach Göttingen. Meine Tätigkeit bei Hilbert bestand teils in der Mithilfe bei der Vorbereitung seiner Vorlesungen und auch der Ausarbeitung mancher Vorlesungen sowie in den Besprechungen über seine Untersuchungen, wobei es viele Diskussionen gab.

Neben dieser Beschäftigung für Hilbert hatte ich bald auch eine Lehrtätigkeit an der Universität Göttingen, an der ich 1919 die venia legendi erhielt. Die hierfür 1918 von mir eingereichte Habilitationsschrift war eine axiomatische Arbeit über den Aussagenkalkul der "Principia Mathematica". Ich versäumte damals, mich um eine baldige Publikation der Arbeit zu bemühen. Sie erschien erst 1926, und auch nur in gekürzter Fassung.

Ich hatte in Göttingen die Gelegenheit, über verschiedene allgemeine Gebiete der Mathematik Vorlesungen zu halten, die in den Jahren kurz nach dem 1. Weltkrieg auch gut besucht waren. (Von 1922 an war ich nichtbeamteter ausserordentlicher Professor.)

Meinerseits hörte ich mir auch Vorlesungen an, so von Emmy Noether, van der Waerden und von Herglotz. (Ich lernte meist lieber durch persönliches Hören als durch Lesen.)

Mit vielen Fachgenossen hatte ich Gedankenaustausch. Die Zeit der akademischen Ferien verbrachte ich regelmässig in Berlin bei der Familie.—Mein Vater lebte damals nicht mehr. Er war schon Ende 1916 gestorben.

1933 wurde mir als "Nicht-Arier" die venia legendi an der Universität Göttingen entzogen. Hilbert behielt mich noch privatim ein halbes Jahr als Assistent. Unsere Familie siedelte aber dann nach der Schweiz über. Wir hatten alle die Schwiezer Staatsangehörigkeit von meinem Vater her, der in seiner Jugend Schweizer geworden war.

Für das Sommersemester 1934 und noch mehrmals danach erhielt ich an der ETH Zürich einen Lehrauftrag. Für das akademische Jahr 1935/36 wurde ich an das Institute for Advanced Study in Princeton eingeladen, wo ich Vorlesungen über mathematische Logik und axiomatische Mengenlehre hielt. Von der Mengenlehre trug ich damals insbesondere über diejenige Axiomatisierung vor, die ich mir einige Jahre zuvor als Umgestaltung des von Neumann'schen Axiomensystems zurechtgelegt hatte, die aber damals noch nicht publiziert war. Ich hatte in Göttingen in einer Vorlesung über Mengenlehre 1931 in einem Schlussteil diese Axiomatisierung vorgeführt, und zuvor auch schon in der Göttinger Mathematischen Gesellschaft darüber vorgetragen. Dass ich mich so lange nicht zum Publizieren entschloss, rührte zum Teil davon her, dass ich die Axiomatisierung in einem gewissen Masse als etwas Künstliches empfand. Ich äusserte auch diesen Gedanken gegenüber Alonzo Church, der mir mit einem tröstlichen Lächeln erwiderte: "That cannot be otherwise." Daraufhin habe ich dann bald die Publikation beschlossen.

Anlässlich der Publikation habe ich dann noch gewisse Aenderungen in der Terminologie und in den Definitionen vorgenommen. Insbesondere habe ich meine vorherige Definition des geordneten Paares zugunsten des Verfahrens von Kuratowski abgeändert und die Definition der Ordinalzahl, anstelle einer vorherigen, von Raphael M. Robinson übernommen.

Im Herbst 1939 wurde mir die venia legendi an der ETH Zürich erteilt, und im Herbst 1945 wurde ich dort ausserordentlicher Professor. Meine Vorlesungen an der ETH betrafen folgende Gebiete der Mathematik: Algebraische Zahlkörper, Mengenlehre, Elliptische Funktionen, Geometrische Konstruktionen und Zahlbegriff, Grundbegriffe der Analysis, Mathematische Logik, Theorie des Lebesgue'schen Integrals, Einführung in die Beweistheorie, Zahlentheorie, Theorie der Verbände, Konstitution des Kontinuums.

Ich meinerseits hörte noch Vorlesungen bei verschiedenen Kollegen, so bei Michel Plancherel, bei Beno Eckmann und bei Eduard Stiefel. Auch aus Seminarien von Heinz Hopf, den ich schon von Göttingen her kannte und mit dem ich befreundet war, habe ich Etliches gelernt.

Im Philosophischen kam ich in näheren Kontakt mit Ferdinand Gonseth, an dessen philosophischen Seminarien ich mich mehrmals beteiligte. Ich war aufgrund meiner gedanklichen Auseinandersetzungen mit der Kant-Fries-Nelson'schen Philosophie den Ansichten Gonseth's sehr nahe gekommen, und so schloss ich mich seiner philosophischen Schule an. Seitdem nahm ich an etlichen von Gonseth veranstalteten Symposien ("Entretiens") teil und gehöre dem leitenden Komitee der von ihm gegründeten philosophischen Revue "Dialectica" an. Auch wurde ich Mitglied der von Père S. Dockx gegründeten Internationalen Gesellschaft für Philosphie der Wissenschaften; während zweier Jahre war ich deren Präsident.

In der Zeit von 1956 bis 1965 wurde ich dreimal als "visiting professor" an die University of Pennsylvania in Philadelphia und 1959/60 an das Institute for Advanced Study in Princeton eingeladen.

Gross ist die Zahl der Fachgenossen in meinem engeren und weiteren Fachgebiet, mit denen ich in persönliche Beziehung gekommen bin, und von denen ich Anregungen empfangen habe. Mit so manchen von ihnen bin ich auch in freundschaftliche Beziehung gekommen.

*Paul Bernays*

# LIST OF PUBLICATIONS*
## of Paul Bernays

### 1910–1919

1. "Das Moralprinzip bei Sidgwick und bei Kant", *Abhandlungen der Friesschen Schule*, III. Band, 3. Heft (1910).
2. "Über die Darstellung von positiven, ganzen Zahlen durch die primitiven, binären quadratischen Formen einer nicht-quadratischen Diskriminante", Dissertation, Göttingen (1912).
3. "Zur elementaren Theorie der Landauschen Funktion $\phi(\alpha)$", *Vierteljahresschrift der Naturforschenden Gesellschaft in Zürich* **58** (1913), Habilitationsschrift Universität Zürich.
4. "Über den transzendentalen Idealismus", *Abhandlungen der Friesschen Schule*, IV. Band, 2. Heft (1913), 367–394.
5. "Über die Bedenklichkeiten der neueren Relativitätstheorie", *Abhandlungen der Friesschen Schule*, IV. Band, 3. Heft (1913).
6. "Zum Beweise der Legendreschen Bedingung in der Variationsrechnung", *Archiv der Mathematik und Physik*, III. Reihe XXVII (1918).

### 1920–1929

7. "Über Hilberts Gedanken zur Grundlegung der Arithmetik". *Jahresbericht der Deutschen Mathematiker-Vereinigung*, XXXI, 1. Abteilung, Heft 1/4 (1922), 10–19 (lecture at the mathematical congress in Jena, Sept. 1921).
8. "Zur mathematischen Grundlegung der kinetischen Gastheorie", *Mathematische Annalen* **85** (1922), 242–255.
9. "Die Bedeutung Hilberts für die Philosophie der Mathematik", *Die Naturwissenschaften* **10** (1922), 93–99.
10. "Erwiderung auf die Note von Herrn Aloys Müller: 'Über Zahlen als Zeichen'", *Mathematische Annalen* **90** (1923), 159–163.
11. "Axiomatische Untersuchung des Aussagenkalkuls der 'Principia Mathematica'", *Mathematische Zeitschrift* **25** (1926), 305–320

*Kindly prepared by Paul Bernays for this volume; the distinction, originally proposed by him, between publications on mathematics and foundations of mathematics on the one hand and those on general philosophy on the other hand, was abandoned by the editor to make for ease of reference. In most cases this distinction can be reextracted by a look at the titles.

(Habilitationsschrift, Universität Göttingen (1918); abridged for publication).

12. "Probleme der theoretischen Logik", *Unterrichtsblätter für Mathematik und Naturwissenschaften* 33 (1927), 369–377.
13. (With M. Schönfinkel) "Zum Entscheidungsproblem der mathematischen Logik", *Mathematische Annalen* 99 (1928), 342–372.
14. "Über Nelsons Stellungnahme in der Philosophie der Mathematik", *Die Naturwissenschaften*, 16. Jahrgang, Heft 9 (1928).
15. "Die Grundbegriffe der reinen Geometrie in ihrem Verhältnis zu Anschauung" (criticism of a book with the same title by R. Strohal), *Die Naturwissenschaften*, 16. Jahrgang, Heft 12 (1928), 197–203.

1930–1939

16. "Die Grundgedanken der Friesschen Philosophie in ihrem Verhältnis zum heutigen Stand der Wissenschaft", *Abhandlungen der Friesschen Schule*, neue Folge, Band V, Heft 2 (1930), 99–113.
17. "Die-Philosophie der Mathematik und die Hilbertsche Beweistheorie", *Blätter für deutsche Philosophie* 4 (1930), 326–367.
18. "Methoden des Nachweises von Widerspruchsfreiheit und ihre Grenzen", in: *Internationaler Kongress Zürich* II (1932), 342–343 (Orell Füssli Verlag, Zürich-Leipzig).
19. (With D. Hilbert) "*Grundlagen der Mathematik*", Band. I (Springer, Berlin, 1934, 2nd edition 1968) XV + 473 pp.
20. "Hilberts Untersuchungen über die Grundlagen der Arithmetik", in: *David Hilbert—Gesammelte Abhandlungen*, 3. Band (Springer, Berlin, 1935), 196–216.
21. "Sur le platonisme dans les mathématiques", *L'Enseignement Mathématique* XXXIV (1935/36), 52–69.
22. "Quelques points essentiels de la métamathématiques", *L'Enseignement Mathématique* XXXIV (1935/36), 70–95.
23. "Logical Calculus". Mimeographed lectures at the Institute for Advanced Study 1935/36, Princeton (1936) 125 pp.
24. "Grundsatzliche Betrachtungen zur Erkenntnistheorie". *Abhandlungen der Friesschen Schule*, neue Folge 6, Heft 3/4 (1937), 279–290.
25. "Thesen und Bemerkungen zu den philosophischen Fragen und zur Situation der logisch-mathematischen Grundlagenforschung", in: *Travaux du IX$^e$ Congrès international de Philosophie* (Hermann et Cie., Paris, 1937), 104–110.
26. "A system of axiomatic set theory", Part I, *Journal of Symbolic Logic* 2 (1937), 65–77.
27. "Zum Begriff der Dialektik". *Dialectica* 1 (1946), 172–175.

28. (With D. Hilbert) "Grundlagen der Mathematik", Band II (Springer, Berlin, 1939, 2nd edition 1970), XII + 561 pp.

## 1940–1949

29. "Sur les questions méthodologiques actuelles de la théorie Hilbertienne de la démonstration", in: *Entretiens de Zürich 1938* (Leemann & Co., Zürich, 1941), 144–152.
30. "A system of axiomatic set theory", Part II, *Journal of Symbolic Logic* 6 (1941), 1–17.
31. Part III, ibid. 7 (1942), 65–89.
32. Part IV, ibid. 7 (1942), 133–145.
33. Part V, ibid. 8 (1943), 89–106.
34. "Quelques points de vue concernant le problème de l'évidence", *Synthese* V (1946), 321–326.
35. "Grundsätzliches zur 'philosophie ouverte'", Les deuxièmes Entretiens de Zürich, *Dialectica* 6 (1948).
36. "Die Erneuerung der rationalen Aufgabe", in: *Proceedings of the Xth international congress of philosophy*, Amsterdam (1948), 42–50.
37. "Über die Ausdehnung des Begriffes der Komplementarität auf die Philosophie", *Synthese* VII (1948/49), 66–70.
38. "A system of axiomatic set theory", Part VI, *Journal of Symbolic Logic* 13 (1948), 65–79.
39. "Bemerkungen zu den Grundlagen der Geometrie", in: *Courant Anniversary Volume* (1948), 29–44.

## 1950–1959

40. "Logique et Science", in: *XVI^e Congrès Internationale de Philosophie de science*, Paris 1949 (Hermann & Cie., Paris, 1951), 1–5.
41. "Mathematische Existenz und Widerspruchsfreiheit", in: *Etudes de Philosophie des sciences en hommage à Ferdinand Gonseth* (Editions du Griffon, Neuchatel 1950), 11–25.
42. "Über das Induktionsschema in der rekursiven Zahlentheorie", in: *Kontrolliertes Denken, Festschrift für Wilhelm Britzelmayr*, eds. A. Menne, A. Wilhelmy and H. Angstl (Freiburg (Breisgau)—München, 1951), 10–17.
43. "Über die Verwendung der Polygoninhalte an Stelle eines Spiegelungsaxioms in der Axiomatik der Planimetrei", *Elemente der Mathematik* VIII/5 (1953), 102–107.
44. "Über die Friessche Annahme einer Wiederbeobachtung der unmittelbaren Erkenntnis", in: *Leonard Nelson zum Gedächtnis* (Verlag öffentliches Leben, Frankfurt a/M.-Göttingen, 1953), 113–131.

45. "A system of axiomatic set theory", Part VII, *Journal of Symbolic Logic* **19** (1954), 81–96.
46. "Die Mathematik als ein zugleich Vertrautes und Unbekanntes", Vortrag zur Gedächtnisfeier für B. Nieuwentijt in Purmerend, *Synthese* **IX** (1954), 465–471.
47. "Zur Beurteilung der Situation in der beweistheoretischen Forschung", *Revue Internationale de Philosophie* **27/28** (1954), 1–5.
48. "Über den Zusammenhang des Herbrand'schen Satzes mit den neueren Ergebnissen von Schütte und Stenius", Proc. International Congress Amsterdam (1954).
49. "Bemerkungen zu der Betrachtung von Alexander Wittenberg: über adäquate Problemstellung in der mathematischen Grundlagenforschung", *Dialectica* **8** (1954), 147–151.
50. "Betrachtungen über das Vollständigkeitsaxiom und verwandte Axiome", *Mathematische Zeitschrift* **63** (1955), 219–229.
51. "Zur Frage der Anknüpfung an die Kantische Erkenntnistheorie", *Dialectica* **9** (1955), 23–65 and 195–221.
52. "Vereinfachte Begründung der Proportionenlehre". Supplement II to the 8th edition of Hilbert's 'Grundlagen der Geometrie', Stuttgart (1956), 241–245.
53. "Betrachtungen zum Paradoxen von Thoralf Skolem", Avhandlinger utgitt av Det Norske Videnskaps-Akademi i Oslo, Oslo (1957), 3–9, Aschehoug.
54. "Von der Syntax der Sprache zur Philosophie der Wissenschaften", *Dialectica* **11** (1957) 233–246.
55. "Remarques sur le problème de la décision en logique élémentaire", Le Raisonnement en mathématiques et en sciences expérimentales, Editions du Centre National de la Recherche Scientifique, Paris (1958), 39–43.
56. *Axiomatic set theory* (with a historical introduction by Abraham Fraenkel) (North-Holland, Amsterdam 1958), VIII + 226 pp.
57. "Über eine natürliche Erweiterung des Relationskalkuls", in: *Constructivity in Mathematics*, ed. A. Heyting, Proceedings of the Colloquium held at Amsterdam, 1957 (North-Holland, Amsterdam, 1959), 1–14.
58. "Die Mannigfaltigkeit der Direktiven für die Gestaltung geometrischer Axiomensysteme", in: *The Axiomatic Method*, eds. L. Henkin, P. Suppes and A. Tarski; Proceedings of an international Symposium at Berkeley 1957–58 (North-Holland, Amsterdam, 1959), 1–15.
59. "Betrachtungen zu Ludwig Wittgensteins 'Bemerkungen über die Grundlagen der Mathematik'", *Ratio* **1** (1959), 1–18.

1960–1969

60. "Charakterzüge der Philosophie Gonseths", *Dialectica* **14** (1960), 151–156.
61. "Zur Rolle der Sprache in erkenntnistheoretischer Hinsicht", *Synth-ese* **XIII** (1961), 185–200.
62. "Die hohen Unendlichkeiten und die Axiomatik der Mengenlehre", in: *Infinitistic Methods*, Proceedings of the Symposium on Foundations of Mathematics, Warsaw, 2–9 September 1959 (Pergamon Press, Oxford, 1961), 11–20.
63. "Zur Frage der Unendlichkeitsschemata in der axiomatischen Mengenlehre", in: *Essays on the foundations of mathematics*, dedicated to Prof. A. A. Fraenkel (Magnes Press, Jerusalem, 1961), 3–49.
64. "Remarks about formalization and models", in: *Logic, Methodology and Philosophy of Science*, Proceedings of the 1960 international Congress, eds. E. Nagel, P. Suppes and A. Tarski (Stanford University Press, Stanford, Calif., 1962), 176–180.
65. Supplements to the 9th edition of 'Grundlagen der Geometrie' (Teubner, Stuttgart, 1962).
66. "Über den Unterschied zwischen realistischer und konservativer Tendenz in der heutigen theoretischen Physik", Coll. de l'Académie internat. de philosphie des Sciences, Paris 1961, Office internat. de Librairie (1962), 17–21.
67. "Remarks to 'The End of a Phase'" (Remarks to an article by Errol E. Harris) *Dialectica* **16** (1963), 49–50.
68. "Reflections on Karl Popper's Epistemology", in: *The Critical Approach*, in Honor of Karl R. Popper's 60th Birthday, ed. Mario Bunge (The Free Press, Glencoe, 1964), 32–44.
69. "Betrachtungen zum Sequenzen-Kalkül", in: *Contributions to Logic and Methodology, in Honor of J. M. Bochenski*, eds. Anna-Teresa Tymieniecka and Charles Parsons (North-Holland, Amsterdam, 1965), 1–44.
70. "Some Empirical Aspects of Mathematics" (translated from the French), in: *Information and Prediction in Science*, Proceedings of a Symposium, Brussels 1962, eds. S. Dockx and P. Bernays (Academic Press, New York and London, 1965), 123–128.
71. "Gedanken zu dem Buch 'Bildung und Mathematik (Mathematik als exemplarisches Gymnasialfach)' von Alexander Israel Wittenberg", *Dialectica* **20** (1966), 27–41.
72. "Scope and Limits of Axiomatics", in: *Lecture at the Delaware Seminar in the Foundations of Physics*, ed. M. Bunge, 1967 (Springer, Berlin–Heidelberg, 1967), 188–201.

73. Article on Hilbert's work on foundations in: *The Encyclopedia of Philosophy* (Macmillan, 1967).
74. "What do some recent results in Set Theory suggest?" Lecture with discussion at the International Conference in the Philosophy of Science in London, 1965, in: *Problems in the Philosophy of Mathematics* (North-Holland, Amsterdam, 1967), 109–117.
75. "On the original Gentzen Consistency Proof for Number Theory", in: *Proceedings of the Summer Conference on Intuitionism and Proof Theory*, Buffalo, N.Y. (1968), 409–417.
76. "Remarks to the paper by Dr. Sandra Rosenthal: 'The Cognitive Status of Theoretical Terms'", *Dialectica* **22** (1968).
77. "Bemerkungen zur Philosophie der Mathematik", in: *Akten des XIV. Internationalen Kongresses für Philosophie*, Wien, Sept. 1968, vol. VI (Herder, Wien, 1969), 192–198.

1970–1976

78. "Die schematische Korrespondenz und die idealisierten Strukturen", *Dialectica* **24** (1970), 53–66.
79. Introductory remarks to 'Leonard Nelson. Gesammelte Schriften in neun Bänden':

    Vol. I, 'Zum Geleit' (1970), IX–XI.

    Vol. III, Introduction to 'Bemerkungen über die nichteuklidische Geometrie und den Ursprung der mathematischen Gewissheit' (1974), 4–6;

    An introduction to 'Bemerkungen zu den Paradoxien von Russell und Burali-Forti' (1974), 96–97;

    Critical remarks in the footnotes to this paper.
80. "Causality, Determinism and Probability", in: *Perspectives in Quantum Theory – Essays in Honor of Alfred Landé*, eds. Wolfgang Yourgrau and Alwyn van der Merwe (MIT Press, Cambridge, Mass., 1971), 260–269.
81. "Bemerkungen zur Rolle der Methode in den Wissenschaften", Colloque 'Problèmes de Méthodologie', Lausanne 1969, *Archives de Philosophie* **34** (1971), 575–580.
82. "Zum Symposium über die Grundlagen der Mathematik, *Dialectica* **25** (1971), 171–195.
83. "Bemerkung über eine Ordnung der zahlentheoretischen Funktionen mittels eines additiven 0–1-Masses für die Mengen natürlicher Zahlen", in: *Theory of sets and topology, in Honor of Felix Hausdorff (1868–1942)*, eds. G. Asser, J. Flachsmeyer and W. Rinow (VEB Deutscher Verlag der Wissenschaften, Berlin, 1972), 39–43.

84. "Concerning rationality", in: *The Philosophy of Karl Popper*, Vol. I, ed. Paul A. Schilpp (The Library of Living Philosophers, Vol. XIV), Open Court, La Salle, Ill. (1974), 597–605.

85. "Zu den Maximalprinzipien der Mengenlehre", in: *Proceedings of the Tarski-Symposium*, June 1971 (Am. Math. Soc., Providence, R.I., 1974), 289–296.

86. "Zu der Abhandlung von Raymond L. Weiss 'Historicism and Science: Thoughts on Quine'", *Dialectica* **29** (1975), 167–172.

87. "Mathematics as a domain of theoretical science and of mental experience", in: *Logic Colloquium '73*, Proceedings of the Logic Colloquium, Bristol, July 1973, eds. H. E. Rose and J. C. Shepherdson (North-Holland, Amsterdam, 1975), 1–4.

88. *Abhandlungen zur Philosophie der Mathematik* (Wiss. Buchgesellschaft, Darmstadt, 1976) X + 213 pp. (containing the papers 12, 17, 25, 41, 46, 53, 58, 59, 61, 77, 78 and 82, and German translations of 21 and 34).

89. "A system of axiomatic set theory", this volume, 1–120 (slightly revised version of 26, 30–33, 38 and 45).

90. "On the problem of schemata of infinity in axiomatic set theory", this volume, 121–172 (Revised version of 63, translated into English).

91. "Bemerkungen zu Lorenzen's Stellungnahme in der Philosophie der Mathematik", in: *Festschrift zum 60. Geburtstag von Paul Lorenzen*, ed. K. Lorenz, to appear.

# A SYSTEM OF AXIOMATIC SET THEORY*

## Paul BERNAYS
### *Zurich, Switzerland*


**PART I****

Introduction. The system of axioms for set theory to be exhibited in this paper[1] is a modification of the axiom system due to von Neumann.[2] In particular it adopts the principal idea of von Neumann, that the elimination of the undefined notion of a *property* ("definite Eigenschaft"),[3] which occurs in the original axiom system of Zermelo,[4] can be accomplished in such a way as to make the resulting axiom system elementary, in the sense of being formalizable in the logical calculus of first order, which contains no other bound variables than individual variables and no accessory rule of inference (as, for instance, a scheme of complete induction).[5]

The purpose of modifying the von Neumann system is to remain nearer to the structure of the original Zermelo system and to utilize at the same time some of the set-theoretic concepts of the Schröder logic and of *Principia mathematica* which have become familiar to logicians. As will be seen, a considerable simplification results from this arrangement.

The theory is not set up as a pure formalism, but rather in the usual manner of elementary axiom theory, where we have to deal with propositions which are understood to have a meaning, and where the reference to the domain of facts to be axiomatized is suggested by the names for the kinds of individuals and for the fundamental predicates.

On the other hand, from the formulation of the axioms and the methods used in making inferences from them, it will be obvious that the theory can be formalized by means of the logical calculus of first order ("Prädikatenkalkul" or

---

* Almost unchanged reproduction of seven papers under the same general title. Reprinted by permission of the publisher, the Association for Symbolic Logic, from *The Journal of Symbolic Logic*, Volumes **2** (1937) 65–77; **6** (1941) 1–17; **7** (1942) 65–89, 133–145; **8** (1943) 89–106; **13** (1948) 65–79; **19** (1954) 81–96.

** Cf. *J. Symbolic Logic* **2** (1937) 65–77.

[1] This system was first introduced by the author in a lecture on "Mathematical Logic" at the University of Göttingen, 1929–30.

[2] VON NEUMANN (1925), (1928), (1929).

[3] This elimination was first carried out, in two different ways, by Th. Skolem and A. Fraenkel. See SKOLEM (1923) and FRAENKEL (1922), (1925), (1927), (1928).

[4] ZERMELO (1908a).

[5] It may be observed that the von Neumann axiom system for set theory is the first example of an axiom system which is at once adequate to arithmetic and elementary in the sense just described.

"engere Funktionenkalkül") with the addition of the formalism of equality and the $\iota$-symbol[6] for "descriptions" (in the sense of Whitehead and Russell).

### 1. Fundamental concepts, notations, derived notions.

According to the leading idea of the von Neumann set theory we have to deal with two kinds of individuals, which we may distinguish as *sets* and *classes*. The distinction may be thought of in this way, that a set is a multitude forming a proper thing, whereas a class is a predicate regarded only with respect to its extension.

We shall indicate this distinction by using small italics to refer to sets and capital italics for classes (the letters $a, \cdots, t, A, \cdots, T$ will be used as free variables, $u, \cdots, z, U, \cdots, Z$ as bound variables). Sometimes a letter will be chosen as a proper name (symbol) for a particular set or class, and in this case a small Greek letter will be taken for a set, a capital Greek letter for a class.

To denote expressions (including, in particular, expressions consisting of a single letter), German letters will be used.

"Being the same individual" will be denoted by the symbol $=$. As in the usual postulate theory, the identity, $=$, is not regarded as a primitive predicate of the system, but as a logical concept immediately connected with the idea of an individual.

Corresponding to the two kinds of individuals we have two primitive relations, one between sets,

$$a \epsilon b,$$

to be read *a is in b* or *a is an element of b*, and one between a set and a class,

$$a \eta B,$$

to be read, *a belongs to B* or *a is an element of B*. We assume that for any sets $a, b$ it is uniquely determined whether $a \epsilon b$ or not, and that for a set $a$ and a class $B$ it is always uniquely determined whether $a \eta B$ or not.

Observe that a class never occurs as an element; nor are there elements of any other kind than sets.[7]

The relations $\epsilon, \eta$ are the only primitive predicates of our system. Some derived notions are immediately obtained from them by applying logical terms. Thus $a \in b$, or *a is a subset of b*, means that every element of $a$ is also an element of $b$; and $A \in B$, or *A is a subclass of B*, means that every element of $A$ is also an element of $B$; and the relations $a \in B$ and $A \in b$ are to be defined in quite the same way. Likewise, $a \subset b$, or *a is a proper subset of b*, means that $a \in b$ but not $b \in a$; and $A \subset B$, or *A is a proper subclass of B*, means that $A \in B$ but not

---

[6] Cf. HILBERT and BERNAYS (1934), §8.

[7] The original Zermelo system admits the existence of elements which are not sets. Zermelo insists on this point for the sake of generality. And in his axiomatization of set theory ZERMELO (1930) he explicitly introduces *Urelemente*.

In the systems of Fraenkel and v. Neumann, on the other hand, it is assumed that every element is a set. This idea of avoiding elements which are not sets was apparently first suggested by P. Finsler.

Whether the one procedure or the other is preferable depends on the purpose for which the system is intended.

$B \mathbin{\text{-}\in} A$; and the relations $a \mathbf{C} B$ and $A \mathbf{C} b$ are to be defined in the same way.

That the set $a$ *represents* the class $A$ means that $a \mathbin{\text{-}\in} A$ and $A \mathbin{\text{-}\in} a$. A set $c$ is said to be *reflexive* if $c \epsilon c$. A set $c$ is said to be *transitive* if every element of an element of $c$ is also an element of $c$. A set or class is said to be *empty* if there is no element of it.

In order to make clear the logical character of these definitions, it is desirable to write them down by means of the logical symbols:

| $\overline{\mathfrak{A}}$ | "Not $\mathfrak{A}$" | (negation) |
|---|---|---|
| $\mathfrak{A}$ & $\mathfrak{B}$ | "$\mathfrak{A}$ and $\mathfrak{B}$" | (conjunction) |
| $\mathfrak{A} \vee \mathfrak{B}$ | "$\mathfrak{A}$ or $\mathfrak{B}$" | (disjunction) |
| $\mathfrak{A} \to \mathfrak{B}$ | "If $\mathfrak{A}$, then $\mathfrak{B}$" | (implication) |
| $(\mathfrak{w})\mathfrak{A}(\mathfrak{w})$ | "For every set $\mathfrak{w}$, $\mathfrak{A}(\mathfrak{w})$" | (universal quantification) |
| $(E\mathfrak{w})\mathfrak{A}(\mathfrak{w})$ | "For some set $\mathfrak{w}$, $\mathfrak{A}(\mathfrak{w})$" | (existential quantification) |

Definition of

$$
\begin{aligned}
a \mathbin{\text{-}\in} b: & \quad (x)(x \epsilon a \to x \epsilon b). \\
a \mathbin{\text{-}\in} B: & \quad (x)(x \epsilon a \to x \eta B). \\
A \mathbin{\text{-}\in} b: & \quad (x)(x \eta A \to x \epsilon b). \\
A \mathbin{\text{-}\in} B: & \quad (x)(x \eta A \to x \eta B). \\
a \mathbf{C} b: & \quad a \mathbin{\text{-}\in} b \ \& \ \overline{b \mathbin{\text{-}\in} a}.
\end{aligned}
$$

Similarly $a \mathbf{C} B$, $A \mathbf{C} b$, $A \mathbf{C} B$ are to be defined.

$$
\begin{aligned}
a \text{ represents } A: & \quad a \mathbin{\text{-}\in} A \ \& \ A \mathbin{\text{-}\in} a. \\
c \text{ is reflexive}: & \quad c \epsilon c. \\
c \text{ is transitive}: & \quad (x)(y)(x \epsilon y \ \& \ y \epsilon c \to x \epsilon c). \\
c \text{ is empty}: & \quad \overline{(Ex)(x \epsilon c)}, \text{ or } (x)\overline{(x \epsilon c)}. \\
c \text{ is non-empty}: & \quad (Ex)(x \epsilon c).
\end{aligned}
$$

Similarly $C$ *is empty* is to be defined.

In regard to the formalization of the identity, it may be remarked that, for deductive operation with the symbol $=$, the following formulas, to be used as initial formulas (formal axioms) are sufficient:

$$
\begin{aligned}
& a = a. \\
& a = b \to (a \epsilon c \to b \epsilon c). \\
& a = b \to (c \epsilon a \to c \epsilon b). \\
& a = b \to (a \eta C \to b \eta C).
\end{aligned}
$$

Instead of $\overline{a = b}$ we shall usually write $a \neq b$ ("$a$ is another set than $b$").

**2. The axioms, first part.** We shall now state the axioms of the system which we are presenting. As in the Hilbert system of axiomatic geometry, the axioms are distributed in several series.

The first axioms are almost the same as in the Zermelo system.

I. AXIOMS OF EXTENSIONALITY.

(1) If the set $a$ has the same elements as the set $b$, then $a$ is the same set as $b$. (This can be expressed by the formula $a \mathbin{\text{-}\in} b \ \& \ b \mathbin{\text{-}\in} a \to a = b$.)

(2) If the class $A$ has the same elements as the class $B$, then $A$ is the same class as $B$.

*Remarks.*

1. Instead of employing the logical concept of identity and introducing the axiom I(1), there would be, as A. Fraenkel pointed out,[8] the possibility of introducing equality as a derived notion, by defining $a = b$ as $a \in b$ & $b \in a$, and taking as axioms the properties of equality which are expressed by the formulas,

$$a = b \rightarrow (a \epsilon c \rightarrow b \epsilon c),$$
$$a = b \rightarrow (a \eta C \rightarrow b \eta C).$$

This reduction, or a similar one, may be useful in the investigation of consistency. But for setting up the theory the method of defining the equality $a = b$ does not seem to be advantageous, since the meaning of several of the axioms is complicated by it.

2. The axiom I(2) will be used only for the purpose of defining a class by saying what elements belong to it. Since such a definition is a case of a description and, according to a theorem of logic,[9] descriptions generally can be eliminated, the introduction of the axiom I(2) could be avoided, and we could get along without speaking anywhere of identity between classes.

At all events, if the system of our axioms with exception of I(2) can be shown to be consistent, the consistency including this axiom is a consequence.

## II. AXIOMS OF DIRECT CONSTRUCTION OF SETS.

(1) There exists a set which has no element.

(2) To a set $s$ can be adjoined as element any set $c$ which is not already in $s$.

In other words, given a set $s$ and a set $c$ not in $s$, there exists a set $t$, such that $s \mathbf{C} t$ and $c$ is the only element of $t$ which is not in $s$.

*Immediate consequences, notations.* Combining the axioms II(1), (2) with I(1), we find that for both the former axioms the set asserted to exist can be shown also to be uniquely determined. Thus we have:

1. There is a unique set characterized by the property of having no element. It may be called the *null set* and denoted by 0.

2. For any two sets $s$ and $c$ there is a unique set characterized by the property that its elements are those and only those sets which either are in $s$ or are identical with $c$. (Observe that the case $c \epsilon s$ need not be excluded, since in this case $s$ itself is the unique set having the required property.)

In particular, taking $s = 0$, we find that, corresponding to any set $c$, there is a unique set whose only element is $c$. It may be denoted by $(c)$.

Similarly, taking $s = (a)$, we find that, corresponding to any two sets $a$ and $b$, there is a unique set whose only elements are $a$ and $b$. This set will be denoted by $(a, b)$. (If $a = b$, then $(a, b) = (a)$.)

The set $((a), (a, b))$, which is uniquely determined by the sets $a$, $b$ (in the given order), will be called the *pair a, b* and denoted by $\langle a, b \rangle$.[10] Observe that the

---

[8] FRAENKEL (1927a).

[9] Cf. HILBERT and BERNAYS (1934) §8.

[10] This manner of representing the ordered pair is due to C. Kuratowski, see KURATOWSKI (1921).

relation, $\langle a, b \rangle = c$, as well as the assertion, "$c$ is a pair," can be expressed by means of $\epsilon$, $=$, and our logical symbols.

If $\langle a, b \rangle = \langle c, d \rangle$, then $a = c$ and $b = d$. Indeed, for $c = d$ we have:

$$\langle c, d \rangle = ((c), (c, d)) = ((c));$$
$$\therefore \quad ((a), (a, b)) = ((c)),$$
$$(a) = (a, b) = (c),$$
$$a = c, \quad b = c, \quad b = d.$$

And for $c \neq d$ we have:

$$(c) \neq (c, d), \quad (a) \neq (c, d);$$
$$(a) \epsilon ((c), (c, d)), \quad (a) = (c), \quad a = c;$$
$$(c, d) \epsilon ((a), (a, b)), \quad (a, b) = (c, d),$$
$$(a) \neq (a, b), \quad a \neq b, \quad b \neq c, \quad b = d.$$

Thus if $\langle a, b \rangle = c$, the sets $a$, $b$ are uniquely determined by the set $c$. We call $a$ the *first member*, and $b$ the *second member*, of the pair $\langle a, b \rangle$.

The pair $\langle b, a \rangle$ will be said to be *converse* to $\langle a, b \rangle$. The pair $\langle \langle a, b \rangle, c \rangle$ will be said to arise from $\langle a, \langle b, c \rangle \rangle$ by *coupling to the left*, and $\langle a, \langle b, c \rangle \rangle$ will be said to arise from $\langle \langle a, b \rangle, c \rangle$ by *coupling to the right*.

### III. Axioms for construction of classes.[*]

a(1) Corresponding to any set $a$ there exists a class whose only element is $a$.

a(2) Corresponding to any class $A$ there exists a class to which a set belongs if and only if it does not belong to $A$ (*complementary class to $A$*).

a(3) Corresponding to any two classes $A$, $B$ there exists a class to which a set belongs if and only if it belongs both to $A$ and to $B$ (*intersection* of $A$ and $B$, or, as we shall also say, of $A$ with $B$).

b(1) There exists a class whose elements are those sets which have one and only one element.

b(2) There exists a class whose elements are those pairs $\langle a, b \rangle$ for which $a \epsilon b$.

b(3) Corresponding to any class $A$ there exists a class whose elements are those pairs $\langle a, b \rangle$ for which $a \eta A$.

c(1) Corresponding to any class $A$ of pairs there exists a class whose elements are the first members of the elements of $A$ (*domain* of $A$).

c(2) Corresponding to any class $A$ of pairs there exists a class whose elements are the pairs which are converse to the elements of $A$ (*converse class* to $A$).

c(3) Corresponding to any class $A$ of pairs of the form $\langle a, \langle b, c \rangle \rangle$ there exists a class whose elements are the pairs which arise from the elements of $A$ by coupling to the left.

*Immediate consequences.* In consequence of I(2), each of the assertions of the axioms III can be supplemented by the remark that there is only one class having the postulated property. Hence we may speak of *the* class whose only element is $a$, *the* complementary class to $A$, *the* intersection of $A$ and $B$, and so on.

Combining the axioms III among themselves, we are led to further classes, which again are uniquely determined in consequence of I(2):

1. The intersection of the class whose only element is 0 with the class whose only element is (0) is the *empty class*. The complementary class to this is the *class of all sets*. The class of the pairs $\langle a, b \rangle$ for which $a$ belongs to the class of all sets is the *class of all pairs*.

---

* Axiom b(1) is redundant; cf. Section 20 (*editor*).

2. The complementary class of the intersection of the complementary classes of $A$ and $B$ has as its elements the sets $a$ characterized by the property, "Either $a$ belongs to $A$ or $a$ belongs to $B$." We call it the *sum* of $A$ and $B$.

3. The converse class to the class of pairs whose first member belongs to $B$ is the class of pairs whose second member belongs to $B$. The intersection of the class of pairs whose first member belongs to $A$ and the class of pairs whose second member belongs to $B$ is the class of pairs $\langle a, b \rangle$ such that $a\eta A$ and $b\eta B$.

4. The domain of the converse class of a class $A$ of pairs is the class of second members of elements of $A$. We call it the *converse domain* of $A$. The sum of the domain and the converse domain of a class $A$ of pairs is the *field* of $A$. Its elements are the members of the elements of $A$.

5. Starting from a pair $\langle\langle a, b\rangle, c\rangle$, passing to the converse, then coupling to the left, then passing again to the converse, coupling again to the left, and finally again passing to the converse, we get the pair $\langle a, \langle b, c\rangle\rangle$. Thus from a class $A$ of pairs of the form $\langle\langle a, b\rangle, c\rangle$, by application of III c(2) and c(3) we obtain the class of pairs which arise from elements of $A$ by coupling to the right—i.e. the process of applying III c(3) can be inverted. The process of applying III c(3) may be denoted briefly as *coupling to the left*, the inverse process as *coupling to the right*.

6. By III a(3), b(1), b(2), b(3), c(2) we may obtain the intersection of the class of pairs $\langle a, b\rangle$ such that $a\epsilon b$ and the class of pairs $\langle a, b\rangle$ such that $a$ and $b$ have each one and only one element. The converse domain of this intersection has as its elements the sets of the form $((c))$. But since $((c))$ is the same as $\langle c, c\rangle$, this gives us the class of all pairs $\langle a, b\rangle$ such that $a=b$.[11]

7. Let $c$ be a set. By III a(1), a(3), b(2), b(3), c(2) we may obtain the intersection of the class of pairs $\langle a, b\rangle$ such that $a\epsilon b$ and the class of pairs whose second member is $c$. The domain of this intersection has the same elements that $c$ has. Thus every set represents a class. But, as we shall see, not every class is represented by a set.

**3. Predicates and classes.** Before going on to consideration of the remaining axioms it will be desirable to have a certain survey of the consequences of the axioms III. For this purpose we shall prove a metamathematical theorem concerning the possibility of making classes correspond to certain predicates of sets, the term *predicate* being taken in the wider sense, so as to include predicates of several subjects (relations).

The predicates here in question are defined by means of certain expressions, which, in general, contain besides the *arguments*, or variables corresponding to subjects, still other variables as *parameters*.

These expressions are the following: first the *primary expressions*, $\mathfrak{a}\epsilon\mathfrak{b}$, and $\mathfrak{a}=\mathfrak{b}$, and $\mathfrak{a}\eta\mathfrak{B}$, where $\mathfrak{a}$ and $\mathfrak{b}$ denote free variables for sets (small italics) and $\mathfrak{B}$ denotes a free variable for a class (capital italics); further the expressions obtainable from primary expressions by the logical operations, conjunction, dis-

---

[11] This inference depends on the special form of the definition which we have adopted for the ordered pair. We could avoid this dependency by taking instead of our axiom III b(1) an axiom saying that there exists a class whose elements are the pairs of the form $\langle c, c\rangle$.

junction, implication, negation, and the quantifiers, every quantifier changing a free variable into a bound one, but with the restriction that the quantifiers are to be applied only to variables for sets.

These expressions will be called here *constitutive expressions.*

A constitutive expression, with some of the free variables *for sets* taken as arguments and all other free variables occurring in it taken as parameters, represents, for each system of fixed values of the parameters, a predicate with the places of the subjects marked by the arguments. For instance the expression.

$$(Ex)(a\epsilon x \ \& \ x\epsilon b \ \& \ x\eta C),$$

if $b$ and $C$ are taken as parameters, represents the following property of a set $a$: to be in a set which is a common element of the set $b$ and the class $C$.

Now it is a question of making classes correspond to the predicates defined by constitutive expressions. For this purpose we need the notion of a *k-tuplet* $(k = 1, 2, 3, \cdots)$.

A *k-tuplet* is a set, formed ouf of $k$ sets $a_1, \cdots, a_k$, the *members* of the $k$-tuplet, by the iterated operation of forming pairs, as follows. A 1-tuplet (singlet) formed out of $a$ is $a$ itself. A $(k+1)$-tuplet formed out of $a_1, \cdots, a_{k+1}$ is a pair $\langle u, v \rangle$, where $u$ is a $p$-tuplet, $v$ is a $q$-tuplet, $p+q=k+1$, the members of $u$ are some $p$ of the sets $a_1, \cdots, a_{k+1}$, and the members of $v$ are the remainder of those sets.

Under this definition a 2-tuplet (doublet) formed out of $a$ and $b$ is one or other of the pairs $\langle a, b \rangle$, $\langle b, a \rangle$ and the members of the doublet are the same as the members of the pair under our previous definition.

Observe that a set $c$ which is a $(k+1)$-tuplet is also a $k$-tuplet, but that the members of $c$ as a $k$-tuplet are not the same as the members of $c$ as a $(k+1)$-tuplet.

If in the formation of a $k$-tuplet we replace the members in order by the variables $a_1, \cdots, a_k$, we obtain the *schema* of the $k$-tuplet. Thus the schema of a quadruplet $\langle\langle a, b \rangle, \langle c, b \rangle\rangle$ is $\langle\langle a_1, a_2 \rangle, \langle a_3, a_4 \rangle\rangle$.

The number of different $k$-tuplet schemata formed out of the variables $a_1, \cdots, a_k$ can be shown to be

$$\frac{(2k-2)!}{(k-1)! \, k!}.$$

In the schema of a $k$-tuplet each of the variables has a *degree*, i.e. the number of brackets $\langle \ \rangle$ by which it is enclosed. In the $k$-tuplet itself we define the degree of a member to be the degree of the corresponding variable in the schema of the $k$-tuplet.

A $k$-tuplet will be called normal if, in the succession of members $a_1, \cdots, a_k$, each member $a_p$, where $p < k$, has the degree $p$, and $a_k$ has the degree $k-1$. Thus, for instance, a normal quintuplet has the form $\langle a_1, \langle a_2, \langle a_3, \langle a_4, a_5 \rangle\rangle\rangle\rangle$. (All singlets and doublets are normal.)

The possible differences between $k$-tuplets formed out of the same members consist in the order of the members and the positions of the brackets $\langle \ \rangle$. A change in the positions of the brackets, preserving the order of the members, will be called a *rebracketing.*

A $k$-tuplet will be said to *correspond* to a series (system of values) $a_1, \cdots, a_k$ if $a_1, \cdots, a_k$ are the members of the $k$-tuplet in order.

Now the theorem to be proved can be formulated as follows: *If* $\mathfrak{P}(v_1, \cdots, v_k)$ *is a constitutive expression with* $v_1, \cdots, v_k$ *as arguments, then for every system of fixed values of the parameters there exists, by virtue of the axioms* III, *a class the elements of which are the normal $k$-tuplets corresponding to those systems of values of* $v_1, \cdots, v_k$ *for which the predicate* $\mathfrak{P}(v_1, \cdots, v_k)$ *holds for the fixed values in question of the parameters.*

In order to prove this we consider first the case that $\mathfrak{P}(v_1, \cdots, v_k)$ is a primary expression. Then it has one of the forms $v_1 \eta \mathfrak{C}$, $v_1 \epsilon r$, $r \epsilon v_1$, $v_1 = r$, $r = v_1$, $v_1 \epsilon v_2$, $v_2 \epsilon v_1$, $v_1 = v_2$, $v_2 = v_1$, where $\mathfrak{C}$ denotes a parameter referring to classes and $r$ a parameter referring to sets.

In all of these cases the existence of a class with the required property is easily seen, since the normal singlet corresponding to a value of $v$ is just that value itself, and the normal doublet corresponding to a system of values $a_1, a_2$ of $v_1, v_2$ is the pair $\langle a_1, a_2 \rangle$. Indeed, for $v_1 \eta \mathfrak{C}$ the class taken as value for $\mathfrak{C}$ is the required class. For $v_1 = r$ or $r = v_1$ the existence of a class with the required property follows immediately from III a(1). For $v_1 \epsilon v_2$ or $v_2 \epsilon v_1$ it follows from III b(2), c(2). For $v_1 = v_2$ or $v_2 = v_1$ it follows from the consequence 6 of the axioms III, derived above (§2). For $v_1 \epsilon r$ it follows from consequence 7 of the axioms III. And in a similar way it follows for $r \epsilon v_1$ by the axioms III a(1), a(3), b(2), b(3), c(1), c(2).

Now going on to constitutive expressions formed by means of the logical operations, we first remark that on account of the equivalence of $\mathfrak{A} \vee \mathfrak{B}$ to $\overline{\mathfrak{A} \& \mathfrak{B}}$, of $\mathfrak{A} \to \mathfrak{B}$ to $\overline{\mathfrak{A} \& \mathfrak{B}}$, and of $(w)\mathfrak{A}(w)$ to $\overline{(Ew)\mathfrak{A}(w)}$ we need consider only the three operations, conjunction, negation, and existential quantification. Concerning these three operations we have at once the following:

1. If $C$ is a class of the required property with respect to a constitutive expression $\mathfrak{P}(v_1, \cdots, v_k)$ and a fixed system of values for the parameters, then the intersection of the complementary class of $C$ with the class of all normal $k$-tuplets has the required property with respect to $\overline{\mathfrak{P}(v_1, \cdots, v_k)}$ and the same system of values for the parameters. The existence of the class of all normal $k$-tuplets, for a given $k$, follows by the consequences 1 and 3 of the axioms III.

2. If $C$ is a class of the required property with respect to a constitutive expression $\mathfrak{P}(v_1, \cdots, v_k)$ $(k > 1)$ and a fixed system of values for the parameters, then the converse domain of $C$ has the required property with respect to the expression $(Eu)\mathfrak{P}(u, v_2, \cdots, v_k)$ and the same system of values for the parameters, $u$ being a variable which does not occur in $\mathfrak{P}(v_1, \cdots, v_k)$.

3. If $\mathfrak{P}(u_1, \cdots, u_r)$ and $\mathfrak{Q}(v_1, \cdots, v_s)$ are constitutive expressions which have no argument in common and if, for a fixed system of values of the parameters which occur, $A$ is a class of the required property with respect to $\mathfrak{P}(u_1, \cdots, u_r)$ and $B$ is a class of the required property with respect to $\mathfrak{Q}(v_1, \cdots, v_s)$, then by consequence 3 of the axioms III (§2 above) there exists a class whose elements are those $(r+s)$-tuplets $\langle a, b \rangle$, $a$ being a normal $r$-tuplet corresponding to a system of values $a_1, \cdots, a_r$, and $b$ a normal $s$-tuplet corresponding to a system of values $b_1, \cdots, b_s$, for which

$$\mathfrak{P}(a_1, \cdots, a_r) \,\& \, \mathfrak{Q}(b_1, \cdots, b_s)$$

holds for the fixed system of values of the parameters.

Looking at these results 1–3 from the point of view of what has to be proved, we see that 1 and 2, concerning negation and existential quantification, are sufficient. (In connection with 2, note that there is no loss of generality in the assumption that the existential quantifier is applied to the first one of the arguments in the given constitutive expression, because the order $v_1, \cdots, v_k$ of these arguments may be arbitrarily chosen.) In 3, however, two things are lacking: the case that the expressions $\mathfrak{P}(u_1, \cdots, u_r)$ and $\mathfrak{Q}(v_1, \cdots, v_s)$ have common arguments is not included, and the class of $(r+s)$-tuplets which is proved to exist is, in the case $r > 1$, not a class of normal $(r+s)$-tuplets. Thus in order to complete the proof of our theorem we have still to remove these two deficiencies.

Concerning the first of them we remark that the case of common arguments of the expressions $\mathfrak{P}(u_1, \cdots, u_r)$ and $\mathfrak{Q}(v_1, \cdots, v_s)$ can be treated by first taking all the arguments as different from one another and afterwards in the conjunction

$$\mathfrak{P}(u_1, \cdots, u_r) \ \& \ \mathfrak{Q}(v_1, \cdots, v_s)$$

identifying some of the arguments. The identifications can be performed successively, so that at each step only two variables are identified. And by performing permutations on the arguments we can arrange that the arguments identified are, at each step, the first two.

In connection with the other deficiency, concerning the form of the $(r+s)$-tuplets in 3, note that these $(r+s)$-tuplets all have the same schema and that each of them corresponds to a system of values of the arguments $u_1, \cdots, u_r$, $v_1, \cdots, v_s$ for which the predicate represented by the expression

$$\mathfrak{P}(u_1, \cdots, u_r) \ \& \ \mathfrak{Q}(v_1, \cdots, v_s)$$

holds (for the fixed system of values of the parameters). Thus the transition from the class of $(r+s)$-tuplets in 3 to the class which is to be proved to exist in the case of the constitutive expression

$$\mathfrak{P}(u_1, \cdots, u_r) \ \& \ \mathfrak{Q}(v_1, \cdots, v_s)$$

(with $u_1, \cdots, u_r, v_1, \cdots, v_s$ all different) will consist only in a rebracketing, the same for each $(r+s)$-tuplet.

Hence for the completion of our proof it will be sufficient to establish the following two things:

4. If in the case of the constitutive expression $\mathfrak{A}(v_1, \cdots, v_k)$ $\ (k > 1)$ a class with the property required by our theorem exists for a fixed system of values of the parameters, then a class with the required property exists in the case of each of the expressions resulting from $\mathfrak{A}(v_1, \cdots, v_k)$ by a permutation of the arguments $v_1, \cdots, v_k$, and also in the case of the expression $\mathfrak{A}(v_2, v_2, \cdots, v_k)$ with the $k-1$ arguments $v_2, \cdots, v_k$ (where it is understood each time that the values of the parameters are preserved).

5. Corresponding to any class $C$ of $k$-tuplets which all have the same schema there exists a class the elements of which are the normal $k$-tuplets obtained from the elements of $C$ by rebracketing.

Moreover, proof of 4 reduces to proof of the two following things:

4a. If the same permutation is applied to the members of each element of a class $C$ of normal $k$-tuplets, the resulting class of normal $k$-tuplets also exists.

4b. Corresponding to any class $C$ of normal $(k+1)$-tuplets there exists the class obtained from $C$ by omitting all the $(k+1)$-tuplets in which the first two members are different and then canceling the first member of each of the remaining $(k+1)$-tuplets (so as to obtain a normal $k$-tuplet).

Of these, 4b may be proved as follows. By the axiom III b(3) and the consequence 6 of the axioms III (see §2 above), there exists the class of all sets of the form $\langle\langle a, a\rangle, b\rangle$, from which we obtain by coupling to the right (consequence 5 of the axioms III) the class of all sets of the form $\langle a, \langle a, b\rangle\rangle$. If $C$ is a class of normal $(k+1)$-tuplets, then in the case $k>1$ the intersection of $C$ with the class of sets having the form $\langle a, \langle a, b\rangle\rangle$ is the class of those $(k+1)$-tuplets of $C$ in which the first two members are equal. In the case $k=1$ the corresponding subclass of $C$ is obtained as the intersection of $C$ with the class of pairs $\langle c, c\rangle$ (consequence 6). Thus in both cases we have a class $C^*$ arising from $C$ by omitting the $(k+1)$-tuplets in which the first member is different from the second. And the converse domain of $C^*$ is the class obtained from $C^*$ by canceling the first member of each $(k+1)$-tuplet.

The assertions 4a and 5 can be combined into the following: If the same permutation is applied to the members of each element of a class $C$ of $k$-tuplets which all have the same schema and at the same time each element of $C$ is rebracketed so as to render it a normal $k$-tuplet, the resulting class of normal $k$-tuplets exists. And in order to prove this it will be sufficient to prove the two following things:

6. The passage, by permutation and rebracketing, from a given $k$-tuplet to a prescribed normal $k$-tuplet with the same members, can be performed by a succession of steps of the following kind:

$s_1{}^k$. Replacing a $k$-tuplet, regarded as a pair, by the converse pair.

$s_2{}^k$. Coupling to the left or to the right, applied to a $k$-tuplet, i.e., replacing a $k$-tuplet $\langle \mathfrak{a}, \langle \mathfrak{b}, \mathfrak{c}\rangle\rangle$ by $\langle\langle \mathfrak{a}, \mathfrak{b}\rangle, \mathfrak{c}\rangle$ or inversely.

$s_3{}^k$. Replacing a $k$-tuplet $\langle \mathfrak{a}, \langle \mathfrak{b}, \mathfrak{c}\rangle\rangle$ by $\langle \mathfrak{a}, \langle \mathfrak{c}, \mathfrak{b}\rangle\rangle$, or a $k$-tuplet $\langle\langle \mathfrak{a}, \mathfrak{b}\rangle, \mathfrak{c}\rangle$ by $\langle\langle \mathfrak{b}, \mathfrak{a}\rangle, \mathfrak{c}\rangle$, i.e., replacing a pair which is a member of a pair $\mathfrak{p}$ ($\mathfrak{p}$ being a $k$-tuplet) by its converse.

$s_4{}^k$. Coupling to the left or to the right applied to a member of a pair $\mathfrak{p}$ ($\mathfrak{p}$ being a $k$-tuplet).

(Note that $s_3{}^k$ is the application of a process $s_1{}^h$   $(h<k)$   and $s_4{}^k$ the application of a process $s_2{}^h$   $(h<k)$   to one or other of the members of a pair which is a $k$-tuplet.)

7. If $C$ is a class of $k$-tuplets such that a process $\mathbf{P}$, which is one of the steps $s_1{}^k$, $s_2{}^k$, $s_3{}^k$, $s_4{}^k$, can be applied to each of its elements, then the class exists whose elements are the $k$-tuplets arising from the elements of $C$ by the process $\mathbf{P}$.

In order to prove 6 we proceed as follows. We first prove that, in the case of any $k$-tuplet, if $\mathfrak{a}$ is a member of degree higher than 1, we can, by means of the processes $s_1{}^k$ and $s_2{}^k$, lower the degree of $\mathfrak{a}$ by one. Indeed the $k$-tuplet, of which $\mathfrak{a}$ is a member of second or higher degree, must have one of the forms $\langle \mathfrak{p}, \langle \mathfrak{q}, \mathfrak{r}\rangle\rangle$ or $\langle\langle \mathfrak{q}, \mathfrak{r}\rangle, \mathfrak{p}\rangle$, $\mathfrak{a}$ being part of $\langle \mathfrak{q}, \mathfrak{r}\rangle$. If it has the form $\langle \mathfrak{p}, \langle \mathfrak{q}, \mathfrak{r}\rangle\rangle$ and $\mathfrak{a}$ is either part of $\mathfrak{r}$ or $\mathfrak{r}$ itself, we get by coupling to the left the $k$-tuplet $\langle\langle \mathfrak{p}, \mathfrak{q}\rangle, \mathfrak{r}\rangle$, in which the degree of $a$ is less by one—since in $\langle\langle \mathfrak{p}, \mathfrak{q}\rangle, \mathfrak{r}\rangle$ the number of brackets enclosing $\mathfrak{r}$, and therefore also the number of brackets enclosing $a$, is less by one than in $\langle \mathfrak{p}, \langle \mathfrak{q}, \mathfrak{r}\rangle\rangle$. If it has the form $\langle \mathfrak{p}, \langle \mathfrak{q}, \mathfrak{r}\rangle\rangle$ and $a$ is either part of $\mathfrak{q}$ or $\mathfrak{q}$ itself, we get, by taking the converse of the pair $\langle \mathfrak{p}, \langle \mathfrak{q}, \mathfrak{r}\rangle\rangle$ and then coupling to the right, the $k$-tuplet $\langle \mathfrak{q}, \langle \mathfrak{r}, \mathfrak{p}\rangle\rangle$, in which the degree of $a$ is less by one. And the case that the given $k$-tuplet has the form $\langle\langle \mathfrak{q}, \mathfrak{r}\rangle, \mathfrak{p}\rangle$ is handled in an entirely analogous way.

Being able, by means of the processes $s_1{}^k$, $s_2{}^k$ to lower the degree of a member $a$ of a $k$-tuplet by one, as long as it is higher than 1, we can, by iterated applications of these processes, bring the degree down to 1. The $k$-tuplet we obtain in this way has one of the forms $\langle a, \mathfrak{b}\rangle$ or $\langle \mathfrak{b}, a\rangle$; and from $\langle a, \mathfrak{b}\rangle$ we can pass to $\langle \mathfrak{b}, a\rangle$ by the process $s_1{}^k$. Thus from a $k$-tuplet of which $a$ is a member $(k>1)$ we can pass by means of the processes $s_1{}^k$, $s_2{}^k$ to a $k$-tuplet of the form $\langle \mathfrak{b}, a\rangle$.

Now in order to pass from a given $k$-tuplet to the normal $k$-tuplet,

$$\langle a_1, \langle a_2, \cdots, \langle a_{k-1}, a_k\rangle \cdots \rangle\rangle,$$

where $a_1, \cdots, a_k$ are the members of the given $k$-tuplet in some arbitrarily chosen order, we can proceed as follows.

First, by applying the processes $s_1{}^k$, $s_2{}^k$, we can pass from the given $k$-tuplet to a $k$-tuplet $\langle \mathfrak{b}, a_k\rangle$, where $\mathfrak{b}$ is a $(k-1)$-tuplet having $a_1, \cdots, a_{k-1}$ as its members. If $k=2$, then $\langle \mathfrak{b}, a_k\rangle$ is already the normal $k$-tuplet desired.

Let $k$ be greater than 2. Then by applying the processes $s_1{}^{k-1}$, $s_2{}^{k-1}$ to $\mathfrak{b}$ we can pass from $\mathfrak{b}$ to a $(k-1)$-tuplet $\langle \mathfrak{c}, a_{k-1}\rangle$, where $\mathfrak{c}$ is a $(k-2)$-tuplet having the members $a_1, \cdots, a_{k-2}$. This operation, carried out within the $k$-tuplet $\langle \mathfrak{b}, a_k\rangle$, leads to $\langle\langle \mathfrak{c}, a_{k-1}\rangle, a_k\rangle$. The processes involved are applications of $s_1{}^{k-1}$ and $s_2{}^{k-1}$ to one of the members of a pair (the pair being a $k$-tuplet); i.e. they are applications of $s_3{}^k$ and $s_4{}^k$. Then from $\langle\langle \mathfrak{c}, a_{k-1}\rangle, a_k\rangle$ by coupling to the right we get $\langle \mathfrak{c}, \langle a_{k-1}, a_k\rangle\rangle$. If $k=3$, then this $k$-tuplet is already the one desired.

Let $k$ be greater than 3. Then by the processes $s_1{}^{k-2}$, $s_2{}^{k-2}$ applied to $\mathfrak{c}$ we can pass from $\mathfrak{c}$ to a $(k-2)$-tuplet $\langle \mathfrak{d}, a_{k-2}\rangle$, where $\mathfrak{d}$ is a $(k-3)$-tuplet having the members $a_1, \cdots, a_{k-3}$. Therefore by the processes $s_3{}^k$, $s_4{}^k$ we can pass from $\langle \mathfrak{c}, \langle a_{k-1}, a_k\rangle\rangle$ to $\langle\langle \mathfrak{d}, a_{k-2}\rangle, \langle a_{k-1}, a_k\rangle\rangle$, and from this by coupling to the right we get $\langle \mathfrak{d}, \langle a_{k-2}, \langle a_{k-1}, a_k\rangle\rangle\rangle$. If $k=4$, then this is the normal $k$-tuplet desired.

If $k$ is greater than 4 we continue in the same way.

After at most $k-1$ repetitions we will come to the desired normal $k$-tuplet,

$$\langle a_1, \langle a_2, \cdots, \langle a_{k-1}, a_k\rangle \cdots \rangle\rangle,$$

the steps applied all being of the kinds $s_1{}^k$, $s_2{}^k$, $s_3{}^k$, or $s_4{}^k$.

Turning now to the proof of 7, we note that if $\mathbf{P}$ is one of the processes $s_1{}^k$, $s_2{}^k$ the desired result follows immediately from the axioms III c(2), c(3) and consequence 5 of these axioms (§2). Thus we need consider only the cases that $\mathbf{P}$ is $s_3{}^k$ or $s_4{}^k$.

LEMMA. *If $A$ and $B$ are classes of pairs, there exists the class of all those pairs $\langle a, b\rangle$ for which there exists a set $x$ such that $\langle a, x\rangle\eta A$ and $\langle x, b\rangle\eta B$.*

Indeed by the axiom III b(3) there exists the class $C$ of all pairs $\langle\langle a, c\rangle, b\rangle$

such that $\langle a, c \rangle \eta A$. By the axioms III b(3), c(2) there exists the class of all pairs $\langle a, \langle c, b \rangle \rangle$ such that $\langle c, b \rangle \eta B$, and hence by III c(3) the class $D$ of all pairs $\langle \langle a, c \rangle, b \rangle$ such that $\langle c, b \rangle \eta B$. The intersection of $C$ and $D$ is the class of all sets $\langle \langle a, c \rangle, b \rangle$ such that $\langle a, c \rangle \eta A$ and $\langle c, b \rangle \eta B$. Taking the converse class of this class and coupling to the left, we obtain the class $H$ of those pairs $\langle \langle b, a \rangle, c \rangle$ for which $\langle a, c \rangle \eta A$ and $\langle c, b \rangle \eta B$. The converse class of the domain of $H$ is the class whose existence is asserted by the lemma.

The operation of passing from a class $A$ of pairs and a class $B$ of pairs to the class of those pairs $\langle a, b \rangle$ for which there exists an $x$ such that $\langle a, x \rangle \eta A$ and $\langle x, b \rangle \eta B$ (i.e. the class whose existence is asserted by the lemma just proved) will be called *composition of A with B*, and the lemma will be called the *composition lemma*.

The assertion 7, for the case that **P** is one of the processes $s_3{}^k$, $s_4{}^k$, is easily reduced, by means of the composition lemma and the axiom III c(2), to the two following assertions:

8. There exists the class of all sets of the form $\langle \langle a, b \rangle, \langle b, a \rangle \rangle$.

9. There exists the class of all sets of the form $\langle \langle a, \langle b, c \rangle \rangle, \langle \langle a, b \rangle, c \rangle \rangle$.

Proof of 8 is as follows. By consequence 6 of the axioms III, and the axioms III b(3), c(2), c(3), there exists the class of all sets of the form $\langle \langle \langle a, b \rangle, b \rangle, c \rangle$. From this class we obtain by coupling to the right the class of sets having the form $\langle \langle a, b \rangle, \langle b, c \rangle \rangle$. The intersection of this class with its converse is the class of all sets of the form $\langle \langle a, b \rangle, \langle b, a \rangle \rangle$.

Proof of 9 is as follows. By composition of the class of all sets of the form $\langle \langle a, b \rangle, \langle b, a \rangle \rangle$ with itself, we obtain the class of all sets of the form[12] $\langle \langle a, b \rangle, \langle a, b \rangle \rangle$. From this class we get by coupling to the left the class of all sets of the form $\langle \langle \langle a, b \rangle, a \rangle, b \rangle$, and hence, applying the axiom III b(3) and twice coupling to the right, the class of all sets of the form $\langle \langle a, b \rangle, \langle a, \langle b, c \rangle \rangle \rangle$. Taking the converse of the latter class, applying III b(3), and then again coupling to the right, we obtain the class $M$ of all sets which have the form

$$\langle \langle a, \langle b, c \rangle \rangle, \langle \langle a, b \rangle, d \rangle \rangle.$$

On the other hand as we have seen (in the proof of 8) there exists the class of all sets of the form $\langle \langle b, c \rangle, \langle c, e \rangle \rangle$. From this class, applying III b(3), c(2), and coupling to the left, we obtain the class of all sets of the form $\langle \langle a, \langle b, c \rangle \rangle, \langle c, e \rangle \rangle$. And by composition of this class with the class of sets of the form $\langle \langle a, b \rangle, \langle b, a \rangle \rangle$ we obtain the class $N$ of all sets of the form

$$\langle \langle a, \langle b, c \rangle \rangle, \langle e, c \rangle \rangle.$$

The intersection of $M$ and $N$ (III a(3)) is the class of all sets of the form

$$\langle \langle a, \langle b, c \rangle \rangle, \langle \langle a, b \rangle, c \rangle \rangle.$$

Herewith the demonstration of our theorem on the correspondence between predicates and classes is completed. We shall call this theorem briefly the *class*

---

[12] Of course this class can be shown to exist also in other ways. For example it can be obtained as the intersection of the class of all pairs $\langle c, c \rangle$ with the class of those pairs $\langle r, s \rangle$ in which $r$ belongs to the class of all pairs.

*theorem*; in the further development of the present system we shall have occasion to use it constantly.

The following immediate consequences may be stated at once.

Corresponding to any class $C$ there exists:

1) A class which is the intersection of the elements of $C$, i.e., a class whose elements are the sets which are in every element of $C$.

2) A class which is the sum of the elements of $C$, i.e., a class whose elements are the sets which are in at least one element of $C$.

3) A class whose elements are the subsets of $C$.

The constitutive expressions with argument $a$ and parameter $C$ to which these classes correspond (under the class theorem) are, respectively,

$$(x)(x\eta C \rightarrow a\epsilon x),$$

$$(Ex)(x\eta C \ \& \ a\epsilon x),$$

$$(x)(x\epsilon a \rightarrow x\epsilon C).$$

Instead of the parameter $C$, referring to classes, we may take a parameter $b$, referring to sets, at the same time replacing $\eta$ by $\epsilon$; i.e., we may employ the constitutive expressions,

$$(x)(x\epsilon b \rightarrow a\epsilon x),$$

$$(Ex)(x\epsilon b \ \& \ a\epsilon x),$$

$$(x)(x\epsilon a \rightarrow x\epsilon b).$$

Applying the class theorem to these, we find that corresponding to any set $b$ there exists:

1) A class which is the intersection of the elements of $b$.

2) A class which is the sum of the elements of $b$.

3) The class of all subsets of $b$.

**PART II**[13]

**4. The axioms, second part.** For the formulation of the remaining axioms we need the notions of a *function* and of a *one-to-one correspondence*.

We define a *function* to be a class of pairs in which different elements always have different first members; or, in other words, a class $F$ of pairs such that, to every element $a$ of its domain there is a unique element $b$ of its converse domain determined by the condition $\langle a, b \rangle \eta F$. We shall call the set $b$ so determined the *value* of $F$ for $a$, and denote it (following the mathematical usage) by $F(a)$.

A set which represents a function—i.e., a set of pairs in which different elements always have different first members—will be called a *functional set*.

If $b$ is the value of the function $F$ for $a$, we shall say that $F$ *assigns* the set $b$ to the set $a$; and if a functional set $f$ represents $F$, we shall say also that $f$ *assigns* the set $b$ to the set $a$.

A class of pairs will be called a *one-to-one correspondence* if both it and its converse class are functions. We shall say that there exists a one-to-one correspondence between the classes $A$ and $B$ (or of $A$ to $B$) if $A$ and $B$ are domain and converse domain of a one-to-one correspondence. Likewise we shall say that there exists a one-to-one correspondence between the sets $a$ and $b$ (or of $a$ to $b$) if $a$ and $b$ respectively *represent* the domain and the converse domain of a one-to-one correspondence. In the same fashion we speak of a one-to-one correspondence between a class and a set, or a set and a class.

IV. AXIOM OF CHOICE. Every class $C$ of pairs has a subclass which is a function and has the same domain as $C$.

*Consequences.*

1. For every class $C$ of non-empty sets there exists a function, having $C$ as its domain, which assigns to every set belonging to $C$ one of its elements.—For, by the axioms III, the class of pairs $\langle a, b \rangle$ such that $a \eta C$ and $b \epsilon a$ exists; and we apply the axiom of choice to this class.

2. For every function $F$ there exists an *inverse function*, i.e., a function which is a subclass of the converse class of $F$ and whose domain is the converse domain of $F$.—This follows immediately by applying the axiom IV to the converse class of $F$.

*Remark.* If the consequence 2 (just stated) is taken as an axiom, then the axiom IV can be inferred from it. In fact, by the class theorem, for every class $C$ of pairs there exists the class of all pairs of the form $\langle \langle a, b \rangle, a \rangle$ where $\langle a, b \rangle \eta C$. This class is a function whose converse domain is the domain of $C$. If for every function there is an inverse function, we may infer the existence of a function, having the same domain as $C$, whose elements are of the form $\langle a, \langle a, b \rangle \rangle$ where $\langle a, b \rangle \eta C$. The converse domain of this function is a function having the same domain as $C$ and is a subclass of $C$.

Thus the axiom IV is equivalent in content to the assumption that for every function there exists an inverse function.

V. Axioms concerning the representation of classes by sets.[14]

a. If a class is represented by a set, every subclass of it is also represented by a set. (Subclass axiom.)

b. If the domain of a one-to-one correspondence is represented by a set, the converse domain is also represented by a set. (Axiom of replacement.)

c. For every set $a$, the class which is the sum of the elements of $a$ is represented by a set. (Sum axiom.)

d. For every set $a$, the class of all subsets of $a$ is represented by a set. (Power axiom.)

*Consequences* (1–9). Since, by consequence 7 of the axioms III, every set represents a class, we have as an immediate consequence of V a:

1. Every subclass of a set is represented by a set.

As a consequence of 1 we have:

2. The intersection of the elements of a non-empty class or of a non-empty set is represented by a set.—For, if $a$ is an element of a class $C$ (or of a set $c$), the intersection of the elements of $C$ (or of $c$) is a subclass of $a$.

From V b we infer:

3. If the domain of a function is represented by a set, the function itself is represented by a functional set; and conversely, the domain of a function represented by a functional set is represented by a set.—For, by the class theorem, if $F$ is a function, the class of pairs $\langle a, \langle a, b \rangle \rangle$ such that $\langle a, b \rangle \eta F$ exists; this class is a one-to-one correspondence, its domain is the domain of $F$, and its converse domain is the class $F$ itself.

As a particular application of 3, we note the following. The condition that there exists a one-to-one correspondence between the sets $a$ and $b$ is equivalent to the condition that there is a set representing a one-to-one correspondence between $a$ and $b$. The latter condition can be symbolically formulated by a constitutive expression, since it amounts to the condition that there is a set $s$ of pairs such that (1) different elements of $s$ always differ in both their first and their second members, and (2) the elements of $a$ are just those sets which occur as first members of elements of $s$ and the elements of $b$ are just those sets which occur as second members of elements of $s$. Hence, by the class theorem, there exists the class of all pairs $\langle a, b \rangle$ for which a one-to-one correspondence between $a$ and $b$ exists.

---

[14] The axioms V a, c, d correspond respectively to Zermelo's *Axiom der Aussonderung, Axiom der Vereinigung,* and *Axiom der Potenzmenge.* Cf. Zermelo (1908a). Axiom V b is a modification of Fraenkel's *Axiom der Ersetzung.* Cf. Fraenkel (1922) and (1927).

From IV, V a, and V b follows:

4. If the domain of a function is represented by a set, the converse domain is also represented by a set.—For let $F$ be a function whose domain $A$ is represented by a set, and let $B$ be the converse domain of $F$. By consequence 2 of the axiom IV, there is an inverse function $G$ to $F$, whose domain is $B$, and which is a subclass of the converse class $C$ of $F$. The converse class of $G$ is a one-to-one correspondence between a subclass $A_1$ of $A$, and $B$. Since $A$ is represented by a set, it follows from V a that $A_1$ is represented by a set, and hence, by V b, that $B$ is represented by a set.

*Remark.* The consequence 4, which we have just derived from the axioms IV, V a, V b, will be called the *theorem of replacement*. It has about the same content as Fraenkel's axiom of replacement in its original form.

If 4 is taken as an axiom, V a and V b become provable as theorems. This is obvious in the case of V b. To prove V a we must show that a subclass $S$ of a class $A$ represented by a set is represented by a set. This is immediate if $S$ is empty. Otherwise let $c$ be an element of $S$. By the class theorem, there exists the class of those pairs $\langle a, b \rangle$ for which, either $b = a$ and $a \eta S$, or $b = c$ and $a \eta A$ but not $a \eta S$. This class is a function whose domain is $A$ and whose converse domain is $S$. Since $A$ is represented by a set, it follows from 4 (taken as an axiom) that $S$ is represented by a set.

Thus we have the possibility of replacing the axioms V a, b by the theorem of replacement taken as an axiom (which we shall refer to as axiom V*). This modification is appropriate in connections where the intention is to get along as far as possible without the axiom of choice.

A further remarkable possibility is that of taking instead of V a, b, c the following axiom, which we shall call V**: If the domain of a function is represented by a set, then the sum of the elements of the converse domain (i.e., the sum of the values of the function) is represented by a set.

In fact, from V** we can obtain V c and the theorem of replacement, from which latter, as we have just seen, V a and V b can be derived. If $a$ is any set, there exists, by the class theorem, the class of those pairs $\langle c, c \rangle$ for which $c \epsilon a$. Since this class is a function whose domain is $a$ and whose converse domain is $a$, we conclude that the sum of the elements of $a$ is represented by a set. Moreover, by the class theorem, if $F$ is any function, there exists the class of those pairs $\langle c, d \rangle$ for which $c$ belongs to the domain of $F$ and $d = (F(c))$. Since this class is a function, and the sum of the values of this function is the class of the values of $F$—i.e., the converse domain of $F$—we conclude that if the domain of $F$ is represented by a set the converse domain is also represented by a set.

On the other hand V** follows directly from the theorem of replacement and V c; hence it may be derived as a theorem from IV, V a, V b, V c. We shall call this theorem—whose statement coincides with that of the axiom V**—the *sum theorem*.

As a consequence of 3 and 4 above, we have:

5. If a function is represented by a functional set, its domain and its converse domain are each represented by a set.

*Definition.* If $f$ is a functional set representing a function $F$, we shall call the set representing the domain of $F$ the *domain of $f$*, and the set representing the converse domain of $F$ the *converse domain of f*. Thus the domain and the converse domain of a functional set are, by definition, sets.

From IV and V b, there follows:

6. If $s$ is a set of which 0 is not an element, and if no two elements of $s$ have a common element, then there exists a set $c$, such that every element of $c$ is in some element of $s$, and $c$ has one and only one element in common with each element of $s$.[15]—For let $S$ be the class represented by $s$ (consequence 7 of the axioms III). Then, by consequence 1 of the axiom IV, there exists a function $F$, with $S$ as its domain, which assigns to every element $a$ of $S$ one of the elements of $a$. Since no two elements of $S$ have a common element, $F$ is a one-to-one correspondence. Hence, by the axiom of replacement, the converse domain of $F$ is represented by a set $c$; and it is easily seen that this set $c$ has the required properties.

As we thus see, 6 results from combining a statement about the existence of a function (consequence 1 of our axiom IV) with the axiom of replacement. This was pointed out by Fraenkel.[16]

From V c we obtain:

7. If the classes $A$ and $B$ are represented by sets, their sum is represented by a set.—For if $A$ and $B$ are represented by $a$ and $b$, the sum of $A$ and $B$ is the sum of the elements of the set $(a, b)$.

From V b, c we infer:

8. If the classes $A$ and $B$ are represented by sets, the class of those pairs $\langle a, b \rangle$ for which $a \eta A$ and $b \eta B$ is represented by a set.—For, by the axioms III, corresponding to every fixed element $a$ of $A$ there exists the class of those pairs $\langle b, \langle a, b \rangle \rangle$ for which $b \eta B$. Since this class is a one-to-one correspondence and its domain $B$ is represented by a set, the converse domain is, by V b, also represented by a set. Thus for every element $a$ of $A$ there exists the *set* of those pairs $\langle a, b \rangle$ for which $b \eta B$. Moreover, by the class theorem, there exists the class $C$ of those pairs $\langle a, c \rangle$ whose first member $a$ belongs to $A$, and whose second member $c$ is the set of all pairs having $a$ as first member and an element of $B$ as second member. It follows that the domain of $C$ is $A$. Hence, by the axiom of replacement, since $C$ is a one-to-one correspondence and $A$ is represented by a set, the converse domain of $C$ is represented by a set. Hence, by V c, the sum

---

[15] This is the assertion of the *multiplicative axiom*, which was first introduced by Russell (in RUSSEL (1906) as a modification of the original Zermelo choice postulate (cf. ZERMELO (1904) p. 516) and was independently stated by Zermelo as *axiom of choice*, from which he was able to infer, within his axiom system, the assertion of his former postulate (cf. ZERMELO (1908) p. 110, and (1908a), 266 and pp. 273–274).

[16] FRAENKEL (1922).

of the elements of the converse domain of $C$ is represented by a set.    But this sum is just the class of those pairs $\langle a, b \rangle$ for which $a\eta A$ and $b\eta B$.

We can also derive 8 from V a, c, d in the following way.    If the classes $A$ and $B$ are represented by sets, it follows from 7 (which is a consequence of V c) that the sum of $A$ and $B$ is represented by a set $s$.    By V d, the class of subsets of $s$ is represented by a set $t$, and the class of subsets of $t$ by a set $u$.    Now every pair $\langle a, b \rangle$ for which $a\eta A$ and $b\eta B$ is an element of $u$; for we have $a\epsilon s$ and $b\epsilon s$, hence $(a)\epsilon t$ and $(a, b)\epsilon t$, hence $((a), (a, b))\epsilon u$, i.e., $\langle a, b \rangle \epsilon u$ —since, by definition, $\langle a, b \rangle = ((a), (a, b))$.    Consequently the class of pairs whose first members belong to $A$ and second members to $B$ is a subclass of $u$, and so, by V a, is represented by a set.

This method of proving 8 is more familiar to most mathematicians than that by V b, c.    There is also another method of proving 8, namely by means of IV, V a, V b without using V c or V d, which we shall indicate later on.

Finally, from V a, c, d we obtain the consequence:

9. If $a$ and $b$ are sets, there exists a set whose elements are those functional sets having $a$ as domain and a subset of $b$ as converse domain.—For, since every set represents a class, it follows from 8 that, given sets $a$ and $b$, there exists a set $c$ whose elements are those pairs $\langle k, l \rangle$ for which $k\epsilon a$ and $l\epsilon b$.    Every functional set whose domain is $a$ and whose converse domain is a subset of $b$ is a subset of $c$; hence the class $M$ of all such functional sets—which exists by the class theorem—is a subclass of the class $D$ of all subsets of $c$.    Now, by V d, $D$ is represented by a set.    Hence, by V a, $M$ is represented by a set $m$, which is the set whose existence is asserted in 9.

VI. AXIOM OF INFINITY.    There exists a set of which there is a one-to-one correspondence to a proper subclass.    Or, in other words, there exists a one-to-one correspondence of a class to a proper subclass, the domain of the one-to-one correspondence being represented by a set.

From this axiom, with either V a or V b, we get the *immediate consequence*: There exists a set of which there is a one-to-one correspondence to a proper subset.    This assures the existence of a set representing an infinite class, under the Dedekind definition of infinity,[17] according to which a class is called infinite if there exists a one-to-one correspondence between it and a proper subclass of it.

We shall later discuss the question of the equivalence of this axiom VI to other forms of an axiom of infinity, i.e., of an axiom guaranteeing the existence of an infinite set.

*Remark.*    The axiom of infinity in *Principia mathematica* is of quite a different kind from the axioms of infinity with which we are here concerned.    For it deals with the existence of infinitely many individuals—which, in our system, is a consequence of the axioms II.

---

[17] Cf. DEDEKIND (1888), §5. Of course Dedekind makes no distinction between *classes* anu *sets*; as a matter of fact he uses neither word, but speaks of *systems*.

VII. Restrictive axiom.[18] To every non-empty class $A$ there belongs a set $b$ such that there is no common element of $A$ and $b$. Or, in other words, there is no non-empty class $A$ every element of which has an element belonging to $A$.

Since every set represents a class, an immediate consequence of VII is:

1. Every non-empty set $a$ has an element $b$ such that $a$ and $b$ have no common element.

On the other hand, from this assertion taken as an axiom (call it axiom VII*) axiom VII can be derived as a theorem—as we shall show later—either[19] by means of V a, b, c, d and VI or by means of IV, V a, V b, VI.

From 1 we infer:

2. There is no reflexive set.—For if $a\epsilon a$, the set $(a)$ would contradict 1.

In an analogous way there follows:

3. There are no sets $a$, $b$ such that $a\epsilon b$ and $b\epsilon a$. There are no sets $a$, $b$, $c$ such that $a\epsilon b$ and $b\epsilon c$ and $c\epsilon a$.

4. The null set is an element of every non-empty transitive set.—For let $a$ be a non-empty transitive set. By 1, $a$ has an element $c$ which has no element that is an element of $a$. But, $a$ being transitive, every element of $c$ is an element $a$. Therefore $c$ is the null set.

**5. Foundations of the theory of ordinal numbers.** In axiomatic set theory, the ordinal numbers can be introduced without referring in the definition to the concept of order, so that the theory of ordinals is obtained independently of the theory of ordered sets.

Such an independent general theory of ordinals was obtained by Zermelo (about 1915) but has not been published.

A rather convenient form of this independent theory of ordinals has recently been exhibited by Raphael M. Robinson in connection with his modification of the von Neumann system.[20] We shall follow his method, the simplicity of which will perhaps appear still more clearly in the adaptation to our system.

The only axiom required for this purpose in addition to the elementary axioms I–III is the restrictive axiom VII. As we shall see later, the necessity for axiom VII can be avoided by a modification in the definition of an ordinal, but in that case the axiom V a becomes necessary.

*Definition.* An *ordinal* (or an *ordinal number*) is a transitive set such that, if $a$ and $b$ are any two different elements of it, either $a\epsilon b$ or $b\epsilon a$.

---

[18] The idea of this axiom was first conceived by von Neumann (see von Neumann (1925) p. 239, axiom VI 4). From the original form of it he passed to the present form of the axiom, or to a somewhat stronger axiom in a form adapted to his system, (see von Neumann (1929) p. 231). Zermelo independently introduced this axiom, calling it *Axiom der Fundierung*, (see Zermelo (1930) p. 31).

[19] This dependency was stated by Gödel.

[20] See Robinson (1937).

In consequence of this definition, by the class theorem, the *class of all ordinals* exists.

For the development of the elementary theory of ordinals, we require the following lemmas about reflexive and transitive sets, proofs of which are obvious.

Lemma 1. Every reflexive set has at least one reflexive element.

Lemma 2. If all the elements of a non-empty class are transitive, the set representing the intersection of the elements of the class is also transitive.

Lemma 3. If all the elements of a non-empty class are transitive, a set representing the sum of the elements of the class must also be transitive.

*Definition.* By consequence 2 of the axioms I, II, there is, corresponding to any set $c$, a unique set whose elements are $c$ itself and the elements of $c$. This set will be called $c'$.

Lemma 4. If $a$ is a transitive set, $a'$ is also transitive.

Let us extend the notion of transitivity to classes as well as sets, calling a class transitive if every element of an element of it is an element of it—or, in other words, if every element of it is a subset of it. Then, corresponding to lemma 2 we have: The intersection of the elements of a class of transitive sets is a transitive class.

We now go on to the fundamental theorems on ordinals.

Theorem 1. Every transitive proper subclass of an ordinal is represented by an element of the ordinal.

For let $n$ be an ordinal and $M$ a transitive proper subclass of $n$. If then $D$ is the class of those elements of $n$ not belonging to $M$, $D$ is not empty. By VII, there exists an element $c$ of $D$ such that there is no common element of $c$ and $D$. Now $n$ (as an ordinal) is transitive. Hence every element of $c$ is in $n$ and, since it cannot belong to $D$, must belong to $M$. Therefore $c$ is a subset of $M$.

On the other hand, since $c \eta D$, $c$ does not belong to $M$; and, because $M$ is transitive, $c$ cannot be in an element of $M$. Thus if $a \eta M$, neither $a = c$ nor $c \epsilon a$. But $a \epsilon n$ (since $M$ is a subclass of $n$), and $n$ is an ordinal. Therefore $a \epsilon c$; and, since $a$ was an arbitrary element of $M$, it follows that $M$ is a subclass of $c$.

Since $M$ is a subclass of $c$ and $c$ is a subset of $M$, we have the result that $c$ represents $M$.

As a corollary of this theorem we have: Every transitive proper subset of an ordinal is an element of it. In particular, if $a$ and $b$ are ordinals, and $a \subset b$, then $a \epsilon b$.

Theorem 2. The intersection of the elements of a non-empty class of ordinals is represented by a set belonging to this class.

For if $C$ is a non-empty class of ordinals, and $D$ is the intersection of the elements of $C$, then, by the generalization of lemma 2, $D$ is a transitive class. Let $a$ be any element of $C$; then $D$ is a subclass of $a$. If $D$ is represented by $a$, theorem 2 is verified. Otherwise $D$ is a transitive proper subclass of $a$ and consequently, by theorem 1, is represented by a set $d$ which is an element of $a$. However, $D$ must be represented by *some* element of $C$, because otherwise $d$ would be an element of every element of $C$, and from this would follow $d \eta D$, and therefore $d \epsilon d$, in contradiction to consequence 2 of axiom VII.

*Consequences.* Since every set represents a class, it follows that a set, representing the intersection of the elements of a non-empty set $c$ whose elements are ordinals, is itself in $c$. This applies in particular to the case that $c$ is a set $(a, b)$, $a$ and $b$ being ordinals. Hence follows that the intersection of two ordinals is one of them. I.e., if $a$ and $b$ are distinct ordinals, either $a \subset b$ or $b \subset a$.

Thus the ordinals are *ordered* by the relation "$\subset$" ("being a proper subset of"). Of two ordinals, the one which is a proper subset of the other will be called the *lower*, and the other one, the *higher*. This ordering of the ordinals is a *well-ordering*; in fact it follows from theorem 2 that *among the elements of a non-empty class of ordinals there is always a lowest one*.

Notice that we are here using the words *ordering* and *well-ordering* in the ordinary mathematical sense. Definitions of them within our system, which are here not yet required, will be given later on.

Since, if $a$ and $b$ are ordinals, the relation $a \subset b$ entails $a \epsilon b$, we have that, of any two different ordinals, the lower one is an element of the higher. Thus if $a$ and $b$ are distinct ordinals, either $a \epsilon b$ or $b \epsilon a$.

From this there follows further that *every transitive set of ordinals is an ordinal*.

Theorem 3. Every element of an ordinal is an ordinal.

For let $n$ be an ordinal and $c$ an element of it. Since $n$ is transitive, $c$ is a subset of $n$. Therefore if $a$ and $b$ are any two different elements of $c$, either $a \epsilon b$ or $b \epsilon a$. But $c$ is also transitive; for if $a \epsilon b$ and $b \epsilon c$, the possibilities $a = c$ and $c \epsilon a$ are excluded by consequence 3 of axiom VII; therefore, since $a$ and $c$ are both elements of the ordinal $n$, we must have $a \epsilon c$. Thus $c$ is an ordinal.

Combining with theorem 3 our results concerning the ordering of ordinals, we obtain: *Every ordinal $n$ represents the class of ordinals lower than $n$*.

Since every transitive set of ordinals is an ordinal, we have further, by theorem 3 and lemma 4: *If $a$ is an ordinal, $a'$ is also an ordinal*.

In a similar way, using lemma 3 instead of lemma 4, we obtain: If a set represents the sum of the elements of a class of ordinals, it is itself an ordinal.

The following results are also easily obtained. 0 is the lowest ordinal. If $a$ is an ordinal, the next higher ordinal is $a'$. If $a$ and $b$ are ordinals, and $a' = b'$, then $a = b$. An ordinal $a'$ has $a$ as its highest element; and conversely, an ordinal having a highest element $a$ must be $a'$. If $C$ is a class of ordinals which has no highest element, and there is an ordinal which is higher than every element of $C$, then the sum of the elements of $C$ is represented by a set, namely by the lowest of those ordinals which are higher than every element of $C$.

We have also the negative result that *the class of all ordinals cannot be represented by a set*. In fact, such a set would be a transitive set of ordinals, by theorem 3, and would consequently be itself an ordinal; but this would make it reflexive, contrary to consequence 2 of axiom VII.

Now it is readily verified that the applications of axiom VII which we have made in connection with the theory of ordinals all refer to subclasses of ordinals. In consequence, as remarked by R. M. Robinson,[21] it would be possible to avoid the use of this axiom by adjoining to the definition of an ordinal the following

---

[21] See ROBINSON (1937).

additional condition which a set must satisfy in order to be an ordinal: To every non-empty subclass $C$ of the set there belongs a set which has no element belonging to $C$.

But this modified definition does not allow us to infer by means of the class theorem that the class of all ordinals exists, although this result is necessary for our purposes. The difficulty can be removed, however, if we allow the use of V a; for from this axiom it follows that the stated condition on a subclass $C$ is equivalent to the corresponding condition on a subset (cf. consequence 1 of V a).

Indeed, on the basis of the axioms I–III and V a, we can derive the theory of ordinals in essentially the same way as before if we replace our former definition of an ordinal by the following alternative or second definition:

A set $n$ is an ordinal if (1) $n$ is transitive, and (2) for any two different elements $a$ and $b$ of $n$ either $a \epsilon b$ or $b \epsilon a$, and (3) every non-empty subset $s$ of $n$ has an element $c$ such that $c$ and $s$ have no common element.

Only the two following points then have to be taken into account:

1. In order to conclude that every transitive set of ordinals is itself an ordinal, we must now also show that such a set satisfies the condition (3) of our (second) definition of an ordinal; but this follows at once from the fact that in every non-empty set of ordinals there is a lowest ordinal.

2. In the proof of theorem 3 we have to show that every element of an ordinal satisfies the condition (3); but this is immediate, since an ordinal is transitive and so every element of it is a subset of it.

We add the following remarks:

1) The equivalence of our second definition of an ordinal to the first definition, which obviously subsists on the basis of axiom VII, ceases to be provable with V a in the place of VII. For without VII we cannot exclude, e.g., the possibility of a reflexive set which is its own only element—as we shall show later on by means of a model. Such a set would be an ordinal under our first definition, but not under the second.

We shall usually understand the word *ordinal* in the sense of our second definition—but this can be replaced by the simpler first definition in the case that axiom VII is assumed.

2) With the aid of axiom VII we can prove that a transitive set all of whose elements are transitive is an ordinal. In fact, let $n$ be a transitive set all of whose elements are transitive, and let $S$ be the class of those elements of $n$ which are not ordinals. If $S$ were not empty, there would follow from axiom VII the existence of an element $c$ of $S$ having no element belonging to $S$. Since $n$ is transitive, every element of $c$ would be an element of $n$ not belonging to $S$ and consequently an ordinal. Moreover, as an element of $n$, $c$ would be transitive. But a transitive set of ordinals is itself an ordinal; so $c$ would be an ordinal and could not belong to $S$. The class $S$ must therefore be empty. Thus $n$ is a transitive set of ordinals and is therefore itself an ordinal.

The converse of this theorem is an immediate consequence of theorem 3. Thus if axiom VII is assumed we can characterize the ordinals as those transitive sets whose elements are transitive. The ordinals were defined in this way by Gödel in his lectures at Vienna in 1937.

That this characterization of the ordinals is no longer sufficient if the axiom VII is dropped can be seen by considering again the possibility of a set which is its own only element.

3) Using V a, we can prove that a transitive set, every transitive proper subset of which is an element of it, is an ordinal. For let $n$ be a transitive set, and suppose that every transitive proper subset of $n$ is an element of $n$. By V a, the class of ordinals in $n$ is represented by a set $s$; and, by theorem 3 and the transitivity of $n$, this set $s$ is transitive. Thus $s$ is a transitive set of ordinals and therefore an ordinal. This ordinal must be higher than every ordinal in $n$ and consequently cannot be an element of $n$. Since every transitive proper subset of $n$ is an element of $n$, it follows that $s$ cannot be a proper subset of $n$. Therefore $s = n$, and $n$ is an ordinal.

Since the converse of this follows from theorem 1, the ordinals can be characterized as those transitive sets having the property that every transitive proper subset is an element. We could take this as the definition of an ordinal and, using V a, could develop the theory of ordinals from this definition almost as easily as from the definition we have used. The main difference would be that instead of our theorem 1 we would have to prove that an ordinal cannot have a reflexive element; this we could do by showing that, for every ordinal $n$, the class of those elements of $n$ which do not have a reflexive element is represented by $n$ itself.

4) The definition of an ordinal on which Zermelo based his independent theory of ordinals, referred to at the beginning of this section, was stated in terms of his axioms for set theory (which have no distinction between classes and sets). It can, however, also be formulated with reference to our present system, as follows:[22]

A set $n$ is an ordinal if (1) either $0 = n$ or $0 \epsilon n$, and (2) if $a \epsilon n$ then $a' = n$ or $a' \epsilon n$, and (3) if $s$ is a subset of $n$, the sum of the elements of $s$ is represented by $n$ or by an element $n$.

On the basis of the axioms I–III and V a, this definition can be proved equivalent to our (second) definition. Proofs of the theorems of the Zermelo independent theory of ordinals require in our system no other axioms than I–III and V a.

5) From the axioms I–III and VII it is not possible to prove that a sufficient condition for a transitive set to be an ordinal is that every transitive proper subset of it be an element of it. Likewise it is impossible to prove from these axioms that every set which is an ordinal according to Zermelo's definition, as just given, is also an ordinal under our definition. Both of these independence assertions will be established later by means of a model, or independence example. This model—like the one announced above, concerning the possibility of a set's being its own only element—will be on the basis of number theory as derived from our axioms I–III and VII.

---

[22] We here modify Zermelo's definition slightly, replacing his condition "$0 \epsilon n$" by "$0 = n$ or $0 \epsilon n$," in order that the null set may be counted amongst the ordinals, as it is under our other definitions.

In the applications of ordinals which we shall make, it does not matter which particular definition of an ordinal is chosen. We need only the following properties:

0 *is an ordinal.*

*If $a$ is an ordinal, $a'$ is an ordinal.*

*Every transitive set of ordinals is an ordinal.*

*The ordinals can be ordered by a relation "lower than" in such a way that the elements of an ordinal are all the ordinals lower than it.*

*To every non-empty class of ordinals belongs a lowest ordinal.*

*The class of all ordinals exists.*

**6. Number theory.** From the fundamental theorems about ordinals we can pass to number theory by means of the notion of a *finite ordinal*.

*Definition.* An ordinal is *finite* if both it and every ordinal lower than it are either 0 or of the form $c'$; or, equivalently, if it and every element of it satisfy the condition of either having a highest element or having no element.

From this definition it follows at once that an ordinal lower than a finite ordinal is finite; also, by the class theorem, that the class of all finite ordinals exists. The following consequences are also immediate:

0 is a finite ordinal.

If $n$ is a finite ordinal, then $n'$ is a finite ordinal and $n' \neq 0$.

If $m$ and $n$ are finite ordinals and $m' = n'$, then $m = n$.

If $C$ is a class to which the null set belongs, and if, for every finite ordinal $n$ belonging to $C$, $n'$ also belongs to $C$, then every finite ordinal belongs to $C$. (*Principle of complete induction.*)

In order to prove the principle of complete induction, we may reason as follows. If there were a finite ordinal which did not belong to $C$, the class of finite ordinals not belonging to $C$ (which exists, by the class theorem) would have a lowest element; but this lowest element could be neither the null set nor of the form $c'$; hence a contradiction.

Thus the Peano axioms are satisfied for the finite ordinals if the null set is taken as the number 0 and $n'$ as the successor of $n$.

Moreover the usual method of introducing functions of natural numbers by "recursive definitions" can be justified by an existence theorem.[23] For this purpose we first prove the following *iteration theorem*:

Let $a$ be a set, $A$ a class to which $a$ belongs, and $F$ a function which assigns to every element of $A$ an element of $A$. Then there exists a function $H$ (depending on the parameters $a$ and $F$) which assigns to every finite ordinal an element of $A$, and satisfies the conditions,

$$H(0) = a,$$
$$H(n') = F(H(n))$$

for every finite ordinal $n$.

---

[23] Justification of recursive definition of numerical functions, from the set-theoretic point of view, was first given by Dedekind, see DEDEKIND (1888), §9. We here follow his method, but with the modification that we reduce the recursive definition to the more special case of an iteration.

We show first that, under the given hypotheses, there exists for every finite ordinal $n$ a unique functional set $s$ satisfying the conditions:

(1) The domain of the function represented by $s$ is the class of all ordinals lower than or equal to $n$.

(2) $\langle 0, a \rangle \epsilon s$.

(3) If $\langle k, c \rangle \epsilon s$ and $k \epsilon n$, then $\langle k', F(c) \rangle \epsilon s$.

This we do as follows. The assertion about $n$ that it is a finite ordinal and that there exists a unique functional set satisfying (for this $n$) the conditions (1), (2), (3) is a predicate of $n$ definable by a constitutive expression, with $a$ and $F$ as parameters. Hence, by the class theorem, there exists the class $C$ of those finite ordinals for which there exists a unique functional set $s$ satisfying (1), (2), (3). Moreover we show easily that 0 belongs to $C$, and if a finite ordinal $n$ belongs to $C$ then $n'$ belongs to $C$. Hence by complete induction we infer that $C$ is the class of all finite ordinals.

Now the predicate of $n$ and $b$, that $n$ is a finite ordinal and $b$ is the value assigned to $n$ by a functional set satisfying (1), (2), (3), can be defined by a constitutive expression. Hence, by the class theorem, there exists the class of pairs $\langle n, b \rangle$ such that this predicate holds of $n$ and $b$. It then follows that this class of pairs is a function $H$, whose domain is the class of all finite ordinals, and whose value $H(n)$ for a finite ordinal $n$ is the value assigned to $n$ by the functional set $s$ satisfying (1), (2), (3). The equation $H(0) = a$ obviously holds. That $H(n') = F(H(n))$ for every finite ordinal $n$ can be proved by showing—as is easily done—that the value, assigned to $n$ by the functional set satisfying (1), (2), (3) with $n'$ substituted for $n$, is the same as that assigned to $n$ by the functional set $s$ satisfying (1), (2), (3).

Finally, by an application of complete induction, we see that for every finite ordinal $n$ the value of $H$ belongs to $A$. This completes the proof of the iteration theorem.

*Definition.* If $a$ is a set and $F$ a function, and there exists a class $A$ such that $a \eta A$ and, if $c \eta A$, then $F(c) \eta A$, then the function $H$, which has the class of finite ordinals as its domain and satisfies the conditions $H(0) = a$ and $H(n') = F(H(n))$ for every finite ordinal $n$, will be called the *iterator* of $F$ on $a$.

The constitutive expression by which, under the hypotheses of the iteration theorem, the iterator of $F$ on $a$ is defined, contains $a$ as a parameter, and the variable $n$ ranging over the finite ordinals as an argument. But we may also take $a$ as argument and $n$ as parameter; or $n$ and $a$ may both be taken as arguments. Hence we obtain the following:

*Corollary.* On the hypotheses of the iteration theorem, there exists for every finite ordinal $n$ a function assigning to every element $a$ of $A$ the value that the iterator of $F$ on $a$ has for $n$; this function will be called the *n-fold iteration* of $F$. Likewise there exists a function assigning to every pair $\langle a, n \rangle$, with $a \eta A$ and $n$ a finite ordinal, the value for $n$ of the iterator of $F$ on $a$.

By means of the concept of the $n$-fold iteration of a function, the most familiar arithmetic functions can be defined. Thus for finite ordinals $m, n$:

$m + n$ is the value for the argument $m$ of the $n$-fold iteration of the function which assigns to a finite ordinal $a$ the value $a'$.

$m \cdot n$ is the value for the argument 0 of the $n$-fold iteration of the function which assigns to a finite ordinal $a$ the value $a+m$.

$m^n$ is the value for the argument $0'$ of the function which assigns to a finite ordinal $a$ the value $a \cdot m$.

Under these definitions, we have for all finite ordinals $m$, $n$ the equations,

$$m + 0 = m \qquad\qquad m \cdot 0 = 0 \qquad\qquad m^0 = 0'$$
$$m + n' = (m + n)' \qquad m \cdot n' = m \cdot n + m \qquad m^{n'} = m^n \cdot m$$

—from which the well-known properties of the three arithmetic functions can be derived by complete induction.

It is also possible to show that the ternary relations,

$$a + b = c, \qquad a \cdot b = c, \qquad a^b = c,$$

can be represented by constitutive expressions.

From the iteration theorem we deduce the following *theorem of finite recursion*:

Let $a$ be a set, $A$ a class to which $a$ belongs, and $G$ a function which assigns an element of $A$ to every pair $\langle k, c \rangle$ in which $k$ is a finite ordinal and $c$ is an element of $A$. Then there exists a function $K$ which assigns an element of $A$ to every finite ordinal, and satisfies the conditions,

$$K(0) = a,$$
$$K(n') = G(\langle n, K(n) \rangle)$$

for every finite ordinal $n$.

For let $P$ be the class of all pairs $\langle k, c \rangle$, where $k$ is a finite ordinal and $c \eta A$, and let $F$ be the function obtained from $G$ by replacing every element $\langle \langle k, c \rangle, d \rangle$ of $G$ by $\langle \langle k, c \rangle, \langle k', d \rangle \rangle$. (The existence of such a function follows by means of the axioms III from the existence of the class of pairs $\langle k, k' \rangle$, which in turn follows from the class theorem.) Then $\langle 0, a \rangle \eta P$, and $F$ assigns to every element of $P$ an element of $P$. Now, using the iteration theorem, let $H$ be the iterator of $F$ on $\langle 0, a \rangle$. Then,

$$H(0) = \langle 0, a \rangle,$$
$$H(n') = F(H(n))$$

for every finite ordinal $n$. It follows by complete induction that, for every finite ordinal $n$, $H(n)$ is a pair having $n$ as its first member. Hence

$$F(H(n)) = \langle n', G(H(n)) \rangle.$$

If $K$ is the converse domain of $H$, it follows that $K$ is a function such that, for every finite ordinal $n$,

$$H(n) = \langle n, K(n) \rangle.$$

Then

$$K(0) = a,$$

and, for every finite ordinal $n$,

$$\langle n', K(n') \rangle = \langle n', G(H(n)) \rangle,$$
$$K(n') = G(H(n))$$
$$= G(\langle n, K(n) \rangle).$$

This completes the proof.

*Remark 1.* The theorem of finite recursion obviously could be proved directly in the same way that we proved the iteration theorem (and the iteration theorem itself would then be an immediate corollary). However, it seems to be of interest in itself that a "recursive definition" of the form $K(0) = a$, $K(n') = G(\langle n, K(n) \rangle)$ can be reduced to a definition by mere iteration of a function.[24]

*Remark 2.* As can be seen by examining the proof, there is a *corollary* to the theorem of finite recursion entirely analogous to that which we stated for the iteration theorem.

We have also the means of reproducing definitions of numerical functions employing the concept of "the least number such that." This results from the following considerations.

Let $C$ be a class of pairs whose domain is a class of ordinals and converse domain a subclass of a class $A$. Consider the following predicate of $a$ and $b$: "$a$ belongs to $A$; if $a$ does not belong to the converse domain of $C$, $b$ is the null set; and if $a$ does belong to the converse domain of $C$, then $b$ is the lowest of those ordinals which occur as first member in some pair which belongs to $C$ and has $a$ as second member." This predicate can be defined by a constitutive expression. Hence, by the class theorem, there exists a function having $A$ as its domain and assigning (1) to each element $a$ of $A$ for which there is an ordinal $n$ such that $\langle n, a \rangle \eta C$, the lowest such ordinal, and (2) to other elements of $a$, the null set.

This applies in particular to the case that, for a given $(k+1)$-ary relation $R(a_1, a_2, \cdots, a_k, a_{k+1})$ between finite ordinals which can be represented by a constitutive expression, $C$ is the class (whose existence follows from the class theorem) of those normal $(k+1)$-tuplets $\langle a_{k+1}, \langle a_1, \langle a_2, \cdots, \langle a_{k-1}, a_k \rangle \cdots \rangle \rangle \rangle$, formed out of finite ordinals, for which $R(a_1, a_2, \cdots, a_k, a_{k+1})$ holds. Here the elements of the domain of $C$ are finite ordinals, and the elements of the converse domain are normal $k$-tuplets formed out of finite ordinals.

Thus we obtain the result that, for every $(k+1)$-ary relation $R(a_1, a_2, \cdots, a_k, a_{k+1})$ between finite ordinals which can be represented by a constitutive expression, there exists a function which assigns to every normal $k$-tuplet $\langle a_1, \langle a_2, \cdots, \langle a_{k-1}, a_k \rangle \cdots \rangle \rangle$ whose members are finite ordinals (1) the lowest finite ordinal $a_{k+1}$ such that $R(a_1, a_2, \cdots, a_k, a_{k+1})$ holds, if there is such a finite ordinal $a_{k+1}$ at all, and (2) otherwise the ordinal 0.

With this, we have at our disposition a sufficient basis for the development of number theory.[25]

We shall now indicate how the *theory of finite classes and finite sets* is obtainable from the theory of finite ordinals. For this purpose we require first the following results about finite ordinals.

---

[24] This reduction figures in the investigations of A. Church, J. B. Rosser, and S. C. Kleene on the "$\lambda$-definability" of numerical functions. See KLEENE (1935) pp. 153–173 and 219–244, especially the passage from the theorem 15 IV to 15 V, pp. 220–221.

[25] Cf., e.g., HILBERT and BERNAYS (1934) vol. 1, pp. 401–422.

($\alpha$) If the domain of a function is represented by a finite ordinal, the converse domain is represented by a set.

For let $F$ be the function in question and $n$ the finite ordinal representing the domain of $F$. By complete induction we can show that for every finite ordinal $k$ there exists a set whose elements are those sets $c$ for which there exists an element $\langle l, c \rangle$ of $F$ with $l \epsilon k$. Then taking $n$ for $k$ we have that the converse domain of $F$ is represented by a set.

Corollary 1. Every subclass of a finite ordinal is represented by a set.

For if $S$ is a subclass of a finite ordinal $n$, then either $S$ is empty and is represented by the null set, or for any element $a$ of $S$ the class whose elements are the pairs $\langle c, c \rangle$ for which $c \eta S$ and the pairs $\langle d, a \rangle$ for which $d \epsilon n$ but not $d \eta S$, is a function whose domain is represented by $n$ and whose converse domain is $S$. Hence, by ($\alpha$), $S$ is represented by a set.

Corollary 2. If there is a one-to-one correspondence between a class $A$ and a finite ordinal, then $A$ and the one-to-one correspondence are each represented by a set.

This follows by applying ($\alpha$) to the converse class of the one-to-one correspondence in question, and to the class of triplets of the form $\langle a, \langle b, a \rangle \rangle$ where $\langle b, a \rangle$ belongs to the one-to-one correspondence—since each of these classes is a function whose domain is a finite ordinal.

*Definition.* That there exists a one-to-one correspondence between the class $A$ and the class $B$ will be denoted by $A \backsim B$ ("$A$ one-to-one with $B$").

This relation has the characteristic properties of an equality or equivalence relation. In fact, for every class $A$ we have $A \backsim A$ by consequence 6 of the axioms III, and the axioms III b (3), a (3); if $A \backsim B$ then $B \backsim A$, by III c (2); if $A \backsim B$ and $B \backsim C$, then $A \backsim C$, by the composition lemma.

For sets $a$ and $b$, $a$ representing a class $A$, and $b$ representing a class $B$, the notations $a \backsim b$, $a \backsim B$, $A \backsim b$ will be used to mean the same thing as $A \backsim B$. (Read "$a$ one-to-one with $b$," etc.)

Corollary 3. There exists the class of those pairs $\langle a, b \rangle$ for which $a$ is a finite ordinal and $a \backsim b$.

This follows from corollary 2 by the same method by which in §4 the existence of the class of all pairs $\langle a, b \rangle$ for which $a \backsim b$ was inferred[26] from the consequence 3 of axiom V b. (For the present corollary, of course V b is not required.)

($\beta$) For every proper subset $s$ of a finite ordinal $n$, there exists a one-to-one correspondence between $s$ and an ordinal lower than $n$.

This is proved as follows. By the class theorem and corollary 3 of ($\alpha$) there exists a class $A$ whose elements are those finite ordinals $n$ which satisfy the condition that, for every proper subset $s$ of $n$, there is a one-to-one correspondence between $s$ and an ordinal lower than $n$. Evidently 0 belongs to $A$. Thus, in order to prove ($\beta$), by the principle of complete induction it is sufficient to show that, if a finite ordinal $n$ belongs to $A$, then $n'$ belongs to $A$.

Let $n$ be a finite ordinal belonging to $A$ and $t$ a proper subset of $n'$. If $t=n$, then $t \backsim n$, and so there is a one-to-one correspondence between $t$ and an ordinal lower than $n'$; and this holds also for $t \subset n$, since $n \eta A$. If $t$ is not a subset of $n$,

[26] See p. 15.

then $n\epsilon t$ and there is at least one element of $n$ that is not in $t$. Let $P$ be the class of those elements of $t$ which are different from $n$. By corollary 1 of $(\alpha)$, $P$ is represented by a set $p$. Since $p \subset n$ and $n\eta A$, there exists a one-to-one correspondence $C$ between $p$ and an ordinal $m$ lower than $n$. Now the class, whose elements are the elements of $C$ and in addition the pair $\langle n, m \rangle$, is a one-to-one correspondence between $t$ and $m'$; and $m'$ is an ordinal lower than $n'$. Thus in every case there exists a one-to-one correspondence between $t$ and an ordinal lower than $n'$—as was to be proved.

($\gamma$) There cannot be a one-to-one correspondence between a finite ordinal $n$ and an ordinal different from $n$.

The proof is as follows. By the class theorem and corollary 3 of $(\alpha)$, there exists the class $B$ of those finite ordinals of which there exists a one-to-one correspondence to another ordinal. If this class were non-empty, there would be a lowest ordinal $l$ belonging to it and there would exist an ordinal $k$ different from $l$ such that $l \backsim k$. This ordinal $k$ could not be lower than $l$, since otherwise we would have $k\eta B$ in contradiction to the characterizing property of $l$. Hence $l \subset k$; and consequently the class of those pairs, belonging to the one-to-one correspondence between $l$ and $k$, which have their second member in $l$ would be a one-to-one correspondence between a proper subclass of $l$ and $l$ itself. That subclass being represented, in accordance with corollary 1 of $(\alpha)$, by a set $m$, we should have $m \subset l$ and $m \backsim l$. Moreover, by $(\beta)$, there would exist an ordinal $p$ lower than $l$ such that $m \backsim p$, and from $m \backsim l$ and $m \backsim p$ would follow $p \backsim l$, and hence $p\eta B$, in contradiction to the characterizing property of $l$. It follows that the class $B$ is empty, as was to be proved.

Now we are able to go on to the general definition of finiteness.

*Definition.* A class or set will be called *finite* if there exists a one-to-one correspondence between it and a finite ordinal.

In order to show that this definition is really a generalization of our definition of a finite ordinal, we have to verify that according to it an ordinal is a finite set if and only if it is a finite ordinal. This is now immediate, however, since, on the one hand, every finite ordinal is one-to-one with itself, and, on the other hand, by $(\gamma)$, there cannot be a one-to-one correspondence between an ordinal that is not finite and a finite ordinal.

We note also the existence of the class of all finite sets—which follows from corollary 3 of $(\alpha)$.

As consequences of $(\alpha)$, $(\beta)$, $(\gamma)$, we obtain further the following *theorems on finite classes and sets.*

1. Every finite class is represented by a finite set.—This is an immediate consequence of corollary 2 of $(\alpha)$.

2. Every subclass of a finite class is finite.—This follows by combining corollary 1 of $(\alpha)$ with $(\beta)$.

3. There is only one finite ordinal which is one-to-one with a given finite class (or finite set).—This is an immediate consequence of $(\gamma)$.

*Definition.* We shall call the unique finite ordinal which is one-to-one with a given finite class $A$ (or a given finite set $a$) the *number attributable* to the class $A$ (or to the set $a$).

4. The number attributable to a proper subclass (or a proper subset) of a

finite class (or a finite set) is lower than the number attributable to this class (set).—We obtain this as a consequence of 3 (just stated) and ($\beta$), making use of the fact that every subclass of a finite ordinal is represented by a set.

5. There is no one-to-one correspondence between a finite class and a proper subclass of it.

For let $A$ be a finite class, $B$ a proper subclass of it, and $n$ the number attributable to $A$. Then $n$ is a finite ordinal and there exists a one-to-one correspondence $C$ between $A$ and $n$. The class of those elements of $C$ whose first member belongs to $B$ is a one-to-one correspondence between $B$ and a proper subclass of $n$ that is represented by a set $s$. By ($\beta$), there exists an ordinal $m$ lower than $n$ such that $s \backsim m$. Now if there were a one-to-one correspondence between $A$ and $B$, we should have $A \backsim B$, $n \backsim A$, $B \backsim s$, $s \backsim m$, and consequently $n \backsim m$. But this contradicts ($\gamma$).

Starting from these fundamentals, the theory of finite classes and sets and of the numbers attributable to them can be derived by number-theoretic methods. In particular, the following theorems are to be proved here:

1) If $A$ and $B$ are finite classes and have no common element, and $m$ and $n$ are the numbers attributable to $A$ and $B$ respectively, then the sum of $A$ and $B$ is finite and the number attributable to it is $m+n$.

2) If $A$ and $B$ are finite classes and $m$ and $n$ are the numbers attributable to them, then the class of pairs $\langle a, b \rangle$ such that $a\eta A$ and $b\eta B$ is finite and the number attributable to it is $m \cdot n$.

3) If $A$ is a finite class and $m$ is the number attributable to it, then the class of subsets of $A$ is finite and the number attributable to it is $2^m$, where 2 is the ordinal $0''$.

4) If $A$ is a finite class whose elements are finite, then the sum of the elements of $A$ is finite.

A principal point of the method here set forth for developing number theory and the theory of finite classes and sets is that it is necessary to use for it, besides the axioms I–III, only the restrictive axiom VII or instead of it the subclass axiom V a.

For the foundation of number theory by Dedekind's method—which can also be reproduced within our system—the axiom of infinity VI would be required, as well as V a. Zermelo was the first to show that, for a set-theoretic foundation of number theory and the theory of finite sets, it is possible to do without assuming the existence of an infinite set.[27]

Analogous to this possibility for number theory is the possibility of avoiding the sum axiom V c and the power axiom V d in the development of analysis and of general set theory—as will appear in the next two parts.

---

[27] ZERMELO (1909) and (1909a). See also GRELLING (1910).

## PART III[28]

**7. Axioms of infinity.** The foundation of analysis does not require the full generality of set theory but can be accomplished within a more restricted frame. Just as for number theory we need not introduce a set of all finite ordinals but only a class of all finite ordinals, all sets which occur being finite, so likewise for analysis we need not have a set of all real numbers but only a class of them, and the sets with which we have to deal are either finite or enumerable.

We begin with the definitions of infinity and enumerability and with some consideration of these concepts on the basis of the axioms I–III, IV, V a, V b, which, as we shall see later, are sufficient for general set theory. Let us recall that the axioms I–III and V a suffice for establishing number theory, in particular for the iteration theorem, and for the theorems on finiteness.

*Definitions.* A class or a set is called *infinite* if it is not finite. A class or a set is *enumerable* if there exists a one-to-one correspondence between it and the class of finite ordinals. The latter class (the class of finite ordinals) will be denoted by N.

From this negative definition of infinity we can derive the following positive criterion: A class $A$, or a set $a$, is infinite if and only if for every finite ordinal $n$ there is a subset $s$ of $A$, or of $a$, such that $s \backsim n$.

Indeed, that this condition excludes finiteness follows by our fourth theorem on finite classes and sets (Part II, p. 16), and that on the other hand it is satisfied by any infinite class or set is easily proved by complete induction.

By this criterion it is seen immediately that the class N is infinite, since every finite ordinal is a subset of N. The same thing may be proved also, with the aid of our fifth theorem on finite classes and sets, by showing the existence of a one-to-one correspondence between the class N and a proper subclass of it. There are, in fact, many such one-to-one correspondences, one of them being, for instance, the class of those pairs $\langle a, b \rangle$ for which $a$ is a finite ordinal and $b = a'$.

The fact that the class N is infinite induces a connection between infinity and enumerability. For if $A$ is an infinite class and $A \backsim B$, then $B$ is also infinite; and moreover a class having an infinite subclass is itself infinite, by our second theorem on finite classes and sets. Hence every enumerable class is infinite, and every class which has an enumerable subclass is infinite.

The converse of the last also holds: Every infinite class has an enumerable subclass.

*Proof.* Let $A$ be an infinite class. Then every finite subset of $A$ is a proper subset. By the class theorem, there exists the class of all pairs $\langle a, b \rangle$ for which $a$ is a finite subset of $A$ and $b \eta A$ but not $b \epsilon a$. Applying the axiom of choice to this class, we infer the existence of a function $L$ which has as its domain the class of finite subsets of $A$ and assigns to each of these subsets an element of $A$ which is not in this subset.

Moreover, by the class theorem, there exists the class $F$ of pairs $\langle\langle a, b\rangle, \langle c, d\rangle\rangle$ such that $\langle a, b\rangle \eta L$ and $\langle c, d\rangle \eta L$ and $c$ is the set arising from $a$ by adjoining $b$ to it as an element. Then $F$ is a function which assigns to every element of $L$ an element of $L$, and hence, by the iteration theorem, there exists the iterator of $F$ on $\langle 0, L(0)\rangle$. Let $H$ be this iterator. Then by complete induction it follows that, if $m$ and $n$ are finite ordinals and $m\epsilon n$, the first member of $H(m)$ is a proper subset of the first member of $H(n)$, and the second member of $H(m)$ is in the first member of $H(n)$, but the second member of $H(n)$ is not in the first member of $H(n)$. Hence the class $C$ of pairs $\langle n, r\rangle$, such that $n$ is a finite ordinal and $r$ is the second member of $H(n)$, is a one-to-one correspondence. Since the values of $H$ are elements of $L$, the converse domain of $C$ is a subclass of $A$. Thus $A$ has an enumerable subclass.

A consequence of this theorem (just proved) is that for every infinite class there exists a one-to-one correspondence to a proper subclass. For since the class N, as already stated, has a one-to-one correspondence to a proper subclass, the same thing (by the composition lemma) holds for any enumerable class, and likewise for any class having an enumerable subclass. Conversely, by our fifth theorem on finite classes and sets, a class which has a one-to-one correspondence to a proper subclass of itself is infinite.

Thus we have two conditions, each necessary and sufficient, for a class to be infinite: one that it has an enumerable subclass, the other that there is a one-to-one correspondence between it and a proper subclass of it.

As to sets' being infinite, it follows from our definition of infinity that a set is infinite if and only if it represents an infinite class. Moreover, from the necessary and sufficient conditions for a class to be infinite, just stated, there follow (with the aid of the axiom V a) exactly corresponding necessary and sufficient conditions for a set to be infinite: one that it has an enumerable subset, the other that there is a one-to-one correspondence between it and a proper subset of it.

We can apply the foregoing to our axiom of infinity (axiom VI), which says that there is a one-to-one correspondence of some class represented by a set to a proper subclass. The content of this axiom now proves to be equivalent (on the basis of the axioms I–III, IV, V a, V b) to the existence of an infinite set. This in turn is equivalent to the existence of an enumerable set, and also (by axiom V b) to the existence of a set representing the class N.

Thus we have that our axiom VI is equivalent to the assertion that the class N of finite ordinals is represented by a set.

In this way the equivalence is proved with the aid of the axiom of choice. But the axiom of choice can be avoided here by means of the following more direct reasoning. First, since there exists a one-to-one correspondence between the class N and a proper subclass of it, the assertion of axiom VI can be inferred from the assumption that the class N is represented by a set. On the other hand, by axiom VI there exists a class $A$ which is represented by a set and of which there is a one-to-one correspondence $C$ to a proper subclass $B$. Let $d$ be an element of $A$ that is not in $B$. Then the iterator of $C$ on $d$, as is easily shown by means of complete induction, is a one-to-one correspondence between the class N and a subclass $S$ of $A$. Since $A$ is represented by a set, it follows by V a that $S$ is represented by a set, and hence by V b that N is represented by a set.

Thus, on the basis of the axioms I–III, V a, and V b, the axiom VI is equivalent to the assumption that the class N is represented by a set.

From this we can now also easily infer the equivalence of axiom VI to the Zermelo axiom of infinity, to Fraenkel's generalization of this axiom, and to the von Neumann axiom of infinity. However, for the proofs of the second and third of these equivalences the axioms I–III, V a, V b are not sufficient: for the second equivalence the theorem of replacement, or the axiom V*, will be required, and for the third equivalence the axiom of choice (or else V d and V*) will be required.

The Zermelo axiom of infinity[29] asserts the existence of a set such that 0 is an element of it and if $c$ is an element of it then $(c)$ is also. The equivalence of this axiom to the assumption that the class N is represented by a set, and hence to axiom VI, results as follows. The iterator on 0 of the function assigning to any set $a$ the set $(a)$ is a one-to-one correspondence, as is easily shown by means of complete induction. The domain of this one-to-one correspondence is N. Let $A$ be its converse domain. Then $0\eta A$, and if $c\eta A$ then $(c)\eta A$. Thus, by the axiom V b, if N is represented by a set then $A$ is represented by a set; i.e., the assertion of the Zermelo axiom of infinity holds. On the other hand, if $s$ is a set of the kind whose existence is asserted by the Zermelo axiom of infinity, then $A \subseteq s$, as follows without difficulty by complete induction.[30] Thus, by the axioms V a and V b, the class $A$ and therefore also N is represented by a set.

Of the Zermelo axiom of infinity there is a generalization which was proposed by Fraenkel, and was adopted by R. M. Robinson for his modification of the von Neumann system of set theory.[31] This axiom—let us call it VI*—asserts the following: For every set $a$ and every function $F$, there exists a set $s$, such that $a\epsilon s$ and for every element $b$ of $s$ belonging to the domain of $F$, also $F(b) \epsilon s$.

In order to derive this assertion from the assumption that the class N is represented by a set, we consider the function $G$ which assigns to every element $c$ of the domain of $F$ the value $F(c)$ and to every other set the value $a$. The iterator $H$ of $G$ on $a$ is a function whose domain is N. By our assumption

---

[29] ZERMELO (1908a) "Axiom VII", pp. 266–267.

[30] For typographical reasons we now use the character $\subseteq$ instead of the character $\overline{\in}$ which was introduced in Part I, p. 2.

[31] FRAENKEL (1927) "Axiom VII c", p. 114; ROBINSON (1937) axiom 8.3, p. 31. In Robinson's formulation of the axiom, as in ours following, the express assertion contained in Fraenkel's axiom VII c that there exists at least one set is omitted.

and the theorem of replacement, the converse domain of $H$ is represented by a set. And this set, as is easily seen, is a set of the kind whose existence is asserted by VI*.

On the other hand, from VI* the Zermelo axiom of infinity follows as a special case, and hence, as just shown, there follows by V a and V b that the class N is represented by a set.

The von Neumann axiom of infinity[32] (translated into terms of our system) asserts the existence of a non-empty set every element of which is a proper subset of another element. This assertion is an immediate consequence of the assumption that the class N is represented by a set, since every finite ordinal is a proper subset of every higher finite ordinal. On the other hand, if $s$ is a set of the kind whose existence is asserted by the von Neumann axiom of infinity, then by the class theorem and the axiom of choice there exists a function $F$ assigning to every element $a$ of $s$ another element $b$ of $s$ such that $a \subset b$. Let $c$ be an element of $s$. Then the iterator of $F$ on $c$ is a function whose domain is N and whose converse domain is a subclass of $s$. This function is a one-to-one correspondence, since its value for a finite ordinal $m$ is a proper subset of its value for a finite ordinal higher than $m$. Therefore, by the axioms V a and V b, N is represented by a set.

*Remark.* The application of the axiom of choice in the last proof can be avoided if axiom V d and also V* are available. For from the assumption that every element of $s$ is a proper subset of another element, we first infer by complete induction that for every finite ordinal $m$ there exists a functional set $f$ with the domain $m$ such that $f(0) \, \epsilon \, s$ and, if $k' \epsilon m$, then $f(k) \, \epsilon \, s$, and $f(k') \, \epsilon \, s$, and $f(k) \subset f(k')$. Then $f$ is immediately seen to be a one-to-one correspondence and $m$ therefore to be the number attributable to the converse domain of $f$. Thus for every finite ordinal $m$ there exists a subset of $s$ (namely the converse domain of $f$) the number attributable to which is $m$. Now let $G$ be the function whose domain is the class of subsets of $s$ and which assigns to every finite subset of $s$ the number attributable to it, and to every infinite subset of $s$ the null set. By V d the domain of $G$ is represented by a set, and hence, by V*, the converse domain of $G$ is also represented by a set. But this converse domain is N, and thus we have that N is represented by a set.

In addition let us point out the following equivalence. The assumption that the class N is represented by a set—which, on the basis of the axioms I–III, V a, and V b, can replace our axiom of infinity—is, by axiom V b, obviously equivalent to the assumption that *every enumerable class is represented by a set*.

The latter assumption, if taken as an axiom, may be called the *axiom of the enumerable*. It can be derived more or less directly from VI* and V a, without using V b. For let $A$ be an enumerable class, and $C$ a one-to-one correspondence between N and $A$. Then by the class theorem there exists a function $F$ assigning to every element $a$ of $A$ the set $b$ for which there exists a finite ordinal $n$ such that $\langle n, a \rangle \eta C$ and $\langle n', b \rangle \eta C$. By VI*, there exists a set $s$ such that $C(0) \, \epsilon \, s$ and

---

[32] VON NEUMANN (1925) axiom V 1, p. 226.

⟫ for every finite ordinal $n$ for which $C(n)$ $\epsilon$ $s$, also $C(n')$ $\epsilon$ $s$. Hence by complete induction, $A \subseteq s$, and, by V a, the class $A$ is represented by a set.[30]

Our task now, in regard to the foundation of analysis, is to show that the axiom of the enumerable if added to the axioms I–III and VII—which, as we know, suffice for number theory and the theory of finite classes and sets (axiom VII being replaceable here by V a if desired)—is sufficient for the whole of analysis with the exception merely of a particular kind of inference for which the axiom of choice seems to be required (although only as applied in a certain special way).

As the foundations of analysis are so well known, we may content ourselves for this purpose with the indication of some principal points.

**8. Theorems on enumerability, fraction triplets, real numbers.** As a preliminary, we introduce the following notation. The class of pairs $\langle a, b \rangle$ such that $a \eta A$ and $b \eta B$ will be denoted by $A \times B$ and will be called the *pair class* of $A$ and $B$—or, if $A$ and $B$ are the same class, simply the *pair class* of $A$.

We begin with some *theorems on enumerability*.

1. If $A$ and $B$ are enumerable classes, their pair class $A \times B$ is also enumerable.

In order to prove this, we show first that the class $N \times N$, i.e., the class of pairs of finite ordinals, is enumerable. There are, in fact, various one-to-one correspondences between $N$ and $N \times N$; one of these is the class of triplets $\langle c, \langle a, b \rangle \rangle$ of finite ordinals $c$, $a$, $b$ satisfying the condition that $c' = 2^a \cdot (2b)'$. Thus $N \backsim N \times N$. Now if $A$ and $B$ are enumerable classes, and $C$ and $D$ are one-to-one correspondences between $N$ and $A$ and between $N$ and $B$ respectively, then the class of quadruplets $\langle \langle a, b \rangle, \langle c, d \rangle \rangle$ such that $\langle a, c \rangle \eta C$ and $\langle b, d \rangle \eta D$ is a one-to-one correspondence between $N \times N$ and $A \times B$. So we have $N \times N \backsim A \times B$, and this together with $N \backsim N \times N$ gives $N \backsim A \times B$.

2. Every subclass of an enumerable class is either finite or enumerable.

In order to prove this it is sufficient, in view of the composition lemma, to show that every class of finite ordinals is either finite or enumerable. Let $A$ be any class of finite ordinals. We have the two possibilities, that there is or is not an ordinal which is higher than every ordinal belonging to $A$. In the first case $A$ is a subclass of a finite ordinal and hence, by our second theorem on finite classes and sets, is finite. In the second case there exists a function $F$ assigning to each ordinal $n$ belonging to $A$ the lowest of those ordinals which are higher than $n$ and belong to $A$. If $l$ is the lowest ordinal belonging to $A$, then the iterator of $F$ on $l$, as easily seen, is a one-to-one correspondence between $N$ and $A$, and thus $A$ proves to be enumerable.

3. If the domain of a function is enumerable, the converse domain is either finite or enumerable, and the function itself is enumerable.

For let $F$ be a function whose domain is enumerable, and let $B$ be the converse domain of $F$. Then, by the composition lemma, there exists a function $G$ whose domain is $N$ and whose converse domain is $B$. Consider the class of those elements $\langle n, b \rangle$ of $G$ for which there is no other element $\langle m, b \rangle$ of $G$ (with the same $b$) such that $m \epsilon n$; this class is a one-to-one correspondence whose domain is a subclass $A$ of $N$ and whose converse domain is $B$, in consequence of the fact that for every element $b$ of $B$ there is a lowest of those finite ordinals

$n$ for which $\langle n, b\rangle \eta G$. By the preceding theorem 2 on enumerability, the class $A$ is either finite or enumerable, and consequently the same holds for $B$.

Moreover the class of those pairs $\langle\langle a, b\rangle, a\rangle$ such that $\langle a, b\rangle \eta F$ is a one-to-one correspondence between $F$ and its domain. Since the domain is enumerable, $F$ is also.

Combining this theorem 3 with the first theorem on finite classes and sets, and the axiom of the enumerable, we get the following *consequence*: If the domain of a function is enumerable, then not only the domain but also the converse domain and the function itself are represented by sets.

Thus for the case of a function whose domain is enumerable we have here the same results that were obtained for functions in general on the basis of the axioms IV, V a, V b.[33] Hence we may also in this case, following our definition in §4, define the *domain* and the *converse domain* of a functional set representing a given function to be the sets representing respectively the domain and the converse domain of that function.

Now we are to translate into our system Dedekind's method of introducing the real numbers. For this purpose we do not need the concept of a rational number, but only something corresponding to the arithmetic expressions $\pm m/n$ representing rational numbers. Or instead of these expressions we may consider expressions of the form $(k-l)/n$, in which $k$, $l$, and $n$ are integers, $k \geqq 0$, $l \geqq 0$, and $n > 0$; by this method we avoid certain distinctions of cases in the definitions of the arithmetic operations.

Thus we are led to consider, within the frame of our system, those triplets $\langle\langle a, b\rangle, c\rangle$ in which $a$, $b$, $c$ are finite ordinals and $c \neq 0$. We shall call them, in reference to the use we make of them, *fraction triplets*.

From our first theorem on enumerability follows that the class of all fraction triplets is enumerable. Consequently, by the second theorem on enumerability, every class of fraction triplets is either finite or enumerable, and therefore, by our first theorem on finite classes and sets and by the axiom of the enumerable, every class of fraction triplets is represented by a set.

In order to give the fraction triplets their arithmetic rôle, we have to set up definitions of *sum*, *difference*, and *product* of fraction triplets. These are formulated by the following defining equations, referring to the fraction triplets $\langle\langle a, b\rangle, c\rangle$ and $\langle\langle k, l\rangle, m\rangle$:

$$\langle\langle a, b\rangle, c\rangle + \langle\langle k, l\rangle, m\rangle = \langle\langle (m\cdot a)+(c\cdot k), (m\cdot b)+(c\cdot l)\rangle, c\cdot m\rangle,$$

$$\langle\langle a, b\rangle, c\rangle - \langle\langle k, l\rangle, m\rangle = \langle\langle (m\cdot a)+(c\cdot l), (m\cdot b)+(c\cdot k)\rangle, c\cdot m\rangle,$$

$$\langle\langle a, b\rangle, c\rangle \cdot \langle\langle k, l\rangle, m\rangle = \langle\langle (a\cdot k)+(b\cdot l), (a\cdot l)+(b\cdot k)\rangle, c\cdot m\rangle.$$

*Remark:* We are able to take here the same symbols for the operations with fraction triplets as we use for those with finite ordinals, because a fraction triplet, as is easily seen, is never an ordinal, and thus there is no danger of confusion. A corresponding remark will apply later in connection with the elementary operations with real numbers.

[33] Cf. Part II, pp. 15–16.

We make also the following definitions:

A fraction triplet $\langle\langle a,\ b\rangle,\ c\rangle$ will be called *positive, negative,* or a *null triplet* according as the ordinal $a$ is higher than $b$, lower than $b$, or identical with $b$.

A fraction triplet $p$ will be called, *greater than, less than,* or *equally great as* a fraction triplet $q$ according as the difference $p-q$ is positive, negative, or a null triplet.

The fraction triplet $\langle\langle b,\ a\rangle,\ c\rangle$ will be called the *opposite* triplet of $\langle\langle a,b\rangle,c\rangle$.— Obviously the opposite triplet of a positive triplet is negative, and the opposite triplet of a negative triplet is positive. The sum of a triplet and its opposite triplet is a null triplet.

From these definitions the theory of fraction triplets is easily obtained, including in particular the elementary laws affecting sums, differences, and products of fraction triplets, and the relations *equally great* and *less than*. Also the three following existence theorems are readily proved:

If $r$ is a fraction triplet not a null triplet, then for every fraction triplet $s$ there exists a fraction triplet $q$ such that $s$ is equally great as $q \cdot r$. (This formulates the possibility of division.)

If in particular $r$ and $s$ are positive fraction triplets and $s$ is greater than $r$, then there is a positive fraction triplet $t$ such that $s$ is equally great as $(\langle\langle 1,\ 0\rangle,\ 1\rangle + t)\cdot r$. (Here 1 is the ordinal $0'$. The triplet $\langle\langle 1,\ 0\rangle,\ 1\rangle$ has the property that $\langle\langle 1,\ 0\rangle,\ 1\rangle \cdot r = r$ for every fraction triplet $r$.)

For every fraction triplet there exists a fraction triplet greater than it and another less than it; moreover, if $r$ and $s$ are fraction triplets, and $r$ is less than $s$, there exists a fraction triplet $t$ that is greater than $r$ and less than $s$.

Let us further define, for a finite ordinal $n$ and a fraction triplet $t$, $n \cdot t$ ("$n$ times $t$") and $t^n$ ("$t$ to the $n$th"), by the recursive definitions:

$$0 \cdot t = \langle\langle 0,\ 0\rangle,\ 1\rangle, \quad n' \cdot t = n \cdot t + t.$$

$$t^0 = \langle\langle 1,\ 0\rangle,\ 1\rangle, \quad t^{n'} = t^n \cdot t.$$

By complete induction it can be shown that, for every finite ordinal $n$ and every fraction triplet $\langle\langle k,l\rangle,m\rangle$, $n \cdot \langle\langle k,l\rangle,m\rangle$ is equally great as $\langle\langle n \cdot k, n \cdot l\rangle,m\rangle$, and that, if $r$ is a positive fraction triplet, $(\langle\langle 1,\ 0\rangle,\ 1\rangle + r)^n$ is not less than $\langle\langle 1,\ 0\rangle,\ 1\rangle + n \cdot r$. From this it follows that, for an arbitrary fraction triplet $s$, and every positive fraction triplet $t$, there exists a finite ordinal $n$ such that $n \cdot t$, and *a fortiori* $(\langle\langle 1,\ 0\rangle,\ 1\rangle + t)^n$, is greater than $s$.

In the theory of fraction triplets the theory of *fractions* is included. For the fractions may be defined as fraction triplets of a special kind by agreeing that, if $m$ and $n$ are finite ordinals and $n \neq 0$, the *fraction* $m/n$ shall be the fraction triplet $\langle\langle m,\ 0\rangle,\ n\rangle$. Then from our definitions of the sum and the product of fraction triplets and of *greater than, less than,* and *equally great as* for fraction triplets, there result the usual definitions of the corresponding concepts and operations for fractions. Moreover the class of all fractions exists and is a subclass of the class of all fraction triplets; it is enumerable and therefore is represented by a set.

On the basis of the theory of fraction triplets, the theory of real numbers can now be established.

*Definition.* A set $a$ of fraction triplets will be called a real number if it satisfies the three following conditions: (1) There is a fraction triplet in $a$ and a fraction triplet not in $a$. (2) If a fraction triplet $t$ is in $a$, every fraction triplet less than $t$ or equally great as $t$ is in $a$. (3) For every fraction triplet in $a$ there is a greater fraction triplet in $a$.

From the condition (2) it follows that, if $a$ and $b$ are real numbers, we have either $a \subset b$ or $b \subset a$ or $a = b$. Of two different real numbers, the one which is a proper subset of the other will be called the *less*, and the other one the *greater*. And a real number $c$ will be said to be *between* $a$ and $b$ if $a \subset c$ and $c \subset b$.

In view of the definition of a real number, it follows by the class theorem that the class of all real numbers exists. And notice also that no real number is an ordinal or a fraction triplet.

We also are led rather directly to the *theorem of the least upper bound.*

By an *upper bound* of a class $A$ of real numbers, we understand a real number which is less than no element of $A$. Let $A$ be a non-empty class of real numbers which has an upper bound $b$. The sum of the elements of $A$ is a subclass of $b$; so it is enumerable and therefore is represented by a set $c$. It is easily seen that $c$ is a real number, further that it is an upper bound of $A$, and that there is no upper bound of $A$ less than it. Thus every non-empty class of real numbers which has an upper bound has a *least upper bound.*

By a *lower bound* of a class $A$ of real numbers, we mean a real number which is greater than no element of $A$. For every class $A$ of real numbers there exists the class of all lower bounds of $A$, and every element of $A$ is an upper bound of this class. If $A$ is a non-empty class that has a lower bound, it is readily shown that the least upper bound of the class of lower bounds of $A$ is the *greatest lower bound* of $A$.

Now we have to introduce the *elementary operations* for the real numbers. We define the *sum* $a+b$ of real numbers $a$ and $b$ as the set of those fraction triplets $t$ for which there exists a triplet $r \,\epsilon\, a$ and a triplet $s \,\epsilon\, b$ such that $r+s$ is equally great as $t$. The existence of this set follows by the class theorem, since, as we have seen, every class of fraction triplets is represented by a set. Moreover it can be shown without difficulty that the sum of real numbers $a$ and $b$, as thus defined, is again a real number.

In order to define the difference of real numbers, we first define the sum of a real number and a fraction triplet. By the sum $a+t$ of a real number $a$ and a fraction triplet $t$ we mean the set of those fraction triplets which are equally great as $s+t$ for some element $s$ of $a$. This set is obviously a real number. Then we define the *difference* $a-b$ of real numbers $a$ and $b$ as the set of those fraction triplets $t$ for which $b+t$ is less than $a$. It follows that the difference of two real numbers is again a real number.

As to the laws of computation for sum and difference, those which concern the sum alone are rather obvious. However, the proof of the laws,

$$(a + b) - b = a, \qquad\qquad (a - b) + b = a,$$

is not quite direct; it is desirable to use for it the two following lemmas:

Lemma 1. If $a$ and $b$ are real numbers and $a \subset b$, there exists a positive fraction triplet $t$ such that $a+t \subset b$.

This is a consequence of conditions (2) and (3) in our definition of a real number.

Lemma 2. If $a$ is a real number and $t$ is a positive fraction triplet, then $a \subset a+t$.

For if we had $a+t \subsetneq a$, then, for every triplet $r$ in $a$, $r+t$ would also be in $a$, and hence by complete induction $r + n \cdot t$ would be in $a$ for every finite ordinal $n$. But this is impossible, since on the one hand there is a fraction triplet $s$ which is greater than every triplet in $a$, and on the other hand, $t$ being positive, there is an ordinal $n$ such that $n \cdot t$ is greater than $s-r$.

Of this lemma the following consequence is to be used: If $a$ and $b$ are real numbers and $s$ is a fraction triplet, then $a+s \subset a+b$ if and only if $s \epsilon b$. The proof of this employs the relation $a+(s+t) = (a+s)+t$ for a real number $a$ and fraction triplets $s$, $t$.

In addition to the application of lemma 2 in proving the two above laws, characterizing the difference, we draw from it also the consequence that, for a real number $a$ and a fraction triplet $t$, we have $a+t \subset a$ if and only if $t$ is negative. It follows from this and from our definition of the difference of real numbers that, for any real number $a$, the difference $a-a$ is the set of all negative fraction triplets. Let us denote the latter real number by "$[0]$." We have

$$a - a = [0], \qquad\qquad a + [0] = a,$$

for any real number $a$.

A real number will be called *positive* if it is greater than $[0]$, *negative* if it is less than $[0]$. Then, as is easily seen, a real number is positive if and only if there is a positive fraction triplet in it. Further we define:

$$-a = [0] - a.$$

It is easily shown that the difference $a-b$ of real numbers $a$ and $b$ is negative, $[0]$, or positive according as $a \subset b$, $a = b$, or $b \subset a$; and hence in particular that $-a$ is negative, $[0]$, or positive according as $a$ is positive, $[0]$, or negative. Also easily proved are the relations,

$$-(-a) = a, \qquad\qquad a - b = a + (-b).$$

For every real number $a$ there is one and only one non-negative real number which either is equal to $a$ or is equal to $-a$; this we denote, as is usual, by $|a|$. We say that a real number $a$ *differs from* the real number $b$ *by less than* $d$, where $d$ is a positive real number, if $|a-b| \subset d$.

In order to define the product of real numbers, it seems to be natural to begin with the case of positive real numbers. We first define the product $a \cdot t$ of an arbitrary real number $a$ and a positive fraction triplet $t$ to be the set of those fraction triplets which are equally great as $s \cdot t$ for some element $s$ of $a$. This set is easily seen to be a real number.

Now let $a$ and $b$ be positive real numbers. By the *product* $a \cdot b$ of $a$ and $b$

we mean: the least upper bound of the class of those real numbers $c$ for which there is a positive fraction triplet $t$ such that $t\epsilon b$ and $a \cdot t = c$; or, in other words, the set of those fraction triplets which are in some of the products, $a \cdot t$, of $a$ and a positive triplet $t$ that is in $b$.

This definition can easily be shown to be equivalent to the following:   The product $a \cdot b$ of positive real numbers $a$ and $b$ is the set of those fraction triplets which are either negative or null triplets or equally great as the product of a positive triplet that is in $a$ and a positive triplet that is in $b$.

From the first definition we see that the product of positive real numbers is a real number, and, of course, a positive one.   From the second definition it is evident that, if $a$ and $b$ are positive real numbers, $a \cdot b = b \cdot a$.   The associative law and the distributive law are also easily proved.

The extension of the definition of the product to negative real numbers and [0] is to be made, as usual, by the following defining equations, which refer to positive real numbers $a$ and $b$ and an arbitrary real number $c$:

$$a \cdot (-b) = -(a \cdot b), \qquad (-a) \cdot b = -(a \cdot b), \qquad (-a) \cdot (-b) = a \cdot b,$$

$$c \cdot [0] = [0], \qquad\qquad [0] \cdot c = 0.$$

These conventions, as is known, are necessary and sufficient in order to maintain the distributive law for arbitrary real numbers.   Of course also the commutative and associative character of the product is preserved by them.

We use the notation [1] for the set of those fraction triplets $\langle\langle k, l\rangle, m\rangle$ for which the ordinal $k$ is lower than $l+m$.   This set, as is easily verified, is a positive real number, and it has the property that $a \cdot [1] = a$ for every real number $a$.

We have still to define the quotient of real numbers.   By the *quotient*

$$\frac{a}{b}$$

of positive real numbers $a$ and $b$, we understand the set of those fraction triplets $t$ which either are positive and satisfy the condition $b \cdot t \subset a$ or are negative or null triplets.   Thus the quotient of positive real numbers is again a positive real number.

The proof of the laws,

$$\frac{a \cdot b}{a} = a, \qquad\qquad\qquad b \cdot \frac{a}{b} = a,$$

for positive real numbers is quite analogous to that of the corresponding laws for the difference of real numbers.   To the two lemmas used for that proof there correspond here the two following similar lemmas:

If $a$ and $b$ are positive real numbers and $a \subset b$, there exists a positive fraction triplet $t$ such that $a \cdot (\langle\langle 1, 0\rangle, 1\rangle + t) \subset b$.

If $a$ is a positive real number and $t$ a positive fraction triplet, then $a \subset a \cdot (\langle\langle 1, 0\rangle, 1\rangle + t)$.

The extension of the definition of the quotient is to be made in the usual way by the following defining equations, which refer to positive real numbers $a$ and $b$ and an arbitrary real number $c$:

$$\frac{(-a)}{b} = -\frac{a}{b}, \qquad \frac{a}{(-b)} = -\frac{a}{b}, \qquad \frac{(-a)}{(-b)} = \frac{a}{b}, \qquad \frac{[0]}{c} = [0].$$

Notice that our definitions of the sum and the product of real numbers allow us to represent the relations $a+b = c$ and $a \cdot b = c$ by constitutive expressions, and hence that there exists the class of those triplets $\langle c, \langle a, b \rangle \rangle$ of real numbers $a, b, c$ for which $a+b = c$, and also of those for which $a \cdot b = c$.

*Remark.* The way here outlined of founding the theory of real numbers is, of course, only one among several available methods of carrying out the Dedekind idea within the frame of the axiomatic system which we are considering. The advantage of the one we have chosen is that it allows a rather direct passage from finite ordinals to real numbers. This may be regarded as compensating for the complication of having to deal with fraction triplets instead of fractions— the more so since we can pass immediately to the fraction notation, whenever we wish, by the above given definition of fractions as fraction triplets of a special kind.

**9. Limit point, enumerable sequences, continuous functions, Lebesgue measure.** From the elementary notions concerning real numbers, and their properties, the fundamental concepts and theorems of analysis are to be obtained in the usual manner.

In order to show that this can be done within our axiomatic frame, a number of instances will suffice. We consider first the theorem that *every bounded infinite class of real numbers has a limit point.* Here a class $C$ of real numbers is called *bounded* if it has an upper bound and a lower bound; or, in other words, if there exist real numbers $a$ and $b$ such that, for every element $c$ of $C$, we have $a \subseteq c$ and $c \subseteq b$. And by a *limit point* of a class $C$ of real numbers we understand a real number $a$ such that, for every positive real number $d$, the class of those elements of $C$ which differ from $a$ by less than $d$ is infinite.

The most direct way of proving this theorem is the following. Let $a$ be a lower bound and $b$ an upper bound of the infinite class $C$ of real numbers. From the existence of the class of all real numbers and of the class of all finite sets there follows the existence of a class $D$ whose elements are those real numbers $d$ for which there exists a finite set $s$ whose elements are the elements of $C$ less than $d$. It is immediately seen that $a\eta D$ and $b$ is an upper bound of $D$. Therefore $D$ has a least upper bound $g$. By the definition of the least upper bound and by the theorems on finite classes and sets, for every positive real number $p$ the class of elements of $C$ which are between $g-p$ and $g+p$ is infinite, and thus $g$ is a limit point of $C$.

A more usual method of proving the existence of a limit point for any bounded infinite class of real numbers is the following. Let

$$\frac{a+b}{2}$$

denote the real number $(a+b) \cdot 1/2$. Then, for any class $C$ of real numbers, there exists a function $F$ assigning to any pair $\langle a, b \rangle$ of real numbers the pair

$$\langle a, \frac{a+b}{2} \rangle$$

or the pair

$$\langle \frac{a+b}{2}, b \rangle$$

according as the class of those elements of $C$ which are between $a$ and $\dfrac{a+b}{2}$ is infinite or finite. This follows by the class theorem, since the condition that a class is infinite, or, what comes to the same thing (by the first theorem on finite classes and sets), that it is not represented by a finite set, can be formulated by a constitutive expression.

As before, let $C$ be a bounded infinite class of real numbers and let $a$ be a lower bound and $b$ an upper bound of $C$. Further, let $G$ be the iterator of the function $F$ on the pair $\langle a, b \rangle$. Then $G$ is a function whose domain is the class N of all finite ordinals, and whose values are ordered pairs of real numbers. By our axioms III, there exist the functions $A$ and $B$ with the domain N such that, for any finite ordinal $n$, $A(n)$ is the first, and $B(n)$ the second, member of $G(n)$. By the definition of $F$ and $G$ we have, for any finite ordinal $n$,

$$A(n) \subsetneq A(n'), \qquad A(n) \subset B(n), \qquad B(n') \subsetneq B(n),$$

$$B(n') - A(n') = (B(n) - A(n)) \cdot 1/2,$$

and hence, by complete induction, for any finite ordinals $m$, $n$,

$$A(m) \subset B(n),$$

$$B(n) - A(n) = (b - a) \cdot (1/2)^n.$$

From this it follows that, for any finite ordinal $n$, the real number $B(n)$ is an upper bound of the converse domain of $A$. Let $e$ be the least upper bound of the converse domain of $A$; then, for any finite ordinal $n$,

$$A(n) \subsetneq e, \qquad\qquad e \subsetneq B(n).$$

Now for any positive real number $d$, since $2/1$ is greater than $\langle\langle 1, 0 \rangle, 1 \rangle$, there is, as we know, a finite ordinal $n$ such that $b - a \subset d \cdot (2/1)^n$. For this ordinal $n$,

$$(B(n) - A(n)) \cdot (2/1)^n \subset d \cdot (2/1)^n,$$

$$B(n) - A(n) \subset d,$$

and so every real number between $A(n)$ and $B(n)$ differs from $e$ by less than $d$.

On the other hand, from our assumption that $C$ is infinite and from the definitions of $F$, $G$, $A$, $B$, there follows by complete induction that, for every finite ordinal $n$, the class of those elements of $C$ which are between $A(n)$ and $B(n)$ is infinite.  Hence $e$ is a limit point of $C$.

Let us now see how we may deal with *convergent sequences* and *continuous functions*.

By an *enumerable sequence* we will understand a functional set whose domain is the set of all finite ordinals (representing the class N).  In particular, if the elements of the converse domain are real numbers, such a functional set will be called an *enumerable sequence of real numbers*; or if the converse domain is a subclass of $A$, it will be called *an enumerable sequence of elements of $A$*.  The elements of the converse domain of an enumerable sequence will be called the *members* of the sequence.

*Remarks.*  1.  Notice that the converse domain of an enumerable sequence need not be enumerable but can be finite, since there can be repetitions of members in a sequence.  2.  We do not yet require the general concept of a sequence; it will be introduced later on.

*Definition.*  In what follows, where $f$ is a functional set and $a$ an element of its domain, we shall use the notation $f(a)$ for the value assigned to $a$ by $f$— analogous to the notation $F(a)$ used in the case of a function $F$.

An enumerable sequence $f$ of real numbers will be called *convergent* if, for every positive real number $d$, there exists a finite ordinal $k$ such that, for all finite ordinals $m$ and $n$ both higher than $k$, the real numbers $f(m)$ and $f(n)$ differ from one another by less than $d$.  And an enumerable sequence will be said to have the real number $a$ as its *limit* (or, more briefly, to have *the limit $a$*) if, for every positive real number $d$, there exists a finite ordinal $k$ such that, for every finite ordinal $m$ higher than $k$, the real number $f(m)$ differs from $a$ by less than $d$.

Then the class of all convergent sequences of real numbers exists; and the condition that an enumerable sequence $s$ of real numbers has the limit $a$ can be represented by a constitutive expression with the arguments $s$ and $a$.

The theorems, that an enumerable sequence of real numbers can have only one limit and that it has a limit if and only if it is convergent, now follow in the usual way.  (The proof that every convergent enumerable sequence $f$ of real numbers has a limit may be accomplished by considering the class of those real numbers $c$ for which the condition holds that, given any finite ordinal $k$, there exists a higher finite ordinal $n$ such that $c \subset f(n)$, and showing that this class has an upper bound and that its least upper bound is the limit of the sequence $f$.)

In order to introduce *infinite sums* of real numbers we must define the sequence of *partial sums* which corresponds to an enumerable sequence $f$ of real numbers.  For this purpose we use the theorem of finite recursion.  Let $f$ be an enumerable sequence of real numbers.  Then there exists a function assigning to every pair $\langle n, a \rangle$ of a finite ordinal $n$ and a real number $a$ the real number $a + f(n')$.  Hence by the theorem of finite recursion there exists a function $S$ whose domain is the class N, whose values are real numbers, and which satisfies the conditions,

$$S(0) = f(0),$$

$$S(n') = S(n) + f(n'),$$

for every finite ordinal $n$. This function $S$ is represented by an enumerable sequence of real numbers, which is called *the sequence of partial sums of f*. If the sequence of partial sums of $f$ is convergent we call its limit the *numerical sum* of the sequence $f$, and we then say that the sequence $f$ has a *numerical sum*.

For every sequence $f$ of real numbers there exists a sequence $g$ satisfying the condition that $g(n) = f(n) \cdot f(n)$ for every finite ordinal $n$. The members of $g$ are the *squares* of the members of $f$.

By the class theorem, there exists the class of all those enumerable sequences of real numbers for which the sequence of the squares of the members has a numerical sum. This is needed in particular for the Hilbertian theory of "infinitely many variables."

The obvious way of introducing *continuous functions* is to add to the general concept of a *real function* the condition of *continuity*. It will suffice here to speak of functions of only one argument. A real function of one argument is a function whose domain and converse domain are each a class of real numbers. Frequently the domain of a real function is a class of one of the following kinds:

the class of all real numbers;

the class of all real numbers which are greater than, or are not less than, a certain real number $a$ (e.g., the class of positive real numbers);

the class of real numbers which are between two certain real numbers $a$ and $b$, where $a$ is less than $b$ (we call this *the open interval from a to b*);

the class which is the sum of the open interval from $a$ to $b$ and the class whose elements are $a$ and $b$ (we call this *the closed interval from a to b*).

The condition of continuity of a real function (of one argument) *at the point a* of its domain—the word *point* here being synonymous with *real number*—is to be formulated in the usual way. And the function is called *continuous on its domain* if it is continuous at every point of its domain.

However, this way of defining continuous functions is not sufficient for cases in which we require sequences of continuous functions; for the members of a sequence must be sets. Thus we need a method of characterizing continuous functions by sets. The possibility of such a characterization arises from the fact that a continuous function is determined by its values for the elements of an appropriate enumerable subclass of its domain. Let us explain this for the case of continuous functions having as domain the class of positive real numbers.

For every fraction $m/n$ there is a *corresponding real number* $[1] \cdot m/n$, which, as is easily seen, is the set of fraction triplets less than $m/n$. An enumerable sequence $s$ of fractions will be said to have the limit $c$, $c$ being a real number, if the sequence of real numbers corresponding to the members of $s$ has the limit $c$.

For every positive real number $c$ there is an enumerable sequence of fractions which has the limit $c$. For let $l$ be the lowest finite ordinal $k$, different from $0$, for which $1/k \,\epsilon\, c$ (since $c$ is positive, there exists such a finite ordinal). Then for every finite ordinal $n$ there exists a highest finite ordinal $m \neq 0$ for which

$m/(l+n)$ $\epsilon$ $c$. Thus there exists an enumerable sequence $h$ of finite ordinals such that $h(n)/(l+n)$ is in $c$ but $(h(n)+1)/(l+n)$ is not. And the enumerable sequence which assigns to every finite ordinal $n$ the fraction $h(n)/(l+n)$ can easily be shown to have the limit $c$.

A further remark is that every function whose domain is the class of fractions is represented by a functional set, since the class of fractions is enumerable.

Now we define a *continuous fraction-functional* as a functional set having the following properties:

1) its domain is the set of all fractions;
2) its values are real numbers;
3) to equally great fractions the same value is assigned;
4) given any positive real numbers $c$ and $e$, there exists a positive real number $d$ such that, if $r$ and $s$ are any fractions whose corresponding real numbers differ from $c$ by less than $d$, the values assigned to $r$ and to $s$ differ from one another by less than $e$.

The continuous fraction-functionals, as thus defined, can be taken as a kind of representatives of those continuous functions whose domain is the class of positive real numbers (though not directly representing them). In fact, every continuous function $F$ whose domain is the class of positive real numbers determines the class of all those pairs $\langle r, s\rangle$ for which $r$ is a fraction and $s$ is the value assigned by $F$ to the real number corresponding to $r$. Since this class is a function with an enumerable domain, it is itself enumerable and therefore is represented by a set. This set, which is easily shown to be a continuous fraction-functional, will be said to *correspond* to the function $F$. On the other hand, given any continuous fraction-functional $f$, there exists a unique continuous function to which $f$ corresponds; this can be seen as follows.

For every positive real number $a$ there exists, as we have seen, an enumerable sequence of fractions whose limit is $a$. If $s$ is such a sequence, then by the composition lemma and the axiom of the enumerable there exists an enumerable sequence which assigns to every finite ordinal $n$ the value of $f(s(n))$. This sequence, by condition 4 in the definition of a continuous fraction functional, is convergent, and therefore has a limit $b$. Moreover this limit does not depend on the particular sequence $s$, but is determined by the limit $a$ of $s$. And it is possible to formulate by a constitutive expression $\Re(f, a, b)$ the condition that, $a$ being a positive real number and $b$ a real number and $f$ a continuous fraction-functional, for every enumerable sequence $s$ of fractions, having the limit $a$, the enumerable sequence $t$ which assigns to the finite ordinal $n$ the value of $f(s(n))$ has the limit $b$. Taking the variable $f$ in this constitutive expression as a parameter, we infer the existence of a function $F$ assigning to every positive real number $a$ the uniquely determined real number $b$ for which $\Re(f, a, b)$ holds. Then $F$ can be shown to be continuous, to have $f$ as its corresponding continuous fraction-functional, and to be the only continuous function which does so.

By the class theorem, the class of all continuous fraction-functionals exists, and also the class T of those triplets $\langle\langle f, a\rangle, b\rangle$ for which $\Re(f, a, b)$ holds. This class T is a function assigning to any pair $\langle f, a\rangle$ which has a continuous fraction-functional as its first member and a positive real number as its second member, the value assigned to $a$ by the continuous function to which the continuous fraction-functional $f$ corresponds. Thus any property that a continuous function $F$ of positive real numbers has with respect to its values is immediately expressible by means of the corresponding continuous fraction-functional, since we have, for every positive real number $a$,

$$F(a) = \mathrm{T}(\langle f, a \rangle).$$

Now for the case of continuous functions having as domain (instead of the class of positive real numbers) the open or the closed interval from [0] to [1], our method of characterization by continuous fraction-functionals can be applied quite correspondingly. The only modification required is that we have to take a somewhat different kind of continuous fraction-functionals, differing in that their domain is now not the set of all fractions but the set of *proper fractions*, i.e., the fractions $m/n$ for which the ordinal $m$ is lower than $n$. With this change, the further reasoning is the same as before. For, in the same way that we proved that every positive real number is the limit of an enumerable sequence of fractions, we can show that every positive real number not greater than [1] is the limit of an enumerable sequence of proper fractions; and the number [0] (which belongs to the closed interval from [0] to [1]) is obviously the limit of the enumerable sequence which assigns to each finite ordinal $n$ the proper fraction $1/n''$.

The case of an arbitrary interval as the domain of a continuous function can of course be reduced by a simple transformation to the case of the (open or closed) interval from [0] to [1]. There is also no difficulty in extending our method to continuous functions whose domain is the class of all real numbers: for this purpose we may take, instead of continuous fraction-functionals, functional sets which have the set of all fraction triplets as domain and have otherwise the same properties which we required of continuous fraction-functionals.

Now let us also briefly consider the definition of the Lebesgue measure. We introduce the following definitions in order.

An enumerable sequence of pairs $\langle a, b \rangle$ of real numbers, with $a$ always less than $b$, will be called a *covering sequence* of a class $C$ of real numbers if for every element $c$ of $C$ there exists at least one member $\langle a, b \rangle$ of the sequence such that $a \subsetneq c$ and $c \subsetneq b$.

By the *coordinated sequence* of a covering sequence $s$ of a class $C$ of real numbers we mean the enumerable sequence $t$ determined by the condition that, for every finite ordinal $n$, $t(n)$ is the difference $b - a$, for the pair $\langle a, b \rangle$ assigned to $n$ by $s$. The connection between a covering sequence and its coordinated sequence can be formulated by a constitutive expression.

A real number $d$ will be called a *bound of measure* of the class $C$ of real numbers if there exists a covering sequence of $C$ whose coordinated sequence has a numerical sum not greater than $d$. For every class $C$ of real numbers, the class of its bounds of measure exists.

If $C$ is a non-empty class of real numbers which has a bound of measure, the class of bounds of measure of $C$ is a non-empty class of positive real numbers and hence has a greatest lower bound which is a non-negative real number. This greatest lower bound is called the *Lebesgue exterior measure of C.*

These definitions refer to one-dimensional classes of points. For two-dimensional classes of points, i.e., for classes of ordered pairs of real numbers, the following modifications have to be made:

1. A *covering sequence* of a class $C$ of pairs of real numbers is an enumerable sequence of quadruplets $\langle\langle a, b\rangle, \langle c, d\rangle\rangle$ in which $a$ is always less than $b$ and $c$ less than $d$, such that for every pair $\langle r, s\rangle$ belonging to $C$ there exists a member $\langle\langle a, b\rangle$, $\langle c, d\rangle\rangle$ of the sequence for which $a \subseteq r$, $r \subseteq b$, $c \subseteq s$, $s \subseteq d$.

2. The *coordinated sequence* of a covering sequence $s$ is the enumerable sequence $t$ determined by the condition that, for every finite ordinal $n$, $t(n)$ is the product of differences $(b-a)\cdot(d-c)$, for the quadruplet $\langle\langle a, b\rangle, \langle c, d\rangle\rangle$ assigned to $n$ by $s$.

The notions of a *bound of measure* of $C$ and of the *Lebesgue exterior measure* of $C$ are then introduced in the same way as in the one-dimensional case.

Similarly the corresponding definitions may be made for classes of points of higher dimensions.

Then the Lebesgue measure and, by means of it, the Lebesgue integral can be introduced in the usual manner.

The theory of function spaces[34] also can be treated within our axiomatic frame. This possibility results from the circumstance that the elements of a function space can be characterized by their components (Fourier coefficients) with respect to a complete orthogonal system, or, in other words, from the isomorphism of function spaces to Hilbert space. In fact, Hilbert space is, from the set-theoretic point of view, characterized as a class of enumerable sequences of real numbers.

In sum, it appears that, in the various branches of analysis, real functions occur for the most part only in such a way that they can be characterized by enumerable functional sets. In the case of continuous functions, this possibility is due to the particular character of the functions; in the theory of function spaces the reason for it is that functions are there considered as equal if the class of arguments to which they assign different values has the Lebesgue exterior measure [0].

**10. The special axiom of choice, the second number class.** We still have to consider the application of the axiom of choice in analysis. There are in fact certain reasonings in analysis for which apparently the axiom of choice or a similar principle is necessary—although, as we know, in many cases where application of the axiom of choice suggests itself, the possibility exists of avoiding this axiom, or of reducing the number of applications of it.

As an illustration let us consider briefly the question of choosing convergent sequences out of a class of functional sets. On this there is a theorem of analysis,

---

[34] See for example VON NEUMANN (1929-1930), in particular Kap. I and Anhang I therein.

which is used as an auxiliary theorem in several connections. Before formulating it we introduce the following abbreviating terminologies.

An enumerable sequence which represents a one-to-one correspondence will be called an enumerable sequence *without repetitions*. An enumerable sequence $t$ will be called a *sub-sequence* of an enumerable sequence $s$, if there exists an enumerable sequence $h$ of finite ordinals such that, for every finite ordinal $n$, $h(n) \in h(n')$ and $t(n) = s(h(n))$. Hence, as is easily shown, an enumerable sequence $t$ is a sub-sequence of an enumerable sequence $s$ without repetitions, if every member of $t$ is a member of $s$ and, for every finite ordinal $n$, $t(n')$ is assigned by $s$ to a higher ordinal than $t(n)$ is assigned to.

An enumerable sequence $q$ of functional sets which have a common domain $t$ and whose values are real numbers will be called *convergent at a*, if $a \in t$ and the enumerable sequence assigning to each finite ordinal $n$ the value $(q(n))(a)$ is convergent.

Now the theorem in question asserts that, if $C$ is an infinite class of functional sets which have a fixed enumerable set $t$ as their domain and whose values are real numbers of a certain fixed interval, then there exists an enumerable sequence of elements of $C$ without repetitions which is convergent at every element $a$ of $t$.

Proof of this can be made in the following way, with the aid of the axiom of choice. For any element $a$ of $t$, the class $A$, of real numbers $b$ such that $f(a) = b$ for some functional set $f$ belonging to $C$, is bounded (as follows from the hypothesis on $C$). If $A$ is finite, there exist a real number $c$, and an infinite class of functional sets which belong to $C$ and have the value $c$ for the argument $a$. Then, since every infinite class has an enumerable subclass—a consequence of the axiom of choice, as we have seen—there follows the existence of an enumerable sequence, without repetitions, of functional sets belonging to $C$ which all assign to $a$ the same value $c$; and this sequence is (in a trivial way) convergent at $a$. Otherwise $A$ is infinite and hence has a limit point $c$. Then follows—by a method which involves an application of the axiom of choice and which will be discussed below—that there exists an enumerable sequence $g$ of elements of $A$ without repetitions which has the limit $c$. For every member $r$ of $g$ there exists an element $f$ of $C$ such that $f(a) = r$, and hence by the axiom of choice there exists a function $G$ assigning to each member $r$ of $g$ an element $f$ of $C$ such that $f(a) = r$. Hence we infer—using the composition lemma, and the third theorem on enumerability (§8)—that there is an enumerable sequence of elements of $C$ without repetitions which is convergent at $a$.

Thus for every element $a$ of $t$ there exists an enumerable sequence, without repetitions, of functional sets belonging to $C$ which is convergent at $a$. From this we now have to show that there is a single enumerable sequence, without repetitions, of elements of $C$ which is convergent at every element $a$ of $t$.

For this purpose, we first observe that any infinite subset of $C$ satisfies the assumptions we have made for $C$, and hence that our result applies not only to $C$ but also to any infinite subset of $C$, in particular to the converse domain of any enumerable sequence of elements of $C$ without repetitions. In addition, we must use our assumption that $t$ is enumerable, so that there exists an enumerable sequence $s$ without repetitions which has $t$ as its converse domain.

Using once more the axiom of choice, and applying the theorem of finite recursion, we infer the existence of a function $F$ whose domain is N and which satisfies the condition that, for every finite ordinal $n$, $F(n)$ is an enumerable sequence of elements of $C$ without repetitions which is convergent at $s(n)$, and that $F(n')$ is a sub-sequence of $F(n)$.

Now the enumerable sequence which (by the third theorem on enumerability) represents the function assigning to each finite ordinal $n$ the functional set $(F(n))(n)$ can easily be seen to be convergent at every element $a$ of $t$. Thus our theorem is proved.

This method of proof involves repeated application of the axiom of choice. However we can, by another arrangement, reduce the number of applications to one, as follows.

On the assumptions which we made for the class $C$ of functional sets we can prove without use of the axiom of choice that there is a function $G$ assigning to every pair $\langle q, a \rangle$—where $q$ is an enumerable sequence of elements of $C$ without repetitions and $a$ is an element of $t$—a sub-sequence of $q$ convergent at $a$. Indeed, from the assumptions made for $q$ and $a$ the following disjunction can be inferred, as regards the class $P$ of real numbers which are a value, $(q(n))(a)$, of some member of the sequence $q$, for $a$: Either (i) the class $Q$ of those elements $r$ of $P$ for which there is an infinite class of finite ordinals $n$ such that $(q(n))(a) = r$ has an element, or (ii) for every element $r$ of $P$ there is a finite ordinal $k$ such that for every finite ordinal $n$ higher than $k$ we have $(q(n))(a) \neq r$.

In case (i) there is a least ordinal $l$ among those finite ordinals $n$ for which $(q(n))(a) \, \eta \, Q$. By the iteration theorem there is an enumerable sequence $f$ of finite ordinals, such that $f(0) = l$, and $f(n')$ is the lowest of the finite ordinals $m$ which are higher than $f(n)$ and for which $(q(m))(a) = (q(l))(a)$. The enumerable sequence $h$ assigning to each finite ordinal $n$ the functional set $q(f(n))$ is a sub-sequence of $q$ which is convergent at $a$. Moreover $h$ is uniquely determined by $q$ and $a$, and the relation subsisting between $q$, $a$, and $h$ can be formulated by a constitutive expression $\mathfrak{A}(q, a, h)$.

In case (ii) the class $P$ is infinite and, in consequence of our assumptions on $C$, is bounded. Hence there exists a limit point of $P$, and also a greatest limit point (or *upper limit*) $p$. By the theorem of finite recursion there is an enumerable sequence $f$ of finite ordinals, such that $f(0) = 0$, and $f(n')$ is the lowest of the finite ordinals $m$ which are higher than $f(n)$ and for which $(q(m))(a)$ differs from $p$ by less than $[1] \cdot 1/n$. The enumerable sequence $h$ assigning to each finite ordinal $n$ the value $q(f(n))$ is a sub-sequence of $q$ which is convergent at $a$. Moreover $h$ is again uniquely determined by $q$ and $a$, and its relation to $q$ and $a$ can be formulated by a constitutive expression $\mathfrak{B}(q, a, h)$.

Now if $\mathfrak{C}(q, a, C, t)$ is a constitutive expression formulating that $q$ is an enumerable sequence of elements of $C$ without repetitions and $a \epsilon t$, and if $\mathfrak{M}(q, a)$ and $\mathfrak{N}(q, a)$ are constitutive expressions, with the variables $q$ and $a$, formulating the conditions for cases (i) and (ii) respectively, then, by our assumptions on $C$ and on $t$, the class of all triplets $\langle \langle q, a \rangle, h \rangle$ for which

$$\mathfrak{C}(q, a, C, t) \ \& \ [(\mathfrak{M}(q, a) \ \& \ \mathfrak{A}(q, a, h)) \ \vee \ (\mathfrak{N}(q, a) \ \& \ \mathfrak{B}(q, a, h))]$$

holds is a function $G$, depending on the class $C$, which assigns to every pair $\langle q, a \rangle$ satisfying $\mathfrak{C}(q, a, C, t)$ a sub-sequence $h$ of $q$ that is convergent at $a$.

Now $t$, since it is enumerable, is the converse domain of an enumerable sequence $s$. Thus, applying the theorem of finite recursion, we can infer that, for every enumerable sequence $q$ of elements of $C$ without repetitions, there is a function $F$ whose domain is N, whose values are enumerable sequences of elements of $C$ without repetitions, and which satisfies the conditions that $F(0) = q$ and (for every finite ordinal $n$) $F(n')$ is a sub-sequence of $F(n)$ which is convergent at $s(n)$. And from this follows that the enumerable sequence assigning to each finite ordinal $n$ the functional set $(F(n))(n)$ is an enumerable sequence of elements of $C$ without repetitions and is convergent at every element $a$ of $t$.

Thus in order to complete our proof it only remains to show in consequence of our assumptions on $C$ that there exists an enumerable sequence, $q$, of elements of $C$ without repetitions. This can be done by using the theorem that every infinite class has an enumerable subclass in connection with the third theorem on enumerability. In this way the only application of the axiom of choice in the whole proof is that involved in the theorem that every infinite class has an enumerable subclass.

However the preceding discussion is intended not only to illustrate the possibility in certain cases of reducing the extent of the application of the axiom of choice, but also to present typical instances of the application of the axiom of choice in analysis. In the first of the two proofs which we have given of the theorem on enumerable sequences of functional sets, we find the three following applications of the axiom of choice: (1) for the theorem that every infinite class has an enumerable subclass; (2) in order to prove for an arbitrary limit point $c$ of an infinite class $A$ of real numbers that there exists an enumerable sequence of elements of $A$ without repetitions which has the limit $c$; (3) given a real number $a$, an enumerable sequence $g$ of real numbers without repetitions, and a class $C$ of functional sets, and given that for every member $r$ of $g$ there exists an element $f$ of $C$ such that $f(a) = r$, to prove that there exists a function $G$ assigning to each member $r$ of $g$ an element $f$ of $C$ such that $f(a) = r$.

Of these three consequences of the axiom of choice, the last two apparently cannot be reduced to the first. (It only happens that their use was found to be avoidable in the proof of the particular theorem which we have been considering.)

The third one can be generalized as follows: (4) if for every member $r$ of an enumerable sequence $g$ without repetitions there is a set $s$ such that the pair $\langle r, s \rangle$ belongs to a certain class of pairs $D$, then there exists a function $G$ assigning to each member $r$ of $g$ a set $s$ such that $\langle r, s \rangle \eta D$. And for the proof of (4) we obviously can get along with the following weakened form of the axiom of choice:

Every class of pairs which has N as its domain has a subclass which is a function and has N as its domain.

This *special axiom of choice* will be called $IV_s$.[35] As an immediate consequence of it in connection with the third theorem on enumerability we note the following:

If $C$ is a class of pairs which has N as its domain, there exists a set whose elements are the members of an enumerable sequence which is a subset of $C$.

---

[35] Axiom $IV_S$ is the class-form of the so-called countable axiom of choice $AC^\omega$. In the presence of the axiom of foundation the axioms $IV_{\bar{s}}$ and $AC^\omega$ are equivalent. In the absence of the axiom of foundation, however, $AC^\omega$ does not imply $IV_S$, as can be shown by means of permutation models in the sense of Fraenkel–Mostowski (editor).

*Remark.* If this last be taken as an axiom, the theorems expressing the axiom of the enumerable and the special axiom of choice $IV_s$ follow as immediate consequences of it. Hence we have the possibility of contracting the axiom of the enumerable and the special axiom of choice in a handy way into a single axiom, which can be expressed as follows without using the concept of an enumerable sequence: Every class of pairs whose domain is N has as a subclass a function whose domain is N and whose converse domain is represented by a set.

In what follows, references to the axiom $IV_s$ will be understood as including this immediate consequence of $IV_s$ without explicit mention.

Now we shall show that the axiom $IV_s$—in addition to its adequacy for (3) and (4)—suffices also for the proof of the existential assertions (1) and (2) above.

The proof of (2) by means of $IV_s$ proceeds as follows. Since $c$ is a limit point of $A$, there exists for every finite ordinal $n$ an element of $A$ which is not $c$ but which differs from $c$ by less than $[1] \cdot 1/n$. Hence the class of pairs $\langle n, p \rangle$, satisfying the conditions that $n$ is a finite ordinal, and $p\eta A$, and $p \neq c$, and $p$ differs from $c$ by less than $[1] \cdot 1/n$, has the domain N. Applying the axiom $IV_s$ to this class of pairs, we infer the existence of an enumerable sequence $f$ of elements of $A$ such that, for every finite ordinal $n$, $f(n) \neq c$ and $|f(n) - c|$ is less than $[1] \cdot 1/n$. Hence $f$ has the limit $c$, but $c$ is not a member of $f$. From this it follows in particular that the converse domain $h$ of $f$ is infinite, and therefore that (as the converse domain of an enumerable sequence) it is enumerable. Thus there exists a one-to-one correspondence between N and $h$. This one-to-one correspondence is represented by an enumerable sequence of elements of $A$ without repetitions, which is easily shown to have the limit $c$.

In order to prove by means of the axiom $IV_s$ that every infinite class has an enumerable subclass ((1) above), the method of proof which we used in §7 for this theorem is not applicable, but we can argue instead as follows. If $C$ is an infinite class, then for every finite ordinal $n$ there exists a one-to-one correspondence between $n$ and a subset of $C$, and hence for every finite ordinal $n$ there exists a one-to-one correspondence between the ordinal $2^n$ and a subset of $C$. Consequently the class of pairs $\langle n, s \rangle$ such that $n$ is a finite ordinal and $s$ represents a one-to-one correspondence between $2^n$ and a subset of $C$ has the domain N, and by the axiom $IV_s$ there exists a function $F$ assigning to each finite ordinal $n$ a set representing a one-to-one correspondence between $2^n$ and a subset of $C$. By complete induction, since $2^{n'} = 2^n + 2^n$, it follows that, for every finite ordinal $n$, there is a one-to-one correspondence between an ordinal lower than $2^n$ and the class of those elements of $C$ which for at least one ordinal $k$ lower than $n$ are in the converse domain of $F(k)$. Hence for every finite ordinal $n$ there is in the converse domain of $F(n)$ at least one set $t$ which is not in the converse domain of $F(k)$ for any ordinal $k$ lower than $n$; and among the elements $\langle m, t \rangle$ of $F(n)$ for which $t$ has this property there is one, say $\langle m_1, t_1 \rangle$, for which the ordinal $m$ is lowest. The connection between this element $t_1$ of the converse domain of $F(n)$ and the ordinal $n$ can be formulated by a constitutive expression $\mathfrak{P}(n, t_1, F)$. Moreover the class of pairs $\langle n, t_1 \rangle$ which satisfy the relation $\mathfrak{P}(n, t_1, F)$ is a one-to-one correspondence between N and a subclass of $C$; and the converse domain of this class of pairs is an enumerable subclass of $C$.

On the whole we are led, by our preceding discussions, to delimit analysis within our system of axiomatic set theory as the system based on the axioms I–III, VII, the axiom of the enumerable, and the special axiom of choice $IV_s$. This system will hereafter be referred to briefly as *the system of analysis*.

In this connection let us recall the following facts: (1) that the inclusion of the axiom VII in the system of analysis is required only for the foundations of the theory of ordinals, and that for this purpose VII can be replaced by V a; (2) that the axiom of the enumerable can be deduced from the axioms I–III, V a, V b, and VI (the axiom of infinity), and that the axioms V a and V b can be derived from V*; (3) that the axiom of the enumerable can be derived from the axioms I–III, V a, VI*. Hence each of the three following lists of axioms constitutes a sufficient axiomatic basis for analysis:

I–III, IV, V a, V b, VI.
I–III, $IV_s$, V*, VI.
I–III, $IV_s$, V a, VI*.

*Remark.*[36] There would also be the possibility of deriving $IV_s$ as a theorem from the following weakened form of the axiom of choice, which we shall call IV*:

If $A$ is a class, and $C$ is a class of pairs, and for every element $p$ of $A$ there is an element $q$ of $A$ such that $\langle p, q \rangle \eta C$, then for any element $a$ of $A$ there exists a function $F$ whose domain is N and which satisfies the conditions that $F(0) = a$ and, for every finite ordinal $n$, $F(n) \eta A$ and $\langle F(n), F(n') \rangle \eta C$.

IV* is easily inferred as a theorem from the axiom of choice together with the iteration theorem.

From IV* as an axiom we can deduce $IV_s$ as a theorem, as follows. Let $A$ be a class of pairs having N as its domain. Then there is a set $c$ such that $\langle 0, c \rangle \eta A$. Further, by the class theorem, there exists the class $C$ of all pairs of elements of $A$ which have the form $\langle \langle n, r \rangle, \langle n', s \rangle \rangle$; and for every element $p$ of $A$ there is an element $q$ of $A$ such that $\langle p, q \rangle \eta C$. Then applying IV* (with $\langle 0, c \rangle$ as $a$), we infer the existence of a function $F$ with the domain N satisfying the conditions that $F(0) = \langle 0, c \rangle$ and, for every finite ordinal $n$, $F(n) \eta A$ and $\langle F(n), F(n') \rangle \eta C$. By complete induction it follows that, for every finite ordinal $n$, the first member of $F(n)$ is $n$; and hence it follows that the converse domain of $F$ is also a function with the domain N. The latter function is a subclass of $A$; and thus $IV_s$ is proved.

Axiom IV* surely is at least as natural as $IV_s$. It seems to be a bit stronger than $IV_s$ and thus it might be suitable for some purposes for which $IV_s$ is insufficient.

Finally we give some indications for the development within the system of analysis of *the theory of the Cantor second number class*.

[36] Axiom IV* is the class-form of the axiom of dependent choices $DC^\omega$; IV* is called in Felgner's article (this volume) $DCC^\omega$. As shown there, IV* and $DC^\omega$ are equivalent in the presence of the axiom of foundation. However, $DC^\omega$ does not imply IV* in the absence of the axiom of foundation. R. B. Jensen has shown in 1965 that, in ZF, $DC^\omega$ is not implied by $AC^\omega$. A proof is given in FELGNÉR (1971a) p. 151–159 (*editor*).

The most natural method is to define the *second number class* as the class of enumerable ordinals—the *first number class* being N. Then for the sum of the first and second number classes, i.e., for the class of all finite and all enumerable ordinals, we may use the notation $\Omega$.

By the second theorem on enumerability, every ordinal lower than an enumerable ordinal is either finite or enumerable. Thus $\Omega$ is a transitive class of ordinals.

We shall call an ordinal $a'$ having a highest element $a$ the *successor* of $a$. Such ordinals $a'$ will be called *successors*, and all other ordinals, except 0, will be called *limiting numbers*.

An enumerable sequence $s$ of ordinals will be called *ascending* if, for every finite ordinal $n$, $s(n) \in s(n')$. And an ordinal $l$ will be said to be the *limit* of an ascending enumerable sequence of ordinals if it represents the sum of the members of the sequence, or (what comes to the same thing) if the class of ordinals higher than every element of the sequence is non-empty and has $l$ as its lowest element.

(There will be no danger of confusing this concept of *limit* with that referring to an enumerable sequence of real numbers, since an ordinal cannot be a real number.)

The connection between enumerable limiting numbers and enumerable ascending sequences of ordinal numbers is expressed by the two following theorems:

1. *Every limiting number that is enumerable is the limit of an enumerable ascending sequence of ordinals.*

2. *The sum of the members of an ascending enumerable sequence of finite or enumerable ordinals is represented by an enumerable ordinal which is the limit of the sequence.*

In order to prove 1, it obviously will be sufficient to show that every enumerable sequence $s$ of ordinals which has no highest member has an ascending subsequence $t$ such that the sum of the members of $t$ is the same as the sum of the members of $s$. This can be done by applying the iteration theorem to the function which assigns to each finite ordinal $n$ the lowest of the finite ordinals $m$ such that $s(m)$ is higher than $s(n)$.

The proof of 2 is easily seen to be reducible, with the aid of the axiom of the enumerable, to the proof of the general theorem that *the sum of the members of an enumerable sequence of enumerable sets is enumerable.*

The latter proof, with the aid of the special axiom of choice $IV_s$,[37] can be made as follows. Let $s$ be an enumerable sequence of enumerable sets. By the class theorem, there exists the class $C$ of pairs $\langle n, f \rangle$ in which $n \eta N$ and $f$ is a functional set representing a one-to-one correspondence between N and $s(n)$; and, by our assumption on $s$, the domain of $C$ is N. Hence, by $IV_s$, there exists a function $F$, with the domain N, which is a subclass of $C$. For every finite ordinal $n$, $F(n)$ is an enumerable sequence without repetitions and has the converse domain $s(n)$. So the sum $Q$ of the members of $s$ is identical with the class of

---

[37] The role of the axiom of choice in the theory of the Cantor second number class was generally investigated by Alonzo Church in his dissertation, see CHURCH (1927).

all sets $c$ for which there are finite ordinals $n$ and $m$ such that $(F(n))(m) = c$. In consequence of the class theorem, there exists the class of triplets $\langle\langle n, m\rangle, c\rangle$ such that $(F(n))(m) = c$; and this class obviously is a function whose domain is the pair class of N, which, as we know, is enumerable. Hence, by the composition lemma, there exists a function $G$ whose domain is N and whose converse domain $Q$. Let $H$ be the class of those elements $\langle n, c\rangle$ of $G$ for which there is no element $\langle m, c\rangle$ of $G$ with the same second member $c$ and with $m\varepsilon n$. Then $H$ is a one-to-one correspondence between a subclass of N, and $Q$. But every subclass of N is either finite or enumerable, and hence the same thing holds for $Q$. Because the members of $s$ are enumerable, $Q$ cannot be finite. Therefore $Q$ is enumerable, as was to be proved.

As a consequence of 2, whenever we have an ascending enumerable sequence of ordinals belonging to $\Omega$, we may speak of *its limit*, and this limit will again belong to $\Omega$.

From 1 and 2 combined, the following principle of *generalized induction* may be drawn as a consequence: If $C$ is a class satisfying the three conditions, that 0 belongs to $C$, that, for every element $r$ of $\Omega$ which belongs to $C$, its successor $r'$ also belongs to $C$, and that, for every ascending enumerable sequence of elements of $\Omega$ which belong to $C$, the limit of the sequence also belongs to $C$, then every element of $\Omega$ belongs to $C$. (For if the class of elements of $\Omega$ not belonging to $C$ were non-empty, we would have a contradiction upon considering its lowest element.)

By application of this generalized induction principle we may in particular obtain several extensions of the theorem of finite recursion. Of these we note first the following:

If $A$ is a class, and $a$ is an element of $A$, and $G$ is a function which, to every pair $\langle r, c\rangle$ such that $r\eta\Omega$ and $c\eta A$, assigns a subset of $c$ belonging to $A$, then there exists a function $K$ which to every element of $\Omega$ assigns an element of $A$, in such a way that

$$K(0) = a, \qquad K(r') = G(\langle r, K(r)\rangle) \text{ for every } r \ \eta \ \Omega,$$

and, for every ascending enumerable sequence of elements of $\Omega$, if $l$ is the limit of the sequence, the value $K(l)$ is the set representing the intersection of the values of $K$ for the members of the sequence.

The proof is analogous to that of the theorem of finite recursion (Part II, §6). An extra complication arises from the circumstance that, for a given limiting number $l$, there are many different ascending enumerable sequences having the limit $l$. But in consequence of our assumptions about $G$, and the formal properties of the subset relation, this makes no serious difficulty. It is merely necessary to include as a part of the induction the proof that, if $p\eta\Omega$ and $q\eta\Omega$ and $p\subset q$, the value $K(q)$ is a subset of $K(p)$.

In an entirely similar way we may prove the following recursion theorem:

If $A$ is a class, and $\overline{a}$ is an element of $A$, and $G$ is a function which, to every pair $\langle r, c\rangle$ such that $r\eta\Omega$ and $c\eta A$, assigns a set which belongs to $A$ and of which $c$ is a subset, and if $A$ has the property that the sum of the members of every enumerable sequence of elements of $A$ is represented by an element of $A$, then there exists a function $K$ which to every element of $\Omega$ assigns an element of $A$, in such a way that

$$K(0) = a, \qquad K(r') = G(\langle r, K(r) \rangle) \text{ for every } r \, \eta \, \Omega,$$

and, for every ascending enumerable sequence of elements of $\Omega$, if $l$ is the limit of the sequence, the value $K(l)$ is the set representing the sum of the values of $K$ for the members of the sequence.

As a special case of this theorem, using 2 above, we obtain:

If $a \eta \Omega$, and $G$ is a function which assigns to every pair $\langle r, c \rangle$ of elements of $\Omega$ an element of $\Omega$ higher than $c$, there exists a function $K$ assigning to every element of $\Omega$ an element of $\Omega$, in such a way that

$$K(0) = a, \qquad K(r') = G(\langle r, K(r) \rangle) \text{ for every } r \, \eta \, \Omega,$$

and, whenever $l$ is the limit of an ascending enumerable sequence $s$ of elements of $\Omega$, the value $K(l)$ is the limit of the sequence whose members are the values of $K$ for the members of $s$.

With this we have the foundations of the Cantor theory of the second number class.

PART IV[38]

**11. Elementary one-to-one correspondences, fundamental theorems on power.**
Our task in the treatment of general set theory will be to give a survey for the
purpose of characterizing the different stages and the principal theorems with
respect to their axiomatic requirements from the point of view of our system of
axioms. The delimitation of "general set theory" which we have in view differs
from that of Fraenkel's general set theory, and also from that of "standard
logic" as understood by most logicians. It is adapted rather to the tendency
of von Neumann's system of set theory—the von Neumann system having
been the first in which the possibility appeared of separating the assumptions
which are required for the conceptual formations from those which lead to the
Cantor hierarchy of powers. Thus our intention is to obtain general set theory
without use of the axioms V d, V c, VI.

It will also be desirable to separate those proofs which can be made without
the axiom of choice, and in doing this we shall have to use the axiom V*—i.e.,
the theorem of replacement taken as an axiom. From V*, as we saw in §4,
we can immediately derive V a and V b as theorems, and also the theorem that
a function whose domain is represented by a set is itself represented by a functional set; and on the other hand V* was found to be derivable from V a and V b
in combination with the axiom of choice.[39] (These statements on deducibility
are of course all on the basis of the axioms I–III.)

In the development of general set theory we shall always have V a at our
disposal, in some contexts as an axiom, in others as a theorem. But, as we have
seen, V a in connection with the axioms I–III enables us to obtain the fundamental theorems on ordinals, and also the iteration theorem and number theory.
Hence we shall be able to dispense with the axiom VII throughout our treatment of general set theory.

For this first more elementary part of general set theory we introduce an
axiom which we shall call the *pair class axiom*, and which asserts that the pair
class $A \times B$ is represented by a set if the classes $A$ and $B$ are represented by
sets. This was obtained in §4 as a consequence of V b, c, and also as a consequence of V a, c, d.[40] Later we shall show that it is also derivable from IV,
V a, V b, and hence, on the basis of the axiom of choice, can be dispensed with
as an axiom for general set theory.[41]

---

[38] Cf. *J. Symbolic Logic* **7** (1942) 133–145.

[39] Part II, pp. 15–16, consequence 3, consequence 4, and remark.

[40] Part II, pp. 17–18, consequence 8.

[41] Here and in similar cases, the basic axioms I–III are presupposed as a means of deduction
without being expressly mentioned.

From the pair class axiom we are able to deduce by means of V a, b—hence also by means of V*—the theorem, stated in §4 as a consequence of V c,[42] that the sum of the classes $A$ and $B$ is represented by a set if $A$ and $B$ are represented by sets. In fact we may first reduce this theorem to the case that $A$ and $B$ have no common element. For if $B_1$ is the class of elements of $B$ which do not belong to $A$, then the sum of $A$ and $B$ is the same as that of $A$ and $B_1$; the classes $A$ and $B_1$ have no common element, and if $A$ and $B$ are represented by sets, so likewise are $A$ and $B_1$ (by V a). Moreover the assertion of the theorem is obvious if one of the classes $A$, $B$ has no element or has only one element. Thus we may assume that $A$ and $B$ have no common element and that there are elements $p$, $q$ of $A$ and elements $r$, $s$ of $B$ such that $p \neq q$ and $r \neq s$. But then the class of triplets $\langle\langle a, b\rangle, c\rangle$ such that either $a\eta A$ & $b=r$ & $c=a$, or $a=p$ & $b\eta B$ & $b\neq r$ & $c=b$, or $a=q$ & $b=s$ & $c=r$ is a one-to-one correspondence between a subclass of $A \times B$ and the sum of $A$ and $B$. By the pair class axiom the class $A \times B$ is represented by a set, and hence by V a and V b the sum of $A$ and $B$ is represented by a set.

We introduce at once some notations and definitions.

By the *set-sum* of the sets $a$ and $b$ we mean the set representing the sum of the classes represented by $a$ and $b$, or in other words the set whose elements are those sets which are in $a$ or in $b$. (Its existence, by the proof just given, follows from V a, b and the pair class axiom.) We shall denote the sum of $A$ and $B$ by $A+B$, and likewise the set-sum of $a$ and $b$ by $a+b$.

By the *difference* of the classes $A$, $B$ we mean the intersection of $A$ with the complementary class of $B$; and by the *set-difference* of the sets $a$, $b$ we mean the set representing the difference of the classes represented by $a$, $b$ (the existence of such a set follows from V a). We shall denote the difference of $A$ and $B$ by $A \div B$, and the set-difference of $a$ and $b$ by $a \div b$.

The *pair set* of $a$ and $b$, which we shall denote by $a \times b$, is the set representing the pair class of the classes represented by $a$ and $b$, or in other words the set of pairs $\langle c, d \rangle$ such that $c\epsilon a$ and $d\epsilon b$. (Its existence follows from the pair class axiom.)

The *class of mappings of the set c into the class A*, which we denote by $A^{[c]}$, is the class of functional sets which have $c$ as domain and whose values belong to $A$.

Going on now to our survey, we first observe that there is an introductory discipline of class theory, namely the Boolean algebra (in the elementary sense) dealing with sum and intersection of classes, and the complementary class of a class, considered with respect to equalities and the subclass relation. In order to obtain this Boolean algebra, our axioms I (2), II (1), III a (1), (2), (3) suffice.[42a]

We have also a number of formal laws, of similar character, which concern the pair class $A \times B$ and the class of mappings $A^{[c]}$.

---

[42] Part II, p. 17, consequence 7.

[42a] This kind of a derivation of Boolean algebra of course is not an independent foundation, but the fundamental operations and relations of Boolean algebra are reduced, by means of the logical concepts, to the relation of a thing (set) belonging to a class.

The four laws concerning the pair class which assert that, for any classes $A, B, C,$

$$A \times B \backsim B \times A, \qquad A \times (B \times C) \backsim (A \times B) \times C,$$

$$A \times (B + C) = (A \times B) + (A \times C), \quad A \times (B \div C) = (A \times B) \div (A \times C),$$

are deducible by means of the axioms I–III.[43] (Notice that the first two laws assert merely a one-to-one correspondence, but the other two, an identity.)

The formal laws which concern $A^{[c]}$ are less elementary, since they require the axiom V* and the pair class axiom, or else axioms (such as IV, V a, V b) from which these two axioms can be derived as theorems. These laws for $A^{[c]}$ are as follows (all of them assert one-to-one correspondences):

For any classes $A, B$ and any set $c,$

$$(A \times B)^{[c]} \backsim A^{[c]} \times B^{[c]}.$$

For any class $A$, and for any sets $b, c$ having no common element,

$$A^{[b+c]} \backsim A^{[b]} \times A^{[c]}.$$

For any class $A$ and any sets $b, c,$

$$A^{[b \times c]} \backsim (A^{[b]})^{[c]}.$$

For any set $a$ there is a one-to-one correspondence between the class of subsets of $a$ and the class of mappings of $a$ into the class represented by 2.

Since the translation into our system of the usual method of proving these laws concerning $A^{[c]}$ is rather direct, it will suffice to carry out, as an example, the proof of the first of them. To do this we must, given classes $A, B$ and a set $c$, exhibit a one-to-one correspondence between the functional sets which assign to each element of $c$ an element of $A \times B$, and the pairs of functional sets $\langle f, g \rangle$ such that $f$ assigns to each element of $c$ an element of $A$, and $g$ assigns to each element of $c$ an element of $B$. Such a one-to-one correspondence is the class of triplets $\langle h, \langle f, g \rangle \rangle$ such that $f \eta A^{[c]}$, and $g \eta B^{[c]}$, and $h$ represents the class of triplets $\langle r, \langle s, t \rangle \rangle$ for which $\langle r, s \rangle \epsilon f$ and $\langle r, t \rangle \epsilon g$. In fact this class of triplets $\langle r, \langle s, t \rangle \rangle$ is, for any element $f$ of $A^{[c]}$ and any element $g$ of $B^{[c]}$, a function whose domain is represented by $c$ and which therefore, by axiom V*, is itself represented by a set.

The three remaining laws are to be proved in an analogous direct way.

To the use of these laws on one-to-one correspondences—which are generalizations of laws for finite classes—there is adjoined the method—peculiar to the treatment of infinite classes—of obtaining one-to-one correspondences by means of the *Bernstein theorem* (or *Schröder-Bernstein theorem*), the statement of which is as follows:

If $A, B, C$ are classes, and $A \subset B$, and $B \subset C$, and $A \backsim C$, then $B \backsim C.$

---

[43] See in particular Part I, p. 12, assertions 8 and 9.

Felix Bernstein's proof of this theorem[44] can be carried out within our system in the following way. By hypothesis there exists a one-to-one correspondence $F$ between $C$ and $A$. By the class theorem there exists the class $S$ of those elements $e$ of $C$ for which there is a finite ordinal $n$ and a functional set $f$ such that $n'$ is the domain of $f$, and $f(0)\ \eta\ C \div B$, and $f(n) = e$, and for every element $k$ of $n$, $\langle f(k), f(k')\rangle \eta\ F$.[44a] Let $H$ be the class of those elements $\langle e, a\rangle$ of $F$ for which $e\eta S$. Then it is easily shown that $H$ is a one-to-one correspondence between $S$ and $S \div (C \div B)$. Therefore, since $B = (S \div (C \div B)) + (C \div S)$, and $C = S + (C \div S)$, the sum of $H$ and the class of pairs $\langle b, b\rangle$ such that $b\ \eta\ C \div S$ is a one-to-one correspondence between $C$ and $B$.

For this proof, as can be seen, there are required besides the axioms I–III only the theory of finite ordinals. Thus the Bernstein theorem can be proved on the basis of the axioms I–III and V a (or also with VII replacing V a).

*Remark.* By an application of the class theorem analogous to that at the beginning of the preceding proof we infer the existence, for any class $A$, of the class of all those sets $b$ for which there exists a finite ordinal $n$ and a functional set $f$ such that $n'$ is the domain of $f$, and $f(0)\ \eta\ A$, and $f(n) = b$, and for every element $k$ of $n$, $f(k') \epsilon f(k)$. This class we shall call the *transitive closure* of $A$. It is easily seen to be a transitive class, and a subclass of any transitive class of which $A$ is a subclass. Moreover by the *transitive closure of a set* $a$ we understand the transitive closure of the class represented by $a$.[45] It follows further by the class theorem that the class of pairs $\langle a, b\rangle$ exists such that $b$ belongs to the transitive closure of $a$.

The Bernstein theorem, as is known, has its chief importance in connection with the *foundations of the theory of powers (Mächtigkeiten)*.

The first steps toward the comparison of powers can be made merely on the basis of the axioms I–III, V a. In Cantor's terminology, the classes $A$ and $B$ are said to be *of equal power* if $A \backsim B$; and $A$ is said to be *of lower power* than $B$, and $B$ *of higher power* than $A$, if $A$ is not of equal power with $B$ but is of equal power with some subclass of $B$. We also use the expressions "of equal power," "of lower (higher) power" for sets, in the sense that the relation named holds for the classes represented by the sets; also similarly for a class and a set. That the class $A$ is of lower power than the class $B$ will be symbolized by $A \prec B$; and similarly the notations $a \prec b$, $a \prec B$, $A \prec b$ will be used.

---

[44] Concerning the proofs which have been given of this theorem, see BOREL (1898) Note I, pp. 102–107, KORSELT (1911). In the proofs of Korselt, Zermelo, and Peano, the concept of finite number is eliminated by the Dedekind method of operating with intersections. However, this method of proof is in some respects less elementary, and this has the effect that it is applicable in our system only to the case that the class $C$ (in our above formulation of the Bernstein theorem) is represented by a set.

[44a] The class $S$ can be defined in other words as the class of those elements of $C$ which, for at least one element $a$ of $C \div B$, belong to the converse domain of the iterator of $F$ on $a$—see Part II, §6, p. 25.

[45] The concept of the transitive closure of a set amounts to the same thing as Finsler's concept of the system *der in einer Menge wesentlichen Mengen*, though the latter is defined in a somewhat different way, see FINSLER, (1926) §7, pp. 693–694.

From the definition of the relation $\prec$ the formal laws characterizing it as an ordering relation can be deduced in the usual way. That $\overline{A \prec A}$ for every class $A$ follows immediately; that, for arbitrary classes $A$, $B$, $C$,

$$A \prec B \,\&\, A \infty C \,\to\, C \prec B,$$

$$A \prec B \,\&\, B \infty C \,\to\, A \prec C$$

follows by means of the composition lemma; and that, for arbitrary classes $A$, $B$, $C$

$$A \prec B \,\&\, B \prec C \,\to\, A \prec C$$

is to be proved by means of the Bernstein theorem and the composition lemma.

Among the general theorems on comparison of power which are provable by means of the axioms I–III and V a there belongs also the famous *Cantor theorem* concerning the subsets of a set, which can be formulated as follows: The class of the elements of a set $a$ is of lower power than the class of the subsets of $a$.

The proof proceeds in the well-known way. First there is a one-to-one correspondence between the class $A$ of the elements of $a$ and the class of those non-empty subsets of $a$ which have only one element. On the other hand, if there were a one-to-one correspondence $C$ between $A$ and the class of the subsets of $a$, there would exist the class $S$ of those elements $b$ of $A$ not in $C(b)$. By V a the class $S$ would be represented by a subset $s$ of $a$. This set $s$ would be assigned by $C$ to an element $r$ of $a$. And, by the definition of $S$, the contradiction would result that $r \epsilon s$ if and only if $\overline{r \epsilon s}$.

In this proof the use of V a is essential. This appears from the impossibility of proving, by the method of the preceding reasoning (the Cantor "diagonal procedure"), the assertion that every class is of lower power than the class of its subsets. And in fact this assertion can be immediately seen to be false, since the class of all sets is identical with the class of its subsets.

However, the Cantor argument applies not only to subsets of a set but also to subclasses of a class; and although in our system we have neither classes of classes nor functions assigning classes to sets, nevertheless we can carry out in it the application of the Cantor diagonal procedure to the subclasses of a class. This possibility arises from the following circumstance. To an assignment (in the usual sense) of classes to sets which are the elements of a class $A$, there corresponds the relation between a set $a$ belonging to $A$ and a set $b$ belonging to the class assigned to $a$. If this relation can be formulated by means of a constitutive expression, then the class $C$ exists of pairs $\langle a, b \rangle$ such that the relation in question holds between $a$ and $b$; and the class assigned to an element $a$ of $A$ is the class of sets $b$ for which $\langle a, b \rangle \eta C$.

We shall say that a class $B$ *is assigned to a set $a$ by means of the class of pairs $C$* if $B$ is the class of sets $b$ such that $\langle a, b \rangle \eta C$.

Now we can prove that, for any class $A$, (1) there is a class of pairs by means of which to each element of $A$ a subclass of $A$ is assigned in a one-to-one way, and (2) there is no class of pairs by means of which every subclass of $A$ is assigned to an element of $A$, hence *a fortiori* no class of pairs by means of which such an assignment is made in a one-to-one way. In fact, (1) by means of the class of pairs $\langle c, c \rangle$ such that $c\eta A$ there is assigned to each element $a$ of $A$ the class whose only element is $a$, and this of course is a one-to-one assignment; and (2) if there were a class of pairs $C$ by means of which every subclass of $A$ were assigned to an element of $A$, then the class $S$ of elements $d$ of $A$ such that $\langle d, d \rangle$ did not belong to $C$ would be assigned by means of $C$ to an element $r$ of $A$; but then we should have the contradiction that $\langle r, r \rangle \eta C$ if and only if $\overline{\langle r, r \rangle \eta C}$.

In this way the Cantor theorem can be expressed and proved within the axiomatic frame under consideration, not only for the subsets of a set but also for the subclasses of a class—however without the consequence arising that for every class there is another class of higher power, which of course would lead to a contradiction. We are not even able in general set theory, as we have defined it, to infer from the forms of the Cantor theorem proved that for every set there is a set of higher power. This last follows only by application of the axiom V d (a fact which motivates the designation of this axiom as "power axiom").

However we can infer from the Cantor theorem that for every class represented by a set there exists a class of higher power, or, what amounts to the same thing, that the class of all sets is of higher power than any class which is represented by a set.

This result can also be obtained in another way, by use of the axiom V b. Since every class is a subclass of the class of all sets, every class is either of lower power or of equal power to the class of all sets. Thus if there were a class $C$ represented by a set and not of lower power than the class of all sets, there would exist a one-to-one correspondence between $C$ and the class of all sets; then by V b the class of all sets would be represented by a set, and therefore by V a every class would be represented by a set. But we have seen that the class of all ordinals is not represented by a set.

From these considerations concerning the Cantor theorem and the class of all sets it becomes clear in particular how the set-theoretic paradoxes are avoided in our system by the distinction of classes and sets.

**12. Numeration and well-ordering, cardinal numbers.** A principal point in the theory of power, as is well known, is the question of *comparability* and, in connection with it, the relation between powers and ordinals.

A class $A$ is called *comparable* with the class $B$ if the disjunction holds that

$$A \backsim B \vee A \prec B \vee B \prec A.$$

The comparability of sets is defined in the same way.

By the theorems on finiteness, any finite classes $A$, $B$ are comparable (and likewise any finite sets). In fact it follows easily from the theorems on finiteness that if $A$ and $B$ are finite classes we have $A \backsim B$ or $A \prec B$ or $B \prec A$ according as the number attributable to $A$ is the same as or lower than or higher than the number attributable to $B$. We also can infer that every finite class is of lower power than any infinite class.

For proof of the comparability of arbitrary classes $A$, $B$ rather strong axiomatic assumptions seem to be required. In general set theory we shall prove that any two sets are comparable. Afterwards for the proof that any two classes are comparable we shall have to add the axioms V c, d, and VII (or VII*).

In both these proofs the axiom of choice has an essential rôle. This is not surprising. In fact it is quite natural to use the axiom of choice for the theory of powers, as may be seen from the following considerations.

Cantor's concept of power refers to one-to-one correspondence. But a comparison of powers could just as well be based on the general concept of a function. Indeed we could first introduce a concept, $A$ *is of at least as high a power as $B$*— the notation could be, say, "$A \succsim B$"—defining it to mean that either $B$ is empty or there exists a function with the domain $A$ and the converse domain $B$.[45a] Then we could define the classes $A$, $B$ to be *of equal power* if at the same time $A \succsim B$ and $B \succsim A$; $A$ to be *of higher power than $B$* if $A \succsim B$ but not $B \succsim A$; and $A$ to be *of lower power than $B$* if $B$ is of higher power than $A$. This method of defining equal power, higher power, and lower power is intuitively as well motivated as the usual definition due to Cantor. (For finite classes it comes to the same thing.) And as long as the equivalence of the two definitions is not established, we have two competing concepts of power. Now this equivalence can be expressed by the statement that, for arbitrary classes $A$ and $B$, $A \succsim B$ if and only if $A \backsim B \mathbin{\textbf{v}} B \prec A$ (note that we are using the symbols $\backsim$, $\prec$ in their originally defined signification); and the implication

$$A \backsim B \mathbin{\textbf{v}} B \prec A \ \rightarrow \ A \succsim B$$

follows directly by axioms I–III. So what is in question is the general validity of the implication

$$A \succsim B \ \rightarrow \ A \backsim B \mathbin{\textbf{v}} B \prec A.$$

This, however, follows rather directly from the theorem that every function has an inverse function, which we found to be equivalent to the axiom of choice on the basis of the axioms I–III.[46]

*Remark.*[46a] Apparently the theorem that, if $A$ and $B$ are any classes,

$$A \succsim B \ \rightarrow \ A \backsim B \mathbin{\textbf{v}} B \prec A$$

cannot be deduced from the axioms I–III, V–VII (i.e., from our complete set with exception of the axiom of choice). But a proof of impossibility has not been given. The same thing is to be said of the theorem stating the general validity of the implication

$$A \succsim B \mathbin{\&} B \succsim A \ \rightarrow \ A \backsim B,$$

which of course on the assumption of the axiom of choice is an immediate consequence of the Bernstein theorem.

The inference from $A \succsim B$ to $A \backsim B \mathbin{\textbf{v}} B \prec A$ occurs in particular in Zermelo's

---

[45a] The relation $A \succsim B$ is also written as $B \leqslant^* A$ following Tarski (*editor*).

[46] See Part II, §4, p. 14, consequence 2 and remark.

[46a] The statement $A \succsim B \rightarrow A \backsim B \mathbin{\textbf{v}} B \prec A$ is equivalent to the global axiom of choice IV, as can be seen easily. The impossibility of proving $A \succsim B \rightarrow A \backsim B \mathbin{\textbf{v}} B \prec A$ in I–III, V–VII follows from P. J. Cohen's proof of the independence of AC from ZF (*editor*).

proof of the *generalized Julius König theorem*,[47] which can be formulated as follows: If $f$ and $g$ are functional sets with the same domain $d$ and if, for every element $a$ of $d$, $f(a) \prec g(a)$, then the sum $S$ of the elements of the converse domain of $f$ is of lower power than the class $P$ of functional sets with the domain $d$ which assign to each element $a$ of $d$ an element of $g(a)$.

Let us briefly consider the proof. Two things are to be shown, first that there exists a one-to-one correspondence between $S$ and a subclass of $P$, secondly that there is no one-to-one correspondence between $S$ and $P$.

The first of these results in the following way. By our assumptions on $f$, $g$, the theorem of replacement, and the axiom of choice, there exist functional sets $g_1$, $h$, $t$ with the domain $d$ such that, for every element $a$ of $d$, $g_1(a)$ is a proper subset of $g(a)$, $h(a)$ is a one-to-one correspondence between $f(a)$ and $g_1(a)$, and $t(a) \in g(a) \div g_1(a)$. Let $Q$ be the class of pairs $\langle s, p \rangle$ such that $s \eta S$, $p \eta P$, and, for every element $a$ of $d$, $p(a) = (h(a))(s)$ if $s \in f(a)$, and $p(a) = t(a)$ otherwise. This class is obviously a one-to-one correspondence between $S$ and a subclass of $P$.

The second part of the proof consists in showing that, for every one-to-one correspondence $C$ between $S$ and a subclass of $P$, there exists an element of $P$ not belonging to the converse domain of $C$. For this purpose we notice that, for each element $a$ of $d$, there exists the class of pairs $\langle s, b \rangle$ of an element $s$ of $f(a)$ and an element $b$ of $g(a)$ such that $(C(s))(a) = b$. This class (which depends on $a$) is a function; its domain $M$ is represented by $f(a)$ and its converse domain $N$ is a subclass of $g(a)$. We have $M \succeq N$ and therefore, by the above-mentioned consequence of the axiom of choice, $M \backsim N \lor N \prec M$. Since $f(a) \prec g(a)$, it follows (by the formal properties of the relation "of lower power") that $N$ cannot represent $g(a)$. Thus for every element $a$ of $d$ there exists an element of $g(a)$ which, for every element $s$ of $f(a)$, is different from $(C(s))(a)$. Moreover, by the class theorem, the axiom of choice, and the theorem of replacement, there exists a functional set $q$ with the domain $d$, satisfying the conditions that, for every element $a$ of $d$, $q(a) \in g(a)$ and $(x)(x \in f(a) \to q(a) \neq (C(x))(a))$. And $q$ belongs to $P$, but, as follows immediately, not to the converse domain of $C$.

Thus we prove the generalized König theorem within general set theory.

Going on now to prove, within general set theory, by means of the axioms I–IV, V a, b, that any two sets are comparable, we follow the analogy of the case of finite sets. The comparability of finite sets results from the existence, for any finite set, of a one-to-one correspondence to an ordinal. Thus we have to prove for an arbitrary set the existence of a one-to-one correspondence between this set and an ordinal. As follows from the axiom of replacement, such a one-to-one correspondence must be represented by a functional set. We shall call a functional set representing a one-to-one correspondence between a

---

[47] This theorem was proved by Zermelo in 1904 as a generalization of a theorem presented by Julius König at the Heidelberg Congress of 1904. Cf. KÖNIG, (1905) and ZERMELO (1908a) see theorem 33 and footnote, pp. 277–279. In the following statement and its proof as will be seen, a restricting premiss of both the König and the Zermelo theorem, which was adapted to the theory of powers, is eliminated.

set and an ordinal a *numeration* of the set.   Thus the theorem to be proved can
be formulated as *the numeration theorem*:   Every set has a numeration.

For the proof of this we use the method of Zermelo's first proof of the well-
ordering theorem.[48]

This method yields at the same time a more general theorem whose demonstration is independent of the axiom of choice.   For its formulation we first
make the following definition.   A numeration $h$ of a set $c$ will be called *adapted
to F*, where $F$ is a function assigning to every proper subset $p$ of $c$ an element
of $c \div p$, if for every ordinal $n$ in the domain of $h$ the value $h(n)$ is identical with
the value assigned by $F$ to the proper subset of $c$ which represents the class of
those elements of $c$ assigned by $h$ to the ordinals lower than $n$.

Then we state the following *theorem of adapted numeration*:   For any set $c$
and any function $F$ which assigns to every proper subset $p$ of $c$ an element of
$c \div p$, there exists a numeration of $c$ that is adapted to $F$.

*Proof.*   It is easily seen that the condition that a set be a numeration of a
subset of $c$, adapted to $F$, can be formulated by a constitutive expression.
Therefore the class $L$ exists of those numerations of subsets of $c$ which are
adapted to $F$.   Every element of $L$ is a functional set whose domain is an
ordinal and which represents a one-to-one correspondence.   If $h$ and $k$ are
elements of $L$, and $m$ is the domain of $h$ and $n$ the domain of $k$, and $m$ is a subset
of $n$, then $h$ is a subset of $k$.   For otherwise there would be a lowest ordinal $l$
among those ordinals which are first member of an ordered pair that is in $h$
but not in $k$, and, since $h$ and $k$ are numerations adapted to $F$, we should have
$h(l) = k(l)$, in contradiction to the characterizing property of $l$.   Consequently,
of any two elements of $L$, one is a subset of the other, and so the sum $S$ of the
elements of $L$ is a one-to-one correspondence   The domain of $S$ is a transitive
class of ordinals, and the converse domain of $S$ is the class of those elements of $c$
which are in the converse domain of a numeration of a subset of $c$ adapted to $F$.
By V a, since the converse domain of $S$ is a subclass of $c$, it is represented by a
set; and by V b, since the converse class of $S$ is (like $S$) a one-to-one correspondence, the domain of $S$ and $S$ itself are each represented by a set.   The
set $m$ representing the domain of $S$ is a transitive set of ordinals and so is itself
an ordinal.   Therefore the set $s$ representing $S$ is a numeration of a subset $d$
of $c$, and it is easily shown that this numeration is adapted to $F$.   Moreover $d$
must be identical with $c$.   For otherwise the set $t$ whose elements are the elements of $s$ together with the pair $\langle m, F(d) \rangle$ would be a numeration of a subset
of $c$, adapted to $F$.   And then $t$ would be a subset of $s$; but this is immediately
seen to be impossible.   Therefore $s$ is a numeration of $c$ that is adapted to $F$.—
For this proof, as will be seen, the axioms I–III, V a, b have sufficed.

Now the numeration theorem is easily proved as follows.   Let $c$ be a set.
By the class theorem the class of pairs $\langle a, b \rangle$ exists such that $a \subset c$ and $b \, \epsilon \, c \div a$.
Therefore by the axiom of choice there exists a function $F$ assigning to every
proper subset $p$ of $c$ an element of $c \div p$.   And consequently by the theorem of
adapted numeration, there exists a numeration of $c$ that is adapted to $F$.

---

[48] Cf. ZERMELO (1904).

From the numeration theorem and the theorem of adapted numeration several rather direct consequences are to be drawn.

First we have the result in connection with the theory of powers that *any two sets are comparable*. In fact, since of any two ordinals one is a subset of the other, it follows by the numeration theorem that of any two sets one is of equal power with a subset of the other.

The situation is made more explicit by introduction of the concept of a *cardinal*. By a *cardinal* (or a *cardinal number*) we understand an ordinal for which there exists no lower ordinal of equal power. For any set there exists a unique cardinal to which it has a one-to-one correspondence. For since the class of numerations of a set $c$ is not empty, there is a lowest among the ordinals which occur as domains of numerations belonging to that class—or in other words there is a lowest of the ordinals $m$ such that $m \backsim c$. This lowest ordinal is obviously a cardinal, and there cannot be another cardinal of equal power with $c$.

The uniquely determined cardinal that is of equal power with a set $c$ we shall call *the cardinal number of $c$*, and also *the cardinal number of $C$* if $C$ is the class represented by $c$.

Clearly a set $a$ is of equal power with a set $b$, of lower power than $b$, or of higher power than $b$ according as the cardinal number of $a$ is the same as, lower than, or higher than that of $b$. And the corresponding thing holds for classes which are represented by sets.

By the theorem $(\gamma)$ of §6,[49] every finite ordinal is a cardinal, and the cardinal number of a finite set or class is the number attributable to it.

Another direct consequence of the numeration theorem is the well-ordering theorem.

In our system the easiest way of introducing the concept of *order* is that of defining ordered classes and ordered sets as classes of pairs. As is well known, this can be done as follows.

*Definition.* A class $M$ of pairs is called *an order of a class $C$* if:

1. $\langle a, b \rangle \eta M \rightarrow a \eta C \,\&\, b \eta C$.
2. $a \eta C \,\&\, b \eta C \rightarrow \langle a, b \rangle \eta M \vee \langle b, a \rangle \eta M$.
3. $\langle a, b \rangle \eta M \,\&\, \langle b, a \rangle \eta M \rightarrow a = b$.
4. $\langle a, b \rangle \eta M \,\&\, \langle b, c \rangle \eta M \rightarrow \langle a, c \rangle \eta M$.

We then also say that the class $C$ is *ordered by the class $M$*, and we also speak of *the class $C$ in the order $M$*. An order of a set $c$ is to be defined in the same way; or the definition can be given by saying that an order of a set $c$ is the same as an order of the class represented by $c$.

There can be at most one class $C$ which is ordered by a given class of pairs $M$. For if there is such a class $C$, it must be the same as the class of sets $a$ such that $\langle a, a \rangle \eta M$.

If $a$ and $b$ are two distinct elements of a class or a set which is ordered by a class $M$, then, by conditions 2 and 3 in the definition of order, one and only one of the pairs $\langle a, b \rangle$, $\langle b, a \rangle$ belongs to $M$. We shall say that *a precedes b in the order $M$* if $a \neq b$ and $\langle a, b \rangle \eta M$.

[49] See Part II, §6, p. 29.

*Remark.* It might appear more natural to define an ordering class in such a way that no pair $\langle a, a \rangle$ belongs to it; but this would have the disadvantage that a class or a set with only one element could not be regarded as ordered, or else that the ordered set $(a)$ could not be distinguished from the ordered set $(b)$ or from the ordered null set.

An order $M$ of a class $C$ (or of a set $c$) is called a *well-ordering* if every non-empty subclass of $C$ (or every non-empty subset of $c$) has a *first element* in the order $M$—i.e., an element which precedes every other element in the order $M$.

A well-ordering of a set $c$ can be obtained immediately from a numeration of $c$. Indeed every numeration $h$ of a set $c$ determines an order $M$ of $c$ by the condition that, $a$ and $b$ being elements of $c$, the pair $\langle a, b \rangle$ belongs to $M$ if and only if the ordinal to which $a$ is assigned by $h$ is not higher than the ordinal to which $b$ is assigned. Now this ordering of $c$—let us call it *the order associated with h*—is a well-ordering. For if $s$ is a non-empty subset of $c$, the class of those ordinals to which an element of $s$ is assigned by $h$ has a lowest element; and the value of $h$ for this lowest element is obviously the first element of $s$ in the order in question. Thus from the numeration theorem we can infer that *every set has a well-ordering*. This is the *well-ordering theorem*.

On the other hand from the theorem of adapted numeration it follows that every well-ordering of a set $c$ is associated with a numeration of $c$. For let $c$ be well-ordered by $M$ and (making use of the class theorem) let $F$ be the function whose domain is the class of proper subsets of $c$ and whose value for a proper subset $p$ of $c$ is the first element of $c \div p$ in the order $M$. Then by the theorem of adapted numeration there exists a numeration of $c$ that is adapted to $F$; and it is readily seen that $M$ is the well-ordering associated with this numeration.

Moreover it is easily shown that a well-ordering of a set is associated with only one numeration of the set.

The foregoing applies in particular to the *natural order* of a set of ordinals. By the *natural order of a class, or a set, of ordinals* we mean the class of pairs $\langle a, b \rangle$ such that $a$ and $b$ are elements of the class, or set, and $a$ is not higher than $b$. This order is obviously a well-ordering. Thus of any set of ordinals there is one and only one numeration with which the natural order is associated; we shall call it *the numeration in the natural order*.

We insert here some discussion of the proof of the well-ordering theorem. A natural question is whether we could not follow more closely Zermelo's method of proving this theorem, applying the treatment we have made of numerations directly to well-orderings instead. This indeed would be possible, but would not be advantageous for our purposes, since in any case we want to have the numeration theorem, and the passage from it to the well-ordering theorem is more immediate than the inverse passage. Moreover for the treatment of well-orderings, as we have defined them, we should need the pair class axiom in order to show that any well-ordering of a set is represented by a set—whereas our intention is to derive the pair class axiom by means of the numeration theorem.

This last inconvenience can, however, be avoided by using another way of introducing the notion of order, due to Sierpiński.[50] Thus we come to a proof of the well-ordering theorem which is intermediate between the first proof of Zermelo and his second[51] one. Let us briefly indicate this method.

We start from the following definition. An *ordering class for a set c* is a class $A$ of subsets of $c$ having the three following properties:

1. Of any two elements of $A$, one is a subset of the other.

2. In every element $s$ of $A$ there is one and only one element which is not in any proper subset of $s$ belonging to $A$. This element will be called the *terminal* element of $s$ (with respect to $A$).

3. For every element $b$ of $c$ there is an element $s$ of $A$ such that $b$ is in $s$ but in no proper subset of $s$ belonging to $A$. (In view of 2, this amounts to postulating that every element $b$ of $c$ is the terminal element of some element of $A$.)

From this definition it follows immediately that there is a one-to-one correspondence between any set $c$ and any ordering class for it. Hence it follows by the axiom V b that every ordering class for a set is represented by a set. We shall call a set representing an ordering class for a set $c$ an *ordering set for c*.

By the *order generated by an ordering set t* for $c$ we understand the class of pairs $\langle a, b\rangle$ such that $a\epsilon c$ and $b\epsilon c$ and $a$ is in every element of $t$ in which $b$ is. This class of pairs is obviously an order. And it is easily seen that the order generated by an ordering set $t$ for $c$ is a well-ordering of $c$ if and only if every non-empty subset $s$ of $t$ has an element which is a subset of every element of $s$. If this condition is satisfied by an ordering set $t$ for $c$ we call it a *well-ordering set for c*. (In particular, under this definition, the null set is a well-ordering set for itself.)

Moreover a well-ordering set $r$ for a subset of $c$ will be called *adapted to F*, where $F$ is a function which assigns to every proper subset $p$ of $c$ an element of $c \div p$, if, for every element $b$ of $r$, the terminal element of $b$ is the value of $F$ for the set of the remaining elements of $b$.

Now let $c$ be any set. We are to prove that there exists a well-ordering set for $c$. As before, we conclude that, in virtue of the axiom of choice, there exists a function assigning to every proper subset $p$ of $c$ an element of $c \div p$. Let $F$ be such a function.

First we show that, if $h$ and $k$ are well-ordering sets for subsets of $c$ and are both adapted to $F$, and if $k$ is not a subset of $h$, then there is an element $d$ of $k$ such that $h$ is the set of those elements of $k$ which are proper subsets of $d$. Let $D$ be the class of those elements of $k$ which have a subset that is in one of the sets $h$, $k$ but not in both (notice that the subset in question is not required to be

---

[50] Cf. SIERPINSKI (1921). The Sierpinski concept of order is a modification of that introduced by Kuratowski in his paper, [1921]. The idea of representing any ordering of a set by a class of subsets such that any two distinct subsets $a$ and $b$ belonging to the class satisfy the condition $a \subset b$ ∨ $b \subset a$ goes back to Hessenberg. Cf. HESSENBERG (1906) vol. 1 in particular pp. 674–685 ("Vollständig ordnende Systeme").

[51] ZERMELO (1908), §1, pp. 107–111.

a proper subset). Then $D$ is not empty, since $k$ has an element not in $h$. And since $k$ is a well-ordering set, the subset of $k$ which represents $D$ has an element $d$ which is a subset of every element of $D$. Let $t$ be the set of sets $b$ such that $b\epsilon k$ and $b \subset d$, and let $s$ be the set representing the sum of the elements of $t$ (which sum is a subclass of $c$). Then $d = s + (F(s))$. An element $b$ of $t$ cannot belong to $D$, and consequently, every subset of $b$ (including $b$ itself) is either in both of the sets $h$, $k$ or in neither. From this it follows that $t$ is a subset of $h$, and that every subset of an element of $t$ which is in $h$ is also in $t$. And this entails $t=h$; for otherwise, since $h$ is a well-ordering set adapted to $F$, there would be an element of $h$ which was on the one hand not in $t$ and on the other hand a subset of every element of $h \div t$, and this element of $h$ would be identical with $s + (F(s))$; so we should have $d\epsilon h$, $d\epsilon k$, and at the same time $d$ would be a subset of every element of $D$ and of every element of $h \div t$, and this leads to a contradiction with $d\eta D$. Thus $h$ is the set of those elements of $k$ which are proper subsets of $d$.

Then we consider the class $H$ of those well-ordering sets for subsets of $c$ which are adapted to $F$ (the existence of $H$ following from the class theorem). From the foregoing it follows that the sum of the elements of $H$ is represented by some one of its elements, say $g$. But then $g$ must be a well-ordering set for $c$ itself—since otherwise the set $g + (F(g))$ would be an element of $H$ and thus a subset of $g$, which is impossible. Therefore there exists a well-ordering set for $c$. And the order generated by this well-ordering set is a well-ordering of $c$.

In this way we have also proved at the same time that, for any function $F$ which assigns to every proper subset $p$ of a set $c$ an element of $c \div p$, there exists a well-ordering set for $c$ that is adapted to $F$. And in the proof of this the axiom of choice has not been used.

In regard to this demonstration of the well-ordering theorem, it will be observed that the possibility of imitating within our system of general set theory (with use merely of the axioms I–IV, V a, b) Zermelo's second proof of the well-ordering theorem is due to an essential modification of that proof by which it becomes more elementary. In fact, in order to translate the second proof of Zermelo directly into our system, we should have to apply the axiom V d. Likewise this axiom would be required for translating into our system Hartogs's proof (without use of the axiom of choice) that there exists no set which is of higher power than every well-ordered set.[52]

---

[52] Cf. HARTOGS (1915).

## PART V[53]

**13. General recursion.** We have still to consider the extension of the methods of number theory to infinite ordinals—or to *transfinite numbers* as they may also, as usual, be called.

The means for establishing number theory are, as we know, recursive definition, complete induction, and the "principle of the least number." The last of these applies to arbitrary ordinals as well as to finite ordinals, since every non-empty class of ordinals has a lowest element. Hence immediately results also the following generalization of complete induction, called *transfinite induction*: If $A$ is a class of ordinals such that (1) $0\eta A$, and (2) $a\eta A \rightarrow a'\eta A$, and (3) for every limiting number $l$, $(x)(x\epsilon l \rightarrow x\eta A) \rightarrow l\eta A$, then every ordinal belongs to $A$.

So for the generalization of the methods of number theory to arbitrary ordinals it remains only to inquire how recursive definition is to be generalized. The theorem answering this question (*the theorem of transfinite recursion*) can be derived from a more general theorem on recursion (*the general recursion theorem*) which is one of the fundamental theorems of set theory.[54] Before stating it, we introduce as a preliminary the *general concept of a sequence*.

By a *sequence* we understand a functional set whose domain is an ordinal. In particular, if $n$ is an ordinal, an *n-sequence* is a sequence with the domain $n$. The elements of the converse domain of a sequence will be called the *members* of the sequence—so that a set is a member of a sequence $s$ if and only if it is the second member of a pair which is in $s$.

By a *sequence* (or *n-sequence*) *of elements of* $C$, where $C$ is a class, we mean a sequence ($n$-sequence) whose members belong to $C$. In this sense we speak in particular of a *sequence* (or *n-sequence*) of ordinals. And we speak also of a *sequence* (or *n-sequence*) *of elements of a set* $c$, meaning a sequence whose members are in $c$.

If $G$ is a function whose domain is the class of all ordinals, a sequence which is a subset of $G$ will be called a *segment* of $G$. For any ordinal $n$, the set which (by axiom V b) represents the class of elements $\langle a, c\rangle$ of $G$ such that $a\epsilon n$, is a segment of $G$ and will be called *the n-segment of* $G$. Similarly, if $g$ is an $m$-sequence and $n\epsilon m$, the $n$-sequence representing the class of elements $\langle a, c\rangle$ of $g$ such that $a\epsilon n$, will be called *the n-segment of* $g$.

[53] Cf. *J. Symbolic Logic* **8** (1943) 89–106.

[54] General recursion in the frame of the Fraenkel axiomatic set theory (with the strong form of the *Ersetzungsaxiom*, equivalent to our axiom V*) was established by von Neumann, on the basis of his independent theory of ordinals, in VON NEUMANN (1928a).

According to these definitions we have in particular, for any class $C$, that the null set is a 0-sequence of elements of $C$, and the only one; and likewise for any set $c$ the null set is a 0-sequence of elements of $c$, and the only one. And the 0-segment of any function whose domain is the class of all ordinals, or the 0-segment of any $n$-sequence, where $n$ is an ordinal $\neq 0$, is the null set.

It is easily shown that, if $n$ is an ordinal and $k\epsilon n$, the $k$-segment of the $n$-segment either of a sequence $s$ whose domain is higher than $n$, or of a function $G$ whose domain is the class of all ordinals, is identical with the $k$-segment of $s$, or of $G$.

We insert here at once some remarks on *ascending sequences of ordinals*. A sequence of ordinals will be called *ascending* if it is a numeration in the natural order. As is easily shown by transfinite induction, each member of an ascending sequence of ordinals is at least as high as the ordinal to which it is assigned.

An ascending sequence of ordinals whose domain is a limiting number is said to *have a limit* if the sum of its members is represented by a set. This set is then the lowest of those ordinals which are higher than every member of the sequence, and it is at least as high as the domain of the sequence. We call it *the limit of the sequence*. Every limiting number $l$ is the limit of an ascending sequence of ordinals; for in particular the set of pairs $\langle n, n \rangle$, such that $n\epsilon l$, has the limit $l$.

A limiting number $l$ will be called *irreducible* if every ascending sequence of ordinals whose limit is $l$ has the domain $l$.

For every limiting number $l$ there is a lowest of those limiting numbers $k$ such that there exists an ascending $k$-sequence of ordinals whose limit is $l$. The ordinal so determined is an irreducible ordinal, as follows easily by the composition lemma and axiom V b. We shall call it *the lowest domain for the limit $l$*.

Now we state the *general recursion theorem*: For any class $A$ and any function $F$ which assigns to every sequence of elements of $A$ an element of $A$, there exists a function $G$ whose domain is the class of all ordinals and whose value for an ordinal $n$ is the value assigned by $F$ to the $n$-segment of $G$.

*Proof.* Let us call a sequence $s$ *adapted to $F$* if, for each of its elements $\langle n, c \rangle$, $c$ is the value assigned by $F$ to the $n$-segment of $s$.

If $n$ is an ordinal and $r\epsilon n$, the $r$-segment of any $n$-sequence adapted to $F$ is itself adapted to $F$. By the class theorem, there exists the class $C$ of ordinals $m$ such that there is one and only one $m$-sequence adapted to $F$.

Let $k$ be an ordinal every element of which belongs to $C$. There exists the class of pairs $\langle n, c \rangle$ such that $n\epsilon k$ and $c$ is the value assigned by $F$ to the uniquely determined $n$-sequence which is adapted to $F$. This class, by V b, is represented by a set $s$ which is a $k$-sequence of elements of $A$. We shall now show that $s$ is adapted to $F$. For this purpose we have to verify that, if $n\epsilon k$, the value $s(n)$ is identical with the value of $F$ for the $n$-segment of $s$. Let $n$ be an element of $k$ and let $t$ be the uniquely determined $n$-sequence which is adapted to $F$. If $\langle r, a \rangle \epsilon t$, then $r\epsilon n$, $r\epsilon k$, and $a$ is the value of $F$ for the $r$-segment of $t$. But this $r$-segment, by our remark above, is adapted to $F$; hence it is the uniquely determined $r$-sequence which is adapted to $F$, and $a$ is the value of $F$ for this sequence. Thus we have $t(r) = s(r)$ for every $r \epsilon n$, so that $t$ is the $n$-segment of $s$, and the value $s(n)$, which is the value assigned by $F$ to the $n$-sequence $t$, is the value of

$F$ for the $n$-segment of $s$. So in fact $s$ is adapted to $F$. Furthermore, if $s_1$ is any $k$-sequence adapted to $F$, and $n\epsilon k$, then the $n$-segment of $s_1$ is the uniquely determined $n$-sequence which is adapted to $F$, so that $s_1(n) = s(n)$. Accordingly we have $s_1 = s$. So $s$ is the only $k$-sequence adapted to $F$, and $k\eta C$.

Thus we have that, if every element of an ordinal $k$ belongs to $C$, then $k$ itself belongs to $C$. So the class of ordinals not belonging to $C$ cannot have a lowest element and consequently must be empty; in other words, every ordinal belongs to $C$.

In consequence, it follows by the class theorem that the function $G$ exists whose domain is the class of all ordinals and which assigns to the ordinal $k$ the value of $F$ for the $k$-sequence adapted to $F$. From the above considerations it follows further that, for every ordinal $k$, the $k$-sequence adapted to $F$ is the same as the $k$-segment of $G$, so that $G(k)$ is the value of $F$ for the $k$-segment of $G$. Thus $G$ is the function (depending on $A$ and $F$) whose existence is asserted in our theorem.

For this proof, besides the axioms I–III, only V a, V b are required—and V a only for the theory of ordinals (so that instead of it here axiom VII would suffice).

Of the general recursion theorem there are, of course, many applications. As a particular consequence of it we note first the following theorem: If $A$ is a class of ordinals such that, for every sequence of elements of $A$, there exists an element of $A$ higher than every member of the sequence, then there exists a one-to-one correspondence $C$ between the class of all ordinals and $A$, such that to the higher of any two ordinals is assigned the higher element of $A$—so that every segment of $C$ is an ascending sequence.

This results by applying the general recursion theorem to the case that $F$ is the function whose domain is the class of sequences of elements of $A$ and which assigns to each of these sequences the next higher element of $A$. Thus there follows first the existence of a one-to-one correspondence $C$ between the class of all ordinals and a subclass $B$ of $A$, with the property that every segment of $C$ is an ascending sequence. Then by means of the principle of the least number it is easily shown that $B = A$.

Let us further show how by means of the general recursion theorem we can obtain the Max Zorn *maximum principle*, which for many purposes in connection with abstract algebras may suitably be used instead of the well-ordering theorem, as has been noted by Zorn.[55]

For simpler formulation of the principle we introduce the following definitions of Zorn (slightly modified):

A set of sets is a *chain* if, for every two elements $a$, $b$ of it, either $a \subset b$ or $b \subset a$.

(Under this definition, in particular, the null set is a chain, and, for every set $a$, the set $(a)$ is a chain.)

A class $A$ (or a set $a$) is *closed* if for every chain which is a subset of $A$ (or $a$) the sum of its elements is represented by an element of $A$ (or $a$).

(We note that every closed class, or set, has the null set as an element.)

[55] ZORN (1935).

We further define an element of a class (or a set) to be a *maximal* element if it is not a proper subset of any other element of that class (or set).

Now a formulation of Zorn's principle adapted to our present axiomatic frame is: *Every closed class of subsets of a set has a maximal element.*

Concerning this formulation of the principle we make the following remark. Zorn's original statement is that *every closed set has a maximal element.* From this our statement of the principle follows if we use V d, since by V d and V a every class of subsets of a set is represented by a set. On the other hand, from our statement, that of Zorn follows immediately if we apply V c. However, this application of V c can be avoided: in fact, as we shall see, Zorn's statement of his principle can be derived from our statement on the basis merely of the axioms I–III and V a. Moreover, under our distinction of classes and sets, our form of the statement is more advantageous for the applications for which the principle is intended. So it will be justified to speak here of the "Zorn maximum principle" in the sense of our above formulation, and to distinguish from this the "original statement" of the principle.

In order to derive the Zorn maximum principle from our axioms I–IV, V a, b it will be sufficient to show the following: If $A$ is a closed class satisfying the condition that each of its elements is a proper subset of another element, then the elements of $A$ cannot all be subsets of a set $b$. This in turn will follow if we show that, under the same assumptions on $A$, there exists a function $L$ whose domain is a subclass of the sum $S$ of the elements of $A$ and whose converse domain is the class of all ordinals. In fact, if every element of $A$ were a subset of $b$, then $S$ would be a subclass of $b$, and therefore by V a every subclass of $S$ would be represented by a set; thus from the existence of the function $L$ it would follow by the theorem of replacement that the class of all ordinals were represented by a set, whereas we know it is not so represented.

Now the existence of the function $L$, under the stated conditions on $A$, results as follows, by means of the general recursion theorem. By one of the conditions on $A$, in consequence of the axiom of choice, there exists a function $P$ assigning to each element $c$ of $A$ an element $d$ of $A$ such that $c \subset d$. Moreover, since $A$ is closed, there exists, by the class theorem, a function $F$ assigning to every sequence of elements of $A$ an element of $A$ in such a way that the following relations hold: $F(0) = 0$ $(0 \eta A)$; for every $k'$-sequence $q$, $F(q) = P(q(k))$; for a sequence $q$ whose domain is a limiting number, in case the converse domain of $q$ is a chain, $F(q)$ is the value of $P$ for the element of $A$ which represents the sum of the members of $q$, and in the contrary case $F(q) = 0$. Thus the general recursion theorem can be applied, and it follows by it that there exists a function $G$ whose domain is the class of all ordinals and whose value for an ordinal $k$ is the value of $F$ for the $k$-segment of $G$. This function $G$, as is easily shown with the aid of transfinite induction, has the property that, for every ordinal $m$, $G(m)$ has an element which is not in $G(n)$ for any ordinal $n$ lower than $m$.

Consequently, if $H$ is the sum of the elements of the converse domain of $G$, and $L$ is the function assigning to each element $c$ of $H$ the lowest of the ordinals $m$ such that $c \in G(m)$, the converse domain of $L$ is the class of all ordinals. And the domain of $L$, being the sum of the values of $G$, which are elements of $A$, is a subclass of the sum $S$ of the elements of $A$.—Thus $L$ is a function of the required kind. And so the Zorn principle is seen to be provable by means of our axioms I–IV, V a, b.

There is another principle of a similar kind, intended for the same purposes as is that of Zorn, which was proposed by Oswald Teichmüller—who in his paper, *Braucht der Algebraiker das Auswahlaxiom?*,[56] not knowing of Zorn's publication, showed this principle to be sufficient for abstract algebras. Teichmüller's principle, of which he gives three equivalent statements, can be formulated as follows: *If $A$ is a class of subsets of a set, such that a set $c$ belongs to $A$ if and only if every finite subset of $c$ belongs to $A$, then $A$ has a maximal element.*

This principle can be derived from the Zorn maximum principle. In fact it is easily shown, with an application of V a, that every class satisfying the hypotheses of the Teichmüller principle is closed.

On the other hand, from the Teichmüller principle we can obtain the original statement of the Zorn principle in two steps as follows. Observing first that a set is a chain if and only if every finite subset of it is a chain, we deduce from the Teichmüller principle the *theorem of the maximal chain*, viz.: *The class of those subsets of a set which are chains has a maximal element.*

Now let $a$ be a closed set. By the theorem of the maximal chain, there exists among the subsets of $a$ which are chains a maximal chain $m$; and the sum of the elements of $m$, since $a$ is closed, is represented by an element $s$ of $a$. The set $s$ cannot be a proper subset of an element $t$ of $a$. For if it were, the set $n$ having as elements the sets $c$ such that $c \epsilon m \lor c = t$ would be a subset of $a$ and at the same time a chain, and $m$ would be a proper subset of $n$; but this contradicts the defining property of $m$. Therefore $s$ is a maximal element of $a$. So it results that every closed set has a maximal element.

In this way, finally, we have derived Zorn's original statement of his maximum principle from our statement by means of the axioms I–III, V a.

*Remark.* As has been observed for each of the two maximum principles by its author, there is the possibility of deducing from it the well-ordering theorem, but for this the power axiom V d is necessary. On the other hand, the axiom of choice in the form of our axiom IV, referring to arbitrary classes of pairs, apparently is not deducible from the maximum principles even with the aid of V d.

There is also an easy proof of the theorem of adapted numeration as a consequence of the general recursion theorem, as follows. Let $c$ be a non-empty set (the theorem being obvious in the case of the null set), let $a$ be an element of $c$, and let $F$ be a function which assigns to every proper subset $p$ of $c$ an element of $c \div p$. Then the sum $T$ of $F$ and the class whose single element is $\langle c, a \rangle$ is a function which assigns to every subset of $c$ an element of $c$. Furthermore by the class theorem there exists a function $P$ assigning to every sequence of elements of $c$ the value of $T$ for the converse domain of this sequence. By the general recursion theorem there exists a function $G$ whose domain is the class of all ordinals and which assigns to every ordinal $n$ the value of $P$ for the $n$-segment of

---

[56] TEICHMÜLLER (1939). See the review by Rózsa Péter in PÉTER (1941).

[56a] Zorn's principle is equivalent to the local axiom of choice AC. W. B. Easton showed, that AC does not imply the global axiom of choice. See Felgner's article (in this volume) for a proof (*editor*).

$G$. This function $G$ cannot be a one-to-one correspondence; for if it were, then, since the the converse domain of $G$ is a subclass of $c$ and therefore (by V a) is represented by a set, it would follow by V b that the domain of $G$, namely the class of all ordinals, were represented by a set.

There must, therefore, exist different ordinals for which the value of $G$ is the same; and the class of those ordinals for which the value of $G$ is the same as for some lower ordinal has a lowest element $m$. Now the $m$-segment of $G$, which is a sequence of elements of $c$, is a one-to-one correspondence. Its converse domain must be the set $c$ itself. For if it were a proper subset $p$ of $c$, then $G(m)$, which is the value of $P$ for the $m$-segment of $G$, i.e. $T(p)$, would be identical with $F(p)$ and thus not in $p$; then the $m'$-segment of $G$ would still be a one-to-one correspondence, contrary to the definition of $m$. It follows that the $m$-segment of $G$ is a numeration of $c$; and obviously this numeration is adapted to $F$.

In this way the numeration theorem and the well-ordering theorem can be derived from the general recursion theorem.

We now still have to apply the general recursion theorem, as originally intended, to the derivation of a theorem of transfinite recursion, extending the theorem of finite recursion to arbitrary ordinals. Within general set theory as we have defined it this application is not at all immediate. But a direct passage from the general recursion theorem to a satisfactory theorem of transfinite recursion becomes possible as soon as the axiom V c is adjoined. In fact, as we know, this axiom in combination with the theorem of replacement yields the sum theorem,[57] and from the latter theorem it follows directly that the sum of the members of any sequence is represented by a set. Using this in connection with the general recursion theorem, we obtain immediately the following *strong theorem of transfinite recursion*: If $A$ is a class, $a$ an element of $A$, and $P$ a function assigning, to every pair $\langle n, c \rangle$ of an ordinal $n$ and an element $c$ of $A$, an element of $A$, then there exists a function $K$, uniquely determined by $a$ and $P$, whose domain is the class of all ordinals and which satisfies the conditions that $K(0) = a$, and $K(n') = P(\langle n, K(n) \rangle)$ for every ordinal $n$, and, for every limiting number $l$, $K(l)$ is the set representing the sum of the members of the $l$-segment of $K$.

For the existence of such a function $K$ follows from the general recursion theorem by taking for $F$ the function whose domain is the class of sequences of elements of $A$ and whose value for an $n$-sequence $s$ of elements of $A$ is $a$ if $n = 0$, or, if $n$ is the successor $m'$ of an ordinal $m$, is $P(\langle m, s(m) \rangle)$, or, if $n$ is a limiting number, is the set by which the sum of the members of $s$ is represented (in consequence of the sum theorem). And by transfinite induction it follows immediately that the value of $K$ for an ordinal $n$ is uniquely determined by $n$, $a$, and $P$.

This (strong) theorem of transfinite recursion may be applied to the case that $A$ is the class of all ordinals, and it then allows the introduction of functions of arbitrary ordinals by recursive definitions, in the usual fashion.

In this way a comparatively simple foundation of transfinite arithmetic is possible. And for this purpose it might seem desirable to adjoin the axiom

---

[57] See Part II, §4, p. 16.

V c to the axioms of general set theory—or, what amounts to the same thing, to take the axioms I–IV and V** as basis for general set theory. This stronger conception of general set theory—we shall call the axiomatic system to which it gives rise the *strengthened system of general set theory*—is of course advantageous in some respects. But it conflicts with our idea (expressed in §11) of separating from general set theory the existential statements concerning cardinal numbers which lead to the Cantor hierarchy of powers. In fact, in the strengthened system of general set theory it follows, as a consequence of the theorem that the sum of the members of any sequence is represented by a set, that for every sequence of cardinals which has no highest member there exists a higher cardinal.

If our idea of §11, for general set theory (proper), is to be found practicable, we must show how a general method of transfinite recursion, applying in particular to the recursive introduction of functions of arbitrary ordinals, can be established on the basis merely of the axioms I–IV, V a, b. For this purpose we require a number of preliminary results, including the proof of the pair class axiom from the axioms I–IV, V a, b.

**14. Sum and product of arbitrary ordinals. Proof of the pair class axiom.** We wish next to introduce the notion of the sum of arbitrary ordinals. For this purpose we begin by defining the *sum* $a+n$ *of an arbitrary ordinal* $a$ *and a finite ordinal* $n$ as the value for $n$ of the iterator on $a$ of the function which assigns to every ordinal $c$ the value $c'$. By complete induction it follows that, for an arbitrary ordinal $a$ and any finite ordinals $m$ and $n$, we have $a+(m+n) = (a+m)+n$.

Corresponding to any ordinal $a$ there are ordinals $c$ for which there exists a finite ordinal $n$ such that $a = c+n$; and it is easily seen that the lowest such ordinal $c$ cannot be a successor. Thus for any ordinal $a$ there exist ordinals $b$ and $n$, $n$ being finite and $b$ either 0 or a limiting number, such that $a = b+n$. Moreover, for a given $a$, $b$ and $n$ are uniquely determined, as is easily shown. The finite ordinal $n$ will in particular be called *the finite residual of* $a$.

By means of finite residuals we can extend the familiar distinction between even and odd numbers to arbitrary ordinals, calling an ordinal *even* or *odd* according as its finite residual is expressible in the form $n+n$ or in the form $n+n'$.

If $a$ is a limiting number, the class of pairs $\langle b+n, b+(n+n)\rangle$, such that $b$ is either 0 or a limiting number lower than $a$, and $n$ is a finite ordinal, is readily shown to be a one-to-one correspondence between $a$ and the class of even elements of $a$. Similarly, the class of pairs $\langle b+n, b+(n+n')\rangle$, with $b$ and $n$ satisfying the same conditions as before, is a one-to-one correspondence between $a$ and the class of odd elements of $a$.

Further, if $a$ is any infinite ordinal, $n$ the finite residual of $a$, and $b$ the limiting number for which $a = b+n$, then the class of pairs which have either the form $\langle b+k, k\rangle$ with $k\epsilon n$, or the form $\langle m, n+m\rangle$ where $m$ is a finite ordinal, or the form $\langle r, r\rangle$ where $r$ is an infinite ordinal lower than $b$, is a one-to-one correspondence between $a$ and $b$. Thus every infinite ordinal number $a$ is of equal power with some limiting number not higher than $a$. It follows in particular that *every infinite cardinal number is a limiting number.*

Now we prove readily that *if the classes A and B are represented by sets, their sum is represented by a set.* As previously remarked,[58] we may, in consequence of V a, restrict ourselves to the case that $A$ and $B$ have no common element. Let $r$ and $s$ be the respective cardinal numbers of the sets representing two classes $A$ and $B$ having no common element. Since our conditions on $A$ and $B$ are symmetrical, we may suppose that $r$ is not higher than $s$. If $r$ is finite, we prove by complete induction the existence of a one-to-one correspondence between the ordinal $s+r$ and the class $A+B$, and the latter, by V b, is therefore represented by a set. If $r$ is infinite, $s$ is also infinite, and $r$ and $s$, being cardinals, are limiting numbers. As above, there exists a one-to-one correspondence between $r$ and the class of even elements of $r$. The even elements of $r$ are also even elements of $s$. Further, there exists a one-to-one correspondence between $s$ and the class of odd elements of $s$. From this, using the composition lemma, we infer that there is a one-to-one correspondence between a subclass of $s$ and the class $A+B$, and the latter, by V a and V b, is therefore represented by a set. Thus in either case the sum of $A$ and $B$ is represented by a set.

Now (as we did in §11 on the basis of the pair class axiom) we may define the *set-sum* $a+b$ of sets $a$ and $b$ as the set representing the sum of the classes represented by $a$ and $b$.

From the preceding, in consequence of the Bernstein theorem, it follows also that if a set $a$ is not of higher power than $b$ and $b$ is infinite, then $a+b \backsim b$. Hence if $a \prec c$, and $b \prec c$, and $c$ is infinite, then $a+b \prec c$.

We may now introduce the *sum $a+b$ of arbitrary ordinals $a$ and $b$*, as follows. We first consider the class of pairs $\langle r, 0\rangle$ such that $r\epsilon a$, and the class of pairs $\langle r, 1\rangle$ such that $r\epsilon b$. By V b these classes are represented by sets $p$, $q$, and so their sum is represented by the set-sum $p+q$. A well-ordering of the latter set is constituted by the class of those pairs which have one of the three forms:.

$\langle\langle r, 0\rangle, \langle s, 0\rangle\rangle$ with $s\epsilon a$ and $r=s \lor r\epsilon s$;

$\langle\langle r, 1\rangle, \langle s, 1\rangle\rangle$ with $s\epsilon b$ and $r=s \lor r\epsilon s$;

$\langle\langle r, 0\rangle, \langle s, 1\rangle\rangle$ with $r\epsilon a$ and $s\epsilon b$.

Moreover this well-ordering, by the theorem of adapted numeration, is associated with a certain numeration of $p+q$. The domain of this numeration of $p+q$ we define to be the *sum $a+b$*.

Under this definition, the relation $a+b = c$ between ordinals $a$, $b$, $c$ amounts, as is easily seen, to the following: $a$ is not higher than $c$ (and thus is a subset of $c$) and $b$ is the domain of the numeration of $c \div a$ in the natural order. This relation can be formulated by a constitutive expression, and from the preceding reasoning it follows that, for any ordinals $a$, $b$, there is a unique ordinal $c$ such that $a+b = c$. Hence there exists the class of triplets $\langle\langle a, b\rangle, c\rangle$ such that $a$, $b$, $c$ are ordinals and $a+b = c$; and this class is a function whose domain is the pair class of the class of all ordinals.

An ordinal $b$ for which there exists an ordinal $a$ such that $a+b = c$ will be called a *residual of c.*

From our definition of $a+b$ it follows further that for arbitrary ordinals $a$ and $b$ we have $a+0 = a$ and $a+b' = (a+b)'$. Hence our general definition of

---

[58] See Part IV, §11, p. 57.

$a+b$ is in agreement with the one previously given for the special case that $b$ is finite.

Another consequence of our definition of the sum of ordinals is that, if $a$ and $c$ are ordinals and $c$ is not lower than $a$, there exists an ordinal $b$ such that $a+b = c$. Moreover, for given $a$ and $c$, the ordinal $b$ is uniquely determined. In fact, for arbitrary ordinals $a$, $b$, $c$, as is easily proved, we have $b\epsilon c \rightarrow a+b \,\epsilon\, a+c$. Hence in particular, if $c$ is an ordinal other than 0, every ordinal $a$ is lower than the ordinal $a+c$. And also, if $l$ is a limiting number, the sum $a+l$ is the lowest ordinal that is higher than every sum $a+c$ for $c\epsilon l$; hence if $l$ is a limiting number and $a$ is any ordinal, then $a+l$ is also a limiting number.

That, for arbitrary ordinals $a$ and $b$, $b$ is not higher than $a+b$, can be proved by transfinite induction. Also by transfinite induction we obtain the associative law, $a+(b+c) = (a+b)+c$, for arbitrary ordinals $a$, $b$, $c$.

As for the power of the sum $a+b$ of ordinals $a$ and $b$, since $a+b$ is the set-sum of $a$ and a set of equal power with $b$, it follows from the properties of the set-sum which we derived above, that if at least one of $a$ and $b$ is infinite, then either $a+b \sim a$ or $a+b \sim b$. In particular, if $c$ is an infinite cardinal and $a\epsilon c$ and $b\epsilon c$, then $a+b < c$ and consequently $a+b \,\epsilon\, c$; hence further, if $a\epsilon c$, then $a+c = c$. Thus every residual, $\neq 0$, of an infinite cardinal $c$ is identical with $c$.

We come now to the proof of the pair class axiom as a theorem of general set theory. It will be derived as a consequence of the following *pair class theorem*: If the class $C$ is represented by an infinite cardinal, then $C \times C \sim C$.

*Remark.* Of course the one-to-one correspondence here stated is well known; but we have to show that it can be proved on the basis merely of our axioms I–IV, V a, b. As a matter fact, it will not even be necessary to use the axiom of choice, IV, in the proof.

*Proof.* We first observe that the condition on a cardinal $c$, that $C \times C \sim C$, where $C$ is the class represented by $c$, is equivalent, by V b, to the existence of a functional set representing a one-to-one correspondence between $C \times C$ and $C$. Hence we see that the condition in question can be formulated by a constitutive expression with $c$ as its only free variable. And so the class of those infinite cardinals which do not satisfy the condition exists. Unless this class is empty, there must be a lowest cardinal belonging to it. Consequently it is sufficient to consider the case of an infinite cardinal $c$ such that, for every lower infinite cardinal $q$, the class $Q$ represented by $q$ satisfies the condition $Q \times Q \sim Q$.

A further reduction results from the following consideration. For any class of ordinals $C$, the class exists of those pairs $\langle a, b \rangle$ such that $a\eta C$, $b\eta C$, $a\epsilon b$; let us call it (for purposes of this proof) the *reduced pair class of* $C$. If $E$ is the class of pairs $\langle b, b \rangle$ such that $b\eta C$, and $H$ is the reduced pair class of $C$, and $L$ is the converse class of $H$, then $C \times C = E+(H+L)$.

Obviously $E \sim C$ and $L \sim H$. And if $C$ has at least three elements, it is of equal power with a subset of $H$. Now let $C$ be the class represented by the infinite cardinal $c$. If it can be shown that $H$ is of equal power with a subset of $C$, then by the Bernstein theorem it will follow that $H \sim C$. Moreover, since $C$ is represented by an infinite cardinal, it will follow from $H \sim C$, $E \sim C$, $L \sim H$ that $E+(H+L) \sim C$, or $C \times C \sim C$.

Thus it remains only to show that, if $c$ is an infinite cardinal, $C$ the class represented by $c$, and $H$ the reduced pair class of $C$, then $H$ is of equal power with a subclass of $C$, and for this purpose we may assume that every class represented by an infinite cardinal lower than $c$ is of equal power with its pair class.

We consider[59] the well-ordering $R$ of $H$ constituted by the class of elements $\langle\langle a, b\rangle, \langle d, e\rangle\rangle$ such that $\langle a, b\rangle \eta H$, and $\langle d, e\rangle \eta H$, and either $b\epsilon e$ or $b = e$ & $(a\epsilon d$ ∨ $a = d)$.

Let $F$ be a function assigning to every sequence $s$ of elements of $H$, according as the converse domain $p$ of $s$ is a proper subset of $H$ or represents $H$, the first element of $H$ in the order $R$ which is not in $p$, or the first element of $H$ in the order $R$. By the general recursion theorem there exists a function $G$ whose domain is the class of all ordinals and whose value, for every ordinal $n$, is the value of $F$ for the $n$-segment of $G$.

Three cases must be considered: (1) that $G$ is a one-to-one correspondence between the class of all ordinals and a proper subclass $H_1$ of $H$; (2) that $G$ is a one-to-one correspondenbe between the class of all ordinals and $H$; (3) that $G$ is not a one-to-one correspondence.

Case (1) is, however, impossible. For if $\langle a, b\rangle \, \eta \, (H \div H_1)$, then, by the definition of $F$ and $G$, every element $\langle d, e\rangle$ of $H_1$ must precede $\langle a, b\rangle$ in the well-ordering $R$, and hence either $e\epsilon b$ or $e = b$, and also $d\epsilon e$, therefore $d\epsilon b$. Consequently $H_1$ must be a subclass of the pair class $P$ of the class represented by $b'$. Now if $q$ is the cardinal number of $b'$ (which is the same as the cardinal number of $b$) and $Q$ is the class represented by $q$, then since $q$ is lower than $c$ we have $Q \times Q$ $\sim q$ and therefore $P \sim q$. So by V b it follows that $P$ is represented by a set, and therefore, by V a, $H_1$ is represented by a set. From the one-to-one correspondence between $H_1$ and the class of all ordinals then follows that the latter class is represented by a set; but this is impossible.

In case (3), there exists a one-to-one correspondence between some ordinal $n$ and the class $H$, as follows by an argument which we have used already in our last proof of the theorem of adapted numeration.[60] This one-to-one correspondence, as also the one-to-one correspondence of case (2), has, by the definition of $F$ and $G$, the property that the element of $H$ assigned to the lower of two ordinals (belonging to the domain of the one-to-one correspondence) precedes, in the well-ordering $R$, that assigned to the higher ordinal. Thus in either case (2) or case (3) there exists a one-to-one correspondence $K$ between a transitive class of ordinals and $H$, such that, for all elements $k$ and $l$ of the domain of $K$,

$$k\epsilon l \rightarrow \langle K(k), K(l)\rangle \, \eta \, R.$$

Let $m$ be an element of the domain of $K$. Then $K(m)$ is an element $\langle a, b\rangle$ of $H$, and if $M$ is the class of elements of $H$ which precede $\langle a, b\rangle$ in the well-order-

---

[59] The following argument has been substituted for an earlier one which was more complicated, and which besides required the axiom of choice. This simplification was suggested by Gödel's proofs of the theorems 7.811 and 8.62 in GÖDEL (1940). However, these proofs are based on the theorem 5.18 (proved by means of the power axiom), which coincides with our pair class axiom. Hence we here need to modify Gödel's method of proof.

[60] §13, p. 74.

ing $R$, we have $m \backsim M$. Let $q$ be the cardinal number of $b'$, $Q$ the class represented by $q$, and $B$ the class represented by $b'$. Then $M$ is a subclass of $B \times B$, and

$$B \times B \backsim Q \times Q$$
$$\backsim Q.$$

Therefore the cardinal number of $m$ is not higher than $q$, and consequently $m \epsilon c$.

So the domain of $K$ is a subclass of $C$, and therefore the converse domain of $K$, namely $H$, is of equal power with a subclass of $C$. But just this is what had to be shown.

This now completes the proof of the pair class theorem. (In order to see that the proof really avoids use of the axiom of choice it must be observed that for our definition of the cardinal number of a set, in the special case that this set is an ordinal, the reference to the numeration theorem is not needed.)

As a consequence of the pair class theorem we are now able immediately to prove the pair class axiom as a theorem. For let $a$ and $b$ represent the classes $A$ and $B$ respectively. If $a$ and $b$ are both finite, the pair class $A \times B$, as the sum of the elements of a finite class of finite sets, is finite; so in this case the pair class of $A$ and $B$ is represented by a set. If at least one of the sets $a$, $b$ is infinite, the class $A + B$ and the set-sum $a + b$ are infinite. Let $c$ be the cardinal number of $a + b$, and $C$ the class represented by $c$. Then $A + B \backsim C$, and by the pair class theorem $C \times C \backsim c$, hence by the composition lemma $(A + B) \times (A + B) \backsim c$. Hence by axiom V b the pair class of $A + B$ is represented by a set, and, since $A \times B \subseteq (A + B) \times (A + B)$, we have by V a that $A \times B$ is also represented by a set.

Thus we have generally that the pair class of classes represented by sets is itself represented by a set. We may therefore define the *pair set* $a \times b$ of sets $a$, $b$, in the same way that we did before on the basis of the pair class axiom.

At the same time we obtain, for every infinite set $a$, the one-to-one correspondence $a \times a \backsim a$. Hence by the Bernstein theorem, for every infinite set $a$ and every non-empty set $b$ which is not of higher power than $a$, $a \times b \backsim a$, and $b \times a \backsim a$.

A further one-to-one correspondence obtainable here concerns the *class of mappings* of a set $b$ into the class represented by a set $a$. If $A$ is the class represented by $a$, this class of mappings is $A^{[b]}$; we shall denote it also by $a^{[b]}$.

From the obvious fact that for any set $a$ there exists a one-to-one correspondence between $a$ and a subclass of $2^{[a]}$, it follows readily that for every set $b$,

$$(a^{[b]} \backsim (2^{[a]})^{[b]}) \vee (a^{[b]} < (2^{[a]})^{[b]}).$$

Now by one of the formal laws stated in §11,

$$(2^{[a]})^{[b]} \backsim 2^{[a \times b]};$$

and combining this with the result just obtained concerning the power of the pair set $a \times b$, we have that, if $a$ is not empty and not of higher power than $b$, and $b$ is infinite, then

$$(a^{[b]} \backsim 2^{[b]}) \vee (a^{[b]} < 2^{[b]}).$$

Hence by the Bernstein theorem it follows that, if $a$ is a set with at least two elements, $b$ is an infinite set, and $a$ is not of higher power than $b$, then $a^{[b]} \backsim 2^{[b]}$. In particular, for every infinite set $a$, we have $a^{[a]} \backsim 2^{[a]}$, and thus also the class of subsets of $a$ is of equal power with the class of mappings of $a$ into the class represented by $a$.—

We can also further apply the result concerning the existence of the pair set to the *general definition of the product of ordinals*, analogously to the way in which we have introduced the sum of arbitrary ordinals by using the existence of the set-sum of arbitrary sets. For this purpose we consider, for arbitrary ordinals $a$, $b$, a special well-ordering of the pair set $a \times b$, namely the class of those pairs of elements of $a \times b$ which have one of the three forms:

$\langle q, q \rangle$ with $q \, \epsilon \, a \times b$;

$\langle \langle m, r \rangle, \langle n, r \rangle \rangle$ with $m \epsilon n$, $n \epsilon a$, and $r \epsilon b$;

$\langle \langle m, r \rangle, \langle n, s \rangle \rangle$ with $m \epsilon a$, $n \epsilon a$, $r \epsilon s$, and $s \epsilon b$.

By the theorem of adapted numeration, this well-ordering of $a \times b$ is associated with a numeration of $a \times b$, and we define the domain of this numeration to be the *product* $a \cdot b$ of $a$ and $b$.

Thus the relation $a \cdot b = c$ among the ordinals $a$, $b$, $c$ is defined to mean that there exists a numeration of the pair set $a \times b$ having the domain $c$ and satisfying the condition that, if the element $\langle m, r \rangle$ of $a \times b$ is assigned to a lower ordinal than that to which the element $\langle n, s \rangle$ is assigned, then either $r \epsilon s$, or $r = s$ and $m \epsilon n$. And by the preceding argument it follows that there is always a unique numeration of $a \times b$ with the required properties.

From this it is seen that the relation $a \cdot b = c$ can be formulated by a constitutive expression, so that there exists a function assigning to every pair of ordinals $\langle a, b \rangle$ the value $a \cdot b$, and for every ordinal $a$ there exists a function assigning to every ordinal $b$ the value $a \cdot b$.

As further consequences of the definition of the product, we have, for arbitrary ordinals $a$, $b$, $c$:

$$0 \cdot b = 0, \qquad a \cdot 0 = 0, \qquad a \cdot 1 = a, \qquad a \neq 0 \ \& \ b \neq 0 \rightarrow a \cdot b \neq 0;$$

$$a \cdot (b + c) = a \cdot b + a \cdot c, \quad \text{and hence } a \cdot b' = a \cdot b + a;$$

$$a \neq 0 \ \& \ b \, \epsilon \, c \rightarrow a \cdot b \, \epsilon \, a \cdot c;$$

also if $a \neq 0$ and $l$ is any limiting number, the product $a \cdot l$ is the limit of the ascending $l$-sequence assigning to every element $n$ of $l$ the value $a \cdot n$.

Using the preceding results, we prove by transfinite induction that the equation,

$$a \cdot (b \cdot c) = (a \cdot b) \cdot c,$$

is valid for arbitrary ordinals $a$, $b$, $c$.

As to the cardinal number of the product of ordinals $a$, $b$, it follows from our result concerning the cardinal number of the pair set that, if at least one of the ordinals $a$, $b$ is infinite, and neither is 0, then the cardinal number of $a \cdot b$ is identical with the cardinal number of $a$ or the cardinal number of $b$, whichever is higher, and thus also identical with the cardinal number of $a + b$. —

We now go on to apply our results concerning the existence of the pair set, and its cardinal number, as we intended, to the proof of a theorem of transfinite recursion.

**16. Transfinite recursion. Remarks on formal algebra.** As we saw in §13, there is possible in the strengthened system of general set theory an easy derivation of a theorem of transfinite recursion from the general recursion theorem. The sum theorem, which was required for this, is not available in general set theory, based on the axioms I–IV, V a, b alone. But we do have a certain substitute for it. In fact we shall prove, in general set theory, the following *sum lemma*:

If $p$ is an infinite ordinal, and if $s$ is a sequence such that, for every element $n$ of its domain $k$, the cardinal number of $s(n)$ is not higher than that of $p+n$, then the sum of the members of $s$ is represented by a set whose cardinal number is not higher than that of $p+k$.

*Proof.* From the hypotheses it follows that the cardinal number of any member of $s$ is at most as high as the cardinal number $c$ of $p+k$. As a consequence of the axiom of choice and axiom V b, there exists a sequence $f$, with the domain $k$, which assigns to every element $n$ of $k$ a functional set representing a one-to-one correspondence between $s(n)$ and its cardinal number, which last is a subset of $c$. And by the class theorem there exists the class $R$ of pairs $\langle\langle n, r\rangle$, $\langle n, t\rangle\rangle$ such that $n\epsilon k$, $r \epsilon s(n)$, and $t = (f(n))(r)$. This class $R$ is evidently a one-to-one correspondence. Its converse domain $B$ is a subclass of the pair set $k\times c$, hence by V a is represented by a set, and by V b (applied to the converse class of $R$) the domain $A$ of $R$ is also represented by a set. Moreover the class of pairs $\langle\langle n, r\rangle, r\rangle$ such that $\langle n, r\rangle\eta A$ is a function having the domain $A$, which is represented by a set, hence by the theorem of replacement the converse domain is represented by a set. This converse domain is, however, identical with the sum $S$ of the members of $s$. Therefore $S$ is represented by a set.

By the axiom of choice, $S$ is of equal power with a subclass of $A$. Since $A \backsim B$, we have that $S$ is not of higher power than $B$. But $B$ is a subclass of $k\times c$, and consequently the cardinal number of the set representing $S$ is not higher than the cardinal number of the pair set $k\times c$. Since $c$ is the cardinal number of $p+k$, and $p$ is infinite, the cardinal number of $k\times c$ is not higher than $c$.

Thus we do have the existence of a set which represents the sum of the members of $s$ and whose cardinal number is not higher than the cardinal number of $p+k$.

*Remark.* From the sum lemma we can infer in particular that every infinite cardinal than which there is a next lower cardinal is an irreducible limiting number.

In fact if $c$ is an infinite cardinal and $p$ the next lower cardinal, then the cardinal number of an element of $c$ cannot be higher than $p$. Therefore any ascending sequence of elements of $c$ whose domain $k$ is an element of $c$ has, in consequence of the sum lemma, a limit whose cardinal number is not higher than that of $p+k$. But $p+k \backsim p$. Therefore $c$ cannot be the limit of an ascending sequence of ordinals with a domain lower than $c$, or in other words, $c$ is irreducible.

On the other hand it can easily be shown that every irreducible limiting number is a cardinal.

Now by means of the sum lemma we prove the following *restricted theorem of transfinite recursion*:

If $a$ and $b$ are ordinals, $b$ is infinite, and $P$ is a function which assigns to every pair of ordinals $\langle n, c \rangle$ an ordinal whose cardinal number is not higher than that of $(b+c)+n$, then there exists a function $K$ which assigns to every ordinal an ordinal in such a way that: (1) $K(0) = a$; (2) $K(n') = P(\langle n, K(n) \rangle)$ for every ordinal $n$; (3) for every limiting number $l$, $K(l)$ represents the sum of the members of the $l$-segment of $K$. Moreover, upon the conditions (1), (2), (3) on $K$, the value $K(n)$ for an ordinal $n$ is uniquely determined by $n$, $a$, and $P$, and the cardinal number of $K(n)$ is not higher than that of $(a+b)+n$.

*Proof.* By the class theorem there exists a function $F$ assigning to every sequence of ordinals an ordinal in such a way that for the 0-sequence its value is $a$, for a $k'$-sequence $s$ its value is $P(\langle k, s(k) \rangle)$, for a sequence whose domain is a limiting number and the sum of whose members is represented by a set $c$ its value is $c$, and for all other sequences of ordinals its value is 0. Then by the general recursion theorem there exists a function $K$ whose domain is the class of all ordinals and which assigns to every ordinal $n$ the value of $F$ for the $n$-segment of $K$. Obviously $K$ satisfies conditions (1) and (2). Using the class theorem again, let $C$ be the class of ordinals $n$ for which the cardinal number of $K(n)$ is not higher than that of $(a+b)+n$. We show by transfinite induction that every ordinal belongs to $C$. First obviously $0 \eta C$. Further, by the given condition on $P$ we have $n \eta C \rightarrow n' \eta C$, since, because $b$ is infinite, the cardinal number of $(b+((a+b)+n))+n$ is the highest of the cardinals $a$, $b$, $n$ and therefore identical with the cardinal number of $(a+b)+n'$. Thirdly, if $l$ is a limiting number and every element of $l$ belongs to $C$, then, where $s$ is the $l$-segment of $K$, we have that for every element $n$ of $l$ the cardinal number of $s(n)$ is not higher than that of $(a+b)+n$; also $a+b$ is infinite; hence by the sum lemma the sum of the members of $s$ is represented by a set $c$ whose cardinal number is not higher than that of $(a+b)+l$; consequently $F(s) = c$, $K(l) = c$, and the cardinal number of $K(l)$ is not higher than that of $(a+b)+l$. So in fact for every limiting number $l$ we have $(x)(x \epsilon l \rightarrow x \eta C) \rightarrow l \eta C$. Thus the three premises required for the proof by transfinite induction that every ordinal belongs to $C$ are satisfied. Hence it follows that for every ordinal $n$ the cardinal number of $K(n)$ is not higher than that of $(a+b)+n$; also—on account of the sum lemma—that for every limiting number $l$, $K(l)$ represents the sum of the members of the $l$-segment of $K$, i.e., that $K$ also satisfies condition (3).

It remains only to prove that if $H$ is a function assigning to every ordinal an ordinal in such a way that conditions (1), (2), (3) are satisfied, then for every ordinal $n$, $H(n) = K(n)$. But this follows obviously by transfinite induction.

This (restricted) theorem of transfinite recursion—whose proof is now complete—affords a general method of introducing functions of ordinals. An instance of this method is the *extension of our former definition of $a^b$*, given for finite ordinals, *to arbitrary ordinals*.

Of course an extension of this definition is required only in case that there exist infinite ordinals, and we have to deal, therefore, only with this case. We apply our theorem of transfinite recursion, taking for $a$ the ordinal 1, for $P$ the function assigning to every pair of ordinals $\langle n,\ c\rangle$ the ordinal $c\cdot m$, where $m$ is a fixed ordinal, and for $b$ the lowest infinite ordinal or $m$ according as $m$ is finite or infinite. The required condition on $P$ is satisfied, since the cardinal number of $c\cdot m$ is not higher than that of $b+c$. Thus we infer the existence of a function $K$, uniquely determined for a given $m$, which has the following properties: the domain of $K$ is the class of all ordinals; $K(0) = 1$; for every ordinal $n$, $K(n') = K(n)\cdot m$; and for every limiting number $l$, $K(l)$ represents the sum of the members of the $l$-segment of $K$.

Denoting the value $K(n)$, which depends also on the parameter $m$, by $m^n$, we have, for arbitrary ordinals $m$, $n$:

$$m^0 = 1, \qquad\qquad m^{n'} = m^n \cdot m.$$

Moreover, for every limiting number $l$, $m^l$ is the lowest of those ordinals which are at least as high as every one of the ordinals $m^n$ for $n\epsilon l$ and $m$ fixed.

For an ordinal $m$ higher than 1 it follows by transfinite induction that, for all ordinals $a$, $b$,

$$a\ \epsilon\ b \rightarrow m^a\ \epsilon\ m^b,$$

so that for any limiting number $l$ the class of pairs $\langle n,\ m^n\rangle$, such that $n\epsilon l$, is represented by an ascending sequence of ordinals, and the limit of this sequence is $m^l$.

Moreover by transfinite induction, in virtue of the properties of the sum and product of ordinals, the following equations result, for arbitrary ordinals $a$, $b$, $m$:

$$1^a = 1, \qquad (m^a)\cdot(m^b) = m^{(a+b)}, \qquad (m^a)^b = m^{(a\cdot b)}.$$

And it can also be shown that the class of triplets of ordinals $\langle\langle a,\ b\rangle,\ c\rangle$, such that $a^b = c$, exists.

*Remark.* The general definition of $m^n$ for ordinals $m$, $n$, by transfinite recursion, refers to the general definition of the product of ordinals. We have defined the product of arbitrary ordinals $m$, $n$ by means of a well-ordering of the pair set $m\times n$. But we could as well have extended our definition of the product of finite ordinals to arbitrary ordinals $m$, $n$ by applying the restricted theorem of transfinite recursion (upon the assumption that there exist infinite ordinals) to the case that $m$ is a fixed ordinal, the ordinal $a$ of the theorem is 0, the function $P$ is the class of pairs $\langle\langle n,\ c\rangle,\ c+m\rangle$ with $n$ and $c$ ordinals, and $b$ is the lowest infinite ordinal or $m$ according as $m$ is finite or infinite. The correctness of this procedure is due to the circumstance that in our proof of the restricted theorem of transfinite recursion no reference is made to the concept of the product of arbitrary ordinals.

As regards the concept of the sum of arbitrary ordinals, it has to be observed that the references to it in the sum lemma and in the restricted theorem of transfinite recursion could be avoided. In fact the occurrences of the sum of arbitrary ordinals in these theorems have to do only with the cardinal number of a sum $a+b$ of ordinals $a$, $b$ of which one at least is infinite. But this cardinal number is "the maximum of the cardinal numbers of $a$ and $b$," i.e., it is the cardinal number of $a$ or the cardinal number of $b$ according as $a$ is higher than $b$ or not.   Thus the use of the sum of arbitrary ordinals can be eliminated from the formulation and the proofs of these two theorems.   And it is then also possible, as is easily seen, to base the general definition of the sum of ordinals upon the restricted theorem of transfinite recursion.

Now having established the general basis for the development of transfinite arithmetic within our general set theory, we do not enter into further details. Comparing our method for the foundation of the theory of transfinite numbers, as it is brought about by the restricted axiomatic basis of our general set theory, with the usual method, we see that the difference lies chiefly in a changed order of treatment, certain considerations relating to the notion of power coming in at an earlier place under our method.

From the developments of Parts IV and V, taken altogether, it will appear that the axioms I–IV, V a, b constitute a sufficient axiomatic basis for general set theory.   On the other hand we shall show in Part VI, by a method of von Neumann, that the axioms V c and V d cannot be derived as theorems from I–IV, V a, b, and in fact even that each of V c and V d is independent of all the other axioms I–VII, provided that the axioms I–VI are consistent.   In particular the independence of V d will be proved in the stronger form that the axioms I-IV, V a, b, c, VI, VII are compatible with the additional assumption that every set is either finite or enumerable.

As a supplement to our survey of classical arithmetic which we have made on the basis of our axiomatic system, we insert at this point a brief *discussion of formal algebras*, which could have been made already at the end of §6.

Formal algebras can be treated within our axiomatic system on the basis of the axioms I-III, V a, or else of I-III, VII—either set being, as we have seen, sufficient for number theory and the theory of finite sets.   Let us give here a few indications as to the first steps (in regard to which there is of course a certain amount of arbitrariness).

In formal algebras we have to deal with polynomials formed out of variables and coefficients by means of addition and multiplication.   The coefficients are elements of a ring, i.e., of a class $C$ for whose elements addition, subtraction, and multiplication are defined in such a way that the usual laws of computation are valid.   The identity element for the operation of addition in $C$ we shall call "zero."

As representatives of the variables we take the sets which either belong to the converse domain of the iterator on $((0))$ of the function assigning to every set $p$ the value $(p)$ or else have two elements of which one belongs to this same converse domain and the other is a finite ordinal.   The sets of the latter kind, having two elements, are representatives of variables with numerical subscripts; e.g., $(((0)), 1)$ and $(((0)), 2)$ may be taken as representatives of the variables $x_1$ and $x_2$ respectively.   By this means we have the possibility of formulating theorems in which a numerical subscript of a variable appears as a parameter. The representatives of the variables constitute a class, of which they are the elements, and which we shall call $\Xi$.

In order to define polynomials as sets of a certain kind, we first introduce the notion of a complex.   By a *complex* we understand a functional set the domain of which is a finite subset of $\Xi$ and every value of which is a finite ordinal different from 0. (The null set in particular is a complex, under this definition.) It is then easily seen that the class of all complexes exists.

The complexes are to be representatives of expressions like $x^2 y^3 z$, or $x_1^{k_1} x_2^{k_2} \cdots x_n^{k_n}$ where $k_1$, $k_2$, $\cdots$, $k_n$ are positive integers.

By the *algebraic product of a complex h and a complex k* we understand the functional set whose domain is the set-sum $c$ of the domain $a$ of $h$ and the domain $b$ of $k$ and whose value for an element $t$ of $c$ is $h(t)+k(t)$, or $h(t)$, or $k(t)$, according as $t$ is in both $a$ and $b$, or in $a$ alone, or in $b$ alone. Obviously, under this definition the algebraic product of complexes is again a complex.

An ordered pair whose first member is a complex and whose second member is an element of $C$ will be called a *monomial over $C$*, and its second member will be called the *coefficient of the monomial*.

Now we define a *polynomial over $C$* to be a finite functional set whose elements are monomials over $C$. It is then easily seen that the class of all polynomials over $C$ exists.

In cases where, as below, the class $C$ remains fixed we may speak simply of "monomials" and "polynomials," omitting the qualifying phrase "over $C$."

The null set is a particular polynomial.

A polynomial $p$ is said to be *equal* to a polynomial $q$ if it differs from $q$ only by monomials whose coefficient is zero. This relation obviously has the properties of an equality.

Besides polynomials we also have to consider finite sequences of monomials. For every polynomial $p$ there exists an $n$-sequence of monomials which is a numeration of $p$, $n$ being the number attributable to $p$.

We proceed now to introduce the elementary operations on polynomials. First the algebraic sum of polynomials is to be defined in a manner analogous to our definition of the algebraic product of complexes. By the *algebraic sum* of a polynomial $p$ and a polynomial $q$ we understand the functional set whose domain is the set-sum of the domain $a$ of $p$ and the domain $b$ of $q$ and whose value for an element $t$ of its domain is $p(t)$, or $q(t)$, or the element of $C$ resulting from the addition of $p(t)$ and $q(t)$, according as $t$ is in $a$ alone, or in $b$ alone, or in both $a$ and $b$.

The algebraic sum of polynomials, as thus defined, is obviously also a polynomial. And the algebraic sum of a polynomial equal to $p$ and a polynomial equal to $q$ is equal to the algebraic sum of $p$ and $q$. Further, in consequence of the condition that $C$ is a ring, the commutative and associative laws are valid for the algebraic sum of polynomials.

In order to define the algebraic difference of polynomials we first note that, since $C$ is a ring, there is for each element $a$ of $C$ a uniquely determined element of $C$ whose addition to $a$ yields zero; we shall call it *the opposite element to $a$*. In consequence of this there exists for every polynomial $p$ a uniquely determined polynomial having the same domain as $p$ and assigning to each element $c$ of this domain the opposite element to $p(c)$; this polynomial we shall call *the opposite polynomial to $p$*. Then the *algebraic difference* of a polynomial $p$ and a polynomial $q$ can be defined simply as the algebraic sum of $p$ and the opposite polynomial to $q$.

For the definition of the algebraic product of polynomials we proceed in the following way. First we define the algebraic product of a polynomial $p$ by a monomial $\langle k, b \rangle$ to be the set of pairs $\langle l, c \rangle$ for which there is an element $\langle h, a \rangle$ of $p$ such that $l$ is the algebraic product of the complexes $h$ and $k$, and $c$ is the element of $C$ resulting from the multiplication of $a$ by $b$. Then the algebraic product of a polynomial by a monomial is a polynomial.

Next we define the algebraic product of a polynomial by a finite sequence of monomials. By the theorem of finite recursion, if $p$ is a polynomial and $s$ is an $m$-sequence of monomials, where $m$ is a finite ordinal, there exists a function $K$ assigning to every finite ordinal a polynomial in such a way that $K(0) = 0$, and for every ordinal $n$ lower than $m$, $K(n')$ is the algebraic sum of the polynomial $K(n)$ and the algebraic product of $p$ by the monomial $s(n)$, and for every finite ordinal $n$ not lower than $m$, $K(n') = K(n)$. The value of this function $K$ for the ordinal $m$ is a polynomial which is uniquely determined by the polynomial $p$ and the sequence $s$; we shall call it the algebraic product of $p$ by $s$.

Then, using the class theorem, complete induction, and the commutative and associative laws for the algebraic sum of polynomials, we can show that, if $p$ and $q$ are polynomials, we have for every numeration $s$ of $q$ that the algebraic product of $p$ by $s$ (as just defined) is the same polynomial. I.e., the algebraic product of a polynomial $p$ by a sequence of monomials which is a numeration of a polynomial $q$ is uniquely determined by $p$ and $q$. Hence we define this to be the *algebraic product* of the polynomial $p$ by the polynomial $q$.

Under this definition, polynomials $p$ and $q$ have always a uniquely determined algebraic product, and the algebraic product of a polynomial equal to $p$ by a polynomial equal to $q$ is equal to the algebraic product of $p$ by $q$.

Now it can be proved, for the algebraic sum, algebraic difference, and algebraic product of polynomials over $C$, in consequence of the foregoing definitions, that all the familiar laws of computation, corresponding to the laws of addition, subtraction, and multiplication in the ring $C$, are valid as laws of equality.[61]

This therefore provides a basis for the further development of formal algebras.

---

[61] In order to avoid distinguishing between equality and identity, we may introduce the notion of a proper polynomial, defining a polynomial over $C$ to be a *proper polynomial* if every element of its converse domain is different from zero. As is easily seen, there is for every polynomial a uniquely determined proper polynomial equal to it, which is obtained from it by omitting the elements (monomials) with the coefficient zero. The class of proper polynomials exists. Then we may define the *proper algebraic sum* of proper polynomials $p$ and $q$ as the proper polynomial which is equal to the algebraic sum of $p$ and $q$; and analogously the *proper algebraic difference* and the *proper algebraic product* of proper polynomials can be defined. With respect to the operations thus defined the class of proper polynomials constitutes a ring.

**PART VI**[62]

**16. The rôle of the restrictive axiom. Comparability of classes.** Till now we tried to get along without the axioms Vc and Vd. We found that this is possible in number theory and analysis as well as in general set theory, even keeping in the main to the usual way of procedure.

For the considerations of the present section application of the axioms Vc, Vd is essential. Our axiomatic basis here consists of the axioms I–III, V*, Vc, and Vd. From V*, as we know,[63] Va and Vb are derivable. We here take axiom V* in order to separate the arguments requiring the axiom of choice from the others. Instead of the two axioms V* and Vc, as was observed in Part II, V** may be taken as well.[63]

An obvious consequence of axiom Vd is that there exists for every cardinal a higher one; indeed the class of subsets of a set $a$ is of higher power than $a$,[64] and so the set representing that class (by Vd)—let us call it as usual the "power-set" of $a$—has a higher cardinal number than $a$. From V* and Vc (or from V**), we can infer that for every sequence of ordinals $s$ there exists an ordinal which is at least as high as each one of the members of $s$. For, the sum of the members of $s$ by V* and Vc is represented by a set which is a transitive set of ordinals and thus is itself an ordinal.[65] This ordinal, having each member of $s$ as a subset, must be at least as high as every member of $s$.

As a consequence of the stated theorem, there are two alternatives concerning classes of ordinals: Every class of ordinals $A$ is either represented by a set, and then there exists a numeration of it in the natural order, or there exists a one-to-one correspondence between the class of all ordinals and the class $A$, every segment of which is an ascending sequence. Namely, if there exists a sequence $s$ of elements of $A$ such that there is no ordinal number belonging to $A$ which is higher than every member of $s$, then, by the theorem just proved an ordinal $n$ exists which is not lower than any member of $s$ and thus not lower than any element of $A$; hence $n'$ is higher than each element of $A$, and so $A$ is a subclass of $n'$. Consequently $A$ is represented by a set of ordinals, and of this there exists a numeration in the natural order.[66] In the other case, there exists, for every sequence of elements of $A$, an element of $A$ which is higher than every member of the sequence; then, by a theorem noted in Part V as a consequence of the general recursion theorem,[67] there exists a one-to-one correspondence such as asserted for the second alternative.

---

[62] Cf. *J. Symbolic Logic* **13** (1948) 65–79.
[63] Cf. Part II, §4, p. 16.
[64] Cf. Part IV, §11, p. 60.
[65] See Part, II, §5, lemma 3, p. 20 and pp. 21, 22.
[66] See Part IV, §12, p. 66.
[67] Cf. Part V, §13, p. 71.

Applying this result to the class of all cardinals, we are here able to exclude the first alternative. For, if there existed a set of all cardinals and a numeration of it, this would be a sequence having every cardinal as its member; hence, as proved just above, there would exist an ordinal $m$ which is at least as high as every cardinal. But then the cardinal number of $m$ would be a highest cardinal, whereas in fact, by the consequence of Vd stated above, there exists no highest cardinal. Thus it follows that there exists a one-to-one correspondence between the class of all ordinals and the class of all cardinals, even with the property that every segment of it is an ascending sequence.

At the same time it follows from this reasoning that for every sequence of cardinals there exists a cardinal which is higher than every member of the sequence. This ascendence of powers is a characteristic feature of the full Cantor set theory.

A further characterization of the situation results from an application of the strong theorem of transfinite recursion which, as we stated in Part V,[68] is derivable from the axioms V* and Vc. According to this theorem, as a consequence of Vd, there exists the function $\Psi$ whose domain is the class of all ordinals and whose values are determined by the conditions that (1) $\Psi(0) = 0$, (2) for every ordinal $n$, $\Psi(n')$ is the power-set of $\Psi(n)$, (3) for every limiting number $l$, $\Psi(l)$ is the set representing the sum of the members of the $l$-segment of $\Psi$. Of this function we first state that each of its values is a transitive set. As a preparatory result we show that a set $p$ whose elements are the subsets of a transitive set $t$ is itself transitive. In fact, if $b \in p$ and $a \in b$, then $b \subseteq t$ and thus $a \in t$; and since $t$ is transitive, $a \subseteq t$, and thus $a \in p$.

Now our assertion that every value of $\Psi$ is a transitive set follows by transfinite induction: 0 is a transitive set; if $\Psi(n)$ is transitive, then the set $\Psi(n')$ whose elements are the subsets of $\Psi(n)$ is also transitive; and, for every limiting number $l$ such that $\Psi(n)$ is transitive for the ordinals $n$ lower than $l$, $\Psi(l)$ represents the sum of transitive sets and is therefore transitive.

Further, for every ordinal $n$ we have $\Psi(n) \in \Psi(n')$, and the cardinal number of $\Psi(n)$ is lower than that of $\Psi(n')$. If $l$ is a limiting number and $n \in l$, we have $\Psi(n) \subset \Psi(l)$.

From the stated properties of $\Psi$ by means of transfinite induction it follows readily that for ordinal numbers $m$, $n$,

$$m \in n \rightarrow \Psi(m) \in \Psi(n),$$

$$m \in n \rightarrow \Psi(m) \subset \Psi(n),$$

and for every ordinal number $n$,

$$n \subseteq \Psi(n), n \in \Psi(n').$$

At the same time we get the result that the function $\Psi$ is a one-to-one correspondence, and that if $m$ is an ordinal lower than the ordinal $n$, then the cardinal number of $\Psi(m)$ is lower than that of $\Psi(n)$.

[68] Cf. §13, p. 74.

Now let Π be the sum of the values of Ψ, or in other words, the class whose elements are the sets which, for some ordinal $n$, are in $\Psi(n)$.

Concerning this class Π some remarkable facts are to be stated, which were first set forth by von Neumann in his paper 2996, of course in a form related to his axiomatic system.[69] We shall follow here, in the main, his method of reasoning.

Let us call an element of Π a "Π-set" and a subclass of Π a "Π-class." We immediately state: Every ordinal $n$ is a Π-set, since $n \,\epsilon\, \Psi(n')$. Each element of a Π-set is itself a Π-set; for Π, being the sum of transitive sets, is a transitive class. Hence the class represented by a Π-set is a Π-class. Also, conversely, it is true that every set which represents a Π-class is a Π-set. For the proof of this we use the notion of the *degree* of a Π-set.

By the principle of the least number, for every Π-set $a$ there is a least ordinal $n$ such that $a \,\epsilon\, \Psi(n)$; we call this ordinal, which is uniquely determined by $a$, the "degree of the Π-set $a$." There exists, by the class theorem, the class of pairs $\langle a, n \rangle$ such that $a \,\eta\, \Pi$ and $n$ is the degree of $a$.

Concerning the degree of Π-sets we have the following simple facts: (1) If $n$ is the degree of a Π-set $a$, then for every ordinal $m$ not lower than $n$, $a \,\epsilon\, \Psi(m)$; for $a \,\epsilon\, \Psi(n)$, and $\Psi(n) \subseteq \Psi(m)$. (2) An ordinal which is the degree of a Π-set is always a successor; for it can be neither 0 nor a limiting number. (3) The degree of an element $a$ of a Π-set $b$ is lower than the degree of $b$. For the degree of $b$, as we know from (2), is a successor $n'$, and from $b \,\epsilon\, \Psi(n')$ follows $b \subseteq \Psi(n)$ and thus $a \,\epsilon\, \Psi(n)$; so the degree of $a$ is lower than $n'$. (4) The degree of an ordinal $n$ is $n'$. Namely, since $n \,\epsilon\, \Psi(n')$, $n$ is of no higher degree than $n'$; that it is of no lower degree than $n'$ follows by transfinite induction using the statements (2) and (3).

Now with the aid of the concept of degree we can prove our assertion that every set which represents a Π-class is a Π-set, i.e. every set of Π-sets is a Π-set; the reasoning is as follows: If $c$ is a set of Π-sets, then, by V*, there exists a set $s$ of ordinal numbers $n$ such that there is an element of $c$ whose degree is $n$, and by Vc the sum of the elements of $s$ is represented by a set. This sum, being a transitive set of ordinals, is itself an ordinal $m$, and $m$ is at least as high as each element of $s$; hence, if $a \,\epsilon\, c$, the degree of $a$ is not higher than $m$, so that $a \,\epsilon\, \Psi(m)$. Thus we have $c \subseteq \Psi(m)$, $c \,\epsilon\, \Psi(m')$; and so $c$ is a Π-set, as was to be proved.

From this it results that a set is a Π-set if and only if it represents a Π-class, or, in other words, if its elements are Π-sets. This theorem has the following immediate consequences: (1) Every subset of a Π-set is a Π-set. (2) A set $(c)$, having $c$ as its only element, is a Π-set if and only if $c$ is a Π-set. (3) A pair $\langle a, b \rangle$ is a Π-set if and only if its members $a, b$ are Π-sets. (4) If $a$ and $b$ are Π-sets, then the set–sum $a + (b)$ is a Π-set.

Now, using the proven theorem and the stated corollaries, the following result can be easily verified: If we start from a manifold of sets and classes with rela-

---

[69] Our class Π corresponds to von Neumann's "Bereich Π" (loc. cit. p. 237), our Ψ to his function $\psi$ (p. 236); however, our definition of Ψ is somewhat simpler than von Neumann's definition of $\psi$.

tions $\epsilon$, $\eta$ satisfying the axioms I–III, V*, Vc, and Vd, then the assertions of these axioms remain valid if we reduce the range of sets and classes to that of $\Pi$-sets and $\Pi$-classes. Thus the reduced manifold with the original relations $\epsilon$, $\eta$ constitutes again a model for the axioms I–III, V*, Vc, and Vd. Let us call it the "$\Pi$-model."

*Remark.* Of course by this definition the $\Pi$-model is not independently determined, but merely relative to an original system of sets and classes with relations $\epsilon$, $\eta$.

As an obvious statement about the $\Pi$-model we have: If the original system of sets and classes satisfies the axiom of infinity VI, then this axiom is likewise satisfied by the $\Pi$-model.

Further we observe that, the restrictive axiom VII is at all events satisfied by the $\Pi$-model. For, if $A$ is a non-empty $\Pi$-class, then among the ordinal numbers which are the degrees of the elements of $A$ there is a least one $m$; and if $b$ is an element of $A$ whose degree is $m$, every element of $b$ has a degree lower than $m$; thus there cannot exist a common element of $A$ and $b$. So the assertion of axiom VII holds for the $\Pi$-model.

On the other hand, upon the assumption of axiom VII we can infer that every set is a $\Pi$-set and hence the system of all sets and classes is identical with the $\Pi$-model. Indeed, since every set of $\Pi$-sets, by the theorem proved just above, is itself a $\Pi$-set, a set which is not a $\Pi$-set must have an element which is not a $\Pi$-set. Thus if $A$ is the class of sets which are not $\Pi$-sets and $b$ $\eta$ $A$, then there must be a common element of $A$ and $b$. But from this by axiom VII it follows that $A$ is empty. Hence $\Pi$ is the class of all sets.

So we see that, on the basis of the axioms I–III, V*, Vc, and Vd, the fulfilment of axiom VII is a condition upon which and only upon which the class $\Pi$ is identical with the class of all sets and thus the $\Pi$-model identical with the system of all sets and classes.

In connection with this result we mention the observation of Gödel that on the basis of the axioms just mentioned, with the axiom of infinity VI added, axiom VII can be derived from the weaker axiom VII* which asserts for every non-empty set $a$ there exists an element $b$ such that $a$ and $b$ have no common element.[70]

As a preliminary for this derivation we first prove by the axioms I–III, V*, Vc, and VI that *for every set its transitive closure*[71] *is represented by a set.* By the axioms I–III and V*, from which, as we know, Va is derivable, the iteration theorem holds. By this theorem and Vc, for any set $a$ there exists the iterator on $a$ of the function assigning to each set $c$ the set representing the sum of the elements of $c$. This iterator is a function $B$ having the class N of the finite ordinals as its domain. Since N, by a consequence of axiom VI, is represented by a set, the sum of the values of $B$, by V* and Vc, is also represented by a set. That sum however is easily shown to be the transitive closure of $a$; and so we have that the transitive closure of an arbitrary set $a$ is represented by a set.

---

[70] This observation, mentioned already in Part II (§4, p. 19), was communicated to the author by Gödel in July 1939.

[71] Cf. Part IV, §11, p. 59.

Now, using the proven theorem we can infer VII from VII\*, by proving with the aid of VII\* that every set is a II-set. In fact the assumption that there exists a set $a$ which is not a II-set can be seen to contradict VII\* as follows: The set $a$, not being a II-set, must have an element $e$ which is not a II-set. Let $c$ be the set representing the transitive closure of $a$; then $e \ \epsilon \ c$, and thus the class of those elements of $c$ which are not II-sets is not empty, and likewise the set $q$ representing that class is not empty. Now each element of $q$, not being a II-set, must have an element which is not a II-set. On the other hand, since $q \subseteq c$ and $c$ is transitive, every element of an element of $q$ must be in $c$. So it follows that each element of $q$ must have an element $b$ which is in $c$ but is not a II-set; but such an element $b$, by the definition of $q$, must be in $q$. Thus $q$ is a non-empty set, such that for any element $r$ there exists a common element of $r$ and $q$; and so the assertion of VII\* does not hold.

In this proof we had to use implicitly the definition of the function $\Psi$, since the concept of a II-set refers to it.

A more simple derivation of VII from VII\* is possible if besides axiom VI also the axiom of choice is available; even the weakened form IV\* of the axiom of choice, formulated in Part III[72] (which follows from IV and the iteration theorem), is sufficient for this purpose.

Indeed, using the axioms I–III, IV\*, V\*, and VI we can show that if there is an instance contradicting VII, then VII\* cannot hold either, and so VII\* entails VII. The reasoning is as follows: Let $A$ be a class not satisfying VII, i.e. a non-empty class whose every element has an element belonging to $A$. Then, by IV\* applied to the class of pairs $\langle p, q \rangle$ such that $q \ \epsilon \ p$, there exists a function $F$ with the domain N assigning to every finite ordinal an element of $A$ in such a way that, for each finite ordinal $n$, $F(n') \ \epsilon \ F(n)$. The converse domain $C$ of $F$ is a subclass of $A$ each of whose element has an elements belonging to $C$. Now from VI, as we know, it follows that the class N is represented by a set, and hence, by V\*, the converse domain of $F$, i.e. the class $C$, is also represented by a set $c$. But $c$ is non-empty, and for each element $b$ of $c$ there is a common element of $b$ and $C$, and hence also of $b$ and $c$. So the assertion of VII\* is not satisfied.

Thus on the basis of the axioms I–III, IV\*, V\*, and VI, as well as of the axioms I–III, V\*, Vc, Vd, and VI, axiom VII can be replaced by VII\*.

Considering now the consequences of including the axiom of choice IV among our assumed axioms, so that we have the axioms I–V at our disposal, we are going to prove upon this axiomatic basis the *comparability* not only of any two II-sets, but even *of any two* II-*classes*. This in fact will result from the theorem that *every* II-*class is of equal power with a class of ordinals*. The proof of this theorem by means of the axioms I–V can be given as follows: By the class theorem there exists the function K whose domain is the class of all ordinals and whose value for the ordinal $n$ is the cardinal number of $\Psi(n)$. We are to show that the set-difference $\Psi(n') \div \Psi(n)$, i.e. the set of II-sets of degree $n'$, is of equal power with $K(n') \div K(n)$. For this purpose we distinguish the cases that $n$ is finite or infinite. Since the class of subsets of a finite set is finite, it follows by complete

[72] See §10, p. 52.

induction that for every finite ordinal $n$ the set $\Psi(n)$ is finite. Hence, if $m$ is the cardinal number of $\Psi(n') \div \Psi(n)$, this also is the number attributable to $\Psi(n') \div \Psi(n)$, and we have $K(n) + m = K(n')$. From this equation on the other hand it follows that $m$ is the number attributable to $K(n') \div K(n)$. Thus, if the ordinal $n$ is finite,

(1) $$\Psi(n') \div \Psi(n) \sim K(n') \div K(n).$$

Let now $n$ be infinite; then $\Psi(n)$, whose elements include the finite ordinals, is infinite; and since the cardinal number of $\Psi(n')$ is higher than that of $\Psi(n)$, we have

$$\Psi(n') \div \Psi(n) \sim \Psi(n'),$$

$$K(n') \div K(n) \sim K(n'),$$

and by the definition of $K$: $\Psi(n') \sim K(n')$. Hence (1) holds also for an infinite ordinal $n$. So the relation (1) has been proved for all ordinals $n$.

Now by the class theorem there exists a class of pairs $\langle n, c \rangle$ such that $n$ is an ordinal and $c$ is a one-to-one correspondence between the sets $\Psi(n') \div \Psi(n)$ and $K(n') \div K(n)$. The domain of this class of pairs in virtue of the relation (1), proved to hold for every ordinal, is the class of all ordinals. Hence by the axiom of choice there is a function $F$ assigning to every ordinal $n$ a one-to-one correspondence between $\Psi(n') \div \Psi(n)$ and $K(n') \div K(n)$. The sum $S$ of the elements of the converse domain of $F$ is a one-to-one correspondence. Indeed, if $m$, $n$ are ordinals and $m$ is lower than $n$, then the elements of $\Psi(m') \div \Psi(m)$, being $\Pi$-sets of degree $m'$, all are different from the elements of $\Psi(n') \div \Psi(n)$, which are of degree $n'$; thus the sets $\Psi(m') \div \Psi(m)$, and $\Psi(n') \div \Psi(n)$ have no common element; but neither do $K(m') \div K(m)$ and $K(n') \div K(n)$ have common elements, since $m'$ is not higher than $n$, and so $\Psi(m') \subseteq \Psi(n)$, and consequently $K(m') \subseteq K(n)$.

The domain of $S$, being the sum of the sets $\Psi(n') \div \Psi(n)$, is the class $\Pi$; for, the degree of every $\Pi$-set, as we stated, is a successor, and so every $\Pi$-set is in the sum of the sets $\Psi(n') \div \Psi(n)$. As to the converse domain of $S$, we could show without difficulty that it is the class of all ordinals. But here it is sufficient to use that its elements are ordinals. By this we have that there is a one-to-one correspondence between $\Pi$ and a class of ordinals, and hence every subclass of $\Pi$, i.e. every $\Pi$-class, is of equal power with a class of ordinals, as was to be proved.

Now combining this result with the alternative on classes of ordinals stated in the beginning of this section, we infer that every $\Pi$-class is of equal power either with an ordinal number or with the class of all ordinals. In the first case, by Vb or by V*, the $\Pi$-class is represented by a set, which is a $\Pi$-set. Of course the class $\Pi$ cannot be represented by a set, for otherwise the class of all ordinals, being a subclass of $\Pi$, would also be represented by a set. So *there is a one-to-one correspondence between $\Pi$ and the class of all ordinals*.

We have now shown that any two $\Pi$-classes are comparable and that every $\Pi$-class is either represented by a $\Pi$-set or is of equal power with the class $\Pi$.

This result follows from the axioms I–V. If now axiom VII is added to these, then, as we know, we can infer that every class is a $\Pi$-class, and $\Pi$ is the class of all sets. And so we come to state that any two classes are comparable, and that every class which is not represented by a set is of equal power with the class of all sets. By the last statement we have that a class is represented by a set if and only if it is of lower power than the class of all sets.

The contents of this assertion have been taken as an axiom by von Neumann in his axiomatic system.[73]

As a consequence of our results we note that the class of all cardinals is of equal power with the class of all sets. This, in fact, now follows from our former statement that there is a one-to-one correspondence between the class of all cardinals and that of all ordinals.

Another consequence is that *every class has a well-ordering;* indeed a well-ordering of a class $C$ can be obtained from any one-to-one correspondence between $C$ and a class of ordinals, and such a one-to-one correspondence, as we stated, exists for every class.

Let us further observe that by the given proof of the one-to-one correspondence existing between $\Pi$ and the class of all ordinals a one-to-one correspondence has also been exhibited between the class of $\Pi$-sets of finite degree and the class of finite ordinals. For the proof of this one-to-one correspondence the axioms I–III and Va, or else I–III and VII, are sufficient. In fact the values of $\Psi$ we have to deal with are merely those for finite ordinals, and for the definition of the function assigning to every finite ordinal $n$ the value $\Psi(n)$ and for stating the properties of this function we can get along with the iteration theorem and ordinary complete induction.

**17. Proofs of independence by means of models.** The method of assigning to any model of the system of axioms I–III, V*, Vc, and Vd the corresponding $\Pi$-model, by which the results of the last section were derived, can also be used as a means for setting up models of independence. In fact, by deriving from the $\Pi$-model some more restricted models, we shall now show that in our axiom system I–VII none of the axioms VI, Vb, Vc, Vd, if excluded from the axiomatic basis, can be derived; or in other words, that each of these axioms is independent.

We start from the assumption—to be weakened afterwards—that there exists a model of the axiom system I–VI. The corresponding $\Pi$-model then satisfies the axioms I–VI, and also VII. Now we consider four subclasses of the class $\Pi$, which we shall denote by $\Pi_0$, $\Pi_1$, $\Pi_2$, $\Pi_3$. The definition can be given—denoting by $\omega$, as usual, the least infinite cardinal, i.e. the set representing the class N of all finite ordinals, and by $\omega_1$ the second infinite cardinal, i.e. the set representing the class $\Omega$ of all finite or enumerable ordinals—in the following way: $\Pi_0$ is the class represented by $\Psi(\omega)$, $\Pi_1$ is the class of those elements of $\Psi(\omega_1)$ which themselves as well as each element of their transitive closure are either finite or enumerable, $\Pi_2$ is the class represented by $\Psi(\omega + \omega)$, $\Pi_3$ is the class of those $\Pi$-sets which themselves as well as each element of their transitive closure are of lower power than $\Psi(\omega + \omega)$.

---

[73] It is the axiom IV2, VON NEUMANN (1925), p. 225, VON NEUMANN (1928), p. 675.

Each one of these classes $\Pi_r(r = 0, 1, 2, 3)$ determines a system of sets and classes by saying that the sets of that system are the elements of $\Pi_r$ , and the classes of the system are the subclasses of $\Pi_r$ ; let us call it briefly the $\Pi_r$-system and let its sets and classes be called $\Pi_r$-sets and $\Pi_r$-classes.

Then we first state: $(T_0)$ A $\Pi$-set is a $\Pi_0$-set if and only if it is finite and each of its elements is a $\Pi_0$-set. $(T_1)$ A $\Pi$-set is a $\Pi_1$-set if and only if it is finite or enumerable and each of its elements is a $\Pi_1$-set. $(T_2)$ A $\Pi$-set is a $\Pi_2$-set if and only if its degree is lower than $\omega + \omega$. $(T_3)$ A $\Pi$-set is a $\Pi_3$-set if and only if it is of lower power than $\Psi(\omega + \omega)$ and each of its elements is a $\Pi_3$-set.

These statements are easy to verify, using the facts that (1) for every ordinal $n$ the set $\Psi(n)$ is transitive and therefore every element of $\Psi(n)$ is also a subset of it, (2) for every finite ordinal $n$ the set $\Psi(n)$ as also its elements are finite, (3) among the elements of a finite set of ordinals there is a highest ordinal, (4) for every enumerable sequence of elements of $\Omega$ there exists an ordinal belonging to ·$\Omega$ which is higher than each member of the sequence, and (5) the transitive closure of an element of a set $c$ is a subclass of the transitive closure of $c$, the elements of $c$ belong to the transitive closure of $c$, and each element of the transitive closure of $c$ either is an element of $c$ or belongs to the transitive closure of an elment of $c$.

From $(T_0)$–$(T_3)$ we draw in particular the following obvious consequences (referring to the values 0, 1, 2, 3 of the subscript $r$): If $a$ and $b$ are $\Pi_r$-sets, then $(a)$ and the set-sum $a + (b)$ are also $\Pi_r$-sets. A pair $\langle a, b \rangle$ is a $\Pi_r$-set if and only if $a$ and $b$ are $\Pi_r$-sets. $\Pi_r$ is a transitive class, i.e. every element of a $\Pi_r$-set is a $\Pi_r$-set. Every subset (in the $\Pi$-model) of a $\Pi_r$-set is a $\Pi_r$-set. Now it is easy to verify that each of the $\Pi_r$-systems $(r = 0, 1, 2, 3)$ constitutes a model for the axioms I–III, IV, Va, and VII.

But with regard to the axioms Vb, c, d, and VI the four systems differ from one another. In fact let us consider the four $\Pi_r$-systems one by one with respect to the said axioms, applying for each of them the corresponding statement $(T_r)$. We find the following results:

The $\Pi_0$-system satisfies Vb, c, d: (1) every class which is of equal power with a finite set is represented by a finite set, (2) the sum of the elements of a set, in case that the set itself as also its elements are finite, is a finite class, and therefore is represented by a finite set, (3) the class of the subsets of a finite set is represented by a finite set. The $\Pi_0$-system does not satisfy VI, but rather the following theorem incompatible with VI holds for it, that every $\Pi_0$-set is finite. (It is to be noticed however that there are infinite $\Pi_0$-classes.)

The $\Pi_1$-system satisfies VI and Vb, c: (1) the set $\omega$ representing the class N of finite ordinals is a $\Pi_1$-set, (2) every $\Pi_1$-class which is of equal power with a finite or an enumerable set is represented either by a finite or an enumerable set of $\Pi_1$-sets, (3) as a consequence of the theorem that the sum of the members of an enumerable sequence of enumerable sets is enumerable, which was proved in Part III,[74] the sum of the elements of a set, in case that the set and its elements are finite or enumerable, is a finite or enumerable class and therefore represented

---

[74] Cf. Part III, p. 53.

by either a finite or an enumerable set. The $\Pi_1$-system does not satisfy Vd, we rather have for it the theorem conflicting with Vd, that every $\Pi_1$-set is either finite or enumerable. (There are however non-enumerable $\Pi_1$-classes.)

The $\Pi_2$-system satisfies VI and Vc, d: (1) the set $\omega$ is of degree $\omega'$ and is therefore a $\Pi_2$-set, (2) every $\Pi_2$-set $c$ has a degree $n$ that is lower than $\omega + \omega$, the elements of the elements of $c$ are $\Pi$-sets of degrees lower than $n$, thus the sum of the elements of $c$ is a subclass of $\Psi(n)$ and hence is represented by an element of $\Psi(n')$, i.e. by a $\Pi$-set of degree $n'$, but this then is a $\Pi_2$-set, so the sum of the elements of a $\Pi_2$-set is represented by a $\Pi_2$-set, (3) let $n$ be the degree of a $\Pi_2$-set $c$, then $n$ is lower than $\omega + \omega$, and $c \,\epsilon\, \Psi(n)$, and since $\Psi(n)$ is transitive, $c \subseteq \Psi(n)$; hence every subset of $c$ is a subset of $\Psi(n)$ and thus it is an element of $\Psi(n')$, so the class of subsets of $c$ is a subclass of $\Psi(n')$ and therefore is represented by an element of $\Psi(n'')$, but every element of $\Psi(n'')$, since $n'' \,\epsilon\, \omega + \omega$, is a $\Pi_2$-set; thus the class of subsets of a $\Pi_2$-set is represented by a $\Pi_2$-set. The $\Pi_2$-system does not satisfy Vb; in fact, there exists a one-to-one correspondence between the class of finite ordinals and the class of ordinals lower than $\omega + \omega$. The class of finite ordinals is represented by the $\Pi_2$-set $\omega$; hence if Vb were valid for the $\Pi_2$-system, the class of ordinals lower than $\omega + \omega$ would be represented by a set and so $\omega + \omega$ would be a $\Pi_2$-set, but $\omega + \omega$, by a theorem of the preceding section,[75] has the degree $(\omega + \omega)'$, and so it is not a $\Pi_2$-set.

The $\Pi_3$-system satisfies VI and Vb, d: (1) the set $\omega$ is a $\Pi_3$-set, (2) a $\Pi_3$-class which is of equal power with a $\Pi_3$-set is represented by a $\Pi$-set, this set then is of lower power than $\Psi(\omega + \omega)$ and its elements are $\Pi_3$-sets, so it is a $\Pi_3$-set, (3) as we know from the proof of the existence of a one-to-one correspondence between the class $\Pi$ and the class of all ordinals,[76] the cardinal number $K(\omega + \omega)$ of $\Psi(\omega + \omega)$ is the sum of $K(\omega)$ and the sets $K(\omega + n') \div K(\omega + n)$ with $n$ being a finite ordinal, and so it is the lowest cardinal number which is higher than $K(\omega + n)$ for each finite ordinal $n$, hence if $a$ is a $\Pi_3$-set and $c$ is its cardinal number, then, since $c$ is lower than $K(\omega + \omega)$, $c$ is a subset of $K(\omega + n)$ for some finite ordinal $n$, and so $a$ is of equal power with a subset of $\Psi(\omega + n)$; from this it follows that the $\Pi$-set $b$ which represents the class of the subsets of $a$ is of not higher power than $\Psi(\omega + n')$, and thus of lower power than $\Psi(\omega + \omega)$, moreover its elements are $\Pi_3$-sets, hence it is itself a $\Pi_3$-set; so we have that the class of subsets of a $\Pi_3$-set is represented by a $\Pi_3$-set. $\Pi_3$ does not satisfy Vc. In fact, the enumerable $\Pi$-set whose elements are the sets $\Psi(\omega + n)$ with $n$ being a finite ordinal, is a $\Pi_3$-set, but the set $\Psi(\omega + \omega)$ which represents the sum of the elements of that enumerable set, is not a $\Pi_3$-set.

It will appear that the manner in which we set up the four models of independence required more axiomatic assumptions than is really needed for that purpose. Indeed we started from a model for the system of all axioms I–VI, from which we proceeded to the corresponding $\Pi$-model. In this way we had the advantage that the classes $\Pi_r$ could be defined as certain subclasses of $\Pi$. But by setting up each model separately, modifying either merely the way of defini-

[75] See p. 89.
[76] Cf. p. 92.

tion or also the model itself, we may be able to reduce the axiomatic basis, in particular to eliminate from it the axiom whose independence is to be shown by the model in question.

Let us briefly discuss some possible reductions of this kind which apply to the $\Pi_r$-systems with $r = 0, 1, 2,$ or in other words to the models of independence relative to the axioms VI, Vd, and Vb. (The question here remains undecided if a model of the independence of axiom Vc can be established on the basis of the axioms I–IV, Va, b, d, and VI.)

The class $\Pi_0$ can be defined by first introducing the function $\Psi_0$, with the domain N, which is the iterator on 0 of the function whose domain is the class of finite sets and which assigns to every finite set $a$ the power-set of $a$; $\Pi_0$ is the sum of the values of $\Psi_0$.

For this definition the axioms I–III and Va or else I–III and VII, from which the theory of finite sets can be obtained, as exhibited in Part II, are sufficient. These axioms also allow us to prove the properties of the $\Pi_0$-system, in particular that every $\Pi_0$-set is finite, that there exists a one-to-one correspondence between $\Pi_0$ and N, and as a consequence of these statements, that the $\Pi_0$-system constitutes a model for the system of axioms I–V and VII, however it does not satisfy VI.

For setting up the $\Pi_1$-system and proving that it satisfies all our axioms I–VII except Vd, the axioms I–III, IV, Va, b, and VI are sufficient. Namely on this basis, as was stated in Part III,[77] the axioms of the system of analysis are all available, either directly as axioms, or being derivable. By the system of analysis the theorem mentioned just above is provable that the sum of the members of an enumerable sequence of enumerable sets is enumerable; and from this it follows that the sum of the elements of an enumerable class of finite or enumerable sets is represented by an enumerable set.

Using this we can prove (by the considered axioms) that there exists a class of those sequences $s$ whose domain is an element of $\Omega$ and which satisfy the conditions: $s(0) = 0$; $s(n')$ is, for an element $n'$ of the domain of $s$, a finite or enumerable set of subsets of $s(n)$; and for a limiting number $l$ which is in the domain of $s$, $s(l)$ is the set representing the sum of the members of the $l$-segment of $s$. Let us denote this class by $\Upsilon$. Now the class $\Pi_1$ can be defined as the class of sets $b$ such that, for some $s$ belonging to $\Upsilon$ and some element $n$ of the domain of $s$, $b \in s(n)$. And the degree of a $\Pi_1$-set (i.e. of an element of $\Pi_1$) is definable as the lowest of the ordinals $n$ such that, for some sequence $s$ belonging to $\Upsilon$, $n$ is in the domain of $s$ and the $\Pi_1$-set is an element of $s(n)$. According to these definitions of $\Upsilon$, $\Pi_1$, and "degree," the following can be proved:

(1) Every $\Pi_1$-set is either finite or enumerable. For the degree of a $\Pi_1$-set is a successor $n'$, hence every $\Pi_1$-set is an element of some $s(n')$, with $s \eta \Upsilon$, and so it is a subset of $s(n)$; but every value of a sequence $s$ belonging to $\Upsilon$ is either finite or enumerable as follows by transfinite induction[78] (using the above mentioned theorem of enumerability).

[77] Cf. Part III, p. 52.
[78] Cf. Part V, p. 69.

(2) Every element of $\Omega$ is a $\Pi_1$-set; indeed, as follows directly from the definition of $\Upsilon$, every sequence $s$ whose domain belongs to $\Omega$ and which assigns to each element $k$ of its domain the value $k$, belongs to the class $\Upsilon$.

(3) Every element of a $\Pi_1$-set $b$ is again a $\Pi_1$-set, and of lower degree than $b$. For the degree of $b$ being a successor $n'$, we have $b \,\epsilon\, s(n')$ for some $s$ belonging to $\Upsilon$; and so $b$ is a subset of $s(n)$, hence if $a \,\epsilon\, b$, we have $a \,\epsilon\, s(n)$; thus $a$ is a $\Pi_1$-set whose degree is at most $n$.

(4) The transitive closure of a finite or enumerable set $a$ of $\Pi_1$-sets is a finite or enumerable class of $\Pi_1$-sets. Let $C$ be the transitive closure of $a$, and let $S$ be the class of finite or enumerable subsets of $C$. From our statement (3) we infer by means of complete induction that every element of $C$ is a $\Pi_1$-set, and from the statement (1) it follows that the sum of the elements of any element of $S$ is represented again by an element of $S$. Thus there exists the function $F$ assigning to every set which belongs to $S$ the set representing the sum of its elements and to every other set the null set, and the values of $F$ all belong to $S$. Also $a \,\eta\, S$. So, if $G$ is the iterator of $F$ on $a$, every value of $G$ is an element of $S$, i.e. a finite or enumerable subset of $C$, and also the sum of the values of $G$ (since $G$ is enumerable) is represented by an element of $S$. On the other hand, by the definition of the transitive closure it follows with the aid of complete induction that every element of $C$ belongs to the sum of the values of $G$. Thus indeed $C$ is a finite or enumerable class of $\Pi_1$-sets.

(5) Every finite or enumerable set $a$ of $\Pi_1$-sets is a $\Pi_1$-set and its degree is the lowest of those ordinals which are successors and higher than the degree of any element of $a$. In fact, the sum of the degrees of the elements of $a$, being the sum of the elements of a finite or enumerable class of ordinals belonging to $\Omega$, is represented by an element $m$ of $\Omega$; this is the lowest of those ordinals which are at least as high as the degree of any one element of $a$. Let $C$ (as in the proof of (4)) be the transitive closure of $a$. By (4) the class $C$ is finite or enumerable, and so every subclass of it is represented by a set; further the elements of such a set are $\Pi_1$-sets, and their degrees are not higher than $m$, as follows from our statement (3). So there exists an $m'$-sequence $s$ assigning to every element $n$ of $m'$ the set of those elements of $C$ which have a degree not higher than $n$. We have $s(0) = 0$; for every ordinal $k'$ lower than $m'$, every element of $s(k')$ is a set of $\Pi_1$-sets belonging to $C$ which all, by our statement (3), are of degrees not higher than $k$ and therefore are in $s(k)$, so that every element of $s(k')$ is a subset of $s(k)$, and thus $s(k')$ is a finite or enumerable set of subsets of $s(k)$; for every limiting number $l$ lower than $m'$, $s(l)$ is the set of those elements of $C$ which have a degree lower than $l$, and so it is the sum of the members of the $l$-segment of $s$. Thus it follows that $s \,\eta\, \Upsilon$. Moreover, every element of $a$ is in $s(m)$, so that $a \subseteq s(m)$. Now let $t$ be the $m''$-sequence whose elements are those of $s$ and also the pair $\langle m', (a) \rangle$. Then $t(m') = (a)$, $t(m) = s(m)$, so that $t(m')$ is a finite set of subsets of $t(m)$. Thus $t \,\eta\, \Upsilon$ and $a \,\epsilon\, t(m')$. Hence $a$ is a $\Pi_1$-set, whose degree is not higher than $m'$, but neither can the degree of $a$ be lower than $m'$ since it must be higher than the degree of any element of $a$ and it must be a successor. So $m'$ is the degree of $a$, and it is the lowest ordinal which is a successor and is higher than any degree of an element of $a$.

From the statements (1)–(5) about $\Pi_1$ , it is now quite easy to conclude that the $\Pi_1$-system satisfies all our axioms I–IV, Va, b, c, VI, VII, but not Vd.

As to the axiomatic basis of the exhibited theory of the $\Pi_1$-system, which is a variant of the theory of the $\Pi$-model given before, it is to be observed that instead of the axioms Vb and VI the axiom of the enumerable is sufficient here, and instead of Va axiom VII can be taken. On the other hand, if we keep Va, then instead of the axiom of the enumerable we can take axiom VI*, i.e. Fraenkel's generalization of Zermelo's axiom of infinity, which by the axioms I–III and Va is equivalent to the axiom of the enumerable.[79]

Thus for introducing the $\Pi_1$-system by means of the definition of the class $\Upsilon$, and proving that it satisfies all our axioms I–VII with the exception of Vd, each of the following systems of axioms is sufficient:

I–IV, VII, and the axiom of the enumerable.

I–IV, Va, and the axiom of the enumerable.

I–IV, Va, and VI*.

For the proof of the existence of $\Upsilon$ and $\Pi_1$ , as also of the statements (1)–(5) about $\Pi_1$ , in each of three systems of axioms the axiom of choice IV could be replaced by the special axiom of choice $IV_s$ ; however, then the $\Pi_1$-system is not proved to satisfy IV, but only $IV_s$ .

*Remark.* Upon the basis of all the axioms I–VI it is easy to prove, using the statements (1), (3), (5) of our preceding considerations and applying transfinite induction, that the class $\Pi_1$ , as defined by means of the class $\Upsilon$, is identical with the class of those elements of $\Psi(\omega_1)$ which themselves as well as every element of their transitive closure are either finite or enumerable; and further that the degree of a $\Pi_1$-set, as defined by means of the class $\Upsilon$, is the same as the degree that this set has as a $\Pi$-set. Thus our later definition of $\Pi_1$ and of the degree of a $\Pi_1$-set is in agreement with the former definition.

Now we come to the question of setting up the $\Pi_2$-system without the axiom Vb. Here it is to be noticed that our axiom VI, in case Vb is not at our disposal, gives no way for proving any given infinite class to be represented by a set. So in order to establish the $\Pi_2$-system without Vb, we have to assume instead of VI a strengthened form of the axiom of infinity. Each of the following axioms "$VI_1$", "$VI_2$", (which are both derivable from VI, when the axioms I–III, Va, b are available), will suffice for this purpose:

$VI_1$ . The class of all those sets which themselves as also every element of their transitive closure are finite is represented by a set.

$VI_2$ . There exists a set $c$ such that $0 \in c$, and if $a \in c$ and $b$ is a set of subsets of $a$, then $b \in c$.

Indeed by each one of these axioms, in connection with I–III and Va, the class $\Pi_0$ , whose existence, as we know, follows by means of the iteration theorem and the theorems on finiteness, can be shown to be represented by a set. Now let $\Psi_1$ be the iterator on this set of the function, existing by virtue of Vd, which assigns to every set its power-set. This function henceforth will be denoted briefly as the "power-set function." Then we can define $\Pi_2$ , in accordance with

---

[79] Cf. Part III, pp. 34–36, and p. 52.

our former definition, as the sum of the values of $\Psi_1$. A definition equivalent to this can be given by introducing—by analogy with the simple theory of types—the following concept of "type": A set $a$ is said to be "of type $n$" if $n$ is a finite ordinal, and $a \in \Psi_1(n)$, and, for all $m \in n$, $a$ is not in $\Psi_1(m)$. A set is said to "have a type" if there exists a finite ordinal $n$ such that the set is of type $n$; in this case obviously there is only one ordinal $n$ such that the set is of type $n$, and this finite ordinal then is called "the type of" the set. Using the concept of type we can now define $\Pi_2$ as the class of sets which have a type.

The class of sets of type 0 is $\Pi_0$ and is represented by a set of type 1. For every finite ordinal $n$ the class of sets of type $n'$ is represented by the set-difference $\Psi_1(n') \div \Psi_1(n)$, which is a set of type $n''$. Further we have: A set is of type 0 if and only if it is a finite set of sets of type 0; a set not belonging to $\Pi_0$ is of type $n'$ (for a finite ordinal $n$), if and only if every element of it is of a type not higher than $n$ and at least one of its elements is of type $n$. As a consequence of this, every subset of a set of type $n$ has a type not higher than $n$, and every element of a set of type $n'$ has a type lower than $n'$. The infinite subclass N of $\Pi_0$ is represented by the set $\omega$, which therefore is of type 1, and generally for every finite ordinal $n$, as follows by complete induction, the ordinal $\omega + n$ is of type $n'$. Hence there cannot be an ordinal higher than each of these ordinals $\omega + n$ and having a type, or in other words: every ordinal which belongs to $\Pi_2$ is lower than some ordinal $\omega + n$ with $n \in \omega$.

From these statements it is now easy to infer that the $\Pi_2$-system, i.e. the system of $\Pi_2$-sets and $\Pi_2$-classes, by the new definition of $\Pi_2$ and on the basis of the axioms I–III, Va, Vd together with $VI_1$ or $VI_2$, satisfies all the axioms I–III, Va, c, d, VI, as also $VI_1$ and $VI_2$, whereas it does not satisfy Vb. Axiom VII is also satisfied by the $\Pi_2$-system. For let $A$ be a non-empty $\Pi_2$-class; if the lowest type $k$ occurring for an element of $A$ is $\neq 0$, then for each element $c$ of $A$ whose type is $k$ there cannot be a common element of $A$ and $c$; on the other hand, if there are elements of $A$ which are of type 0, then the class $B$ of these elements is a non-empty subclass of $\Pi_0$, and since, as we know, the $\Pi_0$-system satisfies axiom VII, there is an element $c$ of $B$ which has no element in common with $B$, and hence $A$ and $c$ cannot have a common element either (since this, as a set of type 0, would belong to $B$); thus in both cases the assertion of VII is satisfied.

If the axiom of choice IV is included in the axiomatic basis, then it immediately follows that the $\Pi_2$-system satisfies also this axiom. Thus on the basis of the axioms I–IV, Va, Vd and either $VI_1$ or $VI_2$ we get a model for proving that in our system of axioms I–VII, axiom Vb is independent.

The model here considered has to be modified, if instead of one of the axioms $VI_1$, $VI_2$ we take Zermelo's axiom of infinity. We then are no more able to prove the existence of a set representing the class $\Pi_0$; but it follows from Zermelo's axiom of infinity, in connection with the axioms I–III and Va, that the sum of the values of the iterator on 0 of the function assigning to every set $a$ the set $(a)$ is represented by a set, let us call it $\zeta$. Further let $\Psi_0$ be the iterator on 0 of the power-set function and $\Pi_0$ the sum of the values of $\Psi_0$, what is in accordance with the definition of $\Psi_0$ and $\Pi_0$ given before, upon a basis not including Vd.[80] By the

[80] Cf. p. 96.

corollary of the iteration theorem stated in Part II[81] combined with the class theorem, there exists a function $\Psi^*$ assigning to every pair $\langle k, n \rangle$ of finite ordinals the value for $n$ of the iterator of the power-set function on the set-sum $\zeta + \Psi_0(k'')$.

From the fact that $\zeta$ is transitive and that the power-set of a transitive set is transitive, it follows by complete induction, with respect first to $k$ and then to $n$, that every value of $\Psi^*$ is a transitive set; at the same time it results that, for finite ordinals $k$, $n$, we have $\Psi^*(\langle k, n \rangle) \subseteq \Psi^*(\langle k, n' \rangle)$ and $\Psi^*(\langle k, n \rangle) \subseteq \Psi^*\langle (k', n \rangle)$. Now we define the class $\Pi^*$ as the sum of the values of $\Psi^*$; and for an element $c$ of $\Pi^*$(a "$\Pi^*$-set"), we define its "type" to be the lowest finite ordinal $n$ for which there exists a finite ordinal $k$ such that $c \in \Psi^*(\langle k, n \rangle)$.

As immediate consequences of our definitions of $\Psi^*$ and $\Pi^*$ and "type", and of our statements on $\Psi^*$ we have: (1) Every element as also every subset of a $\Pi^*$-set is a $\Pi^*$-set.    (2) If $a$, $b$ are $\Pi^*$-sets then also $(a)$, $(a, b)$, and the set-sum $a + (b)$ are $\Pi^*$-sets.    (3) A pair $\langle a, b \rangle$ is a $\Pi^*$-set if and only if $a$ and $b$ are $\Pi^*$-sets. (Consequence of (1) and (2).)    (4) The power-set of a $\Pi^*$-set is a $\Pi^*$-set.    For, if $a \in \Psi^*(\langle k, n \rangle)$, then also $a \subseteq \Psi^*(\langle k, n \rangle)$; hence the power-set of $a$ is a subset of $\Psi^*(\langle k, n' \rangle)$, hence it is in $\Psi^*(\langle k, n'' \rangle)$, and so it is a $\Pi^*$-set. (5) The sum of the elements of a $\Pi^*$-set is represented by a $\Pi^*$-set.    For if $a \in \Psi^*(\langle k, n \rangle)$ and $b \in a$, then $b \in \Psi^*(\langle k, n \rangle)$ and also $b \subseteq \Psi^*(\langle k, n \rangle)$. Thus the sum of the elements of $a$ is a subclass of $\Psi^*(\langle k, n \rangle)$ and hence, by Va, is represented by a set; this one, being a subset of $\Psi^*(\langle k, n \rangle)$, is an element of $\Psi^*(\langle k, n' \rangle)$ and so it is a $\Pi^*$-set.    (6) The $\Pi^*$-sets of type 0 are the elements of $\Pi_0$.    For every finite ordinal $n$, the elements of a $\Pi^*$-set of type $n'$ are $\Pi^*$-sets of a type not higher than $n$.

From the statements (1)–(5) it appears that the $\Pi^*$-system, i.e. the system of $\Pi^*$-sets and $\Pi^*$-classes, satisfies our axioms I–III, Va, c, d.    Zermelo's axiom of infinity and axiom VII are also satisfied by the $\Pi^*$-system; for the axiom of infinity this follows from the fact that $\zeta \in \Pi^*$, and for VII it can be inferred from the statement (6), by reasoning just as in the case of the $\Pi_2$-system.

As to the axiom of choice, there is again the possibility (as we had it for the $\Pi_2$-system) of immediately stating that it is satisfied by the $\Pi^*$-system, if this axiom is included in our axiomatic basis.

Likewise, if instead of IV the multiplicative axiom, in the form it was stated in Part II,[82] is assumed among our basic axioms, the assertion of this axiom can be proved to hold for the $\Pi^*$-system.    Indeed, if $s$ is a $\Pi^*$-set of non-empty sets, no two of them having a common element, then by the multiplicative axiom there exists a set $c$ whose every element is in an element of $s$ and which has just one element in common with each element of $s$.    But such a set $c$, being a subset of the sum of the elements of the $\Pi^*$-set $s$, is again a $\Pi^*$-set, since Vc and Va hold for the $\Pi^*$-system.

Axiom Vb, of course, is not satisfied by the $\Pi^*$-system; there is even no $\Pi^*$-set

---

[81] See Part II, p. 25.

[82] Cf. Part II, p. 17. It is noted here as consequence (6) of our axioms. The proof here given is by IV and Vb; a better known proof is by IV and Va, c.

representing the class N, which, as we know, is of equal power with $\zeta$. This can be shown by introducing the concept of the "$\zeta$-degree" of a $\Pi^*$-set $a$; we define it as the lowest finite ordinal $m$ which is the arithmetic sum of finite ordinals $k$, $n$ such that $a \, \epsilon \, \Psi^*(\langle k, n \rangle)$. By this definition every $\Pi^*$-set has a (uniquely determined) $\zeta$-degree; the $\Pi^*$-sets of $\zeta$-degree 0 are the elements of $\zeta$, and for every finite ordinal $m$, which is $\neq 0$, the elements of a $\Pi^*$-set of $\zeta$-degree $m$ have a $\zeta$-degree lower than $m$. From this, and the fact that 0 and 1 are the only ordinals which are elements of $\zeta$ and that every finite ordinal $k'$ is in $\Psi_0(k'')$, it follows by complete induction that every finite ordinal $m'$, considered as a $\Pi^*$-set, has the $\zeta$-degree $m$. Thus there cannot be a $\Pi^*$-set of which every finite ordinal is an element; and so N is not represented by a $\Pi^*$-set.

As a result of our discussion of the $\Pi^*$-system we note: Upon the basis of our axioms I–III, Va, d together with Zermelo's axiom of infinity and the multiplicative axiom, the system of $\Pi^*$-sets and $\Pi^*$-classes constitutes a model for the axiom system consisting of the said axioms and also the axioms Vc and VII.

Now considering that the assumptions on the system of sets which are included in the said axiomatic basis are all derivable from Zermelo's original axioms and that on the other hand the original Zermelo axioms—if the concept of "definite Eigenschaft" is understood in our precise sense[83]—are all satisfied by the system of $\Pi^*$-sets, we can draw from our result the following consequence: If the original Zermelo axiom system is consistent, then no contradiction arises by adding the assumption that every set is a $\Pi^*$-set. Or what comes to the same: From the original Zermelo axioms, provided that they are consistent, no set which is not a $\Pi^*$-set can be proved to exist; in particular it is impossible to prove by them that there exists a set of which every finite ordinal, by our definition of "ordinal", is an element.

[83] Cf. Part I, p. 1, footnote 3.

PART VII[84]

**18. Further models for proofs of independence.** The reader of
Part VI will have noticed that among the set-theoretic models considered
there some models were missing which were announced in Part II for
certain proofs of independence. These models will be supplied now.

Mainly two models have to be constructed: one with the property that
there exists a set which is its own only element, and another in which the
axioms I–III and VII, but not Va, are satisfied. In either case we need not
satisfy the axiom of infinity. Thereby it becomes possible to set up the
models on the basis of only I–III, and either VII or Va, a basis from which
number theory can be obtained as we saw in Part II.

On both these bases the $\Pi_0$-system of Part VI, which satisfies the axioms
I–V and VII, but not VI, can be constructed, as we stated there. An
isomorphic model can also be obtained on that basis, by first setting up
number theory as in Part II, and then proceeding as Ackermann did.[85]
Let us recall the main points of this procedure.

For the sake of clarity in the discussion of this and the subsequent
models, it will be necessary to distinguish precisely between the concepts
which are relative to the basic set-theoretic system, and those which are
relative to the model to be defined.

Unless otherwise stated, the terms are to refer to the basic system, so
that in particular the term "natural number" (or simply "number", when no
ambiguity seems possible) means "finite ordinal of the basic system".
Furthermore in order to indicate the rôle of the natural numbers as constituting the sets of the model we speak of them as "new sets".

We now proceed to the description of Ackermann's number-theoretic
model, which we call briefly the model $\mathfrak{M}$. The sets of the model $\mathfrak{M}$ are
the natural numbers, and the element relation in $\mathfrak{M}$, which we denote by
"$m \,\tilde{\epsilon}\, n$", is defined to mean that the greatest natural number $k$ such that
$k \cdot 2^m \leq n$ is odd. (It may be recalled that the relation $r < s$ between natural
numbers $r$, $s$ in our system is simply $r \,\epsilon\, s$.) The condition amounts to requiring that $2^m$ occurs as a term in the expansion of $n$ as a sum of different
powers of 2. Classes in $\mathfrak{M}$ are number classes, and the relation $m \,\eta\, A$ is the

[84] Cf. *J. Symbolic Logic* **19** (1954) 81–96.
[85] ACKERMANN (1937).

same as in the basic system. Also the identity relation between sets and between classes remains unchanged.

For verifying that the model so defined satisfies all the axioms I–V and VII, it will suffice to give the main ideas.

That the extensionality axiom holds is immediate.

As to the axioms II we have: The number 0 is the null set. The augmentation of a new set $m$ by a further element $n$ consists in the operation $m + 2^n$. — An ordered pair $\langle m, n \rangle$ of new sets is either the number $2^{2^m}$ in case $m = n$, or $2^{2^m} + 2^{2^m + 2^n}$ otherwise.

For the verification of the axioms III we can rely on the following circumstances. There exists the class of natural numbers. The relation $\tilde{\epsilon}$ can be formulated by a constitutive expression,[86] likewise the ternary relation $(a = b \ \& \ c = 2^{2^a}) \ \mathbf{v} \ (a \neq b \ \& \ c = 2^{2^a} + 2^{2^a + 2^b})$. From the latter in particular it follows that, for every class of pairs (in the old sense) of new sets, there exists the class of the corresponding pairs in the model, and inversely. Likewise it is to be noted that for a class of pairs in the model the domain and also the converse domain is (by the definition of the "member" of a new pair) the same as for the class of corresponding pairs in the basic system.— As a consequence of the holding of the axioms III in $\mathfrak{M}$ the class theorem is available for $\mathfrak{M}$.

The validity of the axiom IV in $\mathfrak{M}$ follows from the circumstance that every class of natural numbers has a smallest element. In fact, to a class $A$ of pairs of numbers there exists by the class theorem the subclass of those pairs $\langle m, n \rangle$ such that $\langle m, k \rangle$ does not belong to $A$ for any $k \ \epsilon \ n$.

That the axioms Va–d hold for $\mathfrak{M}$ follows by applying the following elementary fact (which is a consequence of the theorems on finite sets proved in Part II). If $A$ is a finite class of natural numbers, then there exists the sum $\sum\limits_{k \, \eta \, A} 2^k$ of the $k^{\text{th}}$ powers of 2 extended over the elements $k$ of $A$. This indeed amounts to stating that every finite class of new sets is represented in the new sense by a set. For instance, the class of the new subsets of a new set $n$ is in the old sense a class of natural numbers not greater than $n$, so it is a finite class and therefore by the theorem just stated it is represented in the new sense by a set; thus Vd holds for $\mathfrak{M}$.

Axiom VII follows by using that every non-empty class of natural numbers has a smallest element and that each element, in the new sense, of a number $m$ is a number smaller than $m$.

So indeed the Ackermann model $\mathfrak{M}$ is found to satisfy all our axioms besides the axiom of infinity.

Now a slight modification of the method used here allows us to construct the models which were announced in Part II.

---

[86] In the sense of Part I, pp. 6–7; for the proof see Part II, pp. 24–27.

By means of the first, which we shall call $\mathfrak{M}_1$ we are to show that the existence of a set[87] which is its own only element is compatible with the axioms I–III and Va and even with all the axioms I–V.

The model $\mathfrak{M}_1$ is obtained from $\mathfrak{M}$ by merely interchanging $0 \, \tilde{\epsilon} \, n$ and $1 \, \tilde{\epsilon} \, n$ in the definition of elementhood between new sets. Thus the definition of $m \, \tilde{\epsilon} \, n$ for $m \geq 2$ is the same in $\mathfrak{M}_1$ as in $\mathfrak{M}$, but in $\mathfrak{M}_1$ we have $1 \, \epsilon \, n$ if and only if $n$ is odd, and $0 \, \tilde{\epsilon} \, n$ if and only if $n$ is of one of the forms $4k+2$ or $4k+3$. According to this a new set is again determined by its elements. Moreover the number which in $\mathfrak{M}_1$ is the new set with the elements $m_1, \ldots, m_k$ is obtained from the number $2^{m_1} + \ldots + 2^{m_k}$ by replacing the exponent 0, if it occurs, by 1, and likewise 1 by 0.

There is now no difficulty in adapting to $\mathfrak{M}_1$ the verification of the axioms I–V given for the model $\mathfrak{M}$. But axiom VII is not satisfied, since the new set 1 is its only element.

This method of modifying $\mathfrak{M}$ can be sharpened so as to produce models in which the axiom VII is violated in a stronger way. We give two instances.

Let us define $n^*$, for a natural number $n$, as follows: if $n$ is odd, then $n^*$ is $2^n$; if $n = 2^k$ with $k$ odd, then $n^*$ is $k$; in all other cases, $n^*$ is $n$. According to this obviously $(n^*)^* = n$. Now the element relation $m \, \tilde{\epsilon} \, n$ is defined to mean that $m^*$ occurs as an exponent in the dyadic expansion of $n$. The condition can also be expressed in this way: we have $m^* \, \tilde{\epsilon} \, n$, if and only if $m$ occurs as an exponent in the dyadic expansion of $n$. Then again all the axioms I–V can be verified to hold. (Indeed the element relation can again be formulated by a constitutive expression, and likewise the relation between $m$, $n$ and $\langle m, n \rangle$, since the ordered pair $\langle m, n \rangle$ is now $2^{(2^{m^*})^*}$ for $m = n$, and $2^{(2^{m^*})^*} + 2^{(2^{m^*} + 2^{n^*})^*}$ otherwise.) Axiom VII is now violated in such a way that for each odd number $m$ we have $(2^m) = 2^m$. Thus we have an enumerable class of new sets which are their only elements.

The other instance differs from the foregoing only by the definition of the star-function. Namely we define: for $n$ odd, $n^*$ is $2^{n+2}$; for $n = 2^{k+2}$ with $k$ odd, $n^*$ is $k$; in all other cases, $n^*$ is $n$. Here the deviation from axiom VII is such that we have an enumerable class of new sets where the set $a_k$, assigned by the enumeration to the number $k$, has $a_{k+1}$ as its element. Indeed we have $2^{2k+1} = (2^{2k+3}) = ((2^{2k+5}))$, and so on.

*Remark.* The model $\mathfrak{M}_1$ and also the two subsequent models of a set theory not satisfying the axiom VII can be extended to satisfy also the axiom VI (the axiom of infinity), provided this axiom and the axioms V are included in the basic system. Namely we can perform a construction fully parallel to that of the $\Pi$-system with only the following differences: (1) As starting set we take not the null-set but the set of all natural numbers, which exists as a consequence of the axiom VI.

---

[87] Cf. Part II, p. 22.

(2)   Every finite set of natural numbers which is not itself a natural number is left out.

(3)   The element relation between natural numbers is defined in the same way as it is in the model to be extended.

The replacement process (2) has to be repeated at each step of the extension of the system of sets by the successive formations of power sets and sums. In the resulting system of sets, which in the basic system (by the general recursion theorem) is a class $S$, every set, as in the $\Pi$-model, has a degree. For every natural number the degree is null; for other sets it is a successor ordinal.

The classes of the new system are the subclasses of $S$, taken in the basic system. The element relation between sets belonging to $S$ — with the exception of that one newly defined between natural numbers — is the original one, likewise that between sets and classes.

It can be shown that the system of sets and classes so constructed satisfies the axioms I–III, V, VI, and also the axiom IV if this is satisfied in the basis. So from the extended models it follows that, if we can satisfy the axioms I–VI (with or without axiom IV), we can satisfy them in such a way that there exists an infinite set each element of which is its own only element,[88] and also in such a way that there exists an infinite sequence each member of which has the following member as its element.

Now we come to the other announced model,[89] which we call $\mathfrak{M}_2$. By this we are to show that without Va it cannot be proved (a) that a transitive set having every transitive proper subset as an element is an ordinal, nor (b) that a set is an ordinal if it satisfies Zermelo's defining conditions for $n$ being an ordinal, which are: $0 = n \lor 0 \, \epsilon \, n$; $a \, \epsilon \, n \rightarrow a+(a) = n \lor a+(a) \, \epsilon \, n$; if $s \subseteq n$, then the sum of the elements of $s$ is represented either by $n$ or by an element of $n$.

The proofs are impossible not only on the basis of I–III and VII, but even if IV and Vc are added. The availability of Vc is particularly agreeable for the consideration of Zermelo's conditions, since by it the third of these conditions becomes simpler in the sense that the representation of the sum of the elements of $s$ by a set holds already in virtue of Vc. Of course Zermelo in setting up his definition presupposed the holding of Vc.

The model $\mathfrak{M}_2$ is again number-theoretic. As before, the class relation in it is the ordinary one of a number belonging to a class of numbers, and the element relation $\bar{\epsilon}$ is again connected with the dyadic expansion of numbers, but in a more complicated way. In order to facilitate its formulation let us take $\mathrm{Oc}(k, m)$ as an abbreviation for "$k$ occurs as an exponent in the

---

[88] This has been recently shown by another method by Ernst Specker, see SPECKER (1952).
[89] Cf. Part II, p. 23.

dyadic expansion of $m$". Further we use $2/n$ for "$n$ is even" and $2 \not/ n$ for "$n$ is odd". We then have the following definition by cases:[90]

(1)   If $2/n$, then $m \,\tilde{\in}\, n \leftrightarrow 2/m \,\&\, 0\mathrm{c}\left(\dfrac{m}{2}+1, n\right)$,

(2)   if $2 \not/ n$ and $(Ex)(x \neq 0 \,\&\, 2/x \,\&\, 0\mathrm{c}(x, n))$, then $m \,\tilde{\in}\, n \leftrightarrow 0\mathrm{c}(m+1, n)$,

(3)   if $2 \not/ n$ and $(x)(x \neq 0 \,\&\, 0\mathrm{c}(x, n) \to 2 \not/ x)$, then $m \,\tilde{\in}\, n \leftrightarrow 2/m \lor 0\mathrm{c}(m, n)$.

This definition may be explained as follows. The three cases on $n$ correspond to three kinds of new sets:

(1)   those whose transitive closures are finite,

(2)   those which themselves are finite whereas their transitive closures are infinite,

(3)   those which are infinite.

Concerning the elements of a new set $n$, we see that, if $n$ is of the first kind, its elements are the numbers $2k-2$ such that $0\mathrm{c}(k, n)$. If $n$ is of the second kind, then its elements are the predecessors of the exponents $\neq 0$ in its dyadic expansion. If $n$ is of the third kind, then its elements are the even numbers together with the odd exponents in the dyadic expansion of $n$ if there are such exponents.

The idea of this arrangement is that besides "normal sets", which are those finite sets whose transitive closures are finite and which arithmetically (in the basic system) are characterized as the even numbers, we have also the set of all normal sets corresponding to the "old" 1 and all those non-normal sets which are generated from 0 and the old 1 by the iterated operation of adding an element (already obtained) to a set. One also sees that every finite set of normal elements occurs as a normal element, and every other finite set occurs as an element of second kind, and every set which has as elements all normal sets besides (at most) finitely many other sets occurs as a set of third kind.

Now we proceed to verify the axioms I–IV, Vc and VII for this model $\mathfrak{M}_2$.

As to extensionality, one easily sees that sets in $\mathfrak{M}_2$ which have the same elements must be of the same kind and then also must be identical.

For the axioms II, we have first that 0 is the empty set in $\mathfrak{M}_2$. For axiom II(2), we shall explicitly indicate how to obtain from a number $n$ which is a new set the number $\sigma\,(n, m)$ which in $\mathfrak{M}_2$ is the set arising from $n$ by adding a set $m$, not yet in $n$, as an element. Here we have to distinguish three cases relative to the kind of $n$.

(1)   If $n$ is of the first kind, we have to consider two possibilities according as $m$ is even or not. If $m$ is even, then $\sigma(n, m) = n + 2^{\frac{m}{2}+1}$. If $m$ is odd, then $\sigma(n, m) = (n_1 + 1) + 2^{m+1}$, where $n_1$ results from $n$ by replacing every additive term $2^k$ in the dyadic expansion of $n$ by $2^{2k-1}$; indeed $n$

---

[90] We use here "$\leftrightarrow$" instead of "if and only if".

is of the first kind and $\sigma(n, m)$ has to be of the second kind, so that for the representation of the elements by the exponents we have to make the passage from the first to the second case.

(2) If $n$ is of the second kind, we have $\sigma(n, m) = n+2^{m+1}$, since this number is also of the second kind.

(3) If $n$ is of the third kind, $m$ must be odd and we obviously have $\sigma(n, m) = n+2^m$.

In order to define $\sigma(n, m)$ for arbitrary numbers, we need only take $\sigma(n, m) = n$ for the case that the new set $m$ is in the new set $n$.— By means of $\sigma(n, m)$ we can express the function which is the number-theoretic representation of the ordered pair $\langle a, b \rangle$. Indeed, we have $\langle a, a \rangle = \sigma(0, \sigma(0, a))$, and for $a \neq b$, $\langle a, b \rangle = \sigma(\sigma(0, \sigma(0, a)), \sigma(\sigma(0, a), b))$.

For the axioms III and IV the verification can be made in the same way as for the model $\mathfrak{M}$; in particular it is necessary to take into account here that in $\mathfrak{M}_2$ the element relation and also the relation $\langle a, b \rangle = c$ can be formulated by a constitutive expression. As a consequence of the axioms III the class theorem holds again in $\mathfrak{M}_2$.

In order to see that Vc holds in $\mathfrak{M}_2$, it is sufficient, on account of our previous statements about the different kinds of new sets, to observe that the sum of the elements of any new set is either a finite set of new sets or has as elements all normal sets besides at most finitely many non-normal sets.

That axiom VII is also satisfied results as follows. Let $A$ be any non-empty class of $\mathfrak{M}_2$. Two possibilities are to be considered. (a) $A$ has at least one even number as element. Let $n$ be the smallest among them. Then $n$ has no element in common with $A$. For, if $k \,\tilde{\epsilon}\, n$, then $2/k$ and $2^{\frac{k}{2}+1} \leq n$, hence $\dfrac{k}{2} < \dfrac{n}{2}$, $k < n$, and thus $k$ cannot belong to $A$. (b) $A$ has only odd numbers as elements. Among these there is a smallest one $n$. Then again $n$ has no element in common with $A$. Indeed such a common element $k$ would be odd, and since $n$ is of the second or third kind, we should have for an odd element $k$ of $n$ that $2^k \leq n$ or even $2^{k+1} \leq n$, and thus $k < n$.

But axiom Va obviously is not satisfied. Indeed an infinite subclass of 1 or of any new set of the third kind is represented by a set only if it has all even numbers as elements.

Similarly we find that neither Vb nor Vd holds in $\mathfrak{M}_2$. For Vb this follows by considering any one-to-one correspondence of the new set 1 to a proper infinite subclass. As to Vd, let us show that the new set 3 is a counterexample. Indeed $3 = 2^0+2^1$; thus 3 is of the third kind, and its elements are 1 and the even numbers. Now the set of the second kind $1+2^2+2^{2k+1}$ whose elements are 1 and $2k$ is a subset of 3. Since $k$ is arbitrary, there are infinitely many odd numbers (non-normal sets) which are subsets of 3, and thus are elements of the class of all subsets of 3. This class therefore cannot be represented by a set, because a new set of any kind has only finitely many odd numbers as elements.

Now we are able to prove our aforementioned assertion that on the basis of the axioms I–IV, Vc and VII : (a) the conditions on a set that it be transitive and that every proper transitive subset be an element of it are not sufficient for a characterization of ordinals, and (b) likewise the conditions constituting Zermelo's definition of an ordinal formulated in Part II are not sufficient for the same purpose.

This indeed follows from the consideration of the new set 1. In $\mathfrak{M}_2$, 1 is not an ordinal, as can be seen as follows: $4 \ \tilde\epsilon \ 1$, 2 is the only element of 4, and $0 \ \tilde\epsilon \ 2$, therefore 4 is not transitive and thus is not an ordinal; so neither is 1 an ordinal. On the other hand, 1 satisfies the conditions that it be transitive and every proper subset of 1 be an element of 1. For, every element of 1 is a normal set, and each element of a normal set is again such a set; and further every proper subset of 1 must be of the first kind, and therefore is an element of 1.

But also the Zermelo conditions for a set being an ordinal are satisfied by 1. In fact $0 \ \tilde\epsilon \ 1$; if $n \ \tilde\epsilon \ 1$, then $\sigma(n, n) \ \tilde\epsilon \ 1$; and if $s$ is a subset (in the new sense) of 1, then the new sum of the elements of $s$ is either 1, or is a normal set and then is an element of 1.

**19. Reduction of the set-theoretic basis, including classes, to a number-theoretic frame.** Our construction of the models $\mathfrak{M}$, $\mathfrak{M}_1$, $\mathfrak{M}_2$ has been performed in the frame of the axiomatic system consisting of the axioms I–III, VII or else I–III, Va. This basis is wider than that frame of set theory whose consistency, as shown by Ackermann's reasoning (l.c.), results as a consequence of the constructive proofs of the consistency of number theory given by Gentzen, Kalmár, Ackermann, Lorenzen, Schütte and Stenius[91]. Indeed we have here the strengthening by the addition of the classes; however this strengthening is only of a restricted character in so far as we do not apply the concept of class in an impredicative way, so that the introduction of classes serves mainly to embody a part of metamathematics in the axiomatic system itself. This fact suggests the conjecture that it will be possible also for the frame considered to reduce the consistency proof to that of number-theory. A natural idea for this is to represent the classes by Gödel numbers, or more exactly by those of number-theoretic expressions corresponding to the constitutive expressions for them. But here a difficulty arises initially with regard to the $\eta$-relation (of a set belonging to a class). We should tend to express this relation by

[91] STENIUS (1952).

that of a set satisfying a constitutive expression. But this relation, as results from Tarski's theory of the truth concept, transgresses the formal system of number theory. On the other hand, if we replace the satisfaction (Erfüllung) of a constitutive expression by a provable satisfaction, then the holding or not holding of an $\eta$-relation would no longer be exhaustive alternatives.

This dilemma can be overcome by the procedure of Ilse Novak[92] which is based essentially on the method developed by Leon Henkin[93]. We will not presuppose familiarity with these methods, but explain their application to our case independently, making use of a simplification applied by Gisbert Hasenjäger[94] to the method of Henkin.

What we want to get is a model of our basic system, i.e. of the axioms I–III and VII, set up in the frame of the number-theoretic formal system Z of **Grundlagen der Mathematik** with certain additions to be mentioned presently. In making these additions we shall use an accessory result of the cited constructive consistency proofs for number theory, namely that the consistency of the system Z is preserved by the following kinds of additions: first addition of a finite number of primitive recursive definitions, second addition of a verifiable recursive formula as an axiom. Obviously also the consistency is not disturbed by adding numbered individual symbols $u_0, u_1, u_2, \ldots$.

In order now to prepare the Lindenbaum completion process we first assume a fixed Gödel numbering of the expressions of Z with the added functors and individual symbols included. The next step consists in adding as axioms the formulas $(Ex)\mathfrak{A}(x) \rightarrow \mathfrak{A}(u_j)$ where $(Ex)\mathfrak{A}(x)$ is any closed formula of the indicated form and $j$ is the Gödel number of this formula. No contradiction can arise by the addition of these formulas to the former consistent system. For otherwise already finitely many such formulas $(Ex)\mathfrak{A}_p(x) \rightarrow \mathfrak{A}_p(u_{j_p})$ $(p = 1, 2, \ldots \mathfrak{r})$ would yield a contradiction, and if $j_\mathfrak{r}$ is the greatest of the $j_p$, then by the deduction theorem it would follow that from the formulas $(Ex)\mathfrak{A}_p(x) \rightarrow \mathfrak{A}_p(u_{j_p})$ with $p < \mathfrak{r}$ (on the basis of our number-theoretic system) the negation of $(Ex)\mathfrak{A}_\mathfrak{r}(x) \rightarrow \mathfrak{A}_\mathfrak{r}(u_{j_\mathfrak{r}})$ and thus the formulas

[92] Novak (1951).

[93] Henkin (1949). An essential step in Henkin's procedure is the construction of a complete set of formulas from any consistent set of formulas, on some logical basis. This method goes back to A. Lindenbaum; see Tarski (1930), Satz. I. 56, p. 394. We shall therefore refer to this method, which (in the form in which we have to use it) will be explained, as the "Lindenbaum completion process".

[94] Hasenjäger (1953).

$(Ex)\mathfrak{A}_\mathfrak{r}(x)$ and $\mathfrak{A}_\mathfrak{r}(u_{j_\mathfrak{r}})$ could be derived. But then also, since $u_{j_\mathfrak{r}}$ cannot occur within $\mathfrak{A}_p(x)$ for $p < \mathfrak{r}$, $\mathfrak{A}(v)$ would be derivable for any free variable $v$ and thus also $(x)\mathfrak{A}_\mathfrak{r}(x)$. So already the first $r-1$ of the formulas $(Ex)\mathfrak{A}_p(x) \to \mathfrak{A}_p(u_{j_p})$ would lead to a contradiction. However this possibility can be excluded by assuming from the beginning that the index $\mathfrak{r}$ has been chosen as the minimal one for which a contradiction arises from formulas $(Ex)\mathfrak{A}(x) \to \mathfrak{A}(u_j)$ (out of our series) with $j \le \mathfrak{r}$.

Let us denote by $Z_\mathrm{I}$ the formal system which we obtain by adding to the system $Z$ the said recursive definitions— we introduce as many of them as are sufficient for performing the Gödel arithmetization of syntax and the elementary theory of dyadic expansion (as used in our model)—, the individual symbols $u_\mathfrak{t}$, and the accessory axioms $(Ex)\mathfrak{A}(x) \to \mathfrak{A}(u_j)$. As we have seen, $Z_\mathrm{I}$ like $Z$ is a consistent system.—

Now we are to perform Lindenbaum's completion process; however it will be sufficient to do this only implicitly by defining a number-theoretic predicate formulating the property of a number $\mathfrak{k}$ of being the Gödel number of a closed formula which is derivable in the completed system. This predicate corresponds fully to I. Novak's predicate $T$, and we shall denote it by the same letter.

Let us first give the definition of $T(k)$ in an informal way, and afterwards indicate how to formalize it in the frame of $Z_\mathrm{I}$. We begin by introducing the concept of an *extension set* of $Z_\mathrm{I}$. By an extension set of $Z_\mathrm{I}$ we understand a finite set of closed formulas of $Z_\mathrm{I}$ which, if added to $Z_\mathrm{I}$, do not yield a contradiction. An extension set can be indicated by the set of the Gödel numbers of its formulas, and this set can be represented by that number in whose dyadic expansion those Gödel numbers are the exponents which occur. Thus a number $\mathfrak{n}$ will be said to *represent an extension set of* $Z_\mathrm{I}$, if the exponents in the dyadic expansion of $\mathfrak{n}$ are the Gödel numbers of closed formulas which added to $Z_\mathrm{I}$ as axioms preserve consistency. One extension set *deviates* from another, if neither of them is a subset of the other.— Of two extension sets deviating from each other, that one is called *anterior* which contains the formula with the smallest of those Gödel numbers occurring for one of them but not for both. Now $T(k)$ is the following number predicate: "$k$ is the Gödel-number of a formula of some extension set which is anterior to every extension set that deviates from it".

For the formalizing we make use of the primitive recursive relation $\tilde\epsilon$ of our model $\mathfrak{M}$. Further we denote by "$\mathrm{Es}(n)$" the predicate "$n$ represents an extension set of $Z_\mathrm{I}$". The above definition of this predicate obviously can be formalized by means of the Gödel arithmetization of the syntax of $Z_\mathrm{I}$. The concepts "deviating" and "anterior" are formalized by the explicit definitions

$\mathrm{Dv}(k, l) \leftrightarrow (Ex)(x \,\tilde\epsilon\, k \,\&\, \overline{x \,\tilde\epsilon\, l}) \,\&\, (Ex)(\overline{x \,\tilde\epsilon\, k} \,\&\, x \,\tilde\epsilon\, l),$

$\mathrm{Ant}\ (k, l) \leftrightarrow (Ex)[(y)(y < x \,.\to.\, y \,\tilde\epsilon\, k \leftrightarrow y \,\tilde\epsilon\, l) \,\&\, x \,\tilde\epsilon\, k \,\&\, \overline{x \,\tilde\epsilon\, l}].$

Now the formal definition of $T(k)$ is

$$T(k) \leftrightarrow (Ex)[\text{Es}(x) \ \& \ (y)(\text{Es}(y) \ \& \ \text{Dv}(x, y) \rightarrow \text{Ant}(x, y)) \ \& \ k \ \tilde{\epsilon} \ x].$$

This definition of $T(k)$ can be shown by means of complete induction to be equivalent to the following recursive condition: $T(k)$, if and only if $k$ is the Gödel-number of a closed formula which on the basis of $Z_I$ is compatible with all those closed formulas whose Gödel-numbers are lower than $k$ and have the property $T$. Using the consistency of $Z_I$, which is formally expressible by a verifiable primitive recursive formula whose addition to $Z_I$ as an axiom preserves the consistency, we can prove that there are infinitely many numbers $k$ such that $T(k)$. By calling a formula whose Gödel number has the property $T$ a *T-formula*, as we shall do in the following, we can express the last statement by saying that there are infinitely many $T$-formulas.

Also it can be seen that every closed formula provable in $Z_I$ is a $T$-formula, and that every closed formula derivable by means of $Z_I$ from $T$-formulas is again a $T$-formula.

Further with regard to the logical operations we have the statements: (1) $\overline{\mathfrak{A}}$ is a $T$-formula, if and only if $\mathfrak{A}$ is not a $T$-formula. (2) $\mathfrak{A} \ \& \ \mathfrak{B}$ is a $T$-formula, if and only if $\mathfrak{A}$ and $\mathfrak{B}$ are $T$-formulas. (3) $(Ex)\mathfrak{A}(x)$ is a $T$-formula, if and only if there is a number $j$ such that $\mathfrak{A}(u_j)$ is a $T$-formula. We can say even more, namely that $(Ex)\mathfrak{A}(x)$ is a $T$-formula, if and only if, when $\mathfrak{r}$ is its Gödel-number, $\mathfrak{A}(u_{\mathfrak{r}})$ is a $T$-formula. In order to express formally in $Z_I$ the last condition we have to apply the primitive recursive function $\mathfrak{U}(r)$ (which can be composed out of the recursive functions introduced in $Z_I$) whose value for a definite value $\mathfrak{r}$ of $r$ is the Gödel-number of $u_{\mathfrak{r}}$. Statements corresponding to (1)–(3) hold for the other logical connectives in virtue of their expressibility by means of the three mentioned. For illustration let us consider the following example, for which we use the original form of Gödel numbering of formulas. Let $\mathfrak{y}, \hat{\mathfrak{s}}, \mathfrak{p}, \mathfrak{n}$ be the numbers (Zeichennummern) of the symbols $=, + \cdot, 0$, and let $\mathfrak{f}$ be the number of the formula $(x)(x \neq 0 \rightarrow (Ey)(Ez)(x \cdot y = u_{128} + z))$. Then we have

$$T(\mathfrak{f}) \leftrightarrow (x)[\overline{T}(2^{\mathfrak{U}(x)} \cdot 3^{\mathfrak{y}} \cdot 5^{\mathfrak{n}}) \rightarrow (Ey)(Ez)T(2^{\mathfrak{U}(x)} \cdot 3^{\mathfrak{p}} \cdot 5^{\mathfrak{U}(y)} \cdot 7^{\mathfrak{y}} \cdot 11^{\mathfrak{U}(128)} \cdot 13^{\hat{\mathfrak{s}}} \cdot 17^{\mathfrak{U}(z)})].$$

We are now ready to set up our number-theoretic model of the system of the axioms I–III and VII. We do this by describing the model in the frame of the metamathematics of $Z_I$ including the theory of the predicate $T$. The whole reasoning can be formalized in the frame of $Z_I$ with the addition of the consistency formula as an axiom. As this formal frame is shown to be consistent by Gentzen's and the other constructive proofs, from the same proofs it will follow that our system I–III and VII is also consistent, and so the consistency of the system of our axioms I–V and VII proved by the model $\mathfrak{M}$ and the independencies proved by means of the models $\mathfrak{M}_1, \mathfrak{M}_2$ hold also as a consequence of the constructive consistency proofs.

In describing the metamathematical model we do not enter into all the details of the number-theoretic formalization, the method of which is indeed well known. We shall apply the number-theoretic notations, where it seems useful for clarity.

As sets we take the individual-symbols $u_0, u_1 \dots$. Equality between $u_i$ and $u_t$ is not to be understood as simple identity, but rather we define $u_i$ to be equal to $u_t$ if the equation $u_i = u_t$ is a $T$-formula, or what is the same, if $T(2^{\mathfrak{U}(i)}.3^\mathfrak{y}.5^{\mathfrak{U}(t)})$. As we see, this relation, briefly "$i \underset{T}{=} k$", is not directly a predicate of $u_i$ and $u_k$ but rather of $i$ and $k$; yet we can regard it as referring to the symbols $u_j$, since these are assigned in a one-to-one way to their indices.

In a like indirect way we define the element-relation between $u_i$ and $u_t$ by a number-theoretic predicate "$i \underset{T}{\tilde{\epsilon}} k$" which holds for i and f if and only if the result of substituting $u_i$ for $a$ and $u_t$ for $b$ in the number-theoretic formula $\mathfrak{E}(a, b)$ which expresses the relation $a \tilde{\epsilon} b$ (i.e. "$a$ occurs as exponent in the dyadic expansion of $b$") is a $T$-formula.

As classes we take the propositional expressions of our system $Z_\mathrm{I}$, with a distinguished variable $c$ (Nennvariable) as their only free variable. These expressions of course have Gödel numbers and therefore can be enumerated as $\mathfrak{P}_0(c)$, $\mathfrak{P}_1(c)$, $\dots$. It may be noted that the Gödel number of $\mathfrak{P}_t(c)$ depends primitive recursively on f, since we can give a primitive recursive majorant for the sequence of the Gödel numbers of the $\mathfrak{P}_t(c)$ (f $= 0, 1, \dots$).

As the predicate of a set belonging to a class we take the relation "$i \, \eta \, k$" which holds for i and f if the formula $\mathfrak{P}_t(u_i)$ is a $T$-formula. $\quad\quad T$

Finally we define equality between $\mathfrak{P}_i(c)$ and $\mathfrak{P}_t(c)$ to mean that the formula $(x)(\mathfrak{P}_i(x) \leftrightarrow \mathfrak{P}_t(x))$ is a $T$-formula.

We can now show that the axioms I–III and VII are satisfied. For these verifications we have to make repeated use of the fact, already stated, that the predicate "being a $T$-formula" commutes with the logical connectives (including the quantifiers).

From this it follows that first the (preliminary) axioms of equality and the axioms of extensionality are satisfied. Let us illustrate this by the case of the extensionality axiom for sets. What we have to show is that, if for every $u_i$ i $\underset{T}{\tilde{\epsilon}}$ f holds if and only if i $\underset{T}{\tilde{\epsilon}}$ l, then f $\underset{T}{=}$ l. By the mentioned commutativity of the predicate "being a $T$-formula", this comes to the same as:

if
$$(x)(\mathfrak{E}(x, u_t) \leftrightarrow \mathfrak{E}(x, u_\mathfrak{l}))$$

is a $T$-formula, then
$$u_t = u_\mathfrak{l}$$

is a $T$-formula. Now in $Z_\mathrm{I}$ we can prove

$$(x)(\mathfrak{E}(x, u_t) \leftrightarrow \mathfrak{E}(x, u_\mathfrak{l})) \rightarrow u_t = u_\mathfrak{l}.$$

Thus this formula— let us abbreviate it $\mathfrak{A} \to \mathfrak{B}$— is a $T$-formula, and so, if $\mathfrak{A}$ is a $T$-formula, $\mathfrak{B}$ is a $T$-formula. But just this had to be shown.

As to the axiom II 1, we have that the formula $(Ex)(z)(\overline{\mathfrak{E}(z, x)})$ is provable in $Z_I$ and thus is a $T$-formula. Let $\mathfrak{n}_0$ be the Gödel number of this formula; then also $(z)(\overline{\mathfrak{E}(z, u_{\mathfrak{n}_0})})$ is a $T$-formula. Thus $u_{\mathfrak{n}_0}$ has the rôle of the null set. For the verification of II 2, we have to prove

$$(x)(y)(Ez)(v)(v \mathrel{\underset{T}{\tilde{\epsilon}}} z \leftrightarrow v \mathrel{\underset{T}{\epsilon}} x \vee v \mathrel{\underset{T}{=}} y).$$

By the commutativity of the predicate "being a $T$-formula" this is equivalent to stating that the formula

$$(x)(y)(Ez)(v)(\mathfrak{E}(v, z) \leftrightarrow \mathfrak{E}(v, x) \vee v = y),$$

is a $T$-formula. However this results from the fact that this formula is provable in $Z_I$.

For the axioms III the task of verification amounts to showing that in each case the class stated in the axiom to exist is characterized in our model by the condition on the elements $u_i$ that $i \mathrel{\underset{T}{\eta}} \mathfrak{k}$ holds for a certain propositional expression $\mathfrak{P}_{\mathfrak{k}}(c)$. For this a difficulty might seem to arise from the circumstance that in the defining conditions for the classes certain classes occur as parameters. However, since in our model the classes are themselves predicates (i.e. propositional expressions), this is no hindrance. Besides we have everywhere to make use again of the commutativity of the predicate "being a $T$-formula".

Let us illustrate the method of verification for the case of the axiom c(1), which we can satisfy even in the strengthened form (as it occurs in Gödel's monograph[95]): "For every class $A$ there exists a class whose elements are those sets which are the first members of ordered pairs belonging to $A$." In order to express that this assertion holds for our model, we have to translate the condition "$a$ is the first member of an ordered pair belonging to a given class $A$", i.e.

$$(Et)\{(Ex)(Ey)(Ez)(u)(v)(w)[(u \epsilon x \leftrightarrow u = a) \mathbin{\&} (v \epsilon z \leftrightarrow v = a \vee v = y) \mathbin{\&}$$
$$\mathbin{\&} (w \epsilon t \leftrightarrow w = x \vee w = z)] \mathbin{\&} t \eta A\},$$

into a condition for a $u_i$ with respect to a propositional expression $\mathfrak{P}_{\mathfrak{k}}(c)$. This is to be done by the following steps: First we replace the set variables by number variables (ranging over the indices of the $u$-symbols), but we need not change the letters. Further we change every "$\epsilon$" into "$\underset{T}{\tilde{\epsilon}}$", every "$=$" into "$\underset{T}{=}$"; and finally we replace the conjunctive member $t \eta A$ by

[95] Gödel (1940) axiom B5.

$t \, \eta \, k$. Now what we have to recognize is that the resulting formula
$$\begin{aligned}(Et)\{(Ex)(Ey)(Ez)(u)(v)(w)[(u \mathbin{\widetilde{\epsilon}} x \leftrightarrow u = a) \,\&\, (v \mathbin{\widetilde{\epsilon}} z \leftrightarrow v = a \lor v = y) \,\&\, \\ (w \mathbin{\widetilde{\epsilon}} t \leftrightarrow w = x \lor w = z)] \,\&\, t \, \eta \, k\},\end{aligned}$$

with the variable $a$ replaced by the numeral $\mathfrak{i}$ and $k$ by the index $\mathfrak{k}$ of the propositional expression $\mathfrak{P}_{\mathfrak{k}}(c)$ to be substituted for $A$, expresses that, for a certain propositional expression $\mathfrak{P}_{\mathfrak{r}}(c)$, the formula $\mathfrak{P}_{\mathfrak{r}}(u_{\mathfrak{i}})$ is a $T$-formula. But it is easy to find a $\mathfrak{P}_{\mathfrak{r}}(c)$ of this kind. Indeed by virtue of the already repeatedly applied commutativity of the predicate "being a $T$-formula", we get it from our first formula by letting the variables $t$, $x$, $y$, $z$, $u$, $v$, $w$ range over the $u$-symbols instead of over sets, and replacing $a$ by $c$, and every expression $\mathfrak{a} \,\epsilon\, \mathfrak{b}$ by the corresponding $\mathfrak{E}(\mathfrak{a}, \mathfrak{b})$, and the expression $t \, \eta \, A$ by $\mathfrak{P}_{\mathfrak{k}}(t)$.

The method used in this instance applies correspondingly to all the axioms III.

Now it only remains to state that also axiom VII is fulfilled in our model. Its assertion for this model is that for any propositional expression $\mathfrak{P}_{\mathfrak{r}}(c)$ such that there is a $u_{\mathfrak{i}}$ for which $\mathfrak{P}_{\mathfrak{r}}(u_{\mathfrak{i}})$ is a $T$-formula, there is a $u_{\mathfrak{j}}$ for which $\mathfrak{P}_{\mathfrak{r}}(u_{\mathfrak{j}})$ is a $T$-formula, whereas there is no $u_{\mathfrak{l}}$ such that $\mathfrak{E}(u_{\mathfrak{l}}, u_{\mathfrak{j}})$ and $\mathfrak{P}_{\mathfrak{r}}(u_{\mathfrak{l}})$ are both $T$-formulas. Or formally expressed,
$$(z)\{(Ex)(x \, \eta \, z) \to (Ex)[x \, \eta \, z \,\&\, (y)(y \mathbin{\widetilde{\epsilon}} x \to \overline{y \, \eta \, z})]\}.$$

The proof of this can be sketched as follows. In $Z_{\mathrm{I}}$ we can prove
$$\mathfrak{P}_{\mathfrak{r}}(u_{\mathfrak{i}}) \to (Ex)[\mathfrak{P}_{\mathfrak{r}}(x) \,\&\, (y)(y < x \to \overline{\mathfrak{P}_{\mathfrak{r}}(y)}]$$

where $y < x$ stands for $(Ez)(z \neq 0 \,\&\, y{+}z = x)$. Further we have in $Z_{\mathrm{I}}$
$$(Ex)[\mathfrak{P}_{\mathfrak{r}}(x) \,\&\, (y)(y < x \to \overline{\mathfrak{P}_{\mathfrak{r}}(y)})] \to \mathfrak{P}_{\mathfrak{r}}(u_{\mathrm{m}}) \,\&\, (y)(y < y_{\mathrm{m}} \to \overline{\mathfrak{P}_{\mathfrak{r}}(y)})$$

where $\mathrm{m}$ is the Gödel number of the formula standing in the antecedent. Thirdly in $Z_{\mathrm{I}}$ we have $(y)(\mathfrak{E}(y, u) \to y < u)$. Combining the three formulas, we obtain as a provable formula
$$\mathfrak{P}_{\mathfrak{r}}(u_{\mathfrak{i}}) \to \mathfrak{P}_{\mathfrak{r}}(u_{\mathrm{m}}) \,\&\, (y)(\mathfrak{E}(y, u_{\mathrm{m}}) \to \overline{\mathfrak{P}_{\mathfrak{r}}(y)}).$$

From this provability it follows that, if $\mathfrak{P}_{\mathfrak{r}}(u_{\mathfrak{i}})$ is a $T$-formula, then the consequent is also; and by virtue of the often mentioned commutativity of $T$, we get the assertion to be proved.

So now we have shown that all the axioms I–III and VII hold for our metamathematical model. By this, as already mentioned, the consistency of the system of these axioms is established in a constructive sense.

*Remark.* It may be noticed that it is possible also to show that the axioms IV and V are likewise satisfied for our model. But for our purpose this statement is not needed, since indeed the model $\mathfrak{M}$ can be established on the basis of the axioms I–III and VII.

**20. Elimination of one of the axioms III.** Among the axioms III one, as we found, is redundant, namely b(1). We give here its derivation from the other axioms III (without a(1)) and the extensionality axiom I(1) (using also some of the equality axioms.)

The assertion of b(1) is that there exists the class A of all unit sets. We have $A = B - \Gamma$ where B is the class of those sets which have at least one element, and $\Gamma$ the class of the sets with at least two different elements.

(1) We first observe that on the assumption of the existence of B and $\Gamma$ also $B - \Gamma$ exists by a(2), a(3); indeed it is the intersection of B with the complementary class of $\Gamma$. Furthermore the existence of B is immediate from b(2), c(2) and c(1). For, if E is the class required to exist by b(2), then B is the converse domain of E. So it will be sufficient to prove the existence of $\Gamma$.

(2) A set $c$ is an element of $\Gamma$, if and only if there exists a triplet $\langle\langle a, b\rangle, c\rangle$ such that $a \,\epsilon\, c$, $b \,\epsilon\, c$ and $a \neq b$. If $\Delta$ is the class of these triplets, then $\Gamma$ is the converse domain of $\Delta$. Thus the proof of the existence of $\Gamma$ reduces to the proof of the existence of $\Delta$. Now $\Delta$ can be characterized as an intersection of three classes of triplets $\langle\langle a, b\rangle, c\rangle$ : (1) those with arbitrary $a$ and $b \,\epsilon\, c$ (class $\Delta_1$), (2) those with arbitrary $b$ and $a \,\epsilon\, c$ (class $\Delta_2$), (3) those with arbitrary $c$ and $a \neq b$ (class $\Delta_3$). The existence of these three classes, under the provisional assumption of the existence of the class $\Theta$ of all pairs $\langle a, b\rangle$ with $a \neq b$, can be shown as follows: $\Delta_1$ results by coupling to left (c(3)) from the converse class (c(2)) of the class of triplets $\langle\langle b, c\rangle, a\rangle$ with $\langle b, c\rangle \,\eta\,$ E, which exists by b(3). $\Delta_2$ results from the class of triplets $\langle\langle c, a\rangle, b\rangle$, where $\langle c, a\rangle$ belongs to the converse class of E, which class of triplets exists by b(2), c(2), b(3); the passage from this class of triplets to $\Delta_2$ is by applying successively c(2), c(3), c(2), c(3). $\Delta_3$ exists by b(3) as the class of pairs whose first members belong to $\Theta$.

(3) So now it remains only to prove the existence of $\Theta$. By the axiom I(1) and some of the equality axioms, this class can be characterized as the class of the pairs $\langle a, b\rangle$ for which there exists a set $c$ such that either $c \,\epsilon\, a$ & $c \,\phi\, b$ or $c \,\phi\, a$ & $c \,\epsilon\, b$. Thus it is the sum of the classes of pairs $\langle a, b\rangle$ with a $c$ existing of the one kind or the other, respectively. Both these classes exist according to the composition lemma, applied for one to the converse class of E and to $\Phi - $E, where $\Phi$ is the class of all pairs, and for the other to the converse class of $\Phi - $E and to E. Note that the existence of $\Phi$ follows by applying b(3) to the class of all sets, which exists as the sum of the class E and its complement, also that the sum of any two classes is

the complement of the intersection of their complements, and finally that the composition lemma has been derived from the axioms a(3), b(3), c(1), c(2), c(3).[96] — So indeed b(1) can be spared.[97]

We add here the following remark: The axiom b(1) was especially used in Part I to prove the existence of the class of pairs $\langle a, b \rangle$ such that $a = b$; and there we observed that this derivation depended on our special definition of the ordered pair. Now we see that the existence of this class of pairs follows directly and without applying a definition of the ordered pair. Indeed the class in question is nothing else than $\Phi - \Theta$.

*Remark.* We showed how the models $\Pi_0$, $\Pi_1$, $\Pi_2$ can be constructed on a narrower axiomatic basis, in particular avoiding the use of the axiom whose independence is to be proved.

On this point Firestone in his review of Part VI[98] made the observation that generally, if we have a model, based on all the axioms of a system $\mathfrak{S}$, for the independence of a particular axiom $\mathfrak{A}$ from the set $\mathfrak{S}_0$ of the other axioms, then this independence follows under the condition of the consistency of $\mathfrak{S}_0$. For, on the assumption that the axiom $\mathfrak{A}$ is derivable from $\mathfrak{S}_0$, we should be able to construct our model also on the basis of $\mathfrak{S}_0$. In this model we should have the negation $\bar{\mathfrak{A}}$ of $\mathfrak{A}$, and on the other hand, since all axioms of $\mathfrak{S}_0$ are satisfied in the model and these (as is assumed) entail $\mathfrak{A}$, we should likewise have $\mathfrak{A}$. So a contradiction would follow from $\mathfrak{S}_0$.

From the point of view of deducibility this reasoning is of course sufficient. But we are interested not only in the statements of independence resulting from certain models, but also in the models themselves and in the method of their construction. In this respect the above indirect argument certainly cannot replace the second direct constructions of $\Pi_0$, $\Pi_1$, $\Pi_2$. Moreover we have there been able not only to avoid the use of the axiom to be proved independent, but also to obtain some further reductions (e.g. Vc is not used in $\Pi_0$, $\Pi_1$, $\Pi_2$).

Concerning our statement that Zermelo's axioms are satisfied by the system of $\Pi^*$-sets, the reviewer raised the question whether this agrees with

---

[96] See pp. 11–12.

[97] With regard to a remark made by Gödel (l.c., footnote 95, p. 7), it may be noticed that as a consequence of our preceding reasoning Gödel's axioms B7 and B8 are derivable from the axioms III without using b(1).

In fact Gödel's axioms B7 and B8 stand not only for our axiom III c(3), but also for c(2), as results from the derivability of B6 from B4, B5 and B8 stated by A. A. Markov in MARKOV (1948). On the other hand, it may be observed that upon assuming B6, which is the same as our c(2), Gödel's B7 is equivalent to our c(3); thus it follows that B8 is provable from B1–B7.

[98] FIRESTONE (1948).

Zermelo's assumption of "Urelemente" different from the null-set. From Zermelo's paper *Über Grenzzahlen und Mengenbereiche*[99] it appears however that Zermelo included the case in which the empty set is the only ,,Urelement". In fact he speaks of an ,,Einheitsbereich" as a possible kind of a model, although he intended that the axiom system for set theory in view of its applications should not exclude models with more "Urelemente".

## References

ACKERMANN, W. (1937) Die Widerspruchsfreiheit der allgemeinen Mengenlehre. *Math. Annalen* **114**, 305–315.

BOREL, E. (1898) *Leçons sur la théorie des fonctions.* Gauthiers Villars, Paris (1898). 2nd ed. (1914), 260 pp.; 3rd [4th] ed. (1928) [1950]. (Cf. *Math. Annalen* **60**, 194–195 (1905), and *Rev. du Mois* **1**, 248–250 (1906).)

CHURCH, A. (1927) Alternatives to Zermelo's assumption. *Trans. A.M.S.* **29**, 178–208.

CHURCH, A. (1956) *Introduction to mathematical logic—I.* Princeton University Press, Princeton, N.J., 376 pp.

DEDEKIND, R. (1888) *Was sind und was sollen die Zahlen?* 6th ed.: F. Vieweg & Sohn, Braunschweig (1930), 58 pp. Also in Dedekind (1930–1932) III. English ed. by W. W. Beman, in: *Essays on the theory of numbers* by R. Dedekind. Chicago and London (1901).

DEDEKIND, R. (1930–1932) *Gesammelte mathematische Werke.* R. Fricke, E. Noether and O. Ore (Eds.). 3 vols. F. Vieweg & Sohn, Braunschweig.

FINSLER, P. (1926) Über die Grundlegung der Mengenlehre—I. Teil. Die Mengen und ihre Axiome. *Math. Zeitschr.* **25**, 683–713.

FIRESTONE, C. D. (1948) Review of Bernays article: A system of axiomatic set theory—Part VI, *J.S.L.* **13**, 220–221.

FRAENKEL, A. A. (1922) Zu den Grundlagen der Cantor-Zermeloschen Mengenlehre. *Math. Annalen* **86**, 230–237. (Cf. already Jahresber. D.M.V. 30 p. 97 ital. (1921).)

FRAENKEL, A. A. (1922a) Über den Begriff "definit" und die Unabhängigkeit des Auswahlaxioms, *Sitzungsberichte der Preuss. Akademie d. Wiss.*, Phys.–Math. Klasse, pp. 253–257.

FRAENKEL, A. A. (1925) Untersuchungen über die Grundlagen der Mengenlehre. *Math. Zeitschr.* **22**, 250–273.

FRAENKEL, A. A. (1927) *Zehn Vorlesungen über die Grundlegung der Mengenlehre.* Springer, Berlin, 182 pp.

FRAENKEL, A. A. (1927a) Über die Gleichheitsbeziehung in der Mengenlehre. *J. f. Math.* **157**, 79–81.

FRAENKEL, A. A. (1928) *Einleitung in die Mengenlehre.* 3rd ed. Springer, Berlin, 424 pp. Reprinted (1964).

---

[99] ZERMELO (1930).

GÖDEL, K. (1940) *The consistency of the axiom of choice and of the generalized continuum hypothesis with the axioms of set theory.* Annals of Math. Studies, Vol. 3. Princeton University Press, Princeton, N.J., 66 pp. (2nd printing (1951), 74 pp.)

GRELLING, K. (1910) Die Axiome der Arithmetik. (Dissertation, Göttingen.)

HARTOGS, F. (1915) Über das Problem der Wohlordnung. *Math. Annalen* **76**, 438–443.

HASENJAEGER, G. (1953) Eine Bemerkung zu Henkin's Beweis für die Vollständigkeit des Prädikatenkalküls der ersten Stufe. *J.S.L.* **18**, 42–48.

HENKIN, L. (1949) The completeness of the first-order functional calculus. *J.S.L.* **14**, 159–166.

HESSENBERG, G. (1906) *Grundbegriffe der Mengenlehre.* (Abh. der Friesschen Schule, N.S. [1] Heft 4.) Göttingen, 220 pp.

HILBERT, D. and BERNAYS, P. (1934–1939) *Grundlagen der Mathematik* I (1934); II (1939). Springer, Berlin. 471; 498 pp. (2nd ed. (1968; 1970), 488; 575 pp.)

KLEENE, S. C. (1935) A theory of positive integers in formal logic. *American J. of Math.* **57**, 153–173, 219–244 (especially the passage from theorem 15-IV to 15-V, 220–221).

KÖNIG, J. (1905) Zum Kontinuum-Problem. *Math. Annalen* **60**.

KORSELT, A. (1911) Über einen Beweis des Äquivalenzsatzes. *Math. Annalen* **70**, 294–296.

KURATOWSKI, K. (1921) Sur la notion d'ordre dans la théorie des ensembles. *Fund. Math.* **2**, 161–171.

NEUMANN, J. VON (1925) Eine Axiomatisierung der Mengenlehre. *J. f. Math.* **154**, 219–240. Corrections, *ibid.* **155**, 128 (1926). Also in Von Neumann (1961) pp. 34–56.

NEUMANN, J. VON (1928) Die Axiomatisierung der Mengenlehre. *Math. Zeitschr.* **27**, 669–752. Also in Von Neumann (1961) pp. 339–422.

NEUMANN, J. VON (1928a) Über die Definition durch transfinite Induktionen und verwandte Fragen der allgemeinen Mengenlehre. *Math. Annalen* **99**, 373–391. Also in Von Neumann (1961) pp. 320–338. (Cf. Fraenkel (1928) pp. 392–393.)

NEUMANN, J. VON (1929) Über eine Widerspruchsfreiheitsfrage in der axiomatischen Mengenlehre. *J. f. Math.* **160**, 227–241. Also in Von Neumann (1961) pp. 494–508.

NEUMANN, J. VON (1929–1930) Allgemeine Eigenwerttheorie Hermitescher Funktionaloperatoren. *Math. Annalen* **102**, 49–131, in particular Kap. I and Anhang I therein.

NEUMANN, J. VON (1961) *Collected works,* Vol. I. Pergamon, New York. 654 pp.

NOVAK, I. L. (1948) A construction for models of consistent systems. Ph.D. thesis. Harvard.

NOVAK, I. L. (1951) A construction for models of consistent systems. *Fund. Math.* **37**, 87–110.

PÉTER, R. (1941) Review of O. Teichmüller (1939). *J.S.L.* **6** (1941), 65–66.

ROBINSON, R. M. (1937) The theory of classes. A modification of von Neumann's system. *J.S.L.* **2**, 69–72.

RUSSELL, B. (1906) On some difficulties in the theory of transfinite numbers and order types. *Proc. of the London Math. Soc.* **4** (2), 29–53.

SIERPINSKI, W. (1921) Une remarque sur la notion de l'ordre. *Fund. Math.* **2**, 199–200.

SKOLEM, Th. (1923) *Einige Bemerkungen zur axiomatischen Begründung der Mengenlehre.* Wiss. Vorträge gehalten auf dem 5. Kongress der Skandinav. Mathematiker in Helsingfors, pp. 217–232.

SPECKER, E. (1952) Habilitationsschrift.

SPECKER, E. (1957) Zur Axiomatik der Mengenlehre (Fundierungs- und Auswahlaxiom). *Zeitschr. f. math. Logik* **3**, 173–210.

STENIUS, E. (1952) Das Interpretationsproblem der formalisierten Zahlentheorie und ihre formale Widerspruchsfreiheit. *Acta Academiae Aboensis (Math. et Phys.)* **18** (3), Åbo Akademi, Åbo, 102 pp.

TARSKI, A. (1930) Fundamentale Begriffe der Methodologie der deduktiven Wissenschaften I, *Monatshefte für Mathematik und Physik* **37**, Satz I. 56, p. 394.

TEICHMÜLLER, O. (1939) Braucht der Algebraiker das Auswahlaxiom? *Deutsche Mathematik* **4**, 567–577.

ZERMELO, E. (1904) Beweis dass jede Menge wohlgeordnet werden kann. *Math. Annalen* **59**, 514–516. (Cf. A. Schoenflies, E. Borel, P. E. B. Jourdain (1905). *Math. Annalen* **60**, 181–186, 194–195, 465–470.)

ZERMELO, E. (1908) Neuer Beweis für die Wohlordnung. *Math. Annalen* **65**, 107–128.

ZERMELO, E. (1908a) Untersuchungen über die Grundlagen der Mengenlehre—I. *Math. Annalen* **65**, 261–281.

ZERMELO, E. (1909) Sur les ensembles finis et le principe de l'induction complète. *Acta Math.* **32**, 185–193.

ZERMELO, E. (1909a) Über die Grundlagen der Arithmetik. *Atti del IV Congresso Internationale del Matematici* (Roma, 6–11 aprile 1908). Vol. 2, pp. 8–11.

ZERMELO, E. (1930) Über Grenzzahlen und Mengenbereiche. *Fund. Math.* **16**, 29–47.

ZORN, M. (1935) A remark on methods in transfinite algebra. *Bulletin of the A.M.S.* **41**, 667–670.

SETS AND CLASSES; On the work by Paul Bernays
North-Holland Publishing Company (1976) pp. 121–172.

# ON THE PROBLEM OF SCHEMATA OF INFINITY
# IN AXIOMATIC SET THEORY*

Paul BERNAYS

*Zurich, Switzerland*

## Introduction

Zermelo's set theory was substantially extended in 1921 when Fraenkel added his axiom of replacement to the original axioms; for it is this axiom which enables Cantor's general summation process to be carried out. This process is not restricted to forming the union of the elements of a set and its use is essential in proving the existence of cardinalities: together with the axiom of union, general summation provides the limiting process which is used to produce cardinalities. In this way the addition of the axiom of replacement to Zermelo's set theory leads to that immense rise of cardinalities which can be bounded only by "inaccessible" ordinals. It is known that those initial ordinals which we call inaccessible can be completely characterized within the framework of the theory of ordinals. First, we call a limit ordinal $\alpha$ an "irreducible limit" if it can be expressed in the form

$$\alpha = \lim_{k < \lambda} \eta_k \quad \text{(with an increasing sequence } \eta_k)$$

only if $\lambda = \alpha$. Now the inaccessible ordinals can be characterized as those irreducible limits which are at the same time the limit of a sequence of irreducible limits.

Zermelo's concept of a *Grenzzahl* represents a strengthening of the concept "inaccessible ordinal". A *Grenzzahl* can be defined as an inaccessible ordinal $\alpha$ with the property that for each smaller ordinal the cardinality of its set of subsets is less than that of $\alpha$. Tarski uses the term "inaccessible in the strict sense" (*strongly inaccessible*) for the cardinals

---

* Partially revised version of the article "Zur Frage der Unendlichkeitsschemata in der axiomatischen Mengenlehre", in: *Essays on the Foundations of Mathematics*, dedicated to Prof. A. A. Fraenkel (Magnes Press, Jerusalem, 1966) pp. 3–49. Printed by permission of the publisher. Translated into English by J. Bell and M. Plänitz.

associated with *Grenzzahlen*; in fact he introduced this term independently of Zermelo.[1] (In view of the well-ordering theorem, cardinals can
be identified with the corresponding initial ordinals.)

We can dispense with the distinction between ordinals inaccessible in
the wide and in the strict sense if we adopt Cantor's Aleph-Hypothesis
(Generalized Continuum Hypothesis), which automatically makes every
inaccessible ordinal in the weak sense inaccessible in the strict sense. It is
well known that Gödel has demonstrated the consistency of the generalized continuum hypothesis with the axioms of Zermelo–Fraenkel set
theory, assuming that the latter are themselves consistent.

A strong method of introducing inaccessible ordinals was formulated
by MAHLO [1911–1913]. His principle may be expressed as follows: any
unbounded sequence of ordinals (i.e. a sequence which exceeds every
ordinal) has at least one initial segment which tends to an irreducible limit
(i.e. to a "$\pi_0$-number", as Mahlo calls it).

This principle gives rise to an extensive hierarchy of inaccessible
ordinals. But the hierarchy does not lead to something definite. This is
apparent from the fact that each of the inaccessible ordinals thus obtained
satisfies a certain restrictive condition, namely, it can be expressed in
the form $\text{Lim}_{k<\lambda} \eta_k$ in such a way that no initial segment of the sequence
$\eta_k$ ($k < \lambda$) tends to an irreducible limit. The inaccessible ordinals which
Mahlo calls "$\rho_0$-numbers" are characterized by the opposite property: an
irreducible limit $\alpha$ is called a $\rho_0$-number if each increasing sequence of
ordinals which tends to $\alpha$ has an initial segment tending to an irreducible
limit. The transition from $\pi_0$-numbers to $\rho_0$-numbers can be iterated, thus
engendering a transfinite sequence of higher and higher types of inaccessible ordinals ($\tau_\nu$-numbers, $\nu = 0, 1, \ldots, \omega, \ldots$).

The following schema, due to LÉVY [1960], is equivalent to Mahlo's
principle:

(I)          $(Eu)[\text{Scm}^{\text{ZF}}(u) \wedge (x_1) \cdots (x_n)(x_1 \in u \wedge \cdots$

$\wedge x_n \in u. \rightarrow .A \leftrightarrow \text{Rel}(u,A))].$

Here A is a formula whose only free variables are $x_1, \ldots, x_n$, Rel $(u,A)$
denotes the expression which is obtained from A by "relativizing with
respect to $u$", i.e. by replacing each component $(x)P(x)$ (with a bound
variable $x$) by $(x)(x \in u \rightarrow P(x))$ and each component $(Ex)P(x)$ by $(Ex)$
$(x \in u \wedge P(x))$. And $\text{Scm}^{\text{ZF}}(u)$, read "the set $u$ is a standard complete
model for ZF", means that the set $u$ together with the basic relation $\in$

---

[1] For historical background cf. ZERMELO [1930] and TARSKI [1938]; cf. especially
Footnotes 1–3. Deviating from the above definition, Zermelo includes $\omega$ among the
*Grenzzahlen*, and Tarski includes it among the cardinals inaccessible in the strict sense.

forms a model of Zermelo–Fraenkel set theory (without the axiom of choice) and that $u$ satisfies the transitivity condition $(x)(y)$ $(x \in y \wedge y \in u \to x \in u)$. (A more detailed explanation of the expression $\text{Scm}^{\text{ZF}}(u)$ is not needed in the sequel.)

LÉVY [1958], in his dissertation, cast the schema in the following form

(II)        $(x)(A(x) \to (Ey)(x \in y \wedge \text{Scm}^{\text{ZF}}(y) \wedge \text{Rel}(y,A)))$,

where $x$ is the only free variable of $A(x)$. He also considered the restricted schema

(III)        $A \to (Ey)(\text{Scm}^{\text{ZF}}(y) \wedge \text{Rel}(y,A))$,

where A contains no free variables. Notice that (I) is stronger than (II) in two respects: Namely, in (I) the existential quantifier precedes the universal one and, moreover, the conditional is replaced by an equivalence.

Lévy makes the following remarks in connection with schema (I). If instead of the system ZF we use the system $S$, consisting of the axioms of extensionality, subsets, pairing, union, power set and foundation, then the adjunction of a certain weaker version of schema (I), containing the condition $\text{Scm}^S(u)$ in place of $\text{Scm}^{\text{ZF}}(u)$, is equivalent to adding the axioms of infinity and replacement.

In Lévy's schemata two methods of strengthening the deductive machinery are formalized: the model-theoretic reference by the term $\text{Scm}^{\text{ZF}}(u)$, and the procedure of relativizing a proposition (or a predicate) A with respect to a variable not occurring in A.

The object of our discussion is to demonstrate that by sufficiently refining the relativizing procedure we can eliminate the model-theoretic reference in the axiom schema, and Lévy's schema will get its full efficiency only by suitably extending the logical frame. The schema will then be sufficient to establish even the stronger versions of Mahlo's postulates.

We start with form (III) of the schema, replacing the strong and complex condition $\text{Scm}^{\text{ZF}}(y)$ by the relatively weak one Trans $(y)$ (read "$y$ is transitive"), where Trans is defined by

Trans $(a) \leftrightarrow (u)(v)(u \in v \wedge v \in a \to u \in a)$,

so that the schema reads

$A \to (Ey)(\text{Trans}(y) \wedge \text{Rel}(y,A))$.

The meaning of the schema is that each assertion satisfied by the whole universe of sets is already satisfied within a suitably chosen set (i.e. chosen in dependence of the assertion). The problem now is to determine the logico-axiomatic framework within which the schema is to be employed. Initially we shall take a modest framework and later extend it in two ways.

**1.** First we describe our underlying logico-axiomatic system. Its logical formalism is that of the usual predicate logic. In its formulas we distinguish between free and bound variables by using the letters $a$, $b$, $c$, $d$, $f$, $g$, $h$, $k$, $l$, $m$, $n$, $p$, $q$, $r$ for the former type and $t$, $u$, $v$, $w$, $x$, $y$, $z$ or $u_1, u_2, \ldots$ for the latter. The symbols for the propositional operations (conjunction, disjunction, negation, conditional, biconditional) are $\wedge$, $\vee$, $\neg$, $\rightarrow$, $\leftrightarrow$; the quantifiers are written $(x)$, $(Ex)$. Starting with a formula $A(c)$, in which $c$ is free and the bound variable $x$ does not occur, quantification allows us to construct the formula $(x)A(x)$ or $(Ex)A(x)$. The deductive rules are the ones customary for the propositional and predicate calculi.[1] As for atomic formulas, we shall initially use only those of the form $a \in b$ or $a = b$, where $a$ and $b$ are terms; the negation of $a \in b$, $a = b$ will, as usual, be denoted by $a \notin b$, $a \neq b$. We admit the following terms: the free variables, $\iota$-terms of the type $\iota_x A(x)$, and terms obtained from explicit definitions of symbols for individuals and functions. We also introduce predicates by explicit definition.

For equality we have the usual schema

(1) $$a = b \rightarrow (A(a) \rightarrow A(b)),$$

for the $\iota$-symbol the schema ("$\iota$-schema")

(2a) $$A(c) \wedge (x)(A(x) \rightarrow x = c) \rightarrow c = \iota_x A(x)$$

(2b) $$a \in \iota_x A(x) \rightarrow (Ex)(A(x) \wedge (z)(A(z) \rightarrow z = x)).$$

For each formula $A(c)$ which does not contain the bound variable $x$, we shall admit $\iota_x A(x)$ as a term.

Explicit definitions will be made by means of defining axioms which are transparent in the sense that the newly introduced symbols can obviously be eliminated.

We have already introduced Trans $(c)$ as a defined predicate. We now give the usual

DEFINITION. $a \subseteq b \leftrightarrow (x)(x \in a \rightarrow x \in b)$,

from which we immediately obtain

$$a \subseteq a$$

as also

$$a \subseteq b \wedge b \subseteq c \rightarrow a \subseteq c.$$

[1] Cf. BERNAYS [1958], pp. 47–48.

In set theory the equality schema is supplemented by the *axiom of extensionality.*[1]

(3)  $$(x)(x \in a \leftrightarrow x \in b) \rightarrow a = b$$

from which, in particular, the formula $a = a$ can be deduced.

The following will serve as set theoretic existence axioms: the *axiom of pairing* in the form

(4)  $$(Ex)(a \in x \wedge b \in x)$$

and the *axiom of subsets* (Aussonderungsaxiom) in the form of a schema

(5)  $$(Ex)(z)(z \in x. \leftrightarrow .z \in a \wedge A(z)),$$

where we assume that $A(c)$ is a formula. (If the expression (5) as well as $A(c)$ is to be a formula, then the variable $x$ must not occur in $A(z)$.)

The application of (5) to the formula $c \notin a$ as $A(c)$ yields

(6)  $$(Ex)(z)(z \notin x) \quad \text{(existence of an "empty" set)}$$

(Incidentally, we can also obtain this formula from clause (2b) of the $\iota$-schema by substituting the formula $c \in c \wedge c \notin c$ for $A(c)$.)

From the

DEFINITION.  $0 = \iota_x(z)(z \notin x)$

we obtain the formula

(6a)  $$b \notin 0.$$

We now apply (4) and (5) and make the

DEFINITION.  $[a,b] = \iota_x(z)(z \in x. \leftrightarrow .z = a \vee z = b).$

Using also (1)–(3) we obtain:

(7)  $$a \in [a,b], \quad b \in [a,b]$$
$$c \in [a,b] \leftrightarrow c = a \vee c = b.$$

Introducing the

DEFINITION.  $[c] = [c,c],$

we also deduce

(8)  $$a \in [a], \quad c \in [a] \leftrightarrow c = a.$$

---

[1] It has been pointed out, particularly by Fraenkel, that it is possible to dispense with the axiom of extensionality by introducing an explicit definition of equality. However, in what follows, and especially in the application of the operation Rel, it will be simpler to retain equality as a basic predicate. Yet finally we shall return to the method of defining equality.

We can now define the ordered pair in the usual way, following Kuratowski, by the

DEFINITION. $\langle a,b \rangle = [[a],[a,b]]$.

We deduce that

(9) $$\langle a,b \rangle = \langle c,d \rangle \to a = c \wedge b = d.$$

Making still the

DEFINITION. $a \cap b = \iota_x(z)(z \in x \leftrightarrow z \in a \wedge z \in b)$,

and applying (5), we obtain

(10) $$c \in a \cap b \leftrightarrow c \in a \wedge c \in b.$$

We next add as an axiom-schema (in a somewhat extended sense) the simplified form of Lévy's *reflection schema*

(11) $$A \to (Ey)(\text{Trans}(y) \wedge \text{Rel}(y,A)),$$

where A is a formula. (For (11) also to be a formula A must not contain the variable y.) "Rel" signifies the relativization process described in the introduction. However, the application of this process shall be restricted to *reduced formulas*, i.e. to formulas which do not contain occurrences of the $\iota$-symbol or any defined symbol. Nevertheless, in order to avoid any restriction in the statement of the schema, we agree that for an unreduced formula A we shall identify $\text{Rel}(b,A)$ with the expression $\text{Rel}(b,A_1)$ for some reduced formula $A_1$ which is provably equivalent to A. Such a formula $A_1$ can be obtained from A in each case by eliminating the defined symbols and $\iota$-terms.

We begin with the following observation: Taking for A in the reflection schema the formula

$$(Ex)(x = a) \wedge (Ex)(x = b)$$

which is derivable from $a = a$, we get

$$(Ey)(\text{Trans}(y) \wedge (Ex)(x \in y \wedge x = a) \wedge (Ex)(x \in y \wedge x = b))$$

and hence, using $(Ex)(x \in c \wedge x = a) \to a \in c$,

$$(Ey)(a \in y \wedge b \in y).$$

Thus the axiom of pairing (4) is derivable by the reflection schema from $a = a$ and hence from the axiom of extensionality (3).[1]

[1] In the original version of the paper the derivation of the pairing axiom by the reflection schema was not so immediate. That it goes so simply has been observed by K. Gloede.

For further applications of the reflection schema we go on with the following consideration. If $F$ is a provable formula, then the formula $A \to A \wedge F$ is also provable for any formula A; hence we obtain from schema (11), provided the variable $y$ occurs neither in A nor in F,

$$A \to (Ey)(\text{Trans}\,(y) \wedge \text{Rel}\,(y, A \wedge F)).$$

Since Rel $(y, A \wedge F)$ is Rel $(y, A) \wedge$ Rel $(y, F)$, we have the derivable schema

(11a)          $A \to (Ey)(\text{Trans}\,(y) \wedge \text{Rel}\,(y, A) \wedge \text{Rel}\,(y, F)).$

For a sequence of $r$ provable formulas $F_1, \ldots, F_r$ we have analogously:

(11b)     $A \to (Ey)(\text{Trans}\,(y) \wedge \text{Rel}\,(y, A) \wedge \text{Rel}\,(y, F_1) \wedge \cdots \wedge \text{Rel}\,(y, F_r)).$

Our first application of this is made by substituting in (11a) for F the formula $(Ex)(a \in x)$ which is deducible from (3), using (11). Rel $(b, (Ex)(a \in x))$ is the formula $(Ex)(x \in b \wedge a \in x)$; moreover we have

$$\text{Trans}\,(b) \wedge (Ex)(x \in b \wedge a \in x) \to a \in b.$$

Thus it follows from (11a) that

(11c)          $A \to (Ey)(\text{Trans}\,(y) \wedge a \in y \wedge \text{Rel}\,(y, A))$

This yields in particular

$$(Ey)(\text{Trans}\,(y) \wedge a \in y).$$

But we have

$$\text{Trans}\,(b) \wedge a \in b \to (c \in d \wedge d \in a \to c \in b).$$

Hence we obtain

(12)          $(Ey)(z)((Ev)(z \in v \wedge v \in a) \to z \in y).$

But this formula, together with

$$(Ex)(z)(z \in x. \leftrightarrow .z \in b \wedge (Ev)(z \in v \wedge v \in a)),$$

which follows from the axiom of subsets (5), implies by means of the predicate calculus

(12a)          $(Ex)(z)(z \in x \leftrightarrow (Ev)(z \in v \wedge v \in a)),$

which represents the *axiom of union*. This axiom can thus be deduced from schema (11) and the axioms (4) and (5). If we introduce the

DEFINITION.  $\sum (a) = \iota_x(z)(z \in x \leftrightarrow (Ev)(z \in v \wedge v \in a)),$

then we obtain from (12a) by means of the $\iota$-schema and the axiom of extensionality (3):

(12b) $$c \in \sum (a) \leftrightarrow (Ev)(c \in v \wedge v \in a).$$

If in (12a) we substitute the term $[a,b]$ for $a$, then on using (7) and (1), we obtain:

$$(Ex)(z)(z \in x \leftrightarrow z \in a \vee z \in b).$$

Further by introducing the

DEFINITION.   $a \cup b = \iota_x(z)(z \in x \leftrightarrow z \in a \vee z \in b)$

we obtain with application of the axiom of extensionality (3) and the $\iota$-schema (2):

(13) $$c \in a \cup b \leftrightarrow c \in a \vee c \in b.$$

In (11c), let us now replace A by the formula

$$(u)(Ev)(z)(z \in v \leftrightarrow z = u),$$

which is provable from (8). In this case Rel$(b,A)$ is the formula

$$(u)(u \in b \rightarrow (Ev)(v \in b \wedge (z)(z \in b. \rightarrow .z \in v \leftrightarrow z = u))),$$

and by observing that generally an expression $B \rightarrow (C \leftrightarrow D)$ can be transformed by the propositional calculus into $B \wedge C \leftrightarrow B \wedge D$, we see that we can deduce, by means of the definition of Trans and the schema of equality:

Trans $(b) \wedge$ Rel $(b,A) \rightarrow (u)(u \in b \rightarrow (Ev)(v \in b \wedge (z)(z \in v \leftrightarrow z = u)))$.

Besides, substituting in our application of (11c) the symbol 0 for $a$, we obtain by means of (8) and (3):

$$A \rightarrow (Ey)(\text{Trans}\,(y) \wedge 0 \in y \wedge (u)(u \in y \rightarrow (Ev)(v \in y \wedge v = [u]))),$$

and in view of the provability of A we infer from this, by applying (1):

(14) $$(Ey)(0 \in y \wedge (u)(u \in y \rightarrow [u] \in y)).$$

But this is the formula for *Zermelo's axiom of infinity*. Similarly, if in (11c) we replace A by the formula

$$(u)(Ev)(z)(z \in v \leftrightarrow z \in u \vee z = u),$$

which can be deduced from (8) and (13), we obtain the formula

(15) $$(Ey)(0 \in y \wedge (u)(u \in y \rightarrow u \cup [u] \in y)).$$

Let us now make the

DEFINITION.

$$\omega = \iota_x(z)(z \in x \leftrightarrow (v)(0 \in v \wedge (u)(u \in v \rightarrow u \cup [u] \in v). \rightarrow .z \in v)).$$

In the same way as we derived (12b) from (12) via (12a) and the definition of $\Sigma(a)$, we deduce

$$c \in \omega \leftrightarrow (v)(0 \in v \wedge (u)(u \in v \rightarrow u \cup [u] \in v) \rightarrow c \in v),$$

whence

$$(15a) \quad \begin{array}{l} 0 \in \omega, \qquad a \in \omega \rightarrow a \cup [a] \in \omega \\ 0 \in b \wedge (u)(u \in b \rightarrow u \cup [u] \in b). \rightarrow .\omega \subseteq b. \end{array}$$

We have thus shown that the axioms of pairing, of union and of infinity can be deduced from our set-theoretic axioms (3) and (5) (the schemata (1) and (2) indeed, belonging to logic) by means of the reflection schema (11). Let us now examine more closely how we can obtain strengthened versions of the reflection schema by applying itself. This "self-strengthening" of the schema, so to speak, has been observed already when we deduced the schemata (11a), (11b), and (11c).

In (11b) let us replace $F_1$ by the formula

$$(u)(v)(Ex)(z)(z \in x \leftrightarrow z = u \vee z = v)$$

which is obtained from the formula $(u)(v)(Ex)(x = [u,v])$ by means of (7). Rel $(b,F_1)$ then becomes (by a propositional transformation already used just now):

$$(u)(v)(u \in b \wedge v \in b \rightarrow (Ex)(x \in b$$
$$\wedge (z)(z \in b \wedge z \in x \leftrightarrow z \in b \wedge (z = u \vee z = v))))$$

and Trans $(b) \wedge$ Rel $(b,F_1)$ becomes

$$\text{Trans } (b) \wedge (u)(v)(u \in b \wedge v \in b \rightarrow (Ex)(x \in b$$
$$\wedge (z)(z \in x \leftrightarrow z = u \vee z = v))),$$

from which we deduce by means of (7), (3), and (1):

$$\text{Trans } (b) \wedge (u)(v)(u \in b \wedge v \in b \rightarrow [u,v] \in b).$$

Thus in (11b), we obtain as a conjunct in place of Rel $(y,F_1)$, the expression

$$(u)(v)(u \in y \wedge v \in y \rightarrow [u,v] \in y),$$

and this means that the axiom of pairing holds for the range of the elements of $y$.

Similarly, in (11b) let us replace $F_2$ by the formula

$$(u)(Ex)(z)(z \in x \leftrightarrow (Ev)(z \in v \wedge v \in u)),$$

which can be deduced from (12a) by quantifying over the free variable $a$. Then if we make the same substitution for $F_2$ in Trans $(b) \wedge$ Rel $(b, F_2)$, and apply (12b), (3), and (1), we find that in (11b) the conjunct Rel $(y, F_2)$ can be replaced by

$$(u)\left(u \in y \to \sum (u) \in y\right),$$

which says that the axiom of union is satisfied in the range of elements of $y$.

As in the derivation of (11c), we can also insert the conjunct $a \in y$ in (11b); if we now substitute $[a, \omega]$ for $a$, and observe that

$$\text{Trans } (b) \wedge [a, \omega] \in b \to a \in b \wedge \omega \in b,$$

we obtain in (11b) the conjuncts $a \in y, \omega \in y$.

Let us now make the

DEFINITION.

$$\text{Mod}_0 (b) \leftrightarrow (u)(v)\left(u \in b \wedge v \in b \to [u, v] \in b \wedge \sum (u) \in b\right) \wedge \omega \in b.$$

$\text{Mod}_0 (b)$ says that the range of elements of $b$ satisfies the axiom of pairing and union and contains $\omega$ as an element.

In this way we obtain the following strengthened reflection schema

(11d)     $A \to (Ey)(\text{Trans } (y) \wedge \text{Mod}_0 (y) \wedge a \in y \wedge \text{Rel } (y, A)).$

Of course in (11d) we may still insert conjuncts of the form Rel $(y, F)$ within the scope of the existential quantifier $(Ey)$, where F is any provable reduced formula.

Let us also point out that, quite independently of the reflection principle, the range of elements of any transitive set satisfies the axiom of extensionality, provided that the underlying set theory satisfies it. For we have

$$\text{Trans } (b) \to (u)(v)(u \in b \wedge v \in b \wedge$$
$$(z)(z \in b \to (z \in u \leftrightarrow z \in v). \to .(z)(z \in u \leftrightarrow z \in v))).$$

**2.** The results of our previous discussion are merely a beginning. True, we have already seen that the reflection schema makes a number of axioms superfluous, and we have also demonstrated its "self-strengthening" character. Nonetheless in the mode of applications used up to now, the power of the reflection schema is still restricted. As we said in the introduction, the schema is meant to express the fact that each proposition about the total universe of sets is already satisfied within the range of elements of a suitably chosen set. But the schema formalizes this idea only for those propositions which are expressed by proper formulas, as opposed to schemata. If the requirement is to be extended to properties which are expressed by schemata, then we need to enlarge our formal system in such a say as to enable us to replace schemata by formulas. Certainly, this is not necessary for the schemata of logical deduction, but we must replace those schemata which we use as set-theoretic axioms, i.e. the axioms of subsets and replacement.

The usual method of transforming schemata into formulas is to introduce predicate or class variables, i.e. first free variables of this type together with a corresponding substitution rule. We shall use here class variables.

The relation between classes and predicates (as extensions of classes) is formalized by introducing "class terms" $\{x/A(x)\}$, where $A(x)$ is the expression obtained from the formula $A(c)$ by replacing the free variable $c$ by a bound variable $x$ which does not occur in $A(c)$. Generally by a class term we mean either a free-class variable—we take for these variables the letters $A$, $B$, $C$, $D$, $F$, $G$, $H$—or an expression of the form $\{x/A(x)\}$ ("the class of $x$ for which $A(x)$ holds").

The atomic formulas to be added to the previous ones in conjunction with the introduction of class terms will be restricted to those of the form $a \in B$, where $a$ is a set term and $B$ a class term. As a rule of deduction, we have that for a free-class variable an arbitrary class term can be substituted. Moreover, for class terms $\{x/A(x)\}$ we have the *comprehension schema*

(16) $$c \in \{x/A(x)\} \leftrightarrow A(c).$$

There are some definitions immediately connected with the introduction of class terms. Corresponding to the set predicate $a \subseteq b$ we introduce "$A \subseteq B$" by

DEFINITION.    $A \subseteq B \leftrightarrow (x)(x \in A \rightarrow x \in B)$.

The predicates $a \subseteq B$ and $A \subseteq b$ are defined similarly. Equality of classes is specified by the

DEFINITION.    $A \equiv B \leftrightarrow A \subseteq B \wedge B \subseteq A$.

Analogously we make the

DEFINITION.    $a \equiv B \leftrightarrow a \subseteq B \wedge B \subseteq a$,

which means that the set $a$ has the same elements as the class $B$. We then say that the class $B$ is *represented* by the set $a$.

Class equality will be used particularly for formulating definitions of (function) symbols expressing the dependence of classes on sets or classes.

Each set can be associated with the class $a^*$ of its elements:

DEFINITION.   $a^* \equiv \{x \,/\, x \in a\}$.

Thus $a^*$ is a class term for which we always have $a \equiv a^*$. Accordingly, each set represents a class.

We define the union and intersection of classes in the customary fashion:

DEFINITION.   $A \cup B \equiv \{x \,/\, (x \in A \lor x \in B)\}$,
$$A \cap B \equiv \{x \,/\, (x \in A \land x \in B)\}.$$

From these definitions one obtains the usual Boolean identities governing $\cap$, $\cup$, $\subseteq$, $\equiv$. Moreover, it follows from the definitions of $a \cap b$ and $a \cup b$ that

(17)                    $a \cap b \equiv a^* \cap b^*$,      $a \cup b \equiv a^* \cup b^*$.

The introduction of class terms and the associated substitution rule and comprehension schema allow axiom schemata to be replaced by formulas. This is immediate in the case of the equality schema (1); in fact (1) becomes a theorem if we take the formula

(1′)                          $a = b \to (a \in C \to b \in C)$

as our axiom of equality.[1]

By using a class variable we can express the axiom of subsets in the form

(5′)                          $(Ex)(z)(z \in x \leftrightarrow z \in a \land z \in C)$

which is equivalent to (5). From this we obtain at once the pair of formulas

(5a)                          $(Ex)(x \equiv a^* \cap C)$

(5b)                          $B \subseteq a \to (Ex)(x \equiv B)$.

In view of (5a) we can define the intersection of a class and a set as a *set*:

DEFINITION.   $a \cap B = \iota_x (x \equiv a^* \cap B)$.

We now focus our attention on the axiom of replacement. Our aim is to express this axiom as a formula; to achieve this, we require a number of definitions concerning the notion of a function. We shall think of

---

[1] If we wanted, we could reduce the $\iota$-symbol to a class operator $\iota(A)$, thus enabling us to rewrite the $\iota$-schema (2) in terms of formulas. However, this would be of little use for our purpose. It is known that the quantifiers can also be reduced to class operators; cf. especially FEYS [1944], pp. 49–50.

functions as special classes of ordered pairs. If a class of this kind is represented by a set then we call it a *functional set*. The formal definition of a class of pairs, i.e. the class predicate "*A* is a class of pairs", and correspondingly, of a set of pairs, of a function and a functional set, are as follows:

DEFINITION.   $Pr(A) \leftrightarrow (x)(x \in A \rightarrow (Eu)(Ev)(x = \langle u,v \rangle))$,

$Pr(c) \leftrightarrow Pr(c^*)$,

$Fu(A) \leftrightarrow Pr(A) \wedge (u)(v)(w)(\langle u,v \rangle \in A \wedge \langle u,w \rangle \in A$
$\rightarrow v = w)$,

$Fu(f) \leftrightarrow Fu(f^*)$.

The concepts *domain* and *co-domain* refer to classes of pairs and in particular to functions, but we shall give definitions applicable to arbitrary classes.

DEFINITION.   $dom_1 (C) \equiv \{u / (Ev)(\langle u,v \rangle \in C)\}$,

$dom_2 (C) \equiv \{v / (Eu)(\langle u,v \rangle \in C)\}$.

We now formulate the axiom of replacement as follows.

(18)      $Fu (A) \wedge (Ex)(x \equiv dom_1 (A)) \rightarrow (Ex)(x \equiv dom_2 (A))$.

We derive this formula with the aid of the reflection schema. However, we use for this another version of the axiom of replacement which has been formulated as a schema in a recent paper by THIELE [1955]. His schema is equivalent to the following formula at applying class variables:

(19)      $(x)(x \in m \rightarrow (Ez)(\langle x,z \rangle \in A)). \rightarrow .(Ey)(x)(x \in m$
$\rightarrow (Ez)(z \in y \wedge \langle x,z \rangle \in A))$.

In order to establish the derivability of (18) from (19) it is sufficient to show that the formula $(Ex)(x \equiv dom_2 (A))$ can be derived from the formulas $Fu (A)$ and $m \equiv dom_1 (A)$, using (19) and taking $m$ and $A$ as fixed parameters. We proceed as follows.

From the formula $m \equiv dom_1 (A)$ we get, by the definition of $dom_1$, the first part of (19); hence we obtain

$$(Ey)(x)(x \in m \rightarrow (Ez)(z \in y \wedge \langle x,z \rangle \in A)).$$

Indicating this formula briefly by "$(Ey)B(y)$" we have

(a)      $B(b). \rightarrow .a \in m \rightarrow (Ez)(z \in b \wedge \langle a,z \rangle \in A)$.

By the definition of $dom_2 (A)$ it follows that

(b)      $c \in dom_2 (A) \rightarrow (Ex)(\langle x,c \rangle \in A)$.

From $m \equiv \mathrm{dom}_1(A)$ and the definition of $\mathrm{dom}_1$ we obtain

(c)                    $\langle a,c \rangle \in A \to a \in m,$

and from $\mathrm{Fu}(A)$:

$$\langle a,c \rangle \in A \wedge \langle a,d \rangle \in A \to c = d,$$

as also, by applying the axiom of equality:

$$\langle a,c \rangle \in A \wedge \langle a,d \rangle \in A \wedge d \in b \to c \in b,$$

and hence

(d)          $\langle a,c \rangle \in A \wedge (Ez)(\langle a,z \rangle \in A \wedge z \in b) \to c \in b.$

The formulas $(a)$, $(c)$, and $(d)$ yield

$$\mathrm{B}(b) \to (\langle a,c \rangle \in A \to c \in b),$$

and hence

$$\mathrm{B}(b). \to .(Ex)(\langle x,c \rangle \in A) \to c \in b.$$

From this and $(b)$ we infer

$$\mathrm{B}(b) \to (c \in \mathrm{dom}_2(A) \to c \in b)$$

and so

$$\mathrm{B}(b) \to \mathrm{dom}_2(A) \subseteq b.$$

Using the consequence (5b) of the axiom of subsets we infer

$$\mathrm{B}(b) \to (Ex)(x \equiv \mathrm{dom}_2(A)).$$

We thus obtain the required formula $(Ex)(x \equiv \mathrm{dom}_2(A))$ from the formula $(Ey)\mathrm{B}(y)$ which has already been established.

The assertion expressed by (19) is more general than the axiom of replacement. It does not seem possible to derive (19) from (18) without using the axiom of choice, in fact using a version of the axiom of choice stronger than Zermelo's. Our problem is to derive (19) with the aid of the reflection schema. This schema is now extended in as much as we also allow formulas A which contain class variables to occur in it. In this connection, we introduce an extra restriction on reduced formulas, namely, that they should not contain any terms of the form $\{x/A(x)\}$. As before, we shall accept schema (11) for non-reduced formulas A; but Rel $(b,A)$ will be interpreted as Rel $(b,A_1)$, where $A_1$ is a reduced formula (in the new sense) which is provably equivalent to A.

In order to derive (19) we apply the reflection schema in the form (11c), substituting therein $m$ for $a$ and taking for A the formula

$$(x)(x \in m \to (Ez)(\langle x,z \rangle \in A)),$$

which may briefly be denoted by "G", so that we get

(e) $\qquad G \rightarrow (Ey)(\text{Trans}\,(y) \wedge m \in y \wedge \text{Rel}\,(y,G))$.

Within Rel $(y,G)$ we have to eliminate the symbol of the ordered pair by means of its definition (which in turn involves the symbols $[a]$, $[a,b]$). In place of an expression $\langle p,q \rangle \in c$, we thus obtain

$$(Eu)(Ev)(Ew)[p \in u \wedge p \in v \wedge q \in v \wedge (t)(t \in u \rightarrow t = p) \wedge$$
$$\wedge\,(t)(t \in v \rightarrow t = p \vee t = q) \wedge u \in w \wedge v \in w$$
$$\wedge\,(t)(t \in w \rightarrow t = u \vee t = v) \wedge w \in c\,];$$

and in place of G we get

$$(x)(x \in m \rightarrow (Ez)(Eu)(Ev)(Ew)[x \in u \wedge x \in v \wedge z \in v \wedge$$
$$(t)(t \in u \rightarrow t = x) \wedge (t)(t \in v \rightarrow t = x \vee t = z) \wedge u \in w$$
$$\wedge\,v \in w \wedge (t)(t \in w \rightarrow t = u \vee t = v) \wedge w \in A\,]).$$

If we now relativize this last expression to $b$, then the expressions $z \in b$, $u \in b$, $v \in b$, $w \in b$ will appear as components of conjunctions within the scope of the existential quantifiers, and $x \in b$, $t \in b$ will appear as the antecedents of implications within the scope of the universal quantifiers $(x)$, $(t)$.

However, upon the premises Trans $(b)$ and $m \in b$ we can suppress the antecedents $x \in b$ and $t \in b$, and likewise we can omit the conjuncts $u \in b$, $v \in b$. If, after doing this, we reinstate the symbol for the ordered pair, we obtain

Trans $(b) \wedge m \in b \wedge \text{Rel}\,(b,G) \rightarrow$
$$\rightarrow (x)(x \in m \rightarrow (Ez)(Ew)(z \in b \wedge w \in b \wedge w = \langle x,z \rangle \wedge w \in A)).$$

From this by application of the axiom of equality $(1')$ and the predicate calculus we get the formula

$(Ey)(\text{Trans}\,(y) \wedge m \in y \wedge \text{Rel}\,(y,G)) \rightarrow$
$$\rightarrow (Ey)(x)(x \in m \rightarrow (Ez)(z \in y \wedge \langle x,z \rangle \in A)),$$

which, together with (e) immediately gives (19).

Thus, we have derived the axiom of replacement from the reflection schema.

A particular consequence of the axiom of replacement is that, if $a$ is a set, then both the domain and the co-domain of $a^*$ are represented by sets. We can therefore define

$$\text{dom}_1\,(a) = \iota_x(x \equiv \text{dom}_1\,(a^*)),$$
$$\text{dom}_2\,(a) = \iota_x(x \equiv \text{dom}_2\,(a^*)).$$

In deriving the axiom of replacement it was essential to extend our logical formalism by adding class variables. This extension is not sufficient, however, if we wish to apply "self-strengthening" versions of the reflection schema to assertions containing free class variables. Indeed for this purpose we have to take the given assertion as the premise (antecedent of an implication), and the free variables do not suffice to express the universal validity of the premise. We thus are induced to introduce *bound-class variables* $U$, $V$, $W$, $X$, $Y$, $Z$ together with rules for the associated existential and universal quantifiers. These rules are quite similar to those for the quantifiers over set variables.

How can we apply relativization to an expression $(X)A(X)$ or $(EX)A(X)$ with a bound-class variable $X$? The natural method is that employed by Lévy in forming the expression $Scm^Q(u)$: it amounts to interpreting $Rel(b,(X)A(X))$ as the expression $(x)(x \subseteq b \to Rel\,(b,A(x))$ with a set variable $x$, and $Rel\,(b,(EX)A(X))$ as the expression

$$(Ex)(x \subseteq b \wedge Rel\,(b,A(x)).$$

It is pertinent to ask if the reflection schema remains consistent upon these stipulations. Contradictions would indeed arise had we not stipulated that the transition to reduced expressions must be made at the beginning of relativizing. For instance, in schema (11), which we now apply to our extended class of formulas, take for A the provable formula $(EU)(A \subseteq U)$; then immediate reflection would give

$$(Ey)(\text{Trans}\,(y) \wedge (Eu)(u \subseteq y \wedge A \subseteq u)),$$

whence $(Ey)(A \subseteq y)$. But this, together with the axiom of subsets, leads to a contradiction if we substitute for $A$ a class which cannot be represented by a set. If, on the other hand, we observe that $Rel\,(b,A)$ is to be interpreted as $Rel\,(b,A_1)$ where $A_1$ is a *reduced* formula such that $A \leftrightarrow A_1$ is provable, then the contradiction vanishes. For if we replace $A \subseteq U$ by the defining expression

$$(x)(x \in A \to x \in U)$$

and then perform the relativizing, we obtain

$$(Ey)(\text{Trans}\,(y) \wedge (Eu)(u \subseteq y \wedge (x)(x \in y \wedge x \in A \to x \in u))).$$

But this formula can be deduced without the reflection schema, since it follows from $(Ey)(\text{Trans}\,(y) \wedge y \subseteq y \wedge (x)(x \in y \wedge x \in A \to x \in y))$ by the rules of the predicate calculus.

In this and similar examples it is essential that in a reduced expression, a class variable can only occur in the second component of an $\in$-relation, while the first component contains a set variable. If this is a free variable

$a$, then we already know that in schema (11) we can insert the conjunction $a \in y$ within the scope of the existential quantifier $(Ey)$. If, on the other hand, the set variable is bound, then we restrict it to the elements of $b$ by relativizing to $b$. In particular, owing to the structure of $\text{Rel}(b, A)$, assertions of the type $A \subseteq c$ or $(Ez)(A \subseteq z)$ will not appear. But this removes the basis for our fear that the extended reflection schema might be inconsistent.

Another circumstance to be noticed is that in our extended formalism we can no longer maintain the restriction to predicative class formation which is stipulated in all axiomatic set theories based on von Neumann's system of axioms.[1]

For, as observed by Specker, we have the following theorem in our extended system.[2] Let $P(c)$ be any formula of our system (possibly containing bound-class variables); suppose that the variables $x$, $U$ do not occur in $P(c)$ (this can be effected by relabeling if necessary). Then the following formula is provable:

(F) $\qquad\qquad (EU)(x)(x \in U \leftrightarrow P(x))$.

This means that any set predicate P (and hence also such a set predicate which refers to the totality of classes) is associated with a class.

In proving (F) we may assume without loss of generality that $P(c)$ is a reduced formula which does not contain the variable $y$. We apply the reflection schema (11) (in the extended sense) to the formula

$$(U) \to (x)(x \in U \leftrightarrow P(x)),$$

which is indeed a transform of the negation of (F). In this way we obtain

$$(U) \to (x)(x \in U \leftrightarrow P(x)). \to .(Ey)[\text{Trans}(y) \wedge (u)(u \subseteq y \to$$
$$\to (x)(x \in y \to (x \in u \leftrightarrow \text{Rel}(y, P(x)))))],$$

and hence

(G) $\qquad\begin{aligned}(U) \to (x)(x \in U \leftrightarrow P(x)). \to .(Ey)(u)(u \subseteq y \to \\ \to (x)(x \in u \leftrightarrow x \in y \wedge \text{Rel}(y, P(x)))).\end{aligned}$

Here $\text{Rel}(y, P(x))$ is an expression of the form $Q(x, y)$ without bound-class variables. If in the formula (5′) of the axiom of subsets, after changing the variables $x, z$ into $u, x$, we substitute for $C$ the class term

---

[1] The stronger versions of the axiom of choice perhaps constitute an exception to this rule. However, the axiom of choice is of course provable—even in its stronger forms, as Gödel has shown—in a set theory with predicative class formation, but strengthened by the axiom of constructibility.

[2] This observation was communicated to the author by E. Specker.

$\{z/Q(z,a)\}$, we get

$$(Eu)(x)(x \in u \leftrightarrow x \in a \wedge x \in \{z/Q(z,a)\}),$$

and from this

$$(y)(Eu)(x)(x \in u \leftrightarrow x \in y \wedge Q(x,y)),$$

as also

$$(y)(Eu)(u \subseteq y \wedge (x)(x \in u \leftrightarrow x \in y \wedge \text{Rel}\,(y,P(x)))).$$

But this is the negation (transformed by the rules of predicate logic) of the major consequent of implication (G). Therefore, we obtain by contraposition the negation of the antecedent, i.e. formula (F).

This result shows that, given our extension of the reflection schema, it would be inadequate to restrict the class terms $\{x/A(x)\}$ to the original ones. Accordingly, in the formation of class terms $\{x/A(x)\}$ we shall allow bound-class variables to occur in $A(x)$.

It must be admitted that by this way, our class formalism loses its comparatively elementary character. But the extension seems to be necessary in order to give the reflection schema its full efficacy. Let us now see what we gain from this.

3. Considering now the strengthening of the logical formalism and of the reflection schema we show that we obtain a self-strengthening of the reflection schema with respect to the axioms of subsets and replacement, and with this a derivation of the power-set axiom.

Our starting point is the final result of §1, i.e. the schema of formulas (11d) which we derived from (11). As observed there, we can insert Rel $(y,F)$, F being any derivable reduced formula, as a conjunct within the scope of $(Ey)$. And we can use the premise Trans$(y)$ for transforming Rel $(y,F)$.

Let us take for F the formula

$$(U)(v)[(w)(w \in U \rightarrow w \in v) \rightarrow (Ex)(z)(z \in x \leftrightarrow z \in U)],$$

which we obtain from the formula (5b) (directly derived from the axiom of subsets) by binding the free variables $B,a$ and replacing the symbols $\subseteq$ and $\equiv$ by their defining expressions. By relativizing to $b$ a formula results which, by using Trans$(b)$, can be transformed into:

$$(u)(v)(u \subseteq b \wedge v \in b \rightarrow (u \subseteq v \rightarrow (Ex)(x \in b \wedge (z)(z \in x \leftrightarrow z \in u)))).$$

From this we infer, using the axioms of extensionality and equality:

$$(u)(v)(u \subseteq b \wedge v \in b \rightarrow (u \subseteq v \rightarrow u \in b)),$$

and furthermore, using Trans $(b)$ again and the provable formula
Trans $(b) \to (u)(v)(u \subseteq v \wedge v \in b \to u \subseteq b)$:

$$(u)(v)(v \in b \wedge u \subseteq v \to u \in b).$$

We can therefore insert in schema (11d) the expression

$$(u)(v)(v \in y \wedge u \subseteq v \to u \in y)$$

within the scope of $(Ey)$ as a conjunction member. This conjunct expresses that each subset of an element of $y$ is again an element of $y$. A set which satisfies this condition and is also transitive will be called *super-transitive.*[1] The formal definition is

DEFINITION.     Strans $(b) \leftrightarrow$ Trans $(b) \wedge (u)(v)(v \in b \wedge u \subseteq v \to u \in b)$.

We thus obtain the following strengthened version of the reflection schema:

(11e)     $A \to (Ey)(\text{Strans}(y) \wedge \text{Mod}_0(y) \wedge a \in y \wedge \text{Rel}(y,A))$.

From this we deduce in particular:

$$(Ey)((u)(v)(v \in y \wedge u \subseteq v \to u \in y) \wedge a \in y),$$

so that

$$(Ey)(u)(u \subseteq a \to u \in y),$$

whence

(20)     $(x)(Ey)(u)(u \subseteq x \to u \in y)$

("for each set $x$ there is a set $y$ which has all subsets of $x$ as elements").

But this is precisely what the power set axiom asserts: it follows that this axiom is derivable from the reflection schema. Now making the

DEFINITION.     $\pi(a) = \iota_x(z)(z \in x \leftrightarrow z \subseteq a)$,

we can deduce from (20) and the axioms $(5')$ and (3):

(20a)     $c \in \pi(a) \leftrightarrow c \subseteq a.$

We know that in (11e) we can again insert within the scope of $(Ey)$ the conjunct Rel $(y,F)$, where $F$ is any provable reduced formula. We consider two particular formulas $F_1$, $F_2$ of this kind.

Let $F_1$ be the formula

$$(x)(Ev)(u)((z)(z \in u \to z \in x) \to u \in v),$$

---

[1] The word is chosen in analogy to the term "super-complete" used in the same sense by SHEPHERDSON [1951–1953], Part I, §24.

which is readily obtained from (20). We have

Strans $(b) \wedge$ Rel $(b, F_1) \to (x)(x \in b \to (Ev)(v \in b \wedge (u)(u \subseteq x \to u \in v)))$.

In (11e) we therefore can add, within the scope of $(Ey)$, the conjunct

$$(x)(x \in y \to (Ev)(v \in y \wedge (u)(u \subseteq x \to u \in v))),$$

which means that the range of $y$ satisfies the power set axiom. We shall denote this conjunct by "Pt $(y)$".

Let $F_2$ be the formula obtained from (19) by invoking the definition of $\langle a, b \rangle$ to reduce the expression $\langle x, z \rangle \in A$ to primitive terms, binding the variables $m$ and $A$, and replacing $y$ by $w$. In other words, $F_2$ is the formula obtained from

$$(u)(V)[(x)(x \in u \to (Ez)(\langle x, z \rangle \in V)). \to .(Ew)(x)(x \in u \to (Ez)(z \in w$$
$$\wedge \langle x, z \rangle \in V))]$$

by eliminating the symbol for the ordered pair. After relativizing we can, as in the derivation of (19) in §2, reinstate the symbol for the ordered pair. Thus we deduce

Trans $(b) \wedge$ Rel $(b, F_2). \to .(u)(v)(u \in b \wedge v \subseteq b \to$

(h) $[(x)(x \in u \to (Ez)(\langle x, z \rangle \in v)) \to (Ew)(w \in b \wedge (x)(x \in u \to$

$(Ez)(z \in w \wedge \langle x, z \rangle \in v)))])$,

which may briefly be indicated by

Trans $(b) \wedge$ Rel $(b, F_2) \to H(b)$.

Using the method by which we derived (18) from (19), we can now deduce

(k) $H(b) \to (u)(v)(u \in b \wedge v \subseteq b \wedge$ Fu $(v) \wedge (u = \text{dom}_1(v)) \to$
$(Ew)(w \in b \wedge \text{dom}_2(v) \subseteq w))$.

We also have:

(1) Strans $(b) \to [(Ew)(w \in b \wedge \text{dom}_2(f) \subseteq w) \to \text{dom}_2(f) \in b]$,

and

(m) Trans $(b) \wedge$ Fu $(f) \wedge \text{dom}_1(f) \in b \wedge \text{dom}_2(f) \subseteq b \wedge$
$(u_1)(u_2)(u_1 \in b \wedge u_2 \in b \to \langle u_1, u_2 \rangle \in b). \to .f \subseteq b$.

Moreover,

(n) $\text{Mod}_0(b) \to (u_1)(u_2)(u_1 \in b \wedge u_2 \in b \to \langle u_1, u_2 \rangle \in b)$.

From (h), (k), (l), (m), and (n), we obtain:

$$\text{Strans}\,(b) \wedge \text{Mod}_0\,(b) \wedge \text{Rel}\,(b,F_2). \rightarrow .(v)(\text{Fu}\,(v) \wedge \text{dom}_1\,(v) \in b$$
$$\wedge\,\text{dom}_2\,(v) \subseteq b \rightarrow \text{dom}_2\,(v) \in b).$$

The consequent in this last implication means that the range of $b$ satisfies the axiom of replacement. (Indeed in the range of $b$, regarded as a model of axiomatic set theory, the subsets of $b$ correspond to the classes and the elements to the sets.) Let us call this property *functional closure*; formally we have the

DEFINITION. $\quad \text{Clf}\,(b) \leftrightarrow (v)(\text{Fu}\,(v) \wedge \text{dom}_1\,(v) \in b$
$$\wedge\,\text{dom}_2\,(v) \subseteq b \rightarrow \text{dom}_2\,(v) \in b).$$

We therefore finally obtain from (11e), by application to $A \wedge F_1 \wedge F_2$:

(11f) $\quad A \rightarrow (Ey)[\text{Strans}\,(y) \wedge \text{Mod}_0\,(y) \wedge \text{Pt}\,(y) \wedge \text{Clf}\,(y) \wedge a \in y \wedge$
$$\text{Rel}\,(y,A)].$$

If we now make the

DEFINITION. $\quad \text{Mod}\,(b) \leftrightarrow \text{Mod}_0\,(b) \wedge \text{Pt}\,(b) \wedge \text{Clf}\,(b),$

we arrive at

(11g) $\qquad A \rightarrow (Ey)(\text{Strans}\,(y) \wedge \text{Mod}\,(y) \wedge a \in y \wedge \text{Rel}\,(y,A)).$

Here $\text{Mod}\,(b)$ says that $b$ satisfies the axioms of pairing, sum set, power set, replacement, and infinity. (The second component of $\text{Strans}\,(b)$ implies that $b$ satisfies the axiom of subsets.)[1]

We have so far ignored the axioms of choice and foundation. As to the axiom of choice, we shall later apply it implicitly in the form of the well-ordering theorem, or, more precisely, the "numeration theorem" which asserts that the elements of a set can be enumerated by ordinals.[2] It is well known that Zermelo's form of the axiom of choice implies the last assertion. This form of the axiom of choice is also equivalent to

(S) $\qquad \text{Pr}\,(c) \rightarrow (Ex)(x \subseteq c \wedge \text{Fu}\,(x) \wedge \text{dom}_1\,(x) = \text{dom}_1\,(c)).$

(The proof of equivalence can be based on the axiom of replacement or the power set axiom.)

We cannot expect to derive the axiom of choice from the reflection schema. But we can use the schema to deduce a stronger form of the axiom of choice from (S), namely

(T) $\qquad (EV)(\text{Fu}\,(V) \wedge (x)(x \neq 0 \rightarrow (Ez)(z \in x \wedge \langle x,z \rangle \in V))).$

---

[1] See the definition of Strans $(b)$ on p. 139.
[2] A precise version follows in §4.

To accomplish this we use Specker's method described in §2: we derive a contradiction from the negation of (T), i.e. the formula

$$(V)(\text{Fu}\,(V) \to (Ex)(x \neq 0 \wedge (z)(z \in x \to \langle x,z \rangle \notin V)).$$

If we identify A in (11d) with this formula we have to eliminate the symbols Fu and $\langle, \rangle$; they can be reinstated afterwards. We thus obtain, after canceling any components which become superfluous in virtue of the premise Trans $(y)$,

(p)
$$A \to (Ey)[\text{Trans}\,(y) \wedge \text{Mod}_0\,(y) \wedge$$
$$(v)(v \subseteq y \wedge \text{Fu}\,(v) \to$$
$$(Ex)(x \in y \wedge x \neq 0 \wedge (z)(z \in x \to \langle x,z \rangle \notin v)))].$$

On the other hand, we have

$$\text{Trans}\,(b) \wedge \text{Mod}_0\,(b) \to \{w\,/(Ex)(Ez)(w = \langle x,z \rangle \wedge x \in b \wedge z \in x\} \subseteq b,$$

and hence, by the axiom of subsets (5b), we have

(q)
$$\text{Trans}\,(b) \wedge \text{Mod}_0\,(b) \to (Eu)[u \subseteq b \wedge (w)(w \in u \leftrightarrow$$
$$(Ex)(Ez)(w = \langle x,z \rangle \wedge x \in b \wedge z \in x))].$$

Denoting the expression within the scope of $(w)$ by $Q(w,u)$, we get

(r)
$$(w)Q(w,c) \to \text{Pr}\,(c) \wedge (x)(x \in \text{dom}_1\,(c) \leftrightarrow x \in b \wedge x \neq 0) \wedge$$
$$(x)(z)(\langle x,z \rangle \in c \to z \in x).$$

Using (S) we infer from (q) and (r):

$$\text{Trans}\,(b) \wedge \text{Mod}_0\,(b) \to (Ev)(v \subseteq b \wedge \text{Fu}\,(v) \wedge (x)(x \in b \wedge x \neq 0 \to$$
$$(Ez)(z \in x \wedge \langle x,z \rangle \in v))),$$

and from this we deduce the negation of the second component of (p). This implies the negation of A and (T) follows.

Thus, within the context of our system, the stronger version (T) of the axiom of choice does not really constitute a more powerful principle than the weaker version. Now this stronger version can be formalized more easily by introducing the one-place function symbol $\sigma$ for the function whose existence is asserted by (T). The symbol $\sigma$ is taken as a basic symbol, along with the axiom:[1]

(21)                              $a \in c \to \sigma(c) \in c.$

This also enables us to formalize the *axiom of foundation* in the simple

---

[1] The possibility of formalizing the axiom of choice in this way was presumably first noticed by SKOLEM [1929] p. 10, V., I).

form:

(22)                         $a \in c \rightarrow a \notin \sigma(c)$,

which gives together with (21)

(22a)                        $a \in c \rightarrow (Ex)(x \in c \wedge x \cap c = 0)$.

This is a common form of the axiom of foundation, and from it we can deduce the somewhat stronger version

(22b)                        $a \in C \rightarrow (Ex)(x \in C \wedge x \cap C = 0)$,

by using certain of the other axioms.[1]

We can derive (22b) very simply from (22a) by means of our schema (11c), without using any bound-class variables. For if we substitute for A in (11c) the formula

$$a \in C \wedge (x)(x \in C \rightarrow (Ez)(z \in x \wedge z \in C)),$$

then as the second component of the implication we obtain the formula

$$(Ey)(\text{Trans}(y) \wedge a \in y \wedge a \in C \wedge (x)(x \in y \wedge x \in C \rightarrow$$
$$(Ez)(z \in x \wedge z \in y \wedge z \in C))),$$

and using (5′) we have

$$A \rightarrow (Eu)(a \in u \wedge (x)(x \in u \rightarrow (Ez)(z \in x \wedge z \in u))).$$

Now the negation of the second component of this implication results from (22a) by generalization with respect to $c$; this gives the negation of A by contraposition and so (22b) follows immediately.

The axiom of foundation in the form (22a) will be sufficient for our purpose.

For the axiomatization, (21) and (22) can be contracted into a single formula. Accordingly, we extend our class of formulas by adding the function symbol $\sigma$ as a basic symbol, at the same time introducing the axiom

(23)                         $a \in c \rightarrow \sigma(c) \in c \wedge a \notin \sigma(c)$,

which combines both the axioms of choice and foundation.

If the assertion (23) holds in set theory, then it is automatically satisfied within any transitive set. (The formula of equality

$$a = b \rightarrow \sigma(a) = \sigma(b),$$

---

[1] Cf. for example, BERNAYS [1958] p. 202 and 209.

associated with the symbol $\sigma$, is obtained from the schema of equality (1) and the formula $a = a$.)

REMARK. The axiom of foundation is not strictly necessary in set theory, but it simplifies the theory of ordinals. (See p. 146, footnote 1.) As to the avoidance of the axiom of choice in the theory of inaccessible cardinals, see the concluding remark.

4. We shall now use schema (11g), which we obtained from (11), to derive Mahlo's postulates. We first introduce some concepts and results from the theory of ordinals.

Upon assuming the axiom of foundation[1], ordinals can be defined as follows:

DEFINITION. $\text{Od}(c) \leftrightarrow \text{Trans}(c) \wedge \text{Alt}(c)$,

where Alt is defined by the

DEFINITION. $\text{Alt}(c) \leftrightarrow (u)(v)(u \in c \wedge v \in c \rightarrow u = v \vee u \in v \vee v \in u)$.

It then can be verified that

(24) $\qquad \text{Trans}(b) \wedge c \in b \rightarrow (\text{Rel}(b, \text{Od}(c)) \leftrightarrow \text{Od}(c))$.

In the language of model theory, this formula[2] means that the predicate Od is absolute with respect to relativization.

We also make the usual

DEFINITIONS. $a' = a \cup [a]$,

$$\text{Lim}(c) \leftrightarrow \text{Od}(c) \wedge c \neq 0 \wedge (x)(x \in c \rightarrow (Eu)(x \in u \wedge u \in c)).$$

It can again be verified that

(24a) $\qquad \text{Trans}(b) \wedge c \in b \rightarrow (\text{Rel}(b, \text{Lim}(c)) \leftrightarrow \text{Lim}(c))$.

Also one easily states:

(25) $\qquad\qquad\qquad \text{Od}(0), \qquad \text{Od}(a) \rightarrow \text{Od}(a')$

and further, with applications of the axiom of foundation, we obtain

[1] If we do not assume the axiom of foundation, then we must add a conjunct $\text{Fund}(c)$ in the definition of $\text{Od}(c)$, where Fund is defined by

$$\text{Fund}(c) \leftrightarrow (t)(t \subseteq c \wedge t \neq 0 \rightarrow (Eu)(u \in t \wedge u \cap t = 0)).$$

we then have to modify (24), replacing the premise Trans $(b)$ by Strans $(b)$. According to the axiom of foundation, Fund $(c)$ holds for each set $c$.

[2] Strictly speaking, (24) is not a formula but represents one; similarly for (28b) and (32) below.

$$\text{Od}(c) \to c = 0 \lor (Ex)(\text{Od}(x) \land c = x') \lor \text{Lim}(c),$$
$$\text{Od}(c) \land a \in c \to \text{Od}(a) \land c \notin a,$$

(26)
$$a \in b \land b \in c \land \text{Od}(c) \to a \in c,$$
$$\text{Od}(a) \land \text{Od}(c) \to (a = c \lor a \in c \lor c \in a)$$
$$\land (a \subseteq c \leftrightarrow a = c \lor a \in c).$$

Theorems (26) show that the membership relation $\in$ constitutes for the ordinals their "natural ordering" (the "less than" relation) and also that the relation of set inclusion coincides with the "less than or equal to" relation on the ordinals. The natural ordering of the ordinals is a well ordering, i.e. we have

(27)
$$(v)(v \in B \to \text{Od}(v)) \land a \in B \to (Ev)(v \in B$$
$$\land (u)(u \in B \to v = u \lor v \in u)).$$

(Each non-empty class of ordinals has a smallest element.) This smallest number principle is equivalent to the principle of *transfinite induction*:

(27a)
$$(v)(\text{Od}(v) \land (u)(u \in v \to u \in A) \to v \in A)$$
$$\to (v)(\text{Od}(v) \to v \in A).$$

We also note the following consequences of (26):

(26a)
$$(x)(x \in m \to \text{Od}(x)) \land \text{Trans}(m) \to \text{Od}(m),$$
$$(x)(x \in m \to \text{Od}(x)) \to \text{Od}\left(\sum (m)\right).$$

The concept of a *sequence* is based on that of an ordinal number: a functional set is called a sequence if its domain is an ordinal:

DEFINITION.  $\text{Sq}(f) \leftrightarrow \text{Fu}(f) \land \text{Od}(\text{dom}_1(f)).$

If the range of a sequence consists of ordinals, then it is called a *sequence of ordinals*. In particular, an *order-preserving* sequence of ordinals is called an *ordinal sequence*, or formally:

DEFINITION.  $\text{Sqod}(f) \leftrightarrow \text{Sq}(f) \land (x)(z)(u)(v)(\langle x,z \rangle \in f \land \langle u,v \rangle \in f$
$$\text{Od}(v) \land (x \in u \to z \in v).$$

If $f$ is an ordinal sequence whose domain is a limit ordinal, then $\Sigma(\text{dom}_2(f))$ is also a limit ordinal, called the *limit of the sequence f*. We have

(28)
$$\text{Sqod}(f) \land \text{Lim}(\text{dom}_1(f)). \to .\text{Lim}\left(\sum (\text{dom}_2(f))\right)$$
$$\land \text{dom}_2(f) \subseteq \sum (\text{dom}_2(f)) \land \text{dom}_1(f) \subseteq \sum (\text{dom}_2(f)).$$

To prove the last clause of this assertion we use the observation

(28a)                Sqod $(f) \to (\langle a,b \rangle \in f \to a \subseteq b)$,

which is proved by transfinite induction.

It also can be verified that[1]

(28b)        Trans $(b) \wedge f \in b \to (\text{Rel}\,(b,\,\text{Sqod}\,(f))) \leftrightarrow \text{Sqod}\,(f))$.

Using the concept of a sequence we can reduce recursive definitions to explicit ones, following the method employed for number theory by Dedekind [1888]. We briefly recall this procedure, taking as an instance the one place function $\Psi$, which was introduced by von Neumann[2] and which is now frequently used in the model theory of set theory. This function is recursively defined on the domain of ordinals by the conditions:

$$\psi(0) = 0,$$
(N)                $$\text{Od}\,(m) \to \psi(m') = \pi(\psi(m)),$$
$$\text{Lim}\,(l) \to \psi(l) \equiv \{x/(Ez)(z \in l \wedge x \in \psi(z))\}.$$

In order to define $\psi$ explicitly, we first construct a predicate $\Psi(f,m)$ which asserts that $f$ is a sequence satisfying condition (N) with respect to the ordinals in its domain, and that $m$ belongs to this domain. We make the formal

DEFINITION.    $\Psi(f,m) . \leftrightarrow . \text{Sq}\,(f) \wedge m \in \text{dom}_1\,(f) \wedge \langle 0,0 \rangle \in f \wedge$

$$(x)(u)(v)(\langle x,u \rangle \in f \wedge \langle x',v \rangle \in f \to v = \pi(u)) \wedge$$
$$(x)(z)(\text{Lim}\,(x) \wedge \langle x,z \rangle \in f \to z \equiv$$
$$\{w/(Eu)(Ev)(u \in x \wedge \langle u,v \rangle \in f \wedge w \in v)\}).$$

Using this definition, transfinite induction, and the axioms of replacement and union, one proves that

$$\text{Od}\,(m) \to (Et)\Psi(t,m)$$
and
$$\Psi(f,m) \wedge \Psi(g,m) \wedge \langle m,c \rangle \in f \wedge \langle m,d \rangle \in g \to c = d.$$

If we introduce $\psi$ by means of the

DEFINITION.    $\psi(m) = \iota_x(t)(\Psi(t,m) \to \langle m,x \rangle \in t)$,

---

[1] If Od is defined as in Footnote 1, p. 144 (as it must be when the axiom of foundation is omitted), then it seems that the premise "Trans $(b)$" must be strengthened. In any case, Strans $(b) \wedge \text{Mod}\,(b)$ is sufficient.

[2] Cf. Von NEUMANN [1929], see in particular pp. 236–238.

then we can prove $(N)$ from the definition and the indicated properties of $\Psi$, without further using induction.

More generally, we can argue as we did in the case of conditions $(N)$ if, instead of $\tau$, we take any function defined for arbitrary sets and if for each limit ordinal $l$ the value of the function is determined by any function— the intersection, for instance—of the previous range of values. (In the special case of the intersection we can dispense with the axioms of replacement and union.) It is also possible to accommodate an additional parameter in the recursive conditions; this parameter will then appear as an argument of the function defined.

We shall now consider those notions of the theory of ordinals which are of special importance for our purposes.

A limit ordinal is called an *irreducible limit* if it is not the limit of an ordinal sequence whose domain is a smaller limit ordinal. In view of (28) we can state the following formal definition.

DEFINITION.   $\text{Lir}(a) \leftrightarrow \text{Lim}(a) \wedge (t)(\text{Sqod}(t) \wedge \text{Lim}(\text{dom}_1(t))$
$$\wedge\ a = \sum (\text{dom}_2(t)) \rightarrow a = \text{dom}_1(t)).$$

An irreducible limit ordinal $\alpha > \omega$ will be called a *strictly inaccessible ordinal*[1] if it satisfies the condition that, whenever the ordinal $c$ is an element of $\alpha$ then so are all ordinals whose cardinality is that of the set of subsets of $c$. In order to formalize this definition we first introduce the usual concepts: *a is a one–one function* and *a is equipotent with b*:

DEFINITION.   $\text{Crs}(a) \leftrightarrow \text{Pr}(a) \wedge (x)(y)(u)(v)(\langle x,y \rangle \in a$
$$\wedge\ \langle u,v \rangle \in a \rightarrow (x = u \leftrightarrow y = v)),$$

$$a \sim b \leftrightarrow (Ew)(\text{Crs}(w) \wedge \text{dom}_1(w) = a \wedge \text{dom}_2(w) = b).$$

Recall the following well-known facts about equipotency:

$$a \sim a, \qquad a \sim b \wedge a \sim c \rightarrow b \sim c$$
$$a \subseteq b \wedge b \subseteq c \wedge a \sim c \rightarrow a \sim b \qquad \text{(Bernstein's theorem)}.$$

The well-ordering theorem can be reduced to the *numeration theorem*:

(29)                     $(Ex)(\text{Od}(x) \wedge x \sim c).$

---

[1] The concept of an ordinal inaccessible in the wider sense will not be needed in the sequel. We therefore shall use the word "inaccessible" in the sense of "strictly inaccessible".

For the proof of (29) it is recommendable to apply the method of Zermelo's original proof of the well-ordering theorem and to use the axiom of choice in the form given in (21).

For irreducible limits we have in particular,

(30)         $\text{Lir}(c) \wedge a \in c \wedge a \sim b \wedge \text{Od}(b). \rightarrow .b \in c.$

This means that any ordinal lower than an irreducible limit has also lower cardinality; an irreducible is thus an *initial ordinal*.

We now give the definition of an inaccessible ordinal.[1]

DEFINITION.   $\text{In}(m) \leftrightarrow \text{Lir}(m) \wedge (x)(x \in m \rightarrow (Ez)(\pi(x) \sim z \wedge z \in m)) \wedge$
$\quad\quad\quad \omega \in m.$

In view of (29) and (30), this definition can be transformed into the equivalence

(31)         $\text{In}(m) \leftrightarrow \text{Lir}(m) \wedge (x)(z)(x \in m \wedge \pi(x) \sim z$
$\quad\quad\quad\quad \wedge \text{Od}(z) \rightarrow z \in m) \wedge \omega \in m.$

In connection with Lir and In, we have

(32)      $\text{Strans}(b) \wedge \text{Mod}(b) \wedge m \in b. \rightarrow .(\text{Rel}(b, \text{Lir}(m)) \leftrightarrow$
$\quad\quad \text{Lir}(m)) \wedge (\text{Rel}(b, \text{In}(m)) \leftrightarrow \text{In}(m)).$

Returning now to our preceding reasoning we make the general

DEFINITION.   $\mu(c) = c \cap \{x / \text{Od}(x)\},$

so that we have

(33)         $a \in \mu(c) \leftrightarrow a \in c \wedge \text{Od}(a).$

($\mu(c)$ is the set of ordinals which are members of $c$.) We then have

(34)         $\text{Strans}(b) \wedge \text{Mod}(b) \rightarrow \text{In}(\mu(b))$

The proof of (34) runs as follows. By (26), we have $\text{Trans}(b) \rightarrow$ $\text{Trans}(\mu(b))$; moreover $\mu(b) \subseteq \{x / \text{Od}(x)\}$ so that by (26a):

(35)         $\text{Trans}(b) \rightarrow \text{Od}(\mu(b)).$

Also, we have

$\text{Mod}(b) \rightarrow (a \in b \rightarrow a \cup [a] \in b),$

---

[1] The predicate In corresponds to the class $\text{In}_2$ in SHEPHERDSON [1951–1953], Part I, Definition 2.420.

so that, by (33) and (25),

$$\text{Mod}(b) \to (a \in \mu(b) \to a' \in \mu(b)).$$

From this and (35) it follows that

(35a) $\qquad \text{Trans}(b) \wedge \text{Mod}(b) \wedge \mu(b) \neq 0 \to \text{Lim}(\mu(b)).$

Furthermore,

$$\text{Mod}(b) \to \omega \in b,$$

so that

(35b) $\qquad\qquad \text{Mod}(b) \to \omega \in \mu(b),$

which together with (35a) gives

(35c) $\qquad\qquad \text{Trans}(b) \wedge \text{Mod}(b) \to \text{Lim}(\mu(b)).$

Also, we have, by the definitions of Mod and of Clf:

(35d) $\qquad \text{Mod}(b). \to .(t)(\text{Fu}(t) \wedge \text{dom}_1(t) \in b \wedge \text{dom}_2(t) \subseteq b \to$
$$\text{dom}_2(t) \in b \wedge \sum(\text{dom}_2(t)) \in b).$$

Using (33) and (26a), and the fact that $\mu(b) \subseteq b$, we infer from (35d):

$$\text{Mod}(b). \to .(t)(\text{Sqod}(t) \wedge \text{dom}_1(t) \in \mu(b) \wedge \text{dom}_2(t) \subseteq \mu(b) \to$$
$$\to \sum(\text{dom}_2(t)) \in \mu(b)).$$

From this we infer, using (28):

$$\text{Mod}(b). \to .(t)(\text{Sqod}(t) \wedge \text{Lim}(\text{dom}_1(t) \wedge \sum(\text{dom}_2(t)) = \mu(b)$$
$$\to \text{dom}_1(t) \notin \mu(b)).$$

Applying (28) again, and also (26) and (26a), it follows that

$$\text{Mod}(b). \to .(t)(\text{Sqod}(t) \wedge \text{Lim}(\text{dom}_1(t)) \wedge \sum(\text{dom}_2(t)) = \mu(b)$$
$$\to \text{dom}_1(t) = \mu(b)).$$

This, together with (35c) gives

(35e) $\qquad\qquad \text{Trans}(b) \wedge \text{Mod}(b) \to \text{Lir}(\mu(b)).$

In view of (37), (35b) and (35e), (34) will be proved if we can establish

(35f) $\qquad \text{Strans}(b) \wedge \text{Mod}(b). \to .(a \in \mu(b) \wedge \pi(a) \sim c$
$$\wedge \text{Od}(c) \to c \in \mu(b)).$$

We prove (35f) by contradiction: assume the premises and suppose that $c \notin \mu(b)$. Then $\mu(b) \subseteq c$, since $\text{Od}(\mu(b))$ by (35). But we also have $a \in \mu(b) \to a \in b$, and $\text{Mod}(b) \wedge a \in b \to \pi(a) \in b$. Thus the proof will be complete if we can deduce a contradiction from

$$\text{Strans}(b) \wedge \text{Mod}(b) \wedge \mu(b) \subseteq c \wedge \pi(a) \in b \wedge \pi(a) \sim c \wedge \text{Od}(c).$$

We argue as follows. Since $\pi(a) \sim c$ there is a one–one mapping of $\pi(a)$ onto $c$. From this set of ordered pairs we choose a subset consisting of those pairs $\langle k,l \rangle$ of the mapping for which $l \in \mu(b)$. Since $\mu(b) \subseteq c$ this subset is a one–one mapping $f$ of a subset $d$ of $\pi(a)$ onto $\mu(b)$. Thus, we have Fu $(f)$, $\text{dom}_1 (f) = d$, $\text{dom}_2 (f) = \mu(b)$, $d \subseteq \pi(a)$, $\mu(b) \subseteq b$, and $d \in b$, since

$$d \subseteq \pi(a) \wedge \pi(a) \in b \wedge \text{Strans}(b) \rightarrow d \in b.$$

Applying (35d) to $f$ we have, as a consequence of Mod $(b)$, $\text{dom}_2 (f) \in b$, i.e. $\mu(b) \in b$. Using (33) and Od $(\mu(b))$, we infer that $\mu(b) \in \mu(b)$. But this, with (26), leads to a contradiction.

This completes the proof of (34), which of course goes as well formally.

Next, we consider Mahlo's first postulate. This may be stated as follows: Each increasing sequence of ordinals with no upper bound has an initial segment whose elements tend to an irreducible limit. Instead of a sequence we can take here simply a class of ordinals (whose elements have indeed their natural order).[1] The postulate may then be expressed as follows: For each unbounded class of ordinals there is an irreducible limit $\alpha$ which is the limit of the set of elements of the class which are less than $\alpha$. More formally, we have

(36) $(x)(x \in A \rightarrow \text{Od}(x)) \wedge (x)(\text{Od}(x) \rightarrow (Ez)(x \in z \wedge z \in A))$

$$\rightarrow (Et)(\text{Lir}(t) \wedge (x)(x \in t \rightarrow (Ez)(x \in z \wedge z \in t \wedge z \in A))).$$

We now show that this formula can be deduced from our derived schema (11g). For A in this scheme we take the formula

$$(x)(\text{Od}(x) \rightarrow (Ez)(x \in z \wedge z \in A))$$

and obtain (omitting the superfluous clause $a \in y$)

$$A \rightarrow (Ey)(\text{Strans}(y) \wedge \text{Mod}(y) \wedge (x)(x \in y \wedge \text{Od}(x)$$

$$\rightarrow (Ez)(x \in z \wedge z \in y \wedge z \in A))).$$

Now by (33) we have

$$(x)(x \in A \rightarrow \text{Od}(x)). \rightarrow .(a \in b \wedge a \in A \rightarrow a \in \mu(b) \wedge a \in A)$$

---

[1] Lévy proceeds in the opposite direction, so to speak, using the fact that each increasing sequence of ordinals can be extended to a "normal function" by adjoining the limits. (These limits might not themselves be members of the sequence.)

and by (35e):

$$\text{Trans}(b) \wedge \text{Mod}(b) \to \text{Lir}(\mu(b)).$$

This gives

$$(x)(x \in A \to \text{Od}(x)) \wedge A. \to .(Ey)(\text{Lir}(\mu(y)) \wedge (x)(x \in \mu(y)$$
$$\to (Ez)(x \in z \wedge z \in \mu(y) \wedge z \in A))),$$

i.e.

$$(x)(x \in A \to \text{Od}(x)) \wedge A. \to .(Et)(\text{Lir}(t) \wedge (x)(x \in t$$
$$\to (Ez)(x \in z \wedge z \in t \wedge z \in A))).$$

But this is the required formula (36). We also see that by using (34) instead of (35e) we get a stronger result. By this way we deduce a formula "(36a)" which is obtained from (36) by substituting In $(t)$ for Lir $(t)$. This formula means that each unbounded class of ordinals has a subset which tends to an inaccessible number.

Mahlo transcends the infinities which he obtained by applying his stated principle (and to which the hierarchy of $\pi_\nu$-numbers refers). This he does by means of the concept of a $\rho_0$-number. A $\rho_0$-number is an irreducible limit $\alpha$ such that each sequence of ordinals tending to $\alpha$ has an initial segment tending to an irreducible limit. In other words, $\alpha$ is an irreducible limit whose set of ordinal predecessors satisfies Mahlo's principle formalized by (36).

It thereby appears that the existence of $\rho_0$-numbers must be deducible from (36) by the reflection schema. For this purpose it will be required to pass from the free-class variable $A$ to a bound variable, which indeed is available to us in our formal frame. We shall at once derive the result in a strengthened form by replacing "irreducible limit" by "inaccessible number". The property of being a $\rho_0$-number in this extended sense becomes formalized by the predicate Ma $(m)$ ("$m$ is a Mahlo number"), defined as follows:

DEFINITION.    $\text{Ma}(m) \leftrightarrow \text{In}(m) \wedge (u)[u \subseteq m \wedge (x)(x \in m \to$
$$(Ez)(x \in z \wedge z \in u)). \to .(Et)(\text{In}(t) \wedge t \in m \wedge (x)(x \in t \to$$
$$(Ez)(x \in z \wedge z \in t \wedge z \in u)))].$$

In order to establish the existence of Mahlo numbers ($\rho_0$-numbers in the strict sense), using the reflection schema, we first take the formula

$$(36) \quad (U)[(x)(x \in U \to \text{Od}(x)) \wedge (x)(\text{Od}(x) \to (Ez)(x \in z \wedge z \in U)).$$
$$\to .(Et)(\text{In}(t) \wedge (x)(x \in t \to (Ez)(x \in z \wedge z \in t \wedge z \in U)))],$$

derived from (36a) by generalizing with respect to the free-class variable
A.

Denoting this formula by F and applying schema (11g) to A ∧ F, we find
(since A → A ∧ F),

$$A \rightarrow (Ey)(\text{Strans}(y) \wedge \text{Mod}(y) \wedge a \in y \wedge \text{Rel}(y,F) \wedge \text{Rel}(y,A)).$$

In view of (32) and (33), we also have

$$\text{Strans}(b) \wedge \text{Mod}(b). \rightarrow .(\text{Rel}(b,F) \leftrightarrow (u)[u \subseteq \mu(b) \wedge$$
$$(x)(x \in \mu(b) \rightarrow (Ez)(x \in z \wedge z \in u) \rightarrow (Et)(\text{In}(t) \wedge t \in \mu(b) \wedge$$
$$(x)(x \in t \rightarrow (Ez)(x \in z \wedge z \in t \wedge z \in u)))]).$$

Hence, by (34),

$$\text{Strans}(b) \wedge \text{Mod}(b) \wedge \text{Rel}(b,F) \rightarrow \text{Ma}(\mu(b)).$$

Thus, we have the derived schema

(11h)     $A \rightarrow (Ey)(\text{Strans}(y) \wedge \text{Mod}(y) \wedge a \in y$
$$\wedge \text{Ma}(\mu(y)) \wedge \text{Rel}(y,A)),$$

from which we deduce in particular, using (33),

(37)               $\text{Od}(a) \rightarrow (Ev)(\text{Ma}(v) \wedge a \in v);$

in other words, for each ordinal there is a larger Mahlo number (i.e.
$\rho_0$-number in the strengthened sense).

Mahlo proceeds to a transfinite iteration of the process leading from
irreducible limits ("$\pi_0$-numbers") to $\rho_0$-numbers. We now explain how
this iteration can be formalized within our system. For this purpose we
determine a predicate $\text{Ma}(m,k)$ by the following conditions:

$$\text{Ma}(m,0) \leftrightarrow \text{In}(m),$$
$$\text{Od}(k). \rightarrow .\text{Ma}(m,k') \leftrightarrow \text{In}(m) \wedge$$
(M)
$$(u)[u \subseteq m \wedge (x)(x \in m \rightarrow (Ez)(x \in z \wedge z \in u))$$
$$\rightarrow (Et)(\text{Ma}(t,k) \wedge t \in m \wedge$$
$$(x)(x \in t \rightarrow (Ez)(x \in z \wedge z \in t \wedge z \in u)))],$$
$$\text{Lim}(l). \rightarrow .\text{Ma}(m,l) \leftrightarrow (z)(z \in l \rightarrow \text{Ma}(m,z)).$$

Conditions (M) constitute a transfinite recursion for a predicate
$\text{Ma}(m,k)$, with $k$ being restricted to ordinal numbers. Such a definition, as
we applied already, can be reduced to an explicit definition by the method
of Dedekind. For this purpose, we may consider the sequence of classes
$\{x / \text{Ma}(x,k)\}$, where $k$ runs through the ordinals. Yet this is not a sequence
in our formal frame. But we can replace an assertion $m \in \{x / \text{Ma}(x,k)\}$ by

the    equivalent    assertion    $m \in m' \cap \{x/\text{Ma}(x,k)\}$,    where    now
$m' \cap \{x/\text{Ma}(x,k)\}$ is a set, and for defining $\text{Ma}(m,k)$ we need only the
sequence of sets $m' \cap \{x/\text{Ma}(x,k)\}$ with domain $k'$.
Indeed the predicate $\text{Ma}(m,k)$ can be formulated as follows:

"There is a sequence $t$ with domain $k'$ having the following properties:

1. The $0^{\text{th}}$ member of the sequence is the set $m' \cap \{u/\text{In}(u)\}$:
2. If $p$ is a member of the sequence then the next member is the set of
   those elements $v$ of $m' \cap \{u/\text{In}(u)\}$ for which the following holds:
   every subset of $v$ which is confinal with $v$ has an initial segment
   which tends to an element of $p$:
3. If $p$ is a limit number, then the $p^{\text{th}}$ member of the sequence is the
   intersection of the preceding members:
4. $m$ is an element of the $k^{\text{th}}$ member of the sequence."

For the formalizing of this predicate we observe that the expression

$$(x)(x \in c \to (Ez)(x \in z \wedge z \in d))$$

can be replaced by the more brief one

$$c \subseteq \sum (d).$$

By applying this abbreviation, the formal definition of $\text{Ma}(m,k)$ is

DEFINITION.

$$\text{Ma}(m,k). \leftrightarrow .(Et)\Big[\text{Sq}(t) \wedge \text{dom}_1(t) = k' \wedge \sum (\text{dom}_2(t)) \subseteq m'$$

$$\wedge (z)(\langle 0,z \rangle \in t \to (u)(u \in z \leftrightarrow u \in m' \wedge \text{In}(u)))$$

(M*)
$$\wedge (x)(z)(w)(\langle x,z \rangle \in t \wedge \langle x',w \rangle \in t \to (v)(v \in w \leftrightarrow v \in m' \wedge \text{In}(v)$$

$$\wedge (u)(u \subseteq v \wedge v \subseteq \sum (u) \to (ey)(y \in v \wedge y \in z \wedge y \subseteq \sum (y \cap u)))))$$

$$\wedge (x)(w)(\text{Lim}(x) \wedge \langle x,w \rangle \in t \to (u)(u \in w \leftrightarrow (z)(v)(z \in x$$

$$\wedge \langle z,v \rangle \in t \to u \in v))) \wedge (Ew)(\langle k,w \rangle \in t \wedge m \in w)\Big].$$

The formulas (M) can now be derived from this definition. We infer also
from (M*):

(38a)                    $\text{Ma}(m,k) \to \text{Od}(m) \wedge \text{Od}(k),$

(38b)                    $\text{Ma}(m,0') \leftrightarrow \text{Ma}(m),$

and with the aid of transfinite induction

(38c)          $\text{Od}(k) \wedge h \in k \to (\text{Ma}(m,k) \to \text{Ma}(m,h)).$

Furthermore we obtain:

(39)
$$\text{Strans}\,(b)\,\wedge\,\text{Mod}\,(b)\,\wedge\,m\in b\,\wedge\,k\in b.$$
$$\rightarrow.\text{Rel}\,(b,\,\text{Ma}\,(m,k))\leftrightarrow\text{Ma}\,(m,k).$$

Ordinals $m$ satisfying $\text{Ma}\,(m,k)$ will be called *Mahlo numbers of order k.*

We now proceed to derive Mahlo's strengthened postulates with the help of the reflection schema. We have to show that for each ordinal $k$ there are Mahlo numbers of order $k$ and that, furthermore, each unbounded sequence of ordinals has an initial segment whose limit is a Mahlo number of order $k$. Formally:

(40)
$$\text{Od}\,(k).\rightarrow.(U)[(x)(x\in U\rightarrow\text{Od}\,(x))\,\wedge$$
$$(x)(\text{Od}\,(x)\rightarrow(Ez)(x\in z\,\wedge\,z\in U))$$
$$\rightarrow(Et)(\text{Ma}\,(t,k)\,\wedge\,(x)(x\in t$$
$$\rightarrow(Ez)(x\in z\,\wedge\,z\in t\,\wedge\,z\in U)))].$$

This last formula may be briefly indicated as $\text{Od}\,(k)\rightarrow\text{B}(k)$. We prove it by means of that familiar form of transfinite induction which is formalized by the schema

$$\frac{\text{A}(0),\qquad\text{Od}\,(k)\,\wedge\,\text{A}(k)\rightarrow\text{A}(k'),\qquad\text{Lim}\,(l)\wedge(w)(w\in l\rightarrow\text{A}(w))\rightarrow\text{A}(l)}{\text{Od}\,(k)\rightarrow\text{A}(k)}$$

This schema is derivable from (27a) and (26). The proof of (40) therefore amounts to deriving the three formulas

$$\text{B}(0),\qquad\text{Od}\,(k)\,\wedge\,\text{B}(k)\rightarrow\text{B}(k'),\qquad\text{Lim}\,(l)\wedge(w)(w\in l\rightarrow\text{B}(w))\rightarrow\text{B}(l)$$

which we shall call (40a), (40b), and (40c).

(40a) follows immediately from (36b) and the formula $\text{Ma}\,(m,0)\leftrightarrow\text{In}\,(m)$, included in (M). To derive (40b) we use schema (11g), taking for A the formula

$$\text{B}(k)\,\wedge\,(x)(\text{Od}\,(x)\rightarrow(Ez)(x\in z\,\wedge\,z\in A))$$

and substituting $k$ for $a$. Thereby and by means of (39), the second component of the implication becomes

$$(Ey)(\text{Strans}\,(y)\,\wedge\,\text{Mod}\,(y)\,\wedge\,k\in y\,\wedge$$
$$(u)[u\subseteq y\,\wedge\,(x)(x\in u\rightarrow\text{Od}\,(x))$$
$$\wedge\,(x)(x\in y\,\wedge\,\text{Od}\,(x)\rightarrow(Ez)(x\in z\,\wedge\,z\in u))\rightarrow(Et)(t\in y$$
$$\wedge\,\text{Ma}(t,k)\,\wedge\,(x)(x\in t\rightarrow(Ez)(x\in z\,\wedge\,z\in t\,\wedge\,z\in u)))]$$
$$\wedge\,(x)(x\in y\,\wedge\,\text{Od}\,(x)\rightarrow(Ez)(x\in z\,\wedge\,z\in y\,\wedge\,z\in A))).$$

Let us write "H" for this formula.
From (33), (34), and (38a) it follows:

$$\text{H} \to (Ey)(\text{In } \mu(y) \wedge$$
$$(u)[u \subseteq \mu(y) \wedge (x)(x \in \mu(y) \to (Ez)(x \in z \wedge z \in u))$$
$$\to (Et)(t \in \mu(y) \wedge \text{Ma}(t,k) \wedge$$
$$(x)(x \in t \to (Ez)(x \in z \wedge z \in t \wedge z \in u)))]$$
$$\wedge (x)(x \in \mu(y) \to (Ez)(x \in z \wedge z \in y \wedge z \in A))),$$

i.e. in view of the second formula in (M),

$$\text{Od}(k) \wedge \text{H} \to (Ey)(\text{Ma}(\mu(y),k') \wedge (x)(x \in \mu(y)$$
$$\to (Ez)(x \in z \wedge z \in y \wedge z \in A))),$$

as also

$$\text{Od}(k) \wedge \text{H} \wedge (x)(x \in A \to \text{Od}(x)). \to .(Ey)(\text{Ma}(\mu(y),k')$$
$$\wedge (x)(x \in \mu(y) \to (Ez)(x \in z \wedge z \in \mu(y) \wedge z \in A))).$$

This formula, together with the initial implication

$$\text{B}(k) \wedge (x)(\text{Od}(x) \to (Ez)(x \in z \wedge z \in A)). \to .\text{H}$$

yields by the predicate calculus:

$$\text{Od}(k) \wedge \text{B}(k). \to .[(x)(x \in A \to \text{Od}(x)) \wedge (x)(\text{Od}(x)$$
$$\to (Ez)(x \in z \wedge z \in A)). \to .(Et)(\text{Ma}(t,k') \wedge (x)(x \in t$$
$$\to (Ez)(x \in z \wedge z \in t \wedge z \in A)))].$$

Here we can, in the second member of the principal implication, generalize with respect to $A$; we thus obtain B($k'$), and the required formula Od($k$) $\wedge$ B($k$) $\to$ B($k'$) follows.

The proof of (40c) resembles that of (40b). In (11g) we take for A the formula

$$(w)(w \in l \to \text{B}(w)) \wedge (x)(\text{Od}(x) \to (Ez)(x \in z \wedge z \in A))$$

and substitute $l$ for $a$. We thus obtain as the second member of the implication with application of (39), a formula $\text{H}_1$, and for this formula we get, using (33), (34), (38a) and the second formula of (M):

$$\text{Lim}(l) \wedge \text{H}_1 \to (Ey)[(w)(w \in l \to \text{Ma}(\mu(y),w')) \wedge (x)(x \in \mu(y)$$
$$\to (Ez)(x \in z \wedge z \in y \wedge z \in A))].$$

From this formula with the aid of

$$\text{Ma}(m,k') \to \text{Ma}(m,k),$$

which follows from (38c), and of the third formula of (M), we obtain

$$\text{Lim } (l) \wedge H_1 \rightarrow (Ey)(\text{Ma }(\mu(y),l) \wedge (x)(x \in \mu(y)$$
$$\rightarrow (Ez)(x \in z \wedge z \in y \wedge z \in A))),$$

as also

$$\text{Lim } (l) \wedge H_1 \wedge (x)(x \in A \rightarrow \text{Od }(x)) \rightarrow (Ey)(\text{Ma }(\mu(y),l)$$
$$\wedge (x)(x \in \mu(y) \rightarrow (Ez)(x \in z \wedge z \in \mu(y) \wedge z \in A))),$$

and hence

$$\text{Lim } (l) \wedge H_1 \wedge (x)(x \in A \rightarrow \text{Od }(x)) \rightarrow (Et)(\text{Ma }(t,l) \wedge (x)(x \in t$$
$$\rightarrow (Ez)(x \in z \wedge z \in t \wedge z \in A))).$$

This formula, together with the initial implication

$$(w)(w \in l \rightarrow B(w)) \wedge (x)(\text{Od }(x) \rightarrow (Ez)(x \in z \wedge z \in A)) \rightarrow H_1$$

yields

$$\text{Lim } (l) \wedge (w)(w \in l \rightarrow B(w)). \rightarrow .[(x)(x \in A \rightarrow \text{Od }(x))$$
$$\wedge (x)(\text{Od }(x) \rightarrow (Ez)(x \in z \wedge z \in A)) \rightarrow (Et)(\text{Ma }(t,l)$$
$$\wedge (x)(x \in t \rightarrow (Ez)(x \in z \wedge z \in t \wedge z \in A)))].$$

By generalizing here with respect to the variable $A$ in the second member of the principal implication, we immediately obtain the required result,

$$\text{Lim }(l) \wedge (w)(w \in l \rightarrow B(w)) \rightarrow B(l).$$

We have thus established (40)—the formalization of Mahlo's postulates. We can subsequently replace the bound variable $U$ by the free variable $A$. By a particular application of the formula it follows:

$$\text{Od }(k) \wedge \text{Od }(a) \rightarrow (Et)(\text{Ma }(t,k) \wedge a \in t)$$

(for each ordinal $k$ and each ordinal $a$ there is a Mahlo number of order $k$ which exceeds $a$).

To sum up, our results have been established within the formal system consisting of the predicate calculus with class and set variables; the $\iota$-schema (2), the *comprehension schema* (16), and the axioms:

| | |
|---|---|
| $a = b. \rightarrow .(a \in C \rightarrow b \in C)$ | (Axiom of equality) |
| $(x)(x \in a \leftrightarrow x \in b) \rightarrow a = b$ | (Axiom of extensionality) |
| $a \in c \rightarrow \sigma(c) \in c \wedge a \notin \sigma(c)$ | (Axiom of choice and foundation) |
| $(Ex)(z)(z \in x \leftrightarrow z \in a \wedge z \in C)$ | (Axiom of subsets). |

Finally, there is the *reflection schema*

$$A \rightarrow (Ey)(\text{Trans }(y) \wedge \text{Rel }(y,A)).$$

From all this we obtain the remaining axioms of Zermelo–Fraenkel set theory along with strengthened versions of the reflection schema from which Mahlo's postulates can be deduced.

REMARK. In the recent discussion of inaccessible cardinals, there is the tendency to avoid application of the axiom of choice.

We have used this axiom only in transforming the definition of In $(m)$ into the equivalence (31).

As Lévy has pointed out, the axiom of choice can be dispensed with completely if we modify our definition of inaccessibility. Denoting the modified predicate by In*, the following two conditions must be satisfied:

1. If the axiom of choice is assumed, we should be able to prove

(a) $$\text{In*}(m) \leftrightarrow \text{In}(m).$$

2. If not, we should be able to show

(b) $$\text{Strans}(b) \wedge \text{Mod}(b) \rightarrow \text{In*}(\mu(b)).$$

Lévy's definition which satisfies these requirements has been simplified by Montague and Vaught;[1] their version takes the form of the following

DEFINITION. $\text{In*}(m) \leftrightarrow \text{Od}(m) \wedge \omega \in m \wedge \text{Clf}(\psi(m))$,

where $\psi$ is von Neumann's function defined in §4 in connection with transfinite recursion.

A proof of (a) for the predicate In* as defined above is included in the reasonings of SHEPHERDSON [1951–1953].

We sketch a proof of (a).[2] Assuming the axiom of choice one proves

(c) $$\text{In}(m) \wedge k \in m \rightarrow (Ex)(x \in m \wedge \psi(k) \sim x)$$

by induction on the ordinal $k$ using the implications

$$\text{In}(m) \rightarrow (x)(x \in m \rightarrow (Ez)(\pi(x) \sim z \wedge z \in m))$$

(for the case that $k$ is a successor ordinal) and

$$\text{In}(m) \rightarrow \text{Lir}(m)$$

(for the case that $k$ is a limit ordinal).

In order to prove In $(m) \rightarrow \text{In*}(m)$ one need only show

(d) $$\text{In}(m) \rightarrow \text{Clf}(\psi(m)).$$

---

[1] Cf. MONTAGUE and VAUGHT [1959], §6. The definition given here corresponds to their concept of a strongly inaccessible ordinal $> \omega$.

[2] Added for this edition by K. Gloede.

Abbreviating the formula

$$\text{In}(m) \wedge \text{Fu}(f) \wedge \text{dom}_1(f) \in \psi(m) \wedge \text{dom}_2(f) \subseteq \psi(m)$$

by $\text{I}(m,f)$ one obtains from (c) and the third formula of (N):

$$\text{I}(m,f) \to (Ex)(x \in m \wedge \text{dom}_1(f) \sim x).$$

Hence, what remains to prove is

$$\text{In}(m) \wedge \text{Sq}(g) \wedge \text{dom}_1(g) \in m \wedge \text{dom}_2(g) \subseteq \psi(m) \to \text{dom}_2(g) \in \psi(m).$$

This results as follows. To each element $a$ of $\text{dom}_2(g)$ we assign the least ordinal $k$ such that $a \in \psi(k)$. Let $s$ be the set of ordinals assigned in this way to the elements of $\text{dom}_2(g)$. Then $s \subseteq m$, and $s$ is the codomain of a sequence with domain $\text{dom}_1(g) \in m$. Hence from $\text{In}(m)$ we can infer $\Sigma(s) \in m$. On the other hand

$$\text{dom}_2(g) \subseteq \psi\left(\sum(s)\right) \in \psi\left(\sum(s)'\right) \in \psi(m)$$

and thus $\text{dom}_2(g) \in \psi(m)$. Of course this reasoning can be formalized so that we obtain (d).

In order to prove (a), note that

$$\text{In}^*(m) \to \text{Lim}(m) \wedge \text{Clf}(\psi(m)) \wedge \omega \in m$$

from which formula one deduces

$$\text{In}^*(m) \to \text{Strans}(\psi(m)) \wedge \text{Mod}(\psi(m)).$$

Using (34) one obtains

$$\text{In}^*(m) \to \text{In}(\mu(\psi(m))).$$

Since

$$\text{Od}(m) \to \mu(\psi(m)) = \psi(m) \cap \{x/\text{Od}(x)\} = m,$$

we get the desired conclusion

$$\text{In}^*(m) \to \text{In}(m).$$

A proof of (b) (without application of the axiom of choice) amounts, in virtue of (35) and (35b), to a proof of

(e)                    $\text{Strans}(b) \wedge \text{Mod}(b) \to \text{Clf}(\psi(\mu(b))).$

For the proof of (e) we first observe that by (35c) we have

(f)                    $\text{Strans}(b) \wedge \text{Mod}(b) \to \text{Lim}(\mu(b)).$

Further we show

(g)                    $\text{Strans}(b) \wedge \text{Mod}(b) \wedge k \in \mu(b) \to \psi(k) \in b$

by induction on $k$. Thus let us assume

$$\text{Strans}(b) \wedge \text{Mod}(b) \wedge k \in \mu(b).$$

By induction hypothesis,

$$(x)(x \in k \rightarrow \chi(x) \in b)$$

and hence by Strans $(b) \wedge \text{Pt}(b)$:

$$(x)(x \in k \rightarrow \psi(x') \in b).$$

Since Clf $(b)$ we get

$$\psi(k) = \sum \{\psi(x')/x \in k\} \in b.$$

Thus (g) is proved. From (f) and (g) we get

(h) $\qquad \text{Strans}(b) \wedge \text{Mod}(b) \rightarrow \psi(\mu(b)) \subseteq b.$

With the help of (f) and (h) we are now able to derive (e). Assume

$$\text{Strans}(b) \wedge \text{Mod}(b) \wedge \text{Fu}(g) \wedge \text{dom}_1(g) \in \psi(\mu(b)) \wedge \text{dom}_2(g) \subseteq \psi(\mu(b)).$$

Then we have by (h): $\text{dom}_1(g) \in b \wedge \text{dom}_2(g) \subseteq b$, and thereby in virtue of Clf $(b)$, $\text{dom}_2(g) \in b$. Now let $s$ be as in the proof of (d). By $\text{dom}_2(g) \subseteq \psi(\mu(b))$ and $\text{Lim}(\mu(b))$ we have $s \subseteq \mu(b) \subseteq b$, and hence $s \in b$ and $\Sigma(s) \in b$ by $\text{Mod}(b)$. Since $\Sigma(s)$ is an ordinal, $\Sigma(s) \in \mu(b)$. Therefore $\text{dom}_2(g) \subseteq \psi(\Sigma(s)) \in \psi(\mu(b))$.

This completes the proof of (e), and hence (b) follows.


## Appendix

As well known, there is the possibility of avoiding the distinction of two sorts of variables and of terms by identifying each set with the class represented by it. The individuals then are the classes, among which the sets are distinguished as those classes which are in the relation $\in$ to an individual, i.e. which are elements.

This procedure is in fact the one most frequently used in recent formalizations of set theory. We shall outline a modification of our system along these lines.

The interpretation of individuals as classes further suggests to take equality as a relation between classes and to introduce it by the defining equivalence:

DEFINITION. $\quad a = b \leftrightarrow (x)(x \in a \leftrightarrow x \in b).$

Instead of the axioms of equality and extensionality we now have only the axiom of equality:

(1″)                         $a = b \rightarrow (a \in c \rightarrow b \in c)$.

It could seem that we also need a formula of equality for the function symbol $\sigma$:

$$a = b \rightarrow \sigma(a) = \sigma(b).$$

But we shall see in the sequel that this is not required.[1]
The comprehension schema now gets the form

$$c \in \{x/A(x)\} \leftrightarrow (Ez)(c \in z) \wedge A(c).$$

Defining the universal class $\gamma$ by the

DEFINITION.   $\gamma = \{x/x \subseteq x\}$,

we have the theorem:

$$(Ez)(a \in z) \leftrightarrow a \in \gamma.$$

The axiom of subsets may now be expressed as

$$a \subseteq b \wedge b \in \gamma \rightarrow a \in \gamma.$$

This formula (as we shall see below) becomes provable if we substitute Strans $(y)$ for Trans $(y)$ in the reflection schema. With this strengthening the reflection schema now reads:

$$A \rightarrow (Ey)(\text{Strans}\,(y) \wedge (Ez)(y \in z) \wedge \text{Rel*}\,(y,A)),$$

where as before, the expression Rel* $(y,A)$ refers directly only to a reduced formula A, but now we admit class terms $\{x/P(x)\}$ to occur in reduced formulas. Moreover, since there is now one sort of variable (i.e. class variable) only, the operation of relativizing will be different from the operation Rel defined for the language with set and class variables as described in the main part of this paper.

The axioms of choice and foundation retain their original form but become more widely applicable. Both the $\iota$-symbol and the $\iota$-schema become redundant.

Let us now describe in more detail the structure of a formalized axiom system, adapted to our purposes.

There is only one sort of variable: class-variable, and only the one fundamental binary predicate $\in$. The derivations go by the predicate calculus to which the unary function symbol $\sigma$ and the class symbols $\{x/A(x)\}$ are added. The formal axioms are: the axiom of equality (and extensionality)

$$a = b \rightarrow (a \in c \rightarrow b \in c),$$

---

[1] This fact was first stated by MYHILL [1963].

to which belongs the definition of equality

$$a = b \leftrightarrow (x)(x \in a \leftrightarrow x \in b),$$

and the axiom of choice and foundation,

$$a \in c \to \sigma(c) \in c \land a \notin \sigma(c).$$

There are two axiom schemata: the comprehension schema (schema about classes)

$$c \in \{x/A(x)\} \leftrightarrow (Ez)(c \in z) \land A(c),$$

and the reflection schema (schema of set existence)

$$A \to (Ey)(\text{Strans}(y) \land (Ez)(y \in z) \land \text{Rel*}(y,A)),$$

with $y$ not occurring in A. This last one is to be completed by the definitions

$$a \subseteq b \leftrightarrow (x)(x \in a \to x \in b),$$

$$\text{Strans}(b) \leftrightarrow (u)(v)(v \in b \land (u \in v \lor u \subseteq v) \to u \in b)$$

and by the rule of forming Rel*$(y,A)$ from A, which consists in first replacing every defined symbol occurring in A by its defining expression and then replacing each component of the form

$$(x)P(x) \quad \text{by} \quad (x)(x \subseteq y \to P(x))$$

$$(Ex)P(x) \quad \text{by} \quad (Ex)(x \subseteq y \land P(x))$$

$$\{x/P(x)\} \quad \text{by} \quad \{x/x \in y \land P(x)\}$$

and every free variable $a$ by $a \cap y$, where the symbol $\cap$ is defined by[1]

$$a \cap b = \{x/x \in a \land x \in b\};$$

the last replacement, however, can be spared, when A is of the form $a \in t$, ($t$ being any term), or has a conjunction member of this form.

Still the first deductive steps for developing the formal system may be indicated.

---

[1] We are using here and in the following equations as definitions of class terms, treating these equations in the derivations as formal axioms. It might not seem quite trivial that a class symbol $\mathfrak{s}$, defined by an equation $\mathfrak{s} = t$, is everywhere replaceable by the defining term $t$ and inversely. Yet by the definition of equality we immediately have $c \in \mathfrak{s} \leftrightarrow c \in t$, as also $t = \mathfrak{s}$; further by the axiom of equality we get $\mathfrak{s} \in c \leftrightarrow t \in c$. Thus first we have the replaceability in the prime formulas. Moreover, it soon will be shown that for any formula $A(c)$ we have $a = b \to (A(a) \leftrightarrow A(b))$, whereby the replaceability of $A(\mathfrak{s})$ by $A(t)$, and inversely, follows.

Besides we have to regard that in the reflection schema it is expressly required that for the formation of Rel$(b,A)$ the defined symbols in A have to be replaced by their defining expressions.

From the definition of equality we get

$$a = a, \qquad a = b \to b = a$$

and, together with the axiom of equality:

$$((1)) \qquad a = b \to (a \in c \leftrightarrow b \in c).$$

Furthermore, from the axiom of equality, we obtain by substitution

$$a = b \to (a \in \{x/\sigma(a) = \sigma(x)\} \to b \in \{x/\sigma(a) = \sigma(x)\}),$$

and, by the comprehension schema:

$$a = b \to ((Ez)(a \in z) \wedge \sigma(a) = \sigma(a) \to (Ez)(b \in z) \wedge \sigma(a) = \sigma(b)),$$

and hence, using $\sigma(a) = \sigma(a)$:

$$((2)) \qquad a = b \wedge a \in c \to (\sigma(a) = \sigma(b)).$$

Now defining

$$\gamma = \{x/x \subseteq x\},$$

we have, by the comprehension schema and the formula $a \subseteq a$,

$$c \in a \to c \in \gamma,$$

hence

$$((3)) \qquad a \subseteq \gamma$$

and

$$((4)) \qquad (Ez)(c \in z) \leftrightarrow c \in \gamma.$$

The interpretation of this formula is that $(Ez)(c \in z)$ is the necessary and sufficient condition for $c$ being a *set*, and $\gamma$ is the class of all sets.

An application of the reflection schema together with the definition of $\gamma$ gives

$$((4a)) \qquad c \in \gamma \to (Ey)(\text{Strans}(y) \wedge (Ez)(y \in z) \wedge c \in \{x/x \in y$$
$$\wedge (u)(u \subseteq y \to (u \in x \to u \in x))\})$$

and, using the comprehension schema as also the formula ((3)) and the predicate calculus:

$$c \in \gamma \to (Ey)(\text{Strans}(y) \wedge c \in y \wedge y \subseteq \gamma),$$

as also

$$a \subseteq c \wedge c \in \gamma \to (Ey)(\text{Strans}(y) \wedge a \subseteq c \wedge c \in y \wedge y \subseteq \gamma)$$

and finally, by the definitions of Strans and of $\subseteq$,

$$((5)) \qquad a \subseteq c \wedge c \in \gamma \to a \in \gamma.$$

From this formula we get, by using the formulas $a \cap c \subseteq c$, $c \cap a \subseteq c$ (with application of the comprehension schema):

((5a))        $c \in \gamma \to a \cap c \in \gamma$

((5b))        $c \in \gamma \to c \cap a \in \gamma$,

and, using ((4)):

$$(Ez)(c \in z) \to (Ez)(a \cap c \in z)$$
$$(Ez)(c \in z) \to (Ez)(c \cap a \in z).$$

From ((5b)), by substituting $\{x/A(x)\}$ for $a$, we obtain

$$c \in \gamma \to c \cap \{x/A(x)\} \in \gamma$$

as also, using the comprehension schema and the axiom of equality:

((5c))        $c \in \gamma \to \{x/x \in c \wedge A(x)\} \in \gamma$,

which is a formalization of the *Aussonderungsaxiom*, in a strengthened form insofar as within the formula A quantifications over class variables are admitted.

Let us therefore call this derived schema the "selection schema". We are now able to derive the formula

$$a = b \to \sigma(a) = \sigma(b).$$

This will be done indirectly. The negation of the formula to be proved is elementarily transformable into the formula

$$a = b \wedge \to (\sigma(a) = \sigma(b)),$$

which may briefly be denoted by B. Applying the reflection schema to B we have

$$B \to (Ey)(\text{Strans}\,(y) \wedge (Ez)(y \in z) \wedge \text{Rel}^*\,(y, a = b \wedge \to (\sigma(a) = \sigma(b)))),$$

which is of the form

$$B \to (Ey)P(y)$$

where $P(c)$ is the expression

$$\text{Strans}\,(c) \wedge (Ez)(c \in z) \wedge \text{Rel}^*\,(c, a = b \wedge \to (\sigma(a) = \sigma(b))).$$

We thus have, according to the prescriptions concerning the formation of $\text{Rel}^*\,(c, A)$ and by the definition of equality:

[P₁]    $P(c) \to \text{Strans}\,(c)$

[P₂]    $P(c) \to (Ez)(c \in z)$

[P₃]    $P(c) \to (x)(x \subseteq c \to (x \in a \cap c \leftrightarrow x \in b \cap c))$

[P₄]     $P(c) \to (Ex)(x \subseteq c \land \to (x \in \sigma(a \cap c) \leftrightarrow x \in \sigma(b \cap c)))$.

From [P₁] and [P₃] we get, using the formula

$$\text{Strans}(c) \to (d \in c \to d \subseteq c),$$

which follows from the definition of Strans, and the formula $d \in a \cap c \to d \in c$, which follows from the definition of $a \cap c$:

[P₅]                    $P(c) \to (a \cap c = b \cap c)$.

Furthermore, by applying formula ((2)) which immediately gives

$$a = b \land (Ez)(a \in z) \to \sigma(a) = \sigma(b),$$

we get

$$a \cap c = b \cap c \land (Ez)(a \cap c \in z) \to \sigma(a \cap c) = \sigma(b \cap c),$$

and on the other hand, by [P₂] and ((5c)), we have

$$P(c) \to (Ez)(a \cap c \in z).$$

Hence, we get

[P₆]        $P(c) \to (a \cap c = b \cap c \to \sigma(a \cap c) = \sigma(b \cap c))$.

Together, [P₅] and [P₆] yield:

[P₇]                    $P(c) \to \sigma(a \cap c) = \sigma(b \cap c)$.

But, from [P₄] follows

$$P(c) \to (Ex) \to (x \in \sigma(a \cap c) \leftrightarrow x \in \sigma(b \cap c)),$$
$$\to \to (x)(x \in \sigma(a \cap c) \leftrightarrow x \in \sigma(b \cap c))$$

[P₈]        $P(c) \to \to (\sigma(a \cap c) = \sigma(b \cap c))$.

And from [P₇] and [P₈] we obtain, by the logical calculus, successively

$$\to P(c), \qquad (x) \to P(x), \qquad \to (Ey)P(y),$$

which, together with the formula

$$B \to (Ey)P(y),$$

from which we started, gives $\to B$. However, B is the negation of the formula to be derived. Hence, we get this formula

((6))                    $a = b \to \sigma(a) = \sigma(b)$.

Using the definition of equality and the formulas ((1)) and ((6)), as also the schema

$$(x)(A(x) \leftrightarrow B(x)) \to \{x/A(x)\} = \{x/B(x)\},$$

which easily follows from the comprehension schema and which can be specialized to the schema

$$(x)(A(a,x) \leftrightarrow A(b,x)) \rightarrow \{x/A(a,x)\} = \{x/A(b,x)\},$$

we can derive for any formula $A(c)$, by means of the predicate calculus:

$$a = b \rightarrow (A(a) \leftrightarrow A(b)).$$

This results by a metamathematical induction with respect to the construction of the formula $A(c)$ out of prime formulas. Thus, we have at our disposal all the specializations of the equality schema.

We now go on to derive the statements on existence of sets which are usually taken as axioms.[1]

Defining

$$0 = \{x/ \rightarrow x \subseteq x\},$$

we get, using the comprehension schema and the formula $a \subseteq a$:

$$\rightarrow a \in 0,$$

hence $a \in 0 \rightarrow a \in c$, and thus

((7))                                    $0 \subseteq c.$

Taking for A any provable formula in the reflection schema, we get:

$$(Ey)(Ez)(y \in z),$$

and using ((4)):

$$(Ey)(y \in \gamma);$$

and this formula, together with ((5)) and ((7)) yields, by the predicate calculus

((8))                                    $0 \in \gamma.$

Thus 0 is a set.

For the following applications of the reflection schema, we apply an auxiliary reasoning:

In order to form for a formula $C(\gamma)$, which contains $\gamma$, the expression Rel* $(b,C(\gamma))$, we have first to replace $\gamma$ by its defining expression $\{x/x \subseteq x\}$, which then again is to be replaced by $\{x/x \in b \wedge x \subseteq x\}$. Now, by the comprehension schema, we have

$$a \in \{x/x \in b \wedge x \subseteq x\} \leftrightarrow (Ez)(a \in z) \wedge a \in b \wedge a \subseteq a$$

---

[1] The derivations are given in such a way as to be readable, independently of the foregoing.

and hence, using the predicate calculus and the formula $a \subseteq a$, we get

$$a \in \{x/x \in b \wedge x \subseteq x\} \leftrightarrow a \in b,$$

so that the definition of equality yields

$$\{x/x \in b \wedge x \subseteq x\} = b ;$$

and from this, as cases of the equality schema:

$$\mathrm{Rel}^*(b,\mathrm{C}(\gamma)) \rightarrow \mathrm{Rel}^*(b,\mathrm{C}(b)),$$

$$(Ey)(\mathrm{B}(y) \wedge \mathrm{Rel}^*(y,\mathrm{C}(\gamma))) \rightarrow (Ey)(\mathrm{B}(y) \wedge \mathrm{Rel}^*(y,\mathrm{C}(y))).$$

Thus, from any formula of the form $\mathrm{A} \rightarrow (Ey)(\mathrm{B}(y) \wedge \mathrm{Rel}^*(y,\mathrm{C}(\gamma)))$, we get $\mathrm{A} \rightarrow (Ey)(\mathrm{B}(y) \wedge \mathrm{Rel}^*(y,\mathrm{C}(y)))$. Let us briefly call the schema of this passage the "$\gamma$-schema".

Our first application of this schema is for $\mathrm{C}(\gamma)$ being the formula $a \in \gamma \wedge b \in \gamma$.

By the reflection schema, we have

$$a \in \gamma \wedge b \in \gamma \rightarrow (Ey)(\mathrm{Strans}\,(y) \wedge (Ez)(y \in z) \wedge \mathrm{Rel}^*(y,a \in \gamma \wedge b \in \gamma)).$$

From this, by using the $\gamma$-schema, the rule of forming $\mathrm{Rel}^*(y,\mathrm{A})$, the formula ((4)) and the predicate calculus, we get

((9))           $a \in \gamma \wedge b \in \gamma \rightarrow (Ey)(y \in \gamma \wedge a \in y \wedge b \in y).$

Defining now

$$[a,b] = \{x/a = x \vee b = x\},$$

we have by the comprehension schema

$$c \in [a,b] \rightarrow (Ez)(c \in z) \wedge (a = c \vee b = c).$$

From this and the formulas

$$a = c \rightarrow (a \in d \rightarrow c \in d)$$
$$b = c \rightarrow (b \in d \rightarrow c \in d)$$

(which indeed are applications of the axiom of equality), we get by means of the propositional calculus

$$c \in [a,b] \wedge a \in d \wedge b \in d \rightarrow c \in d$$

and hence, by the predicate calculus and the definition of $\subseteq$,

$$(a \in d \wedge b \in d) \rightarrow [a,b] \subseteq d,$$

as also

$$(Ey)(y \in \gamma \wedge a \in y \wedge b \in y) \rightarrow (Ey)(y \in \gamma \wedge [a,b] \subseteq y).$$

This formula, together with formulas ((9)) and ((5)) yields, by the predicate calculus

((10)) $\qquad a \in \gamma \wedge b \in \gamma \rightarrow [a,b] \in \gamma.$

Thus, if $a$ and $b$ are sets, then $[a,b]$ is also a set.

Defining also

$$[a] = [a,a],$$

we get

((11)) $\qquad a \in \gamma \rightarrow [a] \in \gamma$

and

$$[a] = \{x/a = x\}.$$

Taking in the reflection schema for A the formula

$$0 \in \gamma \wedge (z)(z \in \gamma \rightarrow [z] \in \gamma),$$

which is derivable from ((8)) and ((11)), we obtain, using the $\gamma$-schema and formula ((4)):

$$(Ey)(y \in \gamma \ \text{Strans} \ (y) \wedge \text{Rel} \ (y, 0 \in y \wedge (z)(z \in y \rightarrow [z] \in y))).$$

From this we pass, by applying the rule of forming $\text{Rel}^* (y,B)$ as also the formulas

$$\{x/x \in b \wedge \rightarrow x \subseteq x\} = 0,$$
$$a \in b \rightarrow \{x/x \in b \wedge a = x\} = [a],$$

which follow from the comprehension schema together with the formula $a \subseteq a$, the equality axiom and the definition of equality, to the formula

$$(Ey)(y \in \gamma \wedge 0 \in y \wedge (z)(z \in y \rightarrow [z] \in y)).$$

Thereby, Zermelo's axiom of infinity is expressed.

We further derive the axiom of the power set and the axiom of the sum set (Vereinigungsmenge).

Therefore, we use the formula

((12)) $\qquad c \in \gamma \rightarrow (Ey)(\text{Strans} \ (y) \wedge y \in \gamma \wedge c \in y),$

which results as an application of the reflection schema together with the $\gamma$-schema and ((4)).

Defining the power class of $c$:

$$\pi(c) = \{x/x \subseteq c\},$$

we have

$$a \in \pi(c) \leftrightarrow (Ez)(a \in z) \wedge a \subseteq c,$$

and hence, using the definition of Strans:

$$\text{Strans}(b) \wedge c \in b \to (a \in \pi(c) \to a \in b),$$

which gives (by the predicate calculus and the definition of $\subseteq$):

$$\text{Strans}(b) \wedge c \in b \to \pi(c) \subseteq b.$$

From this, using formula ((5)), we obtain

$$\text{Strans}(b) \wedge b \in \gamma \wedge c \in b \to \pi(c) \in \gamma.$$

And this together with ((12)) gives, by the predicate calculus, the formula

((13))                              $c \in \gamma \to \pi(c) \in \gamma,$

which expresses that the power class of a set is again a set.
Defining further the sum class of $c$:

$$\sum(c) = \{x / (Ez)(x \in z \wedge z \in c)\},$$

we have

$$a \in \sum(c) \to (Ez)(a \in z \wedge z \in c).$$

From the definition of Strans follows

$$\text{Strans}(b) \wedge c \in b \wedge d \in c \to d \in b,$$

as also

$$\text{Strans}(b) \wedge c \in b \wedge a \in d \wedge d \in c \to a \in b.$$

Hence by the predicate calculus we get

$$\text{Strans}(b) \wedge c \in b \to \left( a \in \sum(c) \to a \in b \right)$$

as also

$$\text{Strans}(b) \wedge c \in b \to \sum(c) \subseteq b;$$

and from this, using formula ((5)):

$$\text{Strans}(b) \wedge b \in \gamma \wedge c \in b \to \sum(c) \in \gamma.$$

This formula together with ((12)) yields:

((14))                              $c \in \gamma \to \sum(c) \in \gamma,$

whereby is expressed that the sumclass of a set is again a set.
Herewith already all the Zermelo axioms of set theory are obtained.
Yet we can also derive the axiom of replacement, in the strengthened form given by THIELE [1955], which in our formal system is expressed, using the definition of the ordered pair

$$\langle a,b \rangle = [[a],[a,b]],$$

by the formula:[1]

$((15))$    $m \in \gamma \wedge (x)(x \in m \to (Ez)(z \in \gamma \wedge \langle x,z \rangle \in a))$
$\to (Ey)(y \in \gamma \wedge (x)(x \in m \to (Ez)(z \in y \wedge \langle x,z \rangle \in a)))$.

The proof of $((15))$ goes by applying the reflection schema, taking for A the formula

$$m \in \gamma \wedge (u)(v)(u \in \gamma \wedge v \in \gamma \to [u,v] \in \gamma)$$
$$\wedge (x)(x \in m \to (Ez)(z \in \gamma \wedge \langle x,z \rangle \in a)),$$

which we briefly indicate as

$$m \in \gamma \wedge C(\gamma) \wedge D(\gamma).$$

The reflection schema together with the $\gamma$-schema and formula $((4))$ gives:

(F)    $m \in \gamma \wedge C(\gamma) \wedge D(\gamma) \to (Ey)(\text{Strans}(y) \wedge y \in \gamma \wedge m \in y$
$\wedge \text{Rel}^*(y,C(y)) \wedge \text{Rel}^*(y,D(y)))$.

Here, in the first member of the implication, the part $C(\gamma)$ can be left away, as $C(\gamma)$ is derivable, resulting immediately from formula $((10))$. $\text{Rel}^*(y,C(y))$ is (after familiar logical transforming):

$(u)(v)(u \subseteq y \wedge v \subseteq y \wedge u \in y \wedge v \in y$
$\to \{w/w \in y \wedge \text{Rel}^*(y,u=w \vee v=w)\} \in y)$.

Now, this expression can be simplified by using the definition of Strans, from which follow the formulas

$$\text{Strans}(b) \to (a \in b \to a \subseteq b),$$
$$\text{Strans}(b) \to (c \in a \wedge a \in b \to c \subseteq b)$$

In virtue of the first of these formulas, we can, in the first implication member of the expression of $\text{Rel}^*(y,C(y))$ leave out the part $u \subseteq y \wedge v \subseteq y$. Further, applying the second formula together with the axiom of equality, we derive

$(y)(\text{Strans}(y) \to (u)(v)(u \in y \wedge v \in y$
$\to \{w/w \in y \wedge \text{Rel}^*(y,u=w \vee v=w)\}$
$= \{w/u=w \vee v=w\}))$,

hence

(G)    $(y)(\text{Strans}(y) \to (u)(v)(u \in y \wedge v \in y \to \text{Rel}^*(y,[u,v]) = [u,v]))$.

---

[1] Compare this formula with the corresponding formula (19) in our former system with two sorts of variables.

Thus, on the whole we get, using anew the axiom of equality:

(H) $\qquad$ $(y)(\text{Strans}\,(y) \wedge \text{Rel*}\,(y,C(y)) \rightarrow C(y))$,

where $C(y)$ is the expression

$$(u)(v)(u \in y \wedge v \in y \rightarrow [u,v] \in y).$$

We then have to consider the expression $\text{Rel*}\,(y,D(y))$, which (again after familiar transformations) is

$$(x)(x \subseteq y \wedge x \in m \rightarrow (Ez)(z \subseteq y \wedge z \in y \wedge \text{Rel*}\,(y,\langle x,z\rangle) \in (a \cap y))),$$

where

$$\text{Rel*}\,(y,\langle x,z\rangle) = \text{Rel*}\,(y,[[x],[x,z]]).$$

Since this expression stands in a conjunction with $\text{Strans}\,(y)$ and $m \in y$, we can cancel within it the members $x \subseteq y$ and $z \subseteq y$, using again the formulas just stated for Strans. Thereby we also get $x \in y$. The last member $a \cap y$ can be replaced by $a$, obviously in virtue of the formula $c \in a \cap b \rightarrow c \in a$.

Further, we have immediately

$$(y)(C(y) \rightarrow (x)(z)(x \in y \wedge z \in y \rightarrow [x,z] \in y))$$

which also by specializing gives

$$(y)(C(y) \rightarrow (x)(x \in y \rightarrow [x] \in y));$$

these both together with the formula (G) yield

$$(y)(\text{Strans}\,(y) \wedge C(y) \rightarrow (x)(z)(x \in y \wedge z \in y$$
$$\rightarrow \text{Rel*}\,(y,[[x],[x,z]]) = [[x],[x,z]]))$$

and by using (H) and the definition of $\langle a,b\rangle$:

$$(y)(\text{Strans}\,(y) \wedge \text{Rel*}\,(y,C(y)) \rightarrow (x)(z)(x \in y \wedge z \in y$$
$$\rightarrow \text{Rel*}\,(y,\langle x,z\rangle) = \langle x,z\rangle)).$$

Combining this formula with (F), making use of the explicit expression of the member $\text{Rel*}\,(y,D(y))$ in $(F)$ and of $\text{Strans}\,(y)$, we obtain the formula ((15)).

Still, we can eliminate here the occurrences of ordered pairs by using the provable schema:

$$b \in \gamma \wedge c \in \gamma \rightarrow (R(b,c) \leftrightarrow \langle b,c\rangle \in \{w/(Eu)(Ev)(u \in \gamma \wedge v \in \gamma \wedge R(u,v)$$
$$\wedge\, w = \langle u,v\rangle)\}).$$

By this way we obtain from ((15)) the following schema of replacement:

$$m \in \gamma \wedge (x)(x \in m \rightarrow (Ez)(z \in \gamma \wedge R(x,z))) \rightarrow (Ey)(y \in \gamma \wedge (x)(x \in m$$
$$\rightarrow (Ez)(z \in y \wedge R(x,z)))).$$

From this schema one gets the usual schema of replacement by introducing the specializing premise on R

$$(x)(y)(z)(R(x,y) \wedge R(x,z) \rightarrow y = z)$$

and applying the schema of Aussonderung ((5c)). The expression of the schema thus to be obtained is

$$m \in \gamma \wedge (x)(y)(z)(R(x,y) \wedge R(x,z) \rightarrow y = z) \wedge$$
$$(x)(x \in m \rightarrow (Ez)(z \in \gamma \wedge R(x,z)))$$
$$\rightarrow \{z/(Ex)(x \in m \wedge R(x,z))\} \in \gamma.$$

Still $\iota$-terms can be introduced by definition as special class terms. The definition of $\iota_x A(x)$ is

$$\iota_x A(x) = \{u/(Ex)(A(x) \wedge (z)(A(z) \rightarrow z = x) \wedge u \in x)\}.$$

From this definition the two formula schemata (2a) and (2b) can be derived. They have now a generalized application, since the $\iota$-terms now can be proper class terms.

Herewith all the derivative means are obtained which we had before in the formal system of sets and classes, from which we showed in particular the Mahlo postulates to be provable.

## References

BERNAYS, P. (1958) *Axiomatic set theory* (with a historical introduction by A. A. Fraenkel). North-Holland, Amsterdam. 226 pp. (2nd ed. (1968), 235 pp.).

DEDEKIND, R. (1888) *Was sind und was sollen die Zahlen?* 6th ed.: F. Vieweg & Sohn, Braunschweig (1930). 58 pp.; also in DEDEKIND (1930–1932) III. English ed. by W. W. Beman, in: *Essays on the theory of numbers* by R. Dedekind. Chicago and London (1901).

DEDEKIND, R. (1930–1932) *Gesammelte mathematische Werke.* R. Fricke, E. Noether and O. Ore (Eds.). 3 vols. F. Vieweg & Sohn, Braunschweig.

FEYS, R. (1944) *Logistiek.* Philosophische Bibliotheek N.V., Antwerpen and Nijmegen.

LÉVY, A. (1958) Contributions to the metamathematics of set theory. Ph.D. thesis, Jerusalem.

LÉVY, A. (1960) Axiom schemata of strong infinity in axiomatic set theory. *Pacific J. Math.* **10**, 223–238.

MAHLO, P. (1911) Über lineare transfinite Mengen. *Berichte über die Verhandlungen der Königlich Sächsischen Akademie der Wissenschaften zu Leipzig*, Math.-Phys. Klasse, **63**, 187–225.

MAHLO, P. (1912–1913) Zur Theorie und Anwendung der $\rho_0$-Zahlen, *ibid.*, I: **64**, 108–112 (1912); II: **65**, 268–282 (1913).

MONTAGUE, R. and VAUGHT, R. L. (1959) Natural models of set theories. *Fund. Math.* **47**, 219–242.

MYHILL, J. R. (1963) Remark on a system of Bernays. *J.S.L.* **28**, 75–76.

NEUMANN, J. VON (1929) Über eine Widerspruchsfreiheitsfrage in der axiomatischen Mengenlehre. *J. f. Math.* **160**, 227–241; also in VON NEUMANN (1961), pp. 494–508.

NEUMANN, J. VON (1961) *Collected works*. Vol. 1. Pergamon, New York. 654 pp.

SHEPHERDSON, J. C. (1951–1953) Inner models for set theory. *J.S.L.* **16**, 161–190 (1951); **17**, 225–237 (1952); **18**, 145–167 (1953).

SKOLEM, TH. (1929) Über einige Grundlagenfragen der Mathematik. *Skrifter utgit av det Norske Vid.-Akad. i Oslo* I (4), 1–49.

TARSKI, A. (1938) Über unerreichbare Kardinalzahlen. *Fund. Math.* **30**, 68–89.

THIELE, E. J. (1955) Ein axiomatisches System der Mengenlehre nach Zermelo und Fraenkel. *Zeitschr. f. math. Logik* **1**, 173–195.

ZERMELO, E. (1930) Über Grenzzahlen und Mengenbereiche. *Fund. Math.* **16**, 29–47.

SETS AND CLASSES; On the work by Paul Bernays
© North-Holland Publishing Company (1976) pp. 173–215.

# THE ROLE OF CLASSES IN
# SET THEORY

Azriel LÉVY

*Jerusalem, Israel*

## 1. Preliminaries

The present paper is from the book *Foundations of Set Theory* (Chap. II, §7).[1] We shall refer, throughout the paper, to that book as *Foundations*. The only changes made here are those which became necessary as a consequence of the fact that this section is reprinted separately.

We discuss here various systems of set theory which admit, beside sets, also classes. We only discuss such systems which view the sets from the same point of view as the Zermelo–Fraenkel set theory ZF or from a similar point of view, e.g. we do not discuss here the set theory "Mathematical Logic" of QUINE [1951] (see *Foundations* pp. 167–171).

Since we view the sets from the point of view of ZF, that set theory will be the starting point of our investigation of set theories with classes. Therefore, we shall first give a description of ZF.

The language of ZF contains just one kind of individual variable, for which we use lowercase letters. In a general mathematical language the range of the individual variables, the so-called *universe of discourse*, consists of *objects*. Since we are dealing with set theory, it is natural to assume that each of these objects is a member of some set (which is again an object). This is in accordance with one of the tacit principles of Cantor's naive set theory that every object can serve as a building block for sets. That set can be, for example, a set which contains just this single object. However, some of the systems of set theory discussed in the present paper abandon this principle. Yet, as far as ZF is concerned, this principle remains valid; it is implemented by the axiom of pairing. Throughout the present paper we mean by *element* an object which is a member of some object. In ZF the term "element" is synonymous with

---

[1] Complete reference: *Foundations of Set Theory*, second revised edition (First ed.: 1958), by A. A. Fraenkel, Y. Bar-Hillel and A. Lévy, with collaboration of D. van Dalen (North-Holland, Amsterdam, 1973).

the term "object", yet we prefer to use the former so as to facilitate the comparison of ZF with those systems of set theory which we shall discuss here where not all objects are elements.

In the version of ZF presented here we assume that all objects are sets. This is done for the purpose of convenience. Permitting the existence of elements which are not sets (these are usually called *urelements*), would have necessitated some rather trivial changes throughout the paper.

The atomic statements of ZF are of the form $x = y$ and $x \in y$, where $x$ and $y$ are any variables. From the atomic statements we build all statements by means of the connectives $\to$ (not), $\vee$ (or), $\wedge$ (and), $\to$ (if ..., then), $\leftrightarrow$ (if and only if) and the quantifiers $\exists x$ (there exists an $x$ such that) and $\forall x$ (for all $x$).

A statement is said to be *closed* if it contains no free variables. It is said to be *open* if it contains at least one free occurrence of a variable. An open statement in which the variable "$x$" is free will also be called, according to mathematical custom, a *condition on x*. A condition on $x$ can also have free variables other than $x$; these additional variables will be called *parameters*. For example, the statement "$x$ is a member of $y$" can be regarded as a condition on $x$ and $y$ with no parameters, or as a condition on $x$ with the parameter $y$, or as a condition on $y$ with the parameter $x$, just as in ordinary mathematical usage the function $ax + b$ can be regarded as a function of $x$ with $a$ and $b$ as parameters, or as a function of $x$, $a$, $b$, with no parameters, etc.

DEFINITION I. If $y$ and $z$ are sets such that for all $x$ if $x \in y$, then $x \in z$, then we shall write $y \subseteq z$ and say that $y$ is a *subset* of $z$ ($y$ is *included* in $z$).

We now list the axioms I–VII and IX of ZF.

AXIOM (I) OF EXTENSIONALITY. If $x \subseteq y$ and $y \subseteq x$, then $x = y$; in other words, sets containing the same members are equal. In symbols:

$$\forall x \, \forall y \, [\forall z \, (z \in x \leftrightarrow z \in y) \to x = y].$$

AXIOM (II) OF PAIRING. For any two elements $a$ and $b$ there exists the set $y$ which contains just $a$ and $b$ (i.e. $a$ and $b$ and no different member). In symbols:

$$\forall a \, \forall b \, \exists y \, \forall x \, [x \in y \leftrightarrow (x = a \vee x = b)].$$

AXIOM (III) OF UNION. For any set $a$ there exists the set whose members are just the members of the members of $a$. In symbols:

$$\forall a \, \exists y \, \forall x \, [x \in y \leftrightarrow \exists z \, (x \in z \wedge z \in a)].$$

AXIOM (IV) OF POWER SET. **For any set $a$ there exists the set whose members are just the subsets of $a$.** In symbols:

$$\forall a \exists y \forall x \, (x \in y \leftrightarrow x \subseteq a).$$

AXIOM SCHEMA (V) OF SUBSETS (or SEPARATION). **For any set $a$ and any condition $\mathfrak{P}(x)$ on $x$ there exists the set that contains just those members $x$ of $a$ which fulfil the condition $\mathfrak{P}(x)$.** In symbols:

$$\forall z_1 \cdots \forall z_n \, \forall a \, \exists y \, \forall x (x \in y \leftrightarrow x \in a \wedge \mathfrak{P}(x)),$$

where $z_1, \ldots, z_n$ are the free variables of $\mathfrak{P}(x)$ other than $x$, and $y$ is not a free variable of $\mathfrak{P}(x)$.

AXIOM (VI) OF INFINITY. **There exists a set $z$ such that the null set O is a member of $z$, and whenever $x \in z$ also $x \cup \{x\} \in z$.** In symbols:

$$\exists z [\exists y (y \in z \wedge \rightarrow \exists t (t \in y)) \wedge$$
$$\forall x (x \in z \rightarrow \exists y (y \in z \wedge \forall t (t \in y \leftrightarrow t \in x \vee t = x)))].$$

We use "$\mathfrak{P}(t,x)$ as a functional condition" as a shorter version of "for every element $t$ there is at most one element $x$ such that $\mathfrak{P}(t,x)$ holds".

AXIOM SCHEMA (VII) OF REPLACEMENT. **If $\mathfrak{P}(t,x)$ is a functional condition, then for every set $a$ there exists a set which contains exactly those elements $x$ for which $\mathfrak{P}(t,x)$ holds for some $t \in a$.** In symbols:

$$\forall z_1 \cdots \forall z_n [\forall u \, \forall v \, \forall w (\mathfrak{P}(u,v) \wedge \mathfrak{P}(u,w) \rightarrow v = w) \rightarrow$$
$$\forall a \, \exists y \, \forall x (x \in y \leftrightarrow \exists t (t \in a \wedge \mathfrak{P}(t,x)))],$$

where $u$, $v$, $w$, $y$ are not free in the condition $\mathfrak{P}(t,x)$ and $z_1, \ldots, z_n$ are the free variables of $\mathfrak{P}(t,x)$ other than $t$ and $x$.

AXIOM SCHEMA (IX) OF FOUNDATION. **For any condition $\mathfrak{P}(x)$, if there is an element $x$ which fulfils $\mathfrak{P}(x)$ then there is a minimal element $u$ which fulfils $\mathfrak{P}(x)$, i.e. $u$ fulfils $\mathfrak{P}(x)$ but none of its members does.**

This ends our listing of the axioms of **ZF**. An additional axiom, which is very useful in mathematics, is the following.

AXIOM (VIII) OF (LOCAL) CHOICE. **For any set $t$ in which the null set is not contained, there exists a choice function $f$ on $t$, i.e. a function $f$ whose domain is $t$ such that for each member $s$ of $t$, $f(s) \in s$.**

We denote by **ZFC** the set theory obtained from **ZF** by the addition of the axiom of choice.

The axiom of choice asserts the existence of a choice function on every set $t$ of non-empty sets. A concept strongly related to that of a choice function is the concept of a selector. Let **Q** be any set theory which includes **ZF**. A *selector* is a definable unary operation $\sigma(x)$ such that one can prove in **Q** that for every non-empty set $x$, $\sigma(x)$ is a member of $x$. We now see that if **Q** has a selector then the axiom of choice is provable in **Q**. Let $t$ be a set of non-empty sets. Let $f$ be the set $\{\langle x,\sigma(x)\rangle | x \in t\}$, then $f$ is clearly a choice function on $t$. In **ZFC** no selector is available (if **ZF** is consistent—see *Foundations*, p. 71), while in the theory **ZFC⁺**, which is **ZF** with Gödel's axiom of constructibility $V = L$ added, we have a selector.

One can also get from **ZF** a system of set theory with a selector by brute force. This is done as follows. First, the language is enriched by adding the operation $\sigma$ as a new primitive notion, in addition to the membership relation. This enrichment of the language causes our notion of condition to be richer too, since now we can express conditions which we could not express before. We denote with **ZFC**$_\sigma$ the system of set theory formulated in our enriched language whose axioms are all the axioms of **ZF**, where *the notion of condition in the axiom schema of replacement (and subsets) is the wider notion just mentioned*, as well as the additional:

AXIOM (VIII$_\sigma$) OF GLOBAL CHOICE. **For every non-empty set** $z$, $\sigma(z)$ **is a member of** $z$.

As in the case mentioned earlier, of a set theory **Q** with a selector, the axiom of choice is provable in **ZFC**$_\sigma$. Let us now compare **ZFC**$_\sigma$ to **ZFC**. Every theorem of **ZFC** is, obviously, a theorem of **ZFC**$_\sigma$. There are statements which are theorems of **ZFC**$_\sigma$, but do not belong to the language of **ZFC** because they contain the symbol $\sigma$, such as Axiom VIII$_\sigma$ itself. However, every statement which is formulated in the language of **ZFC** and which is a theorem of **ZFC**$_\sigma$ is also a theorem of **ZFC**.[1] This also settles the question of the consistency of **ZFC**$_\sigma$. If one could derive a contradiction in **ZFC**$_\sigma$ then $O \neq O$ would become a theorem of **ZFC**$_\sigma$, and hence also of **ZFC**, making also **ZFC** inconsistent. By Gödel's well-known result that if **ZF** is consistent so is **ZFC**, also **ZF** were inconsistent. Thus we have shown that **ZFC**$_\sigma$ is consistent if and only if **ZF** is.

## 2. The axiom system VNB of von Neumann and Bernays

In the present paper we shall discuss the various systems of set theory which admit, beside sets, also classes. Classes are like sets, except that they can be very comprehensive; an extreme example of a class is the class which contains all sets. We shall analyze in detail the relationship of these systems to **ZF**. The main point which will, in our opinion, emerge

---

[1] FELGNER [1971].

from this analysis, is that set theory with classes and set theory with sets only are not two separate theories; they are, essentially, different formulations of the same underlying theory.

We shall carry out a detailed discussion of an axiom system **VNB** due to von Neumann and Bernays which exhibits the typical features of set theory with classes. Later we shall consider, in somewhat less detail, the other main variants of set theory with classes, ignoring systems which differ only technically from the systems which we shall discuss.

In an exposition of **ZF** one has to use often the metamathematical notion of a *condition* (or the equivalent notion of a *formula*). We used it here in formulating the axioms of subsets, replacement, and foundation. One uses it also in the least ordinal principle and in the (meta)theorem on definition by transfinite induction. When we look at other axiomatic mathematical theories to see whether they also make such a frequent use of the notion of a condition, we see that in some theories, e.g. the elementary theories of groups and fields in algebra, such a metamathematical notion does not occur at all, but in most theories this metamathematical notion is avoided only at the expense of developing the axiomatic theory within set theory, and using the mathematical notion of set instead of the metamathematical notion of condition. Thus, instead of formulating the axiom of induction of number theory as "For every condition $\mathfrak{P}(x)$, if 0 fulfils the condition and if, for every $x$ which fulfils the condition, $x + 1$ fulfils it too, then every natural number $x$ fulfils the condition", we can say "For every set $P$, if $0 \in P$ and for every $x$, if $x \in P$ then $x + 1 \in P$ too, then $P$ contains all natural numbers"; and instead of saying "For every condition $\mathfrak{P}(x)$, if some natural number fulfils the condition then there is a least natural number which fulfils it", we say "Every non-empty set $P$ of natural numbers has a least member". Here, where we axiomatize the notion of set, it may seem at first sight that our task is easier than ever, since we deal with sets anyway, but this is not the case. When one considers a mathematical theory **A** given within set theory, the most basic fact of set theory used in developing **A** is the following principle of comprehenson:

(∗)  *For every condition $\mathfrak{P}(x)$ of the theory **A** there exists a set $Q$ which consists exactly of those objects (of the theory **A**) which fulfil the condition.*

If we apply (∗) to set theory we get the *axiom schema of comprehension*:

*For any condition $\mathfrak{P}(x)$ on $x$ there exists a set which contains exactly those elements $x$ which fulfil this condition.*

This axiom schema is well known to be contradictory (take $x \notin x$ for $\mathfrak{P}(x)$

to obtain Russell's antinomy—see *Foundations*, p. 31). To avoid this contradiction we seem to have no choice but to assume that not all the sets guaranteed by the principle (∗) are sets of set theory. To distinguish between the sets of set theory, i.e. the objects which are the subject matter of **ZF**, and the sets guaranteed by the principle (∗), we shall refer to the latter as classes. Thus we have two kinds of sets; the sets of the first kind are still referred to as sets or, synonymously, as elements, and their behavior is expected to be as determined by the theory **ZF**; the sets of the second kind are called classes and their theory will depend to a large extent on the class axiom of comprehension (∗).

Now we set out to develop an axiom system for set theory with classes. As we shall see, there are several ways of doing that, some of which differ only in technical detail, while others show more fundamental differences. At this point let us make sure that we know what we intend by the notion of class. Having done that, we can write down axioms which, we believe, are true statements about our intended classes. We mean by a "class" the extension of some condition $\mathfrak{P}(x)$, i.e. the class, collection, set, or aggregate, whatever you wish, of all sets $x$ which fulfil the condition $\mathfrak{P}(x)$. Let us recall here what we mean by "condition". A condition is any statement of the language introduced in §1. That language mentions only sets, membership and equality of sets and other notions defined in terms of these. Since we shall now deal with languages which mention also classes, we modify the term "condition" by the adjective "pure", i.e. a *pure condition* is a condition which mentions only sets, membership and equality of sets and other notions defined in terms of these notions. In particular, a pure condition is *not* supposed to mention classes. In §1 all the conditions we dealt with were pure since these were the only conditions we could express in the language of **ZF**. Using our present terminology we say that the classes are intended to be the extensions of the pure conditions.

Let us note, at this point, that our present way of looking at classes as extensions of pure conditions is by no means the only accepted one. In §5 we shall see a different point of view and study its implications concerning the axiomatic theory.

We denote the system of set theory which we are now developing by **VNB** (after von Neumann and Bernays). In most of its details it follows the system proposed by Bernays in 1937.[1]

First, let us describe the language we shall use for **VNB**. Lowercase letters will always stand for sets and capital letters for classes (other than O which still stands for the null set). Now we have two kinds of

---

[1] BERNAYS [this volume].

membership, the membership of a set in a set (as in $O \in \{O\}$), and the membership of a set in a class (as in $O \in B$ where $B$ is, say, the class of all sets which are not members of themselves). Both kinds of membership will be denoted by the same symbol $\in$.[1] Expressions of the form $A \in B$ or $A \in x$ are considered, for the time being, to be meaningless and are not allowed in our language, i.e. our grammatical rules allow the use of "is a member of" only after an expression which denotes a set. (We do not claim that the expressions $A \in B$ and $A \in x$ are *necessarily* meaningless. On the contrary, we shall see later that we can attribute a very natural meaning to these expressions.) We also admit here statements of the form $x = y$ and $A = B$ as basic statements of our language. The possibility of admitting these statements as defined, rather than primitive, notions will be discussed in a short while. Expressions of the form $x = A$ are, for the time being, not allowed in our language. In addition, we have available in our language all the sentential connectives, i.e. ...*or*..., ...*and*..., *if*..., *then*..., ...*if and only if*..., *it is not the case that*... and so on, the quantifiers *for every set x*..., *there exists a set x such that*..., *for every class X*..., *there exists a class X such that*... (in symbols, $\forall x, \exists x, \forall X, \exists X$, respectively). When we go on developing **VNB** we shall use a much richer language since we shall introduce many new notions by means of definitions. We shall refer to the language described here, without any defined symbols, as the *primitive language* of **VNB**, and its symbols will be called the *primitive symbols*.

When one writes down the set theory **ZF** one has the choice of taking equality as a primitive notion (of logic, or set theory) or else as a defined notion. In §1 we chose to adopt equality as a primitive notion of logic, and accordingly we now make the same choice with respect to classes. According to our intended notion of class, namely as the extension of a pure condition, two classes are identical if and only if they have the same members (this is what we mean by "extension"). Therefore we adopt the following axiom.

AXIOM (X) OF EXTENSIONALITY FOR CLASSES. **If for every element $x$, $x$ is a member of $A$ if and only if $x$ is a member of $B$, then $A = B$.** In symbols:

$$\forall x \, (x \in A \leftrightarrow x \in B) \to A = B.$$

Had we chosen in §1 to take equality as a primitive notion of set theory

---

[1] BERNAYS [this volume] denotes the latter kind of membership with $\eta$, i.e. he writes $x \, \eta B$ where we write $x \in B$. Even though we use here just one symbol $\in$ we can differentiate between the two kinds of membership according to whether we have on the right side of the $\in$ symbol a symbol for a set, such as $\{O\}$, or for a class, such as $B$.

(rather than of logic), or as a defined notion (see *Foundations*, pp. 25–26), then we would now still be faced with the same choice with respect to the classes. If we choose to *define* equality of classes, then we would have to define it so that the requirements of reflexivity, symmetry, transitivity, and substitutivity, where, by substitutivity we mean that the statement

$$x = y \rightarrow \mathfrak{P}(x) \leftrightarrow \mathfrak{P}(y)$$

holds for every condition $\mathfrak{P}(x)$. In the case of sets the most direct way of defining equality is to use the requirement of substitutivity for atomic statements as the defining property of equality, i.e. to define

$$x = y =_{\text{Df}} \forall z \, [(z \in x \leftrightarrow z \in y) \land (x \in z \leftrightarrow y \in z)],^1$$

since every other definition of equality must anyway be equivalent to this one (see *Foundations*, p. 27). The atomic statements in which a class variable occurs are all of the form $x \in A$ and hence we would now define that $A = B$ if for every element $x$, $x \in A$ if and only if $x \in B$. As in the case of sets, it is easy to prove that any other definition of equality of classes would necessarily have to be equivalent to this one. This definition conforms also to our intuitive notion of class, as mentioned above. If we define equality of classes this way, and it seems to be the only reasonable way of doing it, then Axiom X of extensionality for classes does not have to be assumed as an axiom since it is now an immediate consequence of the definition of equality.

Considering the intended meaning of the term "class", it seems that the following axiom schema is the most natural axiom of comprehension for classes.

(∗)     *There exists a class which consists exactly of those elements $x$ which fulfil the condition $\mathfrak{P}(x)$, where $\mathfrak{P}(x)$ is any pure condition on $x$.*

The trouble is that (∗) is a bit too weak. There are simple facts which are true about our intended classes which cannot be established by means of (∗). For example, let us consider the statement

(∗∗)     *For every class $A$ there exists a class $B$ which consists of all elements which are not members of $A$.*

This is certainly true for the intended classes since, if $A$ is given by the pure condition $\mathfrak{P}(x)$, then $B$ is given by the pure condition "it is not the case that $\mathfrak{P}(x)$". (∗) is, therefore, sufficient to prove every instance of (∗∗) for any particular class $A$ determined by a pure condition, but is not

---

¹ The symbol "$=_{\text{Df}}$" is short for "is the same, by definition, as".

sufficient to prove (∗∗) in general.[1] Thus we see that if we adopt (∗) as our only axiom of comprehension for classes, our handling of classes will be rather clumsy, which is a great disadvantage, as we introduced classes, to begin with, in order to get a more streamlined treatment. Therefore we prefer to choose the following axiom.

AXIOM (XI) OF PREDICATIVE COMPREHENSION FOR CLASSES.[2] **There exists a class $A$ which consists exactly of those elements $x$ which satisfy the condition $\mathfrak{P}(x)$, where $\mathfrak{P}(x)$ is a condition** which does not contain quantifiers over classes, i.e. $\mathfrak{P}(x)$ does not contain expressions of the form "*for every class $X$...*" or "*there exists a class $X$ such that...*" (but $\mathfrak{P}(x)$ may contain quantifiers over elements).

It immediately follows from the axiom of extensionality for classes that the condition $\mathfrak{P}(x)$ in Axiom XI determines a *unique* class $A$; therefore we can speak of *the* class of all elements $x$ which fulfil $\mathfrak{P}(x)$. Accordingly we lay down

DEFINITION VI. $\{x\,|\,\mathfrak{P}(x)\}$, where $\mathfrak{P}(x)$ is a condition which does not use class quantifiers, is defined to be *the* class of all sets $x$ which fulfil the condition $\mathfrak{P}(x)$. The expressions $\{x\,|\,\mathfrak{P}(x)\}$ will be called *class abstracts*.

Now, let us make clear exactly in which way classes and sets are supposed to be mentioned in $\mathfrak{P}(x)$ in Axiom XI and in Definition VI. Expressions of the form $x \in A$, where $A$ is a class variable, are of course permitted; quantifiers over class variables are forbidden. Which *defined* notions are to be allowed in $\mathfrak{P}(x)$? The criterion is simple—defined notions are allowed only if, when we replace these notions in $\mathfrak{P}(x)$ by their definitions, we obtain a condition expressed in the primitive language which contains no class quantifiers. For example, if $\mathfrak{Q}(x)$ is a condition which does not use any class quantifier, then the expression $\{x\,|\,\mathfrak{Q}(x)\}$ is allowed in $\mathfrak{P}(x)$, since $y \in \{x\,|\,\mathfrak{Q}(x)\}$ can be replaced by $\mathfrak{Q}(y)$ which does not involve any class quantifiers.

To get an idea of what we can do by means of Axiom XI, we now define a few constant classes and operations on classes. Notice that these defined notions satisfy the requirement mentioned above, i.e. they can be replaced in expressions containing them by their definitions, without introducing any quantifiers on class variables.

---

[1] This can be shown rigorously by a method like that used below in §3 to prove that every statement of the language of ZF which is provable in VNB is also provable in ZF.

[2] This axiom is called predicative since it asserts only the existence of those classes which are given by a definition which does not presuppose the totality of all classes, unlike Axiom XII in §6 below.

DEFINITION.

$$\Lambda = \{x \mid x \neq x\} \qquad \text{(the } null \text{ class).}$$

$$V = \{x \mid x = x\} \qquad \text{(the } universal \text{ class).}$$

$$A \cup B = \{x \mid x \in A \text{ or } x \in B\} \qquad \text{(the } union \text{ of } A \text{ and } B\text{).}$$

$$A \cap B = \{x \mid x \in A \text{ and } x \in B\} \qquad \text{(the } intersection \text{ of } A \text{ and } B\text{).}$$

$$-A = \{x \mid x \notin A\} \qquad \text{(the } complement \text{ of } A\text{).}$$

The basic properties of these classes and operations are easily proved from their definitions.

Now we see why we admitted in Axiom XI conditions $\mathfrak{P}(x)$ exactly as stated above. Let us first become convinced that Axiom XI is not too wide for our purposes. To see this let us observe that Axiom XI is indeed true for our intended classes. Let $\mathfrak{P}(x)$ be a condition as in Axiom XI, with the class parameters $A_1, \ldots, A_k$. By our assumption on $\mathfrak{P}(x)$, if it contains symbols other than the primitive symbols, we can replace them by their definitions without introducing class quantifiers, and thus get a condition in the primitive language equivalent to $\mathfrak{P}(x)$. Since in the following there will be no need to distinguish between two equivalent conditions, we can assume that it is already $\mathfrak{P}(x)$ which contains only symbols of the primitive language, without containing any quantifiers over class variables. If $A_1, \ldots, A_k$ are classes as intended, then for some pure conditions $\mathfrak{Q}_1(x), \ldots, \mathfrak{Q}_k(x)$ we have $A_i = \{x \mid \mathfrak{Q}_i(x)\}$, for $1 \leq i \leq k$. Since there are no class quantifiers in $\mathfrak{P}(x)$, the only classes mentioned in it are $A_1, \ldots, A_k$, and the only places in which they are mentioned are expressions of the form $y \in A_i$. Since $y \in A_i$, for $A_i = \{x \mid \mathfrak{Q}_i(x)\}$, can be replaced by $\mathfrak{Q}_i(y)$, $\mathfrak{P}(x)$ is equivalent to a pure condition $\mathfrak{Q}(x)$, and therefore the class $\{x \mid \mathfrak{Q}(x)\}$, which is a class as intended since $\mathfrak{Q}(x)$ is a pure condition, consists exactly of the elements $x$ which fulfil the condition $\mathfrak{Q}(x)$. To sum up, the conditions $\mathfrak{P}(x)$ that we allow in Axiom XI differ essentially from pure conditions only in that they may also contain class parameters; once these parameters are given values which are classes determined by pure conditions, the condition $\mathfrak{P}(x)$ itself becomes equivalent to a pure condition.

We also see in §3 that while Axiom XI is a schema it can be replaced, equivalently, by a finite number of its instances, all of which are simple enough to want to have around if one hopes to deal with classes in a neat way. This is another reason why Axiom XI cannot be said to contain too much.

Having hopefully convinced ourselves that we did not admit in Axiom XI too many conditions, we now have to convince ourselves that Axiom

XI is not too narrow for our purposes. If we were to admit more conditions, and have a natural and simple criterion for which conditions to admit, it seems that we would have to admit at least all the conditions that involve no more than one existential (or universal) class quantifier. However, in this case we would get statements which are not true of our intended classes, since there are conditions $\mathfrak{Q}(x)$ of **VNB**, involving one class quantifier, such that for every pure condition $\mathfrak{P}(x)$ the statement "for all $x$, $\mathfrak{Q}(x)$ if and only if $\mathfrak{P}(x)$" is refutable in **VNB**,[1] and hence there is no intended class $A$ such that, for every element $x$, $x \in A$ if and only if $x$ fulfils $\mathfrak{Q}(x)$.

One can formulate a statement in **VNB** which asserts that there are no classes other than those determined by pure conditions.[2] This is, of course, true of our intended notion of class, but it is not implied by the axioms of **VNB**.[3] Shall we add it as an axiom to **VNB**? Such a statement is relatively complicated and does not seem to be useful for proving theorems which one may ordinarily consider in set theory.[4] Since we are interested in the intended classes only to the extent that using them streamlines set theory, and this has been achieved by Axiom XI, there is no need to add an axiom which rules out all classes other than those determined by pure conditions.

The way in which we introduced the classes is not confined only to set theory; on the contrary, Axiom XI can be used to introduce classes in any mathematical theory. Suppose we start with some mathematical theory **T** formulated in the first-order predicate calculus (with or without equality), and we add to it the following items: (a) a new kind of variables which we call class variables, (b) all the statements of the form $x \in A$, where $x$ is a variable of **T** and $A$ is a class variable, as new atomic statements, (c) all the statements which can be obtained from the old and new atomic

---

[1] Such a condition $\mathfrak{Q}(x)$, with one existential class quantifier in front, is given by the formula *Stsf* of MOSTOWSKI [1951], p. 115, or can be obtained by diagonalization over the pure conditions as in KRUSE [1963].

[2] This statement is formalized by KRUSE [1963] (it is also evident from MOSTOWSKI [1951] how to do it). An even stronger statement is considered in MYHILL [1952].

[3] Provided that the theory **QM** of §6 is consistent. In **QM** we can prove that there is a class which is not determined by a pure condition, since the existence of $\{x | \mathfrak{Q}(x)\}$, where $\mathfrak{Q}(x)$ is as above, is provable in **QM**. This independence result can also be shown to follow from the weaker assumption of the consistency of **VNB**, by combining the methods of EASTON [1964] and FEFERMAN [1965].

[4] In particular any statement which mentions only sets and which is provable in **VNB** using the assumption that all classes are determined by pure conditions is also provable in **VNB** without that assumption. This can be shown by the method used in §3 below to show that every statement which mentions only sets and which is provable in **VNB** is already provable in **ZF**.

statements by means of the logical connectives and the quantifiers, and
(d) Axioms X and XI of extensionality and predicative comprehension for
classes as additional axioms. The theory obtained from T by these
additions is, up to possible trivial differences in notation, the predicative
second-order theory of T.[1]

Until now we set down the axioms we needed for the classes. As for the
sets, we take the axioms of ZF, with some changes which are, essentially,
just technical.

First, we take up all the single axioms of ZF, i.e. the axioms of
Extensionality (I), Pairing (II), Union (III), Power set (IV), and Infinity
(VI). Since the main reason for introducing classes is to avoid
metamathematical notions in the formulation of most of the axioms and
theorems, and since the intended classes are just the extensions of pure
conditions we can now replace the conditions by classes in the axiom
schemas of ZF.

AXIOM ($V^c$) OF SUBSETS. **For every class** $P$ **and for every set** $a$
**there exists a set which contains just those members** $x$ **of** $a$ **which are also
members of** $P$. In symbols:

$$\forall P \, \forall a \, \exists y \, \forall x \, (x \in y \leftrightarrow x \in a \wedge x \in P).$$

Having all but replaced the metamathematical notion of condition by
the mathematical notion of class, we can now apply similar methods to the
metamathematical notions of relation and functional condition. In the
case of a general mathematical theory we cannot handle relations and
functions by means of classes, and we need new kinds of objects, similar
to classes, to represent relations and functions. This is unnecessary in set
theory since, as we shall now see, we can use classes to handle relations
by means of the ordered-pair operation. The *ordered pair* $\langle x, y \rangle$ is defined
by

$$\langle x, y \rangle =_{Df} \{\{x\}, \{x, y\}\}$$

and its characteristic property is that in ZF one can (easily) prove

$$\langle x, y \rangle = \langle x', y' \rangle \leftrightarrow x = x' \wedge y = y'.$$

DEFINITION. A class $A$ is said to be a *relation* if it consists only of
ordered pairs. If $A$ is a class then $\mathfrak{D}(A)$ (the *domain* of $A$) is the class of
all elements $x$ for which there is a $y$ such that $\langle x, y \rangle \in A$, and $\mathfrak{R}(A)$ (the

---

[1] See, e.g. CHURCH [1956], §58. More correct, this is the *monadic* predicative second-
order theory of T (monadic means that we have variables over classes but not over $n$-ary
relations for $n \geq 2$). The monadic predicative second-order theory of T is as powerful as the
full predicative second-order theory of T if a concept of an ordered pair is available in T.

*range* of $A$) is the class of all elements $y$ for which there is an $x$ such that $\langle x,y \rangle \in A$. A class $A$ is said to be a *function* if it is a relation and, for all $x$, $y$, $z$, if $\langle x,y \rangle \in A$ and $\langle x,z \rangle \in A$ then $y = z$. If $F$ is a function, and $x \in \mathfrak{D}(F)$, then we denote by $F(x)$ the element $y$ such that $\langle x,y \rangle \in F$. In symbols:

$$\mathfrak{Rel}(A) =_{\mathrm{Df}} \forall x\ (x \in A \to \exists y\ \exists z\ (x = \langle y,z \rangle)).$$

$$\mathfrak{D}(A) =_{\mathrm{Df}} \{x \,|\, \exists y\ (\langle x,y \rangle \in A)\}, \quad \mathfrak{R}(A) =_{\mathrm{Df}} \{y \,|\, \exists x\ (\langle x,y \rangle \in A)\}.$$

$$\mathfrak{Fnc}(A) =_{\mathrm{Df}} \mathfrak{Rel}(A)\ \&\ \forall x\ \forall y\ (\langle x,y \rangle \in A \wedge \langle x,z \rangle \in A \to y = z).$$

THEOREM (-SCHEMA). Let $\mathfrak{Q}(x,y)$ be a condition on $x$ and $y$ (i.e. a relation in the old, metamathematical, sense), then there is a unique relation $A$ such that, for all $x$ and $y$, $\langle x,y \rangle \in A$ if and only if $\mathfrak{Q}(x,y)$ holds. If $\mathfrak{Q}(x,y)$ is a functional condition, then there is a unique function $F$ such that: $x \in \mathfrak{D}(F)$ if and only if there is a $y$ such that $\mathfrak{Q}(x,y)$ holds, and for every $x$ in $\mathfrak{D}(F)$, $\mathfrak{Q}(x,y)$ holds if and only if $y = F(x)$.

PROOF. Given the condition $\mathfrak{Q}(x,y)$, let $A$ be the class which consists of all sets $z$ which are ordered pairs $\langle x,y \rangle$ such that $\mathfrak{Q}(x,y)$ holds. Obviously, $\mathfrak{Q}(x,y)$ holds if and only if $\langle x,y \rangle \in A$. This immediately implies that $x \in \mathfrak{D}(A)$ if and only if, for some $y$, $\mathfrak{Q}(x,y)$ holds. If, in addition, $\mathfrak{Q}(x,y)$ is a functional condition, then $A$ is obviously a function. For $x \in \mathfrak{D}(A)$ we have, by definition of $A(x)$, $\langle x,A(x) \rangle \in A$; hence $\mathfrak{Q}(x,A(x))$ holds. Since $\mathfrak{Q}(x,y)$ is a functional condition we have that, for all $y$, $\mathfrak{Q}(x,y)$ holds if and only if $y = A(x)$.

AXIOM (VII$^{c}$) OF REPLACEMENT. **If $F$ is a function, and $a$ is a set, then there is a set which contains exactly the values $F(x)$ for all members $x$ of $a$ which are in $\mathfrak{D}(F)$.** In symbols:

$$\forall F\ (\mathfrak{Fnc}(F) \to \forall a\ \exists b\ \forall y\ (y \in b \leftrightarrow \exists x\ (x \in a \wedge x \in \mathfrak{D}(F) \wedge y = F(x)))).$$

Unlike Axiom VII, Axiom VII$^{c}$ does not seem to imply the axiom of pairing, since ordered pairs are used in an essential way in the notion of function on which Axiom VII relies. On the other hand, in the presence of the axiom of pairing Axiom VII$^{c}$ implies Axiom V$^{c}$ (of subsets—the proof is exactly the same as the proof in *Foundations*, Ch. II, §3.7 that Axiom VII implies Axiom V).

AXIOM (IX$^{c}$) OF FOUNDATION. **Every class $P$ which has at least one member has a minimal member $u$, i.e. $u$ is a member of $P$, but no member $x$ of $u$ is a member of $P$.** In symbols:

$$\forall P\ (\exists u\ (u \in P) \to \exists u\ (u \in P \wedge \forall x\ (x \in u \to x \notin P))).$$

Axiom IX$^c$ follows the version IX of the axiom of foundation which is a schema. Alternatively, we can use here one of the versions of the axiom of foundation which are single statements such as

AXIOM IX*.  **If $y$ is a non-empty set, then $y$ has a number $u$ such that** $u \cap y = O$.

The proof of the equivalence of IX* with IX$^c$ is similar to the proof of the equivalence of IX* with IX (see, e.g. *Foundations*, Ch. II, §5.1).

When we compare the classes with the sets, we see that there is a certain amount of overlap; we introduced the classes as the extensions of the pure conditions, but the sets are also the extensions of some of the pure conditions. For every set $y$ we have the class $\{x \mid x \in y\}$ which has exactly the same members (but there is no set which has exactly the same members as the class $\{x \mid x \notin x\}$). It actually turns out that the distinction between the set $y$ and the class $\{x \mid x \in y\}$ serves no purpose. Therefore, to avoid the looks, if not the substance, of such a distinction, let us define as follows.

DEFINITION VII.   $z = A$ (and $A = z$) if $z$ and $A$ have exactly the same members.

$A \in B$ if, for some member $z$ of $B$, $z = A$.

$A \in y$ if, for some member $z$ of $y$, $z = A$.

$A$ is a *set* if, for some $z$, $z = A$.

$A$ is a *proper class* if $A$ is not a set.

Now we have arrived at the convenient situation where equality and membership are defined for any two objects. It is easily seen that we now have full substitutivity of equality (i.e. that $x = A$ implies that $\mathfrak{P}(x)$ holds if and only if $\mathfrak{P}(A)$ holds). Since we have, as immediately seen, $\Lambda = O$ we can, by the full substitutivity of equality, use O and $\Lambda$ synonymously. The operation which we define on classes are also defined for sets since we can replace the class variables in their definitions by set variables. The outcome of such an operation is a class, which may also be·a set (in the sense of Definition VII).

Using our present terminology we can rewrite the axioms of **VNB** as follows:

I        (Extensionality of sets). As in **ZF**.

II       (Pairing). $\{x \mid x \text{ is } a \text{ or } x \text{ is } b\}$ is a set.

III      (Union). $\{x \mid x \text{ is a member of a member of } a\}$ is a set.

IV     (Power set). $\{x \mid x \subseteq a\}$ is a set.

$V^c$     (Subsets). $P \cap y$ is a set.

VI     (Infinity). $\{x \mid x$ *is a finite ordinal*$\}$ is a set.[1]

$VII^c$     (Replacement). If $F$ is a function, then
$\{x \mid x = F(y)$ *for some* $y \in a \cap \mathfrak{D}(F)\}$ is a set.

$IX^c$     (Foundation). $A \neq 0 \to \exists u (u \in A \wedge u \cap A = O)$.

X     (Extensionality of classes). As on p.179.

XI     (Predicative comprehension). As on p.181.

## 3. Metamathematical features of VNB

In the transition from ZF to VNB the axiom schemas of ZF became single axioms of VNB; however, VNB has the extra axiom schema of comprehension—Axiom XI. The conditions $\mathfrak{P}(x)$ permitted in Axiom XI can be assumed, as we have already mentioned, to be formulated in the primitive language. In this language there is only a finite number of ways in which atomic statements can be made up, and only a finite numbers of ways in which more complicated statements can be formed from simpler ones. If we can make appropriate classes correspond to the various statements, and we find out how our construction of statements affects the corresponding classes, we can translate the finitely many rules for the construction of statements into finitely many rules for the construction of classes, and thus replace Axiom XI by a finite number of its instances.[2] Since a general statement involves an arbitrary finite number of free variables $x_1, \ldots, x_n$ we have to deal here also with ordered $n$-tuples; actually, it will suffice to consider only ordered pairs and triples.

The axioms which correspond to the propositional connectives are:

AXIOM XI1. **For every class $A$ there is a class $C$ which consists of all elements $x$ which are not in $A$.**

This axiom corresponds to negation:

$$C = \{x \mid it\ is\ not\ the\ case\ that\ x \in A\} = -A$$

($C$ is called the *complement* of $A$).

---

[1] This can be easily shown to be equivalent to Axiom VI of §1.

[2] This is due to VON NEUMANN [1925] (with some of the ideas originating with FRAENKEL [1922]). For set theories like our VNB, where this is more surprising, it was shown by BERNAYS [this volume] pp. 1–13. We shall see in §6 that the fact that in Axiom XI the statements are not supposed to contain class quantifiers is used here in an essential way.

AXIOM XI2.   **For all classes $A$ and $B$ there is a class $C$ which consists of all common members of $A$ and $B$.**

This axiom corresponds to conjunction:

$$C = \{x \mid x \in A \text{ and } x \in B\} = A \cap B.$$

The axiom which corresponds to the atomic statement $x \in y$ is:

AXIOM XI3.   **There is a relation $E$ such that $\langle x,y \rangle \in E$ just in case that $x \in y$.**[1]

The axiom which corresponds to the existential quantifier "there exists a $y$ such that" is:

AXIOM XI4.   **For every relation $A$ there exists a class $C$ which consists exactly of the first members of the ordered pairs which are members of $A$.**

$C$ is the *domain* of $A$:

$$C = \{x \mid \text{there exists a } y \text{ such that } \langle x,y \rangle \in A\} = \mathfrak{D}(A).$$

The next axiom is needed because statements can contain parameters, and therefore we have to reckon with classes of the form $\{x \mid x \in y\}$ or $\{x \mid x = y\}$.

AXIOM XI5.   **For every set $y$ there exists a class $C$ which consists exactly of all the members of $y$:**

$$C = \{x \mid x \in y\}.$$

Using Definition VII this becomes: for every set there is a class equal to it. An alternative to this axiom is

AXIOM XI5*.   **For every set $y$ there exists a class $C$ which contains $y$ as its only member:**

$$C = \{x \mid x = y\}.$$

Using Definition VII, this becomes: for every singleton set $\{y\}$ there is a class equal to it.

Now we have to add three axioms of a rather technical nature, which are needed in order to handle statements with more than one variable.

AXIOM XI6.   **For every class $A$ there exists a relation $C$ which consists of all ordered pairs $\langle x,y \rangle$ such that $y \in A$:**

$$C = \{\langle x,y \rangle \mid y \in A\}.$$

[1] There is no need for an axiom which corresponds to the atomic statement $x = y$ since it is equivalent to the formula $\forall z \, (z \in x \leftrightarrow z \in y)$ which does not involve equality.

Read: $C$ is the class of all ordered pairs $\langle x,y \rangle$ such that $y \in A$.

Notice that $\{\langle x,y \rangle | y \in A\}$ is a new notation not previously used.

AXIOM XI7. **For every relation $A$ there exists a relation $C$ which consists of all ordered pairs $\langle x,y \rangle$ whose inverses $\langle y,x \rangle$ are in $A$:**

$$C = \{\langle x,y \rangle | \langle y,x \rangle \in A\}.$$

AXIOM XI8. **For every relation $A$ there exists a relation $C$ which consists exactly of all ordered pairs $\langle \langle x,y \rangle, z \rangle$ such that $\langle x,y,z \rangle \, (= \langle x, \langle y,z \rangle \rangle)$ is in $A$:**

$$C = \{\langle \langle x,y \rangle, z \rangle | \langle x,y,z \rangle \in A\}.$$

Using the ideas outlined above, preceding the list of Axioms XI1–XI8, one can prove that Axiom XI follows from these axioms.[1]

Let us compare the systems VNB and ZF. First, we notice that the language of VNB is richer, i.e. every statement of ZF is also a statement of VNB, yet no statement of VNB which involves class variables is a statement of ZF. Moreover, some of the statements of VNB express things which cannot be expressed in ZF at all. To make the latter assertion clearer we point out that this has a twofold meaning; first, there is a closed statement of VNB which is not equivalent in VNB to any statement of ZF;[2] and, second, as we mentioned above (p. 183), there is a condition $\mathfrak{Q}(x)$ of VNB such that for every pure condition $\mathfrak{P}(x)$ (i.e. for every condition $\mathfrak{P}(x)$ of ZF) the statement "$\mathfrak{Q}(x)$ if and only if $\mathfrak{P}(x)$" is refutable in VNB.

Every statement of ZF which is provable in ZF is also provable in VNB. This is easily seen, since all the single axioms of ZF are also axioms of VNB, and all the schemas of ZF immediately follow from the corresponding axioms of VNB, by means of Axiom XI. Let us prove, for example, Axiom V (of subsets) in VNB. Let $a$ be a set and $\mathfrak{P}(x)$ a condition of ZF, i.e. a pure condition. By the axiom of comprehension there is a class $A$ which consists of the elements $x$ which fulfil $\mathfrak{P}(x)$; by Axiom V$^c$ there is a set $y$ which consists of the common members of $a$ and $A$, i.e. of those members of $a$ which fulfil $\mathfrak{P}(x)$.

So far we have seen that whatever we can express and prove in ZF we can also express and prove, respectively, in VNB. We have also seen that some statements can be expressed in VNB but not in ZF. The next natural

---

[1] See the proof in BERNAYS [this volume] p. 6, §3, GÖDEL [1940], pp. 8–11, or MENDELSON [1964], Ch. 4, §1. The original proof is due to VON NEUMANN [1928], Ch. II, §1.

[2] Axiom VIII$^c_\sigma$ of §4 is such a statement. A stronger and more general example can be obtained by combining the method of LÉVY [1965], §7 with the truth definition of ZF of MOSTOWSKI [1951].

question which comes up is whether whatever can be expressed in ZF and proved in VNB can already be proved in ZF; more precisely, if $\mathfrak{S}$ is a statement of ZF which is provable in VNB, is $\mathfrak{S}$ necessarily provable in ZF? We shall give a positive answer to this question, and therefore we can say that even though VNB is a theory richer than ZF in its means of expression, VNB is not richer than ZF as far as proving statements which mention only sets is concerned. Thus, if one is interested only in sets and regards classes as a mere technical device, one should regard ZF and VNB as essentially the same theory, and the differences between those theories as mere technical matters.

Our present task is not as easy as our earlier task of showing that every theorem $\mathfrak{S}$ of ZF is also a theorem of VNB. There we used the fact that the proof of $\mathfrak{S}$ in ZF can be trivially reproduced in VNB. Now, if we are given a proof in VNB of a statement $\mathfrak{S}$ of ZF, there is not always a way in which this proof can be reproduced in ZF, since the proof of $\mathfrak{S}$ in VNB may involve statements which cannot be expressed in ZF. Attacking the problem from a different angle, we observe that if the statement $\mathfrak{S}$ is not provable in ZF, there is no reason why $\mathfrak{S}$ should be provable in VNB; after all, the new axioms of VNB do not give us any information about sets—they just assert the basic facts about the pure conditions, or the classes determined by these conditions, and those facts hold irrespective of whether $\mathfrak{S}$ is true or false. This informal argument can be turned into a precise argument, as we do below.

We shall now show that if the statement $\mathfrak{S}$ of ZF is not provable in ZF, it is also not provable in VNB. Suppose $\mathfrak{S}$ is not provable in ZF; then, by the completeness theorem of the first-order predicate calculus, there is a set $m$ and a binary relation $\in'$ on $m$ (i.e. $\in' \subseteq m \times m$) such that $\langle m, \in' \rangle$ is a model of ZF in which $\mathfrak{S}$ does not hold. We now define "classes" for this model. Let us say that $u$ is a *model class* if for some condition $\mathfrak{P}(x)$ (of ZF) with $n$ parameters and for some $y_1, \ldots, y_n \in m$, $u$ is the subset of $m$ which consists exactly of all the members $x$ of $m$ which satisfy the condition $\mathfrak{P}(x)$ in the model, when the values of the parameters are taken to be $y_1, \ldots, y_n$. By the very arguments which we used in §2 to justify the predicative axiom of comprehension and Axioms $V^c$, $VII^c$, and $IX^c$, one shows that if one interprets the notion of set as "member of $m$", the notion of class as "model-class", that of membership of a set in a set as $\in'$, and that of membership of a set in a class as membership (in a model-class), then all the axioms of VNB become true, while $\mathfrak{S}$ stays false. Thus $\mathfrak{S}$ is not provable in VNB.[1]

We have now shown that if a statement $\mathfrak{S}$ of ZF is provable in VNB it is also provable in ZF, but we did it by means of an indirect argument. Thus, even if we know the proof of $\mathfrak{S}$ in VNB our method above does not show us how to get a proof of $\mathfrak{S}$ in ZF by any method other than the ungainly way of scanning all proofs of theorems in ZF till we find a proof of $\mathfrak{S}$,

[1] This proof is due to NOVAK [1951], ROSSER–WANG [1950] and MOSTOWSKI [1951].

which we know must be among them. To get another method which will actually show how to obtain a proof of $\mathfrak{S}$ in ZF once a proof of $\mathfrak{S}$ in VNB is known, we have to return to the idea mentioned above of reproducing in ZF the proof of $\mathfrak{S}$ in VNB. As we have mentioned there, this is not always possible; however, it turns out that if a statement $\mathfrak{S}$ of ZF has a proof in VNB, we can always change this proof to another proof of $\mathfrak{S}$ in VNB which is particularly simple and can therefore be reproduced in ZF.[1]

A particularly important consequence of what we have discussed just now is that if ZF is consistent so is VNB. Suppose VNB were not consistent then every contradictory statement of ZF, e.g. "some set is a member of itself, and no set is a member of itself", would be provable in VNB. By the metamathematical theorem discussed above, every such contradictory statement is also provable in ZF, hence ZF is inconsistent too. Moreover, if Q is a theory obtained from ZF by adding to ZF a set $T$ of axioms which involve only sets and Q' is the theory obtained from VNB by adding to it the same set $T$ of axioms, then Q' is consistent if and only if Q is consistent.[2] Thus all the well-known results concerning the consistency and the independence of the generalized continuum hypothesis and the axiom of constructibility with respect to ZF go over to corresponding results with respect to VNB. In order to be able to transfer more consistency and independence results from ZF to VNB, let us notice the following. When we showed that a statement $\mathfrak{S}$ of ZF is provable in ZF if and only if it is provable in VNB, it mattered only that VNB contains the axioms of predicative comprehension (XI) and extensionality (X) and that, other than that, VNB consists exactly of the single axioms of ZF and of axioms corresponding to the axiom schemas of ZF. Therefore, the same result applies also to other pairs of corresponding theories. For example, once we know that the axiom of union does not follow from the other axioms of ZF then the results mentioned here imply that the axiom of union does also not follow from the other axioms of VNB. Thus, the many consistency and independence results given in *Foundations*, Ch. II, §§4–6, for ZF apply, literally, also to VNB. In fact, in each particular case it is evident anyway, without using the present general principle, that the

---

[1] The idea, due to Paul J. Cohen, is to change first the proof of $\mathfrak{S}$ in VNB to a cut-free proof (as, e.g. in SCHÜTTE [1950]); the latter can be easily reproduced in ZF. An earlier method is given by SHOENFIELD [1954]. These proofs of Shoenfield and Cohen show that the Gödel number of a proof of $\mathfrak{S}$ in ZF depends on the Gödel number of a proof of $\mathfrak{S}$ in VNB via a primitive recursive function, whereas the proof given above suffices to establish this dependence only via a general recursive function.

[2] This is shown as follows. Q is consistent if and only if no statement $\mathfrak{S}$ which is a negation of a conjunction of finitely many statements out of $T$ is provable in ZF. This, we know, holds if and only if no such statement $\mathfrak{S}$ is provable in VNB, which, in turn, holds if and only if Q' is consistent.

proof of the relative consistency (or independence) applies equally well to **VNB** as it does to **ZF**.

## 4. The axiom of choice in VNB

We can add to **VNB** the local axiom of choice of **ZF**, i.e. Axiom VIII, and obtain thereby a system which we denote with **VNBC**. By the results mentioned above, the statements $\mathfrak{S}$ of **ZF** which are theorems of **VNBC** are exactly the theorems of **ZFC**. However, when one wants to have an axiom of choice in **VNB** one usually chooses a very natural *global* axiom of choice which is strongly related to the global axiom of choice VIII$_\sigma$ of **ZFC**$_\sigma$ and which is presented below.

Suppose that we start with a **ZF**-type set theory **Q** which has a selector $\sigma(x)$ in the sense of §1. It does not matter whether **Q** is obtained from **ZF** by addition of an axiom which allows us to define the selector (such as the axiom of constructibility), or if **Q** is obtained from **ZF** by adding $\sigma$ as a new operation symbol and adding Axiom VIII$_\sigma$ which asserts that $\sigma(x)$ is indeed a selector; but, in the latter case, we have to widen our intended notion of class to also include extensions of conditions which involve selection, in addition to sets and membership. Let us consider, informally, the class $F$ of all sets $x$ which are ordered pairs $\langle y, \sigma(y) \rangle$, where $y$ is a non-void set. This class $F$ is obviously a function, and for every non-void set $y$ we have $F(y) = \sigma(y)$, and since $\sigma(y) \in y$ we have $F(y) \in y$. This leads us to

AXIOM (VIII$_\sigma^c$) OF GLOBAL CHOICE. **There exists a function $F$ whose domain contains all non-void sets, and such that for every non-void set $y$, $F(y)$ is a member of $y$.**[1]

We shall denote with **VNBC**$_\sigma$ the system of set theory obtained from **VNB** by adding to it Axiom VIII$_\sigma^c$. It is easily seen that Axiom VIII of local choice is a theorem of **VNBC**$_\sigma$ (as we observed for **ZFC**$_\sigma$ in §1), and hence all the theorems of **VNBC** are also theorems of **VNBC**$_\sigma$. Let us point out that the language of **VNBC**$_\sigma$ does not contain any selector symbol; Axiom VIII$_\sigma^c$ offers the advantages of a selector without the disadvantage of having to extend the language. The subscript $\sigma$ is used in the designation of Axiom VIII$_\sigma^c$ and **VNBC**$_\sigma$, even though they do not involve the symbol $\sigma$ at all, for the purpose of stressing their close relationship with Axiom VIII$_\sigma$ and **ZFC**$_\sigma$, respectively.

---

[1] For many equivalent versions of Axiom VIII$_\sigma^c$ see RUBIN–RUBIN [1963], Part II; cf. also ISBELL–WRIGHT [1966].

In the same way in which one proves the metatheorem that the theorems of **VNB** which mention only sets are exactly the theorems of **ZF** one can also prove that the theorems of **VNBC**$_\sigma$ which mention only sets are exactly the theorems of **ZFC**$_\sigma$ which do not mention $\sigma$.[1] Since, as we said in §1, the theorems of **ZFC**$_\sigma$ which do not involve $\sigma$ are exactly the theorems of **ZFC**, we know that the theorems of **VNBC**$_\sigma$ which involve only sets are exactly the theorems of **ZFC** and are, hence, also exactly the theorems of **VNBC** which involve only sets. Thus, as far as sets are concerned, **VNBC** and **VNBC**$_\sigma$ are the same theory. On the other hand (assuming the consistency of **VNB**), the two theories do not completely coincide, since Axiom VIII$_\sigma^c$ is not a theorem of **VNBC**.[2]

It follows from what we said above that if **ZFC** is consistent so is **VNBC**$_\sigma$. Moreover, if any set $T$ of statements of **ZFC** which can be added to **ZFC** as new axioms without causing a contradiction, the same addition will not introduce a contradiction in **VNBC**$_\sigma$ either. Thus the generalized continuum hypothesis and the axiom of constructibility are consistent with **VNBC**$_\sigma$. Moreover, the axiom of constructibility (or any other axiom which implies in **ZF** the existence of a selector),[3] implies Axiom VIII$_\sigma^c$ in **VNB**, since a class $F$ as required by Axiom VIII$_\sigma^c$ is given by the class of all ordered pairs $\langle x, \sigma(x) \rangle$, where $x$ is a non-void set and $\sigma$ is some fixed selector.

In **VNBC**$_\sigma$ one can prove, making an essential use of the global axiom of choice and of the axiom of foundation, that *a class $A$ is proper if and only if it is equinumerous to the class* V *of all sets*, where by $A$ being equinumerous to $B$ we mean that there is a one–one function $F$, whose domain is $A$ and whose range is $B$.[4] Indeed, von Neumann chose to introduce a very closely related statement as an axiom which replaces the axioms of (subsets), replacement and global choice.[5]

In **VNBC**$_\sigma$ we can define, in terms of a class $F$ as in Axiom VIII$_\sigma^c$, an operation $\sigma(A)$ (with $F$ as a tacit parameter), which satisfies the following strong versions of the axioms of global

---

[1] Actually, one can also give a natural translation of all the statements $\mathfrak{S}$ of **ZFC**$_\sigma$, including those which mention $\sigma$, into statements of **VNB** such that $\mathfrak{S}$ is a theorem of **ZFC**$_\sigma$ if and only if its translation is a theorem of **VNBC**$_\sigma$.

[2] EASTON [1964]. If Q' is a theory obtained from **VNB** by adding to it axioms which involve only sets, and Axiom VIII$_\sigma^c$ is a theorem of Q' and if Q is the theory obtained from **ZF** by the addition of the same axioms, then there is in Q a relative selector, i.e. a definable *binary* operation $\sigma(y,z)$ for which one can prove in Q that there is a set $y$ such that for every non-empty set $z$, $\sigma(y,z) \in z$. The proof is, again, as at the end of §3.

[3] Or even a relative selector.

[4] This is proved, essentially in BERNAYS [this volume] pp. 87–101, and in VON NEUMANN [1929] (see pp. 195–196 and *Foundations*, p. 95).

[5] See pp. 195–196.

choice and foundation:

$$A \neq 0 \to \sigma(A) \in A,$$
$$\sigma(A) \cap A = 0.[1]$$

## 5. The approach of von Neumann

The way we introduced and motivated **VNB** in §2 is not the way this was done historically for set theory with classes. The first axiom system for set theory with classes was put forth by von Neumann in 1925.[2] The main technical difference between his system and **VNB** is that he used the notion of function as the basic notion rather than those of set and class. Von Neumann recognized that the notions of function and class are interchangeable as basic notions for set theory. He gives, as a reason for his choice of the notion of function, the fact that every axiomatization of set theory uses the notion of function anyway, and hence it is simpler to use the notion of function as the basic notion. Now we are using functions (or functional conditions) mostly in our formulation of the axiom of substitution, but Fraenkel's axiom system (see, e.g. *Foundations*, p. 37), which apparently influenced von Neumann, was also using functions in the axiom schema of subsets. Taking the axiom system of Fraenkel as a starting point, it really seems very reasonable to take the notion of function, rather than that of set, as the basic notion. However, it turned out, in spite of a later simplification of von Neumann's system,[3] that this approach is rather clumsy, and that it is after all simpler to take the notions of set and class, or only that of class alone, as the basic notions of set theory.

What von Neumann regards as the first main feature of his theory is the following. In **ZF** the guiding principle in writing down the axioms can be taken to be the *doctrine of limitation of size*, i.e. we do not admit very comprehensive sets in order to avoid the antinomies. Von Neumann regards as the main idea of his set theory the discovery that the antinomies do not arise from the mere existence of very comprehensive sets, but from their elementhood, i.e. from their being able to be members of other sets. He uses the name "set" not only for what we call sets, but also for what we call classes. To illustrate his ideas better we shall present a system **G** of axioms of set theory with classes which is very close to one given by Gödel.[4]

---

[1] BERNAYS [1958], Ch. VIII. $\sigma(A)$ is defined as $F(t)$ where $t$ is the set of the members of $A$ of minimal rank.
[2] VON NEUMANN [1925] and [1928].
[3] ROBINSON [1937].
[4] GÖDEL [1940]; see also MOSTOWSKI [1939].

In **VNB** we defined a set $a$ and a class $A$ to be equal when they have the same members. For every set $a$ there is a class $\{x|x \in a\}$ equal to it. As far as our theory is concerned, the set $a$ and the class $\{x|x \in a\}$ serve exactly the same purpose. Therefore we can actually identify them and base the system **G** on classes only.

In the theory **G** we have just one kind of variables for which we use capital letters. These variables are understood to refer to classes. The only primitive relation symbol, in addition to equality, is the membership symbol $\in$.[1] We start with a definition.

DEFINITION.   $X$ is a *set* if and only if there is a class $Y$ such that $X \in Y$.

Now, having *defined* the notion of set we can use lowercase variables for sets, in the same way that one uses, e.g. Greek-letter variables for ordinals. In other words, whenever we say "there exists a $y$ such that..." we mean "there exists a $Y$ such that $Y$ is a set and..." and whenever we say "for every $y$..." we mean "for every $Y$ which is a set...".

From this point on we just take up Axioms II, III, IV, $V^c$, VI, $VII^c$, $IX^c$, X and XI of **VNB**. The only difference is that, while the lowercase variables in these axioms were part of the primitive language of **VNB**, they are now defined restricted variables in **G**. It is easy to prove that in **VNB** and **G** we can prove exactly the same theorems[2] (we have, of course, to make sure that we translate correctly, since **VNB** and **G** use different languages).

Von Neumann's system is like **G** in the sense that all sets are also classes.[3] To get the flavor of his approach let us, for a while, call the classes sets and the sets elements. The elements are the sets which are also members of sets. There are some sets which are not elements, such as the set of all elements which are not members of themselves. Thus the doctrine of limitation of size is retained by von Neumann, but only in the sense that very comprehensive sets cannot be members of sets and not in the sense that such sets have to be avoided altogether.

Von Neumann regards, as another major innovation of his system, the fact that, whereas in **ZF** the limitation of size doctrine serves only as a guide to the introduction of axioms, in his system it is actually incorpor-

---

[1] The idea of using in a VON NEUMANN–BERNAYS set theory just one kind of variable and a single binary relation symbol is due to TARSKI; see MOSTOWSKI [1949], p. 144.

[2] See, e.g. KRUSE [1963].

[3] VON NEUMANN'S system also admits urelements. We shall not discuss urelements in the framework of set theory with classes, since admitting urelements here does not give rise to any new interesting discussions. For a system which is like **G** but admits urelements, see MOSTOWSKI [1939].

ated as the following axiom:

(*)    *A set A is an element if and only if there is no function F which maps it on the set V of all elements* (i.e. the domain of F is A and its range is V).[1]

This axiom is equivalent to the conjunction of the axioms of union (III), (subsets—$V^c$), replacement (VII$^c$), and global choice (VIII$^c_\sigma$).[2] (*) is attractive from an aesthetic point of view but, contrary to von Neumann's contention, it does not embody the full limitation of size doctrine. Even though (*) establishes non-equinumerosity with the set V of all elements as a necessary and sufficient condition for elementhood, (*) in itself does not tell us when a given set is equinumerous to V. For instance, the axiom of power set, which clearly falls within the limitation of size doctrine, does not follow from (*) and the other axioms of **G**.[3]

We have explicitly described **VNB** and **G** and mentioned the original systems of von Neumann–Bernays and Gödel. In all these systems essentially the same theorems are provable.[4] As we saw, one can arrive at set theory with classes starting from two different motivations. We started first from the motivation of replacing the metamathematical notion of condition by the mathematical notion of class. This motivation was introduced by Quine and Bernays.[5] Thus classes, or at least proper classes, are regarded as a kind of objects different from sets, and in some sense less real than sets. On the other hand, von Neumann's motivation regards classes and sets as objects of the same kind with the same claim for existence. The only difference between proper classes and sets is that, because of the antinomies, the proper classes cannot be members of classes whereas sets can. In the next two subsections, we shall continue these respective lines of thought, to arrive at new axiomatic systems for set theory with classes.

### 6. Classes taken seriously—the system of Quine and Morse

Adopting von Neumann's point of view, let us, for a short while, call again the classes sets and the sets elements, and let us even use lowercase

[1] VON NEUMANN [1925], Axiom IV2.
[2] See VON NEUMANN [1929] and LÉVY [1968].
[3] To see this, consider the model II$_1$ of BERNAYS [this volume] p. 93, §17 in set theory with the axiom of constructibility.
[4] Provided, of course, that the same attitude towards individuals is adopted. Not all the necessary proofs have been carried out in the literature because the matter is trivial but lengthy.
[5] QUINE [1963], BERNAYS [1958].

variables for the classes. The inconsistent axiom of comprehension of §2 requires that for every given condition $\mathfrak{P}(x)$ there exists a set which contains exactly the sets $x$ which fulfil the condition $\mathfrak{P}(x)$. Zermelo's axiom of subsets (our Axiom V) amends this axiom of comprehension by requiring that the condition $\mathfrak{P}(x)$ in it be of the form "$x \in a$ and $\mathfrak{Q}(x)$", where $a$ is a given set (i.e. a parameter). On the other hand, von Neumann's way of avoiding the antinomies is to require $\mathfrak{P}(x)$ to be of the form "$x$ is a member of *some* set, and $\mathfrak{Q}(x)$" or, equivalently, "$x$ is an element, and $\mathfrak{Q}(x)$". Translating this back to our ordinary terminology and notation we obtain:

AXIOM (XII) OF IMPREDICATIVE COMPREHENSION. **There exists a class $A$ which contains exactly those elements $x$ which satisfy the condition $\mathfrak{P}(x)$, where $\mathfrak{P}(x)$ is any condition.**

This is more than what we have in Axiom XI, in which the condition $\mathfrak{P}(x)$ is not supposed to mention any class quantifiers; indeed, not all the instances of Axiom XII are provable in **VNB**.[1] Axiom XII has been suggested by Quine in 1940 as one of the axioms of a system of his known under the name *Mathematical Logic*.[2] The annexation of Axiom XII to **VNB** is due to A. P. Morse and Wang.[3] Let us denote by **QM** the theory which consists of the axioms of **VNB**, which Axiom XI replaced by Axiom XII.[4]

Let us now study **QM**, comparing it with **VNB**. From the point of view that classes are extensions of pure conditions, **QM** is plain false since, as we saw above (on p. 183), some instances of Axiom XII fail for extensions of pure conditions. Therefore, let us compare **QM** with **VNB** as to its desirability as a system of axioms for set theory, from von Neumann's

---

[1] Provided that **VNB** is consistent—MOSTOWSKI [1951], KRUSE [1963]. Stronger results can be proved by the methods of KREISEL–LÉVY [1968] (Th. 11)—see Footnote 4 on p. 158.

[2] First edition of QUINE [1951]; see *Foundations* Ch. III, §4.

[3] WANG [1949], KELLY [1955]. (Classification axiom-scheme, in the Appendix), MORSE [1965] (see pp. xxi–xxii).

[4] We should have added Axiom XII to **G** rather than to **VNB**, since **G** is more in the line of the von Neumann approach; yet we chose to add it to **VNB** for the purpose of direct comparison of **QM** with **VNB**, since **VNB** and **G** can anyway be regarded as notational variants of each other.

A somewhat more detailed exposition of **QM** is given by STEGMÜLLER [1962], who borrows most of the technical features from BERNAYS [1958]. A very detailed development of a system strongly related to **QM** is carried out in MORSE [1965]. This system has the unorthodox feature of identifying the notions of formula and term, thereby identifying the notions of class and statement (a statement is equal to the null class O if it is false and to the *universal* class V if it is true; a class is true if it contains O). The strict equivalence of Morse's system with **QM** has been verified by TARSKI and PETERSON (MORSE [1965], p. xxiii). For a system which comprises **QM**, see BERNAYS [1961].

point of view mentioned above. The main argument in favor of QM is that once we agree, as von Neumann did, to avoid the antinomies not by forbidding the existence of large classes, but by denying their element-hood, there is no reason at all why we should stop at classes defined by conditions which do not involve class quantifiers and not admit classes defined by other conditions. Another argument in favor of QM is that when we define in VNB a class $\{x \mid \mathfrak{P}(x)\}$ we always have to check whether $\mathfrak{P}(x)$ is equivalent to a condition of the primitive language without class quantifiers. This requires some bookkeeping if one uses many defined notions of set theory.[1] Nothing of this sort is needed in QM where $\{x \mid \mathfrak{P}(x)\}$ is always a class.

A particularly embarrassing fact about VNB is that in VNB, unlike QM, one cannot prove all the instances of the induction schema. "If 0 fulfils the condition $\mathfrak{Q}(x)$ and, for every natural number $n$, if $n$ fulfils $\mathfrak{Q}(x)$ then $n + 1$ fulfils $\mathfrak{Q}(x)$ too, then every natural number fulfils $\mathfrak{Q}(x)$".[2] In VNB the standard proof of the induction schema proves it only for conditions formulated in the primitive language without class quantifiers[3] (and for other conditions which are equivalent to such conditions). In practice, induction is indeed almost always used for such conditions only, but to be on the safe side one has to keep track of uses of class quantifiers not only for the definition of classes, but also for the application of induction.

Another aspect in which VNB and QM differ is that VNB can be given by a finite number of axioms, as we saw in §7.2, whereas QM cannot.[4] The fact that VNB can be given by a finite number of axioms is not without its

---

[1] GÖDEL [1940] keeps track of it by means of the metamathematical concept of a *normal notion*.

[2] Assuming that VNB is consistent—MOSTOWSKI [1951]: (see also Footnote 4 below).

[3] The standard formulation of induction in VNB is by the single statement "For every class $Q$, if $0 \in Q$ and if, for every $n$ in $Q$, $n + 1$, too, is in $Q$, then $Q$ contains all the natural numbers."—BERNAYS [this volume] p. 24. By Axiom XI this clearly implies the schema of induction for conditions $\mathfrak{Q}(x)$ without class quantifiers.

[4] Let VNB* be the system obtained from VNB by adding the induction schema above as an axiom (where $\mathfrak{Q}(x)$ varies over *all* conditions). VNB* is a subsystem of QM since the induction schema is obviously provable in QM. VNB* is strongly semantically closed in the sense of MONTAGUE [1961] since finite sequences of classes can be handled as suggested by ROBINSON [1945] and, hence, no consistent extension of VNB* without new symbols, and in particular QM, which we assume to be consistent, can be determined by a finite number of axioms. Moreover, one can prove that no consistent extension of VNB* can be determined by a set of axioms in the language of VNB with a bounded number of class quantifiers. (This follows from Theorem 5 of KREISEL–LÉVY [1968], by means of a truth definition which uses the ideas of MOSTOWSKI [1951] and LÉVY [1965]. Finally, assuming the consistency of VNB*, not all the instances of Axiom XII are provable in VNB*—this follows from KRUSE [1963] Th. 5.2. Whatever will be said about QM in the present paragraph and in the two following ones applies equally well to the weaker theory, VNB*.

aesthetic appeal, but it is not a serious advantage for the following two reasons. First, there is no simple and direct way of using Axioms XI1–XI8 for the run-of-the-mill theorems of set theory. If one adopts Axioms XI1–XI8, the only reasonable way to develop set theory seems to first present the cumbersome proof of Axiom XI from Axioms XI1–XI8 and then start using Axiom XI. Second, the notion of a *proof* in **VNB** is not simpler than the notion of a proof in **QM**, even though the notion of an axiom of **VNB** is (where we choose Axioms XI1–XI8 to take care of comprehension), since in the proofs one uses rules of inference which are like schemas in the sense that they apply to infinitely many possible statements. For instance, the rule of detachment—*modus ponens*—allows one to derive from the two premises $\mathfrak{P}$ and $\mathfrak{P} \to \mathfrak{Q}$ the conclusion $\mathfrak{Q}$, where $\mathfrak{P}$ and $\mathfrak{Q}$ are any statements out of the infinite set of all statements.[1]

We have not yet discussed the question whether in replacing Axiom XI by Axiom XII we introduce no contradictions. We shall now look into this question, as well as into the more general question of the comparison of the deductive power of **VNB** and **QM**. We know that, assuming that **VNB** is consistent, there is no convincing proof that if **VNB** is consistent so is **QM**. This is shown by means of Gödel's theorem on consistency proofs.[2] However, there is no reason why this should lead us to doubt the consistency of **QM**. We shall see below that if some reasonable set theories, which are formulated in terms of sets only, are consistent, so is **QM**.

We have already mentioned above that some instances of Axiom XII are not provable in **VNB**, assuming, as we shall do throughout the present paragraph, that **VNB** is consistent. In fact, one can prove in **QM** infinitely many statements which involve only sets (or, for that matter, only natural numbers), and which are not provable in **ZF** (or in **VNB**).[3] Thus the transition from **VNB** to **QM** is of a different nature than the transition from **ZF** to **VNB** or from **VNBC** to **VNBC**$_\sigma$, which did not add any new theorems about sets. Still, one has to bear in mind that, as far as it is now known, those new theorems of **QM** are of a metamathematical character and do not seem to be theorems one would consider in a development of set

[1] In fact, axiom schemas can be considered to be rules of inference with 0 premises.
[2] Here one uses the fact that in **QM** one can prove the consistency of **VNB**—see MOSTOWSKI [1951].
[3] KREISEL–LÉVY [1968], Theorems 10 and 11. A particularly interesting such statement is the negation of the Second Axiom of Restriction (*Foundations*, p. 116), which is provable in **QM** (KURATA [1964]), but is not provable in **VNB** (if **VNB** is consistent—SHEPHERDSON [1951–1953] III). On the other hand, if **QM** is consistent then the negation of the axiom of constructibility is unprovable also in **QM** (THARP [1966]).

theory for the ordinary purposes of mathematics. At the same time, the facts expressed by Axiom XII are facts about classes which cannot be presented as facts about sets; one can construct a theorem of QM which is not implied in VNB by any statement which mentions only sets, unless the latter statement is refutable in VNB.[1]

Now that we know that QM is the source of infinitely many new theorems concerning sets which cannot be proved in ZF, we can ask, naturally, whether the notion of class is indeed essential for obtaining these theorems, or whether these will be the theorems of some natural set theory stronger than ZF but still formulated in terms of sets only. The latter happens to be the case. All the theorems of QM which mention only sets are also theorems of some set theory ZM, formulated in terms of sets only, and obtained by adding to ZF a certain axiom schema of strong infinity which implies the existence of many inaccessible cardinals.[2] As a consequence, if ZM is consistent so is QM. Actually, one can verify by a relatively simple argument the following stronger result. Let $ZF^{\#}$ be obtained from ZF by adding to it as an additional axiom the statement that there exists at least one inaccessible number. If the theory $ZF^{\#}$ is consistent then QM is consistent too. Obviously $ZF^{\#}$ is much weaker than ZM.[3]

Adopting von Neumann's attitude of regarding classes as objects of essentially the same kind as sets, we went along with the consequences of this attitude which led us to the system QM.[4] Let us now go back and examine again von Neumann's ideas. His addition of proper classes to the universe of set theory results from his discovery that it is not the existence of certain classes that leads to the antinomies, but rather the

---

[1] Such a theorem is given by the proof of Th. 4 in KREISEL–LÉVY [1968], where one has to use the truth definition for statements of ZF given by MOSTOWSKI [1951], and the result on the equivalence of ZF and VNB.

[2] This is a version of an axiom schema proposed, in essence, by Mahlo—see LÉVY [1960].

[3] Actually, all the theorems of QM which mention only sets are theorems of the theory ZF* whose axioms (and theorems) are all the statements $\mathfrak{S}$ in the language of ZF which can be proved in ZF to hold in every model $R(\theta)$, where $\theta$ is an inaccessible number and $R$ is the function recursively defined by $R(\alpha) = \cup_{\beta < \alpha} PR(\beta)$, where $Px$ denotes the power set of $x$. (This easily follows from the discussion in SHEPHERDSON [1951–1953] II, §3.7, provided we define an inaccessible number as in LÉVY [1960], or else add the local axiom of choice to all the theories which we discuss here.) It is obvious that ZF* is consistent, if and only if, $ZF^{\#}$ is consistent. All the theorems of ZF* are theorems of ZM (see LÉVY [1960]). On the other hand, the theorem of QM: "If there is an inaccessible number than $ZF^{\#}$ is consistent" (which is proved along the lines of MOSTOWSKI [1951]) is not a theorem of $ZF^{\#}$ (if $ZF^{\#}$ is consistent), as follows from Gödel's theorem on consistency proofs.

[4] One additional advantage of QM is that one can formulate in its language a strong axiom schema of infinity of set theory, which agrees neatly with QM—BERNAYS [1961].

assumption of their elementhood, i.e. their being members of other classes; therefore he introduces these classes as proper classes which are not members of classes. This is not a completely satisfactory solution of the problem of the existence of collections as objects, since now, even though proper classes are real objects, collections of proper classes do not exist. The existence of real mathematical objects which cannot be members of even finite classes is a rather peculiar matter, even though in actual mathematical treatment such classes are rarely needed, and can, in case of need, be represented by some classes of sets.[1] One cannot just blame the antinomies for this peculiar situation; we shall see that if one proceeds carefully enough then the assumption that proper classes can be members of classes or of other objects can be seen not to cause any contradiction.

One example of a system in which proper classes are members of some objects is as follows. We introduce a new kind of objects (hyper-classes), which are like classes except that, unlike classes, they can also contain classes as members. We shall use Greek letters as variables for hyper-classes, with the understanding that every class and set is a hyper-class and every set is a class. (We shall not carry out the rather trivial task of describing the formal framework in which this is done.) In addition to all axioms of **QM**, the system contains the following axioms.

(a) *Every member of a hyper-class is a class* (or a set).

(b) (Schema) *There is a hyper-class $\alpha$ which consists of all classes (and sets) $X$ which fulfil the condition $\mathfrak{P}(X)$, where $\mathfrak{P}(X)$ is any condition.*

This system can be seen to be consistent if the system $\mathbf{ZF}^{\#}$ mentioned above is,[2] and yet such comprehensive classes as the class of all sets or the class of all ordinal numbers are members of some objects, namely of hyper-classes.[3]

Another, more extreme example of a system where comprehensive classes can be members of classes, is the following system $ST_2$. The only variables of $ST_2$ are class variables. Its primitive relations are the binary relation of membership—$X \in Y$, and the unary predicate of sethood—$S(X)$ (read: $X$ is a set). Lowercase variables are introduced as defined

---

[1] See, e.g., ROBINSON [1945].

[2] The proof is essentially the same as the proof of the (relative) consistency of **QM** (see Footnote 3 on p. 200).

[3] In this system one can formulate an axiom which asserts the existence of a two-valued measure defined on all classes, which is $\alpha$-additive for every ordinal $\alpha$ (see, e.g. SCOTT [1961] or KEISLER–TARSKI [1964]. This is a strong axiom of infinity, which, in a very natural sense, is much stronger than that mentioned in Footnote 3 on p. 200.

variables which vary over sets. The axioms are:

(a) A sethood axiom: *Every member of a set is a set.*
(b) All the axioms of **QM** (these axioms contain uppercase and lower-case variables). The axiom of replacement is formulated as:

   *If F is a function and a is a set, then there is a set which contains exactly the values F(x) which are sets, for all members x of a which are in the domain of F.*

(c) The axioms of **ZF** with all variables replaced by uppercase ones.

This is a two-tier set theory with sets in the bottom tier and classes in the upper tier. For instance, the class V of all sets is a class, as well as its power class **PV**, which consists of all subclasses of V, its power class—**PPV**, etc. A natural model of this theory can be given in the system $\mathbf{ZF}^{*}$ as follows: We understand by "set" a member of $R(\theta)$, where $R$ is the function defined by $R(\alpha) = \bigcup_{\beta < \alpha} PR(\beta)$, and $\theta$ is a fixed inaccessible number, and by "class" we understand any set. Thus, assuming the consistency of $\mathbf{ZF}^{*}$, the system $\mathbf{ST}_2$ is also consistent. Moreover, every statement about sets which is provable in $\mathbf{ST}_2$ is a theorem of **ZM**.[1]

Before we continue our discussion of the possible ways of handling classes in set theory, let us look into the use of classes in category theory, which is a new branch of algebra. Mathematicians working in that theory have found that even a set theory like **QM** is insufficient for their needs. Categories are classes, which may also be proper classes, and category theory also deals with functions defined on classes of categories and with other kinds of objects which are unavailable in **QM**.[2] Let us refer to the informal framework in which category theorists are working as *category theory*. Let us denote the informal power-class operation with **P**, i.e. for a class $A$, **P**$A$ is the class of all subclasses of $A$ (including the proper subclasses of $A$). Category theory involves only objects which are members of the classes V, **PV**, **PPV**,..., $\mathbf{P}^n$V, where V is the class of all sets and $n$ is some fixed finite number.

Some category theorists proposed to develop category theory within a system of set theory which is, essentially, **ZF** together with an axiom which asserts the existence of arbitrarily large inaccessible numbers.[3] In this system, the sets $R(\theta)$, where $\theta$ is any inaccessible number, are called

---

[1] The proof is along the same lines as the proof of the corresponding statement in Footnote 3 on p. 200.

[2] For the part of category theory which can be developed in **VNB** or in **QM** see MACLANE [1961] and ISBELL [1963].

[3] Grothendieck, Sonner. See KÜHNRICH [1966] and KRUSE [1966] where further references are given.

by the category theorists universes. We shall refer to these sets as *subuniverses*, out of respect for the real universe. This idea is now not to deal with categories related to the universe of all sets, but to deal with categories related to a subuniverse $R(\theta)$. The latter categories are just subsets of $R(\theta)$, or of some $R(\theta + n)$, where $n$ is a finite number; therefore one has sets of such categories, functions over such categories, etc.

A similar, but simpler way of dealing with categories in set theory is to assume only the existence of at least one inaccessible number, to choose for $\theta$ a fixed inaccessible number and to agree to talk only about categories related to the subuniverse $R(\theta)$. The reason why this way was not adopted by category theorists seems to be that they did not want to deprive the sets which are not members of the fixed subuniverse $R(\theta)$ from the blessings of category theory. Since they assumed the existence of arbitrarily large inaccessible numbers, given any set $x$, there is, by the axiom of foundation, a subuniverse $R(\theta)$ which contains $x$, and the category theory for this subuniverse applies to $x$. Looking deeper into the matter we see that even the assumption that every set belongs to some subuniverse is not sufficient for all conceivable needs of category theory; the results of category theory will concern in each case only the members of a subuniverse $R(\theta)$, but not *all* sets. To give an example, suppose $\mathfrak{S}(x,y)$ is some binary relation between groups, and suppose, for the sake of simplicity, that this relation holds or does not hold between $x$ and $y$ independently of the universe (or subuniverse) to which we refer in defining this relation. If we use category theory to prove the existence of a group $g$ such that $\mathfrak{S}(g,h)$ holds for every group $h$, then with respect to the subuniverse $R(\theta)$ this means that there is a group $g \in R(\theta)$ such that $\mathfrak{S}(g,h)$ holds for every group $h \in R(\theta)$; but this does not establish in set theory the existence of a group $g$ such that $\mathfrak{S}(g,h)$ holds for *every* group $h$, irrespective of which subuniverse it belongs to.

The best way of developing category theory within set theory seems to be to use a system of set theory like the system $ST_2$ described above. In $ST_2$ we can use categories related to *all* sets. This seems to be close to the way category theorists think about it when they are caught unawares, since in this approach categories are classes, not necessarily sets, yet, in almost all respects, classes can be treated like sets in $ST_2$. This can still be criticized as follows. Since the classes behave like sets this may mean that the classes of $ST_2$ are really sets, even though they are called classes. Thus, when we say here "all sets" we exclude the proper classes, which should have been included too. Thereby we seem to have arrived again at the situation discussed above where we dealt with a single fixed subuniverse (here we have a universe of classes and a subuniverse of sets).

This criticism can be easily overcome by considering $ST_2$ only as a *façon de parler* for proving theorems about sets in the set theory ZM. We have mentioned above that every theorem of $ST_2$ which concerns sets only is also a theorem of ZM. Since ZM deals with sets only, when we say in ZM "all sets" we mean just that. Categories are, generally, objects of the system $ST_2$, but theorems about sets which are proved by means of categories are also theorems of ZM.

A different variant of $ST_2$ is obtained if we adhere to the limitation of size doctrine by requiring that a small class, e.g. a finite class, be a set even if its members are proper classes. In this variant we drop the sethood axiom (a) of $ST_2$, and amend the axiom of replacement $VIII^c$ in (b) to read: *If F is a function and a is a set, then there is a set which contains exactly the values F(X), which may be sets or classes, for all members X of a which are in the domain of F.* It should be noted that the axiom of union in (b) is: *For every set a, there is a set b whose members are exactly the members of the sets which are members of a.*[1] A natural model of this system is obtained in $ZF^{\#}$ by interpreting "class" as set, and "set" as "set of cardinality $< \theta$".[2]

Stronger and more elaborate systems, which follow the basic ideas of the simple systems given here, are discussed in the literature; yet all such systems turn out not to yield any information concerning sets which is not contained, in one way or another, is some set theory of the ZF type,[3] which for the systems considered here is $ZF^{\#}$ or ZM. This process of adding bigger classes and hyper-classes has to stop somewhere; and we have to decide where to do so. QM is a good place to stop at for reasons of convenience and neatness, yet, apart from these considerations, this choice is as arbitrary as any other one. This arbitrariness is, to some extent, due to the antinomies and hence unavoidable; however, it is also due in part to the decision, originating with von Neumann, to admit classes other than sets as real mathematical objects. As mentioned in §5 above, we can use VNB without adopting von Neumann's point of view. More consistent and radical solutions to the problem of developing a system of set theory in which classes occur for the sake of convenience,

---

[1] This is the correct way of reading the symbolic version of the axiom of union in §1; the verbal version of this axiom in §1 is refutable in the present system.

[2] In the system G* of OBERSCHELP [1964], too, proper classes can be members of sets. However, due to an axiom of comprehension weaker than the one given here, the system G* is essentially equivalent to QM. (One can prove that for a suitably formulated version H of QM which admits individuals, and for the natural translation of the statements of H to the language of G*, a statement is a theorem of H if and only if its translation is a theorem of G*—the proof is essentially given in OBERSCHELP [1964], a more constructive version can be obtained by the method of Paul Cohen mentioned in Footnote 1 on p. 191.

[3] TAKEUTI [1961] and [1969]; SOLOVAY [1966].

while sets are still believed to be the only mathematical objects that exist, are handled in the next subsection.

### 7. Classes not taken seriously—systems of Bernays and Quine

In §2 we introduced classes in **VNB**, in order to be able to neatly handle extensions of pure conditions. If we do not intend to regard classes as real mathematical objects, then a second look suggests that the system **VNB** might be too strong. We know that **VNB** is not too strong in the sense that we can prove in it false theorems about sets, or even about classes, yet **VNB** is too strong in the sense that, as we shall see, the machinery it contains for handling classes is much more than needed for the desired streamlining of set theory.

Bernays introduced[1] an axiom system **B** which differs from **VNB**, in addition to purely technical matters, as follows. While **B** retains the full formalism that **VNB** has for handling sets and also retains the class variables, its language does not admit quantifiers over class variables. To partially compensate for this loss the language of **B** also admits, as primitive notions, the class abstracts $\{x|\mathfrak{P}(x)\}$, where $\mathfrak{P}(x)$ is any condition on $x$ (of the language of **B**). Also, equality of classes is not primitive in **B** but is defined. The axioms of **B** are the axioms of **VNB** with the following changes:

(a)  the universal class quantifiers in front of the axioms of subsets ($V^c$) and replacement ($VII^c$) are dropped,

(b)  the axiom of extensionality (X) is dropped, and

(c)  the axiom of comprehension for classes (XI) is replaced by the schema: $y$ *is a member of the class* $\{x|\mathfrak{P}(x)\}$ *if and only if $y$ fulfils the condition* $\mathfrak{P}(x)$.

Free class variables in a formula are interpreted as if they are universally quantified; e.g. the formula $\forall x\ (x \in A \leftrightarrow x \notin \{x|x \notin A\})$ is read "For every class $A$ and for every element $x$, $x \in A$ if and only if $x \notin \{x|x \notin A\}$".

Even though the apparatus of **B** is more economical than that of **VNB**, it is enough for a streamlined approach to classes, since all the statements of **VNB** which are ordinarily used in mathematical arguments can also be expressed in **B**. **B** is closer to **ZF** than **VNB**. For instance, the proof that every statement of **ZF** which is provable in **B** is also provable in **ZF** is rather trivial (this should be compared to the corresponding proofs for

---

[1] Bᴇʀɴᴀʏs [1958].

VNB—both of which use deep theorems of logic).[1] When one compares B and VNB one has to notice that the primitive symbols $\{x|\mathfrak{P}(x)\}$ of B are defined symbols of VNB. It is obvious that every theorem of B is also a theorem of VNB; but also the converse is true, i.e. every statement of B which is a theorem of VNB is also a theorem of B.[2] It is also worth noting that the embarrassing situation in VNB, viz. that there are conditions for which induction over the natural numbers cannot be proved, is avoided in B since all those conditions of VNB involve class quantifiers.

An even more radical attitude is advocated by Quine.[3] He proposes a system which is just ZF, except that statements of the language of B which involve classes are considered to be shorthand versions of statements of ZF. The translation from shorthand (in the language of B) to longhand (in the language of ZF) is as follows. (The shorthand may sometimes be longer than the longhand.) The language of B contains, in addition to what is in the language of ZF, free class variables and class abstracts—$\{x|\mathfrak{P}(x)\}$. The free class variables are interpreted as metamathematical variables for class abstracts $\{x|\mathfrak{P}(x)\}$ in which the condition $\mathfrak{P}(x)$ has no class parameters; e.g. the statement

(*)           $\exists z \, \forall x \, (x \in z \leftrightarrow x \in A \wedge x \in \{u\,|\,u \notin B\})$

is understood to be a schema, where $A$ and $B$ stand for arbitrary class abstracts, i.e. the schema

$$\exists z \, \forall x \, (x \in z \leftrightarrow x \in \{v\,|\,\mathfrak{P}(v)\} \wedge x \in \{u\,|\,u \notin \{v\,|\,\mathfrak{Q}(v)\}\}).$$

From this point of view the single statements contain no class variables, but they may contain class abstracts. These class abstracts can occur in such a statement only in a context like $y \in \{x|\mathfrak{P}(x)\}$.[4] $y \in \{x|\mathfrak{P}(x)\}$ is taken to be shorthand for $\mathfrak{P}(y)$. Thus the statement (*) above is really shorthand for the schema $\exists z \, \forall x \, (x \in z \leftrightarrow \mathfrak{P}(x) \wedge \rightarrow \mathfrak{Q}(x))$, where $\mathfrak{P}(x)$ and $\mathfrak{Q}(x)$ are any conditions of ZF. Simple checking shows that all the axioms of B are, in the present interpretation, theorems or theorem-schemas of ZF. It can easily be seen that also the logical axioms of B are interpreted as theorems or theorem-schemas of ZF, and that the logical

---

[1] The completeness theorem of the first-order predicate calculus for the proof given on p. 190, and the cut elimination theorem (or the $\epsilon$-theorem) for the proofs mentioned in Footnote 1 on p. 191.

[2] There are two proofs for this fact, both very similar to the proofs mentioned in the previous footnote.

[3] QUINE [1963].

[4] In fact, they may also occur as $\{x|\mathfrak{P}(x)\} = \{y|\mathfrak{Q}(y)\}$ or as $\{x|\mathfrak{Q}(x)\} \in y$, etc. but these are *defined* expressions of the language of B (see the definitions on pp. 180 and 186) and can therefore be eliminated.

rules of inference used in **B** lead us here from theorems and theorem-schemas of **ZF** to other theorems and theorem-schemas of **ZF**. Therefore all the theorems of **B** are also theorems of Quine's system, even though they are interpreted somewhat differently there. On the other hand, there are theorems of Quine's system which cannot be proved in **B**, since there is a statement $\mathfrak{S}(A)$ of **B**, with a free-class variable $A$, such that when interpreted as a schema, all its instances are provable in **ZF**, and yet $\mathfrak{S}(A)$ is refutable in **QM**.[1]

## 8. The system of Ackermann

In the systems **ZF** and **VNB** the guiding principle for choosing the axioms was the limitation of size doctrine. Adherence to this doctrine prevented the occurrence of the known antinomies in those systems. In 1956, Ackermann[2] proposed a system of axioms for set theory which is based on a completely different approach and which retains as axioms only the weakest consequences of the limitation of size doctrine, i.e. that a member of a set and a subclass of a set are sets. It is rather surprising that, as it turned out later, essentially the same theorems are provable in Ackermann's system as in **ZF**. It is also possible to formulate Ackermann's system for set theory with individuals,[3] but we shall follow our earlier practice of considering only set theory without individuals.

In Ackermann's system, which we denote with **A**, the universe consists of objects with a membership relation between these objects, denoted by the symbol $\in$. Two objects which have exactly the same members are equal. Therefore, it stands to reason to refer to these objects as *classes*, which we do from now on. Notice that these are not classes in the sense of extensions of pure conditions as in §2, or, for that matter, extensions of any conditions. These are classes in the vague sense for which we also use the words "collection", "aggregate", etc., i.e. objects completely determined by their membership. Some of the classes are said to be *sets*. Unlike the system **G** of §5, not every class which is a member of some class is a set. The language of **A** is based on the first-order predicate calculus with equality. There is just one kind of variables—class variables; we shall use for them capital letters. The primitive predicate symbols are the binary membership symbol $\in$ and a unary predicate symbol $M$. We shall read $M(A)$ as "$A$ is a set". We shall use lowercase

---

[1] Such a schema was given by Mostowski—see LÉVY [1960], §5. To see that it is refutable in **QM** use the method of MOSTOWSKI [1951].

[2] ACKERMANN [1956].

[3] ACKERMANN [1956], §3.

letters as variables for sets. Lowercase variables are not primitive symbols of the language, we just say "for all $x$..." instead of "for every class $X$ if $M(X)$ then..." and similarly for the existential quantifier.

DEFINITION. If $A$ and $B$ are classes such that every member of $A$ is a member of $B$, we write $A \subseteq B$ and say that $A$ is a *subclass* of $B$. In symbols:

$$A \subseteq B =_{Df} \forall X \, (X \in A \rightarrow X \in B).$$

The axioms are:

AXIOM $(\alpha)$ OF EXTENSIONALITY. **If the classes $A$ and $B$ have exactly the same members then they are equal.** In symbols:

$$\forall X \, (X \in A \leftrightarrow X \in B) \rightarrow A = B.$$

AXIOM $(\beta)$ OF COMPREHENSION FOR CLASSES. **There exists a class $A$ which contains exactly those** *sets* $x$ **which satisfy the condition** $\mathfrak{P}(x)$, where $\mathfrak{P}(x)$ is any condition of **A**.

The class $A$ of this axiom is assumed to contain only the *sets* $x$ which satisfy $\mathfrak{P}(x)$, rather than all classes $X$ which satisfy $\mathfrak{P}(X)$, in order not to obtain here the contradictory axiom schema of comprehension of §2 (with sets replaced by classes). As in §2 we denote with $\{x \mid \mathfrak{P}(x)\}$ the class of *sets* $x$ which satisfy $\mathfrak{P}(x)$; the existence of this class being guaranteed by Axiom $\beta$. Now, if we repeat the proof of Russell's antinomy we find that the class $\{x \mid x \notin x\}$ is not a set.

AXIOM $(\gamma)$ OF HEREDITY. **If $Y$ is a member of the set $x$ then $Y$ is a set, too.** In symbols:

$$Y \in x \rightarrow M(Y).$$

AXIOM $(\delta)$ OF SUBSETS. **If $Y$ is a subclass of the set $x$ then $Y$ is a set too.** In symbols:

$$Y \subseteq x \rightarrow M(Y).$$

Let $V$ be the class $\{x \mid M(x)\}$ of all sets. We saw above that the subclass $\{x \mid x \notin x\}$ of $V$ is not a set, hence, by Axiom $\delta$, $V$ too is not a set.

AXIOM $(\epsilon)$ OF COMPREHENSION FOR SETS. **If the only classes $X$ which satisfy the condition $\mathfrak{P}(X)$ are sets, then there exists a set $w$ which consists exactly of those sets $X$ which satisfy the condition $\mathfrak{P}(X)$,** where $\mathfrak{P}(X)$ is any condition *which does not involve the unary predicate $M$ and which has no parameters other than set parameters.* In symbols:

$$\forall x_1 \forall x_2 \cdots \forall x_n \, [\forall X \, (\mathfrak{P}(X) \rightarrow M(X)) \rightarrow \exists w \, \forall X \, (X \in w \leftrightarrow \mathfrak{P}(X))],$$

where $\mathfrak{P}(X)$ does not involve $M$ and has no parameters other than $x_1, \ldots, x_n$.

This is the main axiom of comprehension for sets in **A** ($\gamma$ and $\delta$, too, are axioms of comprehension for sets). Unlike the axioms of comprehension for sets in **ZF** and **VNB**, and unlike Axioms $\gamma$ and $\delta$, Axiom $\epsilon$ is not motivated by the limitation of size doctrine. Before we discuss the motivation of Axiom $\epsilon$, let us first study the axiom from a technical point of view. If we lift the restriction that the condition $\mathfrak{P}(X)$ should not involve the predicate $M$, then by applying Axiom $\epsilon$ to the condition $M(X) \wedge \mathfrak{P}(X)$ we would obtain that the class $\{x | \mathfrak{P}(x)\}$ is a set, for every condition $\mathfrak{P}(X)$. In particular, the class $\{x | x \notin x\}$ is a set, which immediately yields Russell's antinomy. Thus the restriction that the condition $\mathfrak{P}(X)$ in Axiom $\epsilon$ does not involve the unary predicate $M$ is necessary for the consistency of **A**. Also the second restriction, viz. that $\mathfrak{P}(X)$ may only have set parameters, is necessary in order to avoid Russell's antinomy. Were it not for the restriction on parameters in Axiom $\epsilon$, we could have chosen, for $\mathfrak{P}(X)$ in Axiom $\epsilon$, the condition $X \in Y$, and thereby we would have had "for every class $Y$, if all the members of $Y$ are sets then the class $\{x | x \in Y\}$ is a set". If we substitute for $Y$ the class $\{x | \mathfrak{P}(x)\}$, where $\mathfrak{P}(x)$ is any condition, we get that every class $\{x | \mathfrak{P}(x)\}$ is a set. This again, immediately yields Russell's antinomy.

As a consequence of Axiom $\epsilon$, we get that if $\mathfrak{Q}(x)$ is any condition with no parameters other than set parameters, and which does not involve the predicate $M$, then $\mathfrak{Q}(X)$ cannot be equivalent to $M(X)$. This is shown as follows. Suppose $M(X)$ is equivalent to $\mathfrak{Q}(X)$, then if we take $\mathfrak{Q}(X) \wedge X \notin X$ for $\mathfrak{P}(X)$ in Axiom $\epsilon$, we get that the class $\{x | x \notin x\}$ is a set, which, we know, is a contradiction. In other words, $M(X)$ cannot be defined in **A** by means of the membership relation $\epsilon$ (unless **A** is inconsistent).

Ackermann justifies Axiom $\epsilon$ as follows. Let us consider the sets to be the "real" objects of set theory. Not all the sets are given at once when one starts to handle set theory—the sets are to be thought of as obtained in some constructive process. Thus at no moment during this process can one consider the predicate $M(X)$ as a "well-defined" predicate, since the process of constructing the sets still goes on and it is not yet determined whether a given class $X$ will eventually be constructed as a set or not. As a consequence, a condition $\mathfrak{P}(X)$ can be regarded as "well-defined" only if it avoids using the predicate $M$. Also, parameters are allowed in such a condition $\mathfrak{P}(X)$ only to the extent that they stand for "well-defined" objects, i.e. sets.

Ackermann's justification of Axiom $\epsilon$ is clearly insufficient. While one is not allowed to have in the condition $\mathfrak{P}(X)$ of this axiom a parameter $Y$ which stands for a class which is not a set because membership in such a class is not "well defined", one is allowed to use quantifiers over *all* classes in $\mathfrak{P}(X)$, i.e. $\mathfrak{P}(X)$ may contain expressions like "for all classes $Y...$". If a single class is not "well defined", why is the totality of all classes "well defined"? It is possible to refine Ackermann's justification by some subtler arguments which may overcome the difficulty outlined here. However, taking into consideration all justifications known to the author, Axiom $\epsilon$ is still far from having the intuitive obviousness of, say, the axiom of replacement of ZF. Thus, what makes the system A interesting and trustworthy is not the arguments brought forth in favor of its axioms but rather the beauty of the proofs in A, and the fact that A turned out to be equivalent in a strong sense to ZF, as we shall see below.

The last axiom of A is:

AXIOM ($\xi$) OF FOUNDATION. **If $y$ is a non-empty set, then $y$ has a member $u$ such that $u \cap y = $ O.**[1] In symbols:

$$y \neq 0 \rightarrow \exists u \ (u \in y \wedge u \cap y = O).$$

When we come to compare A with ZF, we write the variables of ZF as lowercase variables, since in ZF all objects are sets. Every statement of (the language of) ZF is therefore also a statement of A. On the other hand, statements of A that mention classes which are not sets are not statements of ZF and have no natural translation into statements of ZF. Therefore, the question which we now ask is: Which statements of ZF are provable in A? It turns out that *the statements of ZF provable in A are exactly the theorems of ZF*. The proof that all the statements of ZF provable in A are theorems of ZF uses metamathematical arguments.[2] In order to prove the converse, namely that all the theorems of ZF are provable in A, it is enough to prove in A all the *axioms* of ZF. Here we shall prove in A all the axioms of ZF other than the axiom schema of replacement. The proof of that axiom schema makes use of Axiom $\xi$ of foundation and involves metamathematical arguments.[3] The other axioms of ZF are proved as follows.

I. *The axiom of extensionality* of ZF follows immediately from Axiom $\alpha$.

---

[1] This is Axiom IX* given on p. 186. It is shown in LÉVY–VAUGHT (1961) that schema IX of §1 is now provable in A, and that if A is consistent without Axiom $\xi$, then A is consistent with Axiom $\xi$. Axiom $\xi$ was not proposed by ACKERMANN [1956], but we need it here for the purpose of comparing A with ZF.

[2] LÉVY [1959].

[3] REINHARDT [1970].

II. *The axiom of pairing*. Given sets $b$ and $c$ we consider the condition "$X = b$ *or* $X = c$". This condition does not mention the predicate $M$, it has only set parameters, and every $X$ satisfying it is a set. Therefore, by Axiom $\epsilon$, there is a set whose members are exactly $b$ and $c$.

III, IV. *The axioms of union and power set* are proved similarly by applying Axiom $\epsilon$ to the conditions "$X$ *is a member of a member of* $b$" and "$X$ *is a subclass of* $b$" and using Axioms $\gamma$ and $\delta$, respectively.

V. *The axiom of subsets*. If $b$ is a set and $\mathfrak{P}(X)$ is any condition, not even necessarily in the language of ZF, then by Axiom $\beta$ there is a class $\{x \mid x \in b \wedge \mathfrak{P}(x)\}$, and by Axiom $\delta$ this class is a set. If we knew that there exists at least one set then the existence of the null set would follow from the axiom of subsets (or directly from Axioms $\beta$ and $\delta$). However, here we have to use Axiom $\epsilon$ to prove that there exists a set at all, so we may as well apply Axiom $\epsilon$ to the condition $X \ne X$ and prove right away the existence of the null set.

VI. *The axiom of infinity*. It is rather surprising that this axiom can be proved in **A** since, unlike the systems of set theory discussed till now, none of the axioms of **A** directly mentions the existence of an infinite set. Let us now prove the strongest version of the axiom of infinity. "There is a set $a$ which contains a memberless set (i.e. the null set) and such that, for all members $y$ and $z$ of $a$, $y \cup \{z\}$, too, is a member of $a$". Let us consider the following condition $\mathfrak{P}(X)$ on $X$: "$X$ is a member of every class $B$ such that $B$ contains a memberless class and such that for all members $Y$ and $Z$ of $B$ there is a member $U$ of $B$ which consists of $Z$ and of the members of $Y$ (informally, $U = Y \cup \{Z\}$)". The class $V$ of all sets satisfies the requirements for $B$ in $\mathfrak{P}(X)$, since there is a memberless set and since, by the axioms of pairing and union which we proved above, if $Y$ and $Z$ are sets then also the class $Y \cup \{Z\}$ is a set. Thus every class $X$ which satisfies $\mathfrak{P}(X)$ is a member of $V$, and hence a set. Therefore the condition $\mathfrak{P}(X)$ satisfies the assumption of Axiom $\epsilon$, and Axiom $\epsilon$ implies the existence of a set $a$ which consists exactly of the sets $X$ which satisfy $\mathfrak{P}(X)$. This set can be easily seen to be as required by the axiom of infinity above.

IX. *The axiom of foundation*, and in particular version IX* (p. 186), follows immediately from Axiom $\xi$.

Having presented the result that the same statements of (the language of) ZF are provable in ZF and in **A**, let us draw some conclusions. First, we get that **A** is consistent if and only if ZF is consistent, since a contradictory statement, say, "There exists a set $x$ which is both a member of itself and not a member of itself", is provable in **A** if and only if it is provable in ZF. Second, we get that if $\mathfrak{S}$ is a statement of ZF, then $\mathfrak{S}$ is consistent with **A** (i.e. not refutable in **A**) if and only if $\mathfrak{S}$ is consistent with **ZF**. Therefore, if **A** is consistent then it is also consistent with the axiom of constructibility and, *a fortiori*, with the axiom of choice and the generalized continuum hypothesis. Also, almost all the independence results of *Foundations*, Ch.II, §4 and §6 still hold when **ZF** is replaced in them by **A**.

Till now we have compared **A** with **ZF**; let us now say something about the relationship of **A** with the system **QM** of §6. As in the case of **A** and **ZF** a natural translation exists only from **QM** to **A**. In this translation the set variables of **QM** are translated as set variables of **A** while the class variables of **QM** are translated as class variables of **A** restricted to classes which consist only of sets. Using the proofs given above of the axioms of **ZF** it is easily seen that the translation of all the axioms of **QM** other than Axioms VII$^c$ of replacement are theorems of **A**. The translation of Axiom VII$^c$ is not provable in **A**; in fact, it is an axiom of strong infinity for **A**.[1] If **A** is consistent then (the translation of) Axiom VIII$^c_\sigma$ of global choice is consistent with **A** since, as we mentioned above, if **A** is consistent then **A** is consistent with the axiom of constructibility, which implies Axiom VIII$^c_\sigma$.

The central objects of **A** are the sets, and, as we saw, we know quite a bit about the sets in **A**. As to classes which are not sets, Axiom $\beta$ asserts the existence of such classes whose members are sets. No axiom handles directly classes which have members that are not sets, yet by means of Axiom $\epsilon$ one can obtain many results about such classes. As a particularly simple example let us prove that there is a class $A$ not all of whose members are sets. If there were no such class then a class $X$ would not be a member of any class $A$ unless $X$ is a set. On the other hand, by the axiom of pairing, which we proved above, every set $X$ is a member of some class. Therefore, the property of being a set would be equivalent to the property of being a member of some class; but we proved above, by means of Axiom $\epsilon$, that the property of being a set is not equivalent to any condition which does not mention the predicate $M$, and thus we have a contradiction. One can also prove much stronger results about classes whose members are not necessarily sets. For instance, by means of the axiom of foundation $\xi$ one can prove the existence of the class $\{V\}$ whose only member is $V$ ($= \{x \mid x = x\}$), and of the class $\mathbf{P}V$ which consists of all the subclasses of $V$, and of the class $\mathbf{PP}V$, etc.[2]

---

[1] This can be shown by the methods of LÉVY [1959] and LÉVY–VAUGHT [1961]—see LÉVY [1959], p. 157.

[2] LÉVY–VAUGHT [1961]. On the other hand, one cannot prove in **A** any statement about classes which cannot be proved in **ZF** about sets—LÉVY [1959].

# References

ACKERMANN, W. (1956) Zur Axiomatik der Mengenlehre. *Math. Annalen* **131**, 336–345.

BAR-HILLEL, Y., POZNANSKI, E. I. J., RABIN, M. O., and ROBINSON, A. (Eds.) (1961) *Essays on the foundations of mathematics*. (Dedicated to A. A. Fraenkel.) Magnes Press, Jerusalem. 351 pp.

BERNAYS, P. (1937–1954) A system of axiomatic set theory. This volume.

BERNAYS, P. (1958) *Axiomatic set theory* (with a historical introduction by A. A. Fraenkel). North-Holland, Amsterdam. 226 pp. (2nd ed. (1968), 235 pp.).

BERNAYS, P. (1961) Zur Frage der Unendlichkeitsschemata in der axiomatischen Mengenlehre. In BAR-HILLEL et al. (1961), pp. 3–49. This volume (English translation—revised version).

BULOFF, J. J., HOLYOKE, T. C., and HAHN, S. W. (Eds.) (1969) *Foundations of mathematics*. (Symposium papers commemorating the sixtieth birthday of Kurt Gödel.) Springer, Berlin. 195 pp.

CHURCH, A. (1956) *Introduction to mathematical logic*—I, Princeton University Press, Princeton, N.J., 376 pp.

EASTON, W. B. (1964) Powers of regular cardinals. Ph.D. thesis. Princeton University, 66 pp.

FEFERMAN, S. (1965) Some applications of the notions of forcing and generic sets. *Fund. Math.* **56**, 325–345.

FELGNER, U. (1971) Comparison of the axioms of local and universal choice. *Fund. Math.* **71**, 43–62.

FRAENKEL, A. A. (1922) Über den Begriff "definit" und die Unabhängigkeit des Auswahlaxioms, *Sitzungsberichte der Preussischen Akademie der Wissenschaften, Phys.–Math. Klasse*, pp. 253–257. (English translation in VAN HEIJENOORT (1967), pp. 284–289.)

GÖDEL, K. (1940) *The consistency of the axiom of choice and of the generalized continuum hypothesis with the axioms of set theory*. Annals of Math. Studies. Vol. 3. Princeton University Press, Princeton, N.J., 66 pp. (2nd printing (1951), 74 pp.).

HEIJENOORT, J. VAN (Ed.) (1967) *From Frege to Gödel—a source book in mathematical logic, 1879–1931*. Harvard University Press, Cambridge, Mass., 660 pp.

ISBELL, J. R. (1963) Two set-theoretical theorems in categories. *Fund. Math.* **53**, 43–49.

ISBELL, J. R. and WRIGHT, F. B. (1966) Another equivalent form of the axiom of choice. *Proc. A.M.S.* **17**, 174.

KEISLER, H. J. and TARSKI, A. (1964) From accessible to inaccessible cardinals. *Fund. Math.* **53**, 225–308. Corrections, *ibid.* (1965) **57**, 119.

KELLY, J. L. (1955) *General topology*. Van Nostrand, New York, 298 pp.

KREISEL, G. and LÉVY, A. (1968) Reflection principles and their use for establishing the complexity of axiomatic systems. *Zeitschr. f. math. Logik* **14**, 97–191.

KRUSE, A. H. (1963) A method of modelling the formalism of set theory in axiomatic set theory. *J.S.L.* **28**, 20–34.

KRUSE, A. H. (1966) Grothendieck universes and the super-complete models of Sheperdson. *Compositio Math.* **17**, 96–101.

KÜHNRICH, M. (1966) Über den Begriff des Universums. *Zeitschr. f. math. Logik* **12**, 37–50.

KURATA, R. (1964) On the existence of a proper complete model of set theory. *Commentarii Math. Universitatis Sancti Pauli* **13**, 35–43.

LÉVY, A. (1959) On Ackermann's set theory. *J.S.L.* **24**, 154–166.

LÉVY, A. (1960) Axiom schemata of strong infinity in axiomatic set theory. *Pacific J. Math.* **10**, 223–238.

LÉVY, A. (1965) A hierarchy of formulas in set theory. *Memoirs A.M.S.* **57**, 76 pp.

LÉVY, A. (1968) On von Neuman's axiom system for set theory. *American Mathematical Monthly* **75**, 762–763.

LÉVY, A. and VAUGHT, R. L. (1961) Principles of partial reflection in the set theories of Zermelo and Ackermann. *Pacific J. of Math.* **11**, 1045–1062.

MACLANE, S. (1961) Locally small categories and the foundations of set theory. *Infinitistic methods.* Warsaw, pp. 25–43.

MENDELSON, E. (1964) *Introduction to mathematical logic.* Van Nostrand, New York, 300 pp.

MONTAGUE, R. (1961) Semantical closure and non-finite axiomatizability—I. *Infinitistic methods.* Warsaw, pp. 45–69.

MORSE, A. P. (1965) *A theory of sets.* Academic Press, New York, 130 pp.

MOSTOWSKI, A. (1939) Über die Unabhängigkeit des Wohlordnungssatzes vom Ordnungsprinzip. *Fund. Math.* **32**, 201–252.

MOSTOWSKI, A. (1949) An undecidable arithmetical statement. *Fund. Math.* **36**, 143–164.

MOSTOWSKI, A. (1951) Some impredicative definitions in the axiomatic set theory. *Fund. Math.* **37**, 111–124. Corrections, *ibid.* (1952) **38**, 238.

MYHILL, J. R. (1952) The hypothesis that all classes are nameable. *Acad. U.S.A.* **38**, 979–981.

NEUMANN, J. VON (1925) Eine Axiomatisierung der Mengenlehre. *J. f. Math.* **154**, 219–240. Corrections, *ibid.* (1926) **155**, 128. Also in VON NEUMANN (1961), pp. 34–56. (English translation in VAN HEIJENOORT (1967), pp. 393–413.)

NEUMANN, J. VON (1928) Die Axiomatisierung der Mengenlehre. *Math. Zeitschr.* **27**, 669–752. Also in VON NEUMANN (1961), pp. 339–422.

NEUMANN, J. VON (1929) Uber eine Widerspruchsfreiheitsfrage in der axiomatischen Mengenlehre. *J. f. Math.* **160**, 227–241. Also in VON NEUMANN (1961), pp. 494–508.

NEUMANN, J. VON (1961) *Collected works.* Vol. 1. Pergamon, New York. 654 pp.

NOVAK, ILSE L. (1951) A construction for models of consistent systems. *Fund. Math.* **37**, 87–110.

OBERSCHELP, A. (1964) Eigentliche Klassen als Urelemente in der Mengenlehre. *Math. Annalen* **157**, 234–260.

QUINE, W. V. (1951) *Mathematical logic* (revised edition). Harvard University Press, Cambridge, Mass. 346 pp. (First edition (1940).)

QUINE, W. V. (1963) *Set theory and its logic.* Belknap Press, Cambridge, Mass., 359 pp. (Revised ed. (1969), 361 pp.)

REINHARDT, W. N. (1970) Ackermann's set theory equals ZF. *Ann. of Math. Logic* 2, 189–249.

ROBINSON, R. M. (1937) The theory of classes—A modification of von Neuman's system. *J.S.L.* 2, 69–72.

ROBINSON, R. M. (1945) On finite sequences of classes. *J.S.L.* 10, 125–126.

ROSSER, J. B. and WANG, H. (1950) Non-standard models for formal logics. *J.S.L.* 15, 113–129. (Errata, *ibid.*, p. iv.)

RUBIN, H. and RUBIN, J. E. (1963) *Equivalents of the axiom of choice.* North-Holland, Amsterdam, 134 pp. (2nd ed. (1970)).

SCHÜTTE, K. (1950) Schlussweisen-Kalküle der Prädikatenlogik. *Math. Annalen* 122, 47–65.

SCOTT, D. (1961) Measurable cardinals and constructible sets. *Bull. Acad. Polon. Sc.* 9, 521–524.

SHEPHERDSON, J. C. (1951–1953) Inner models for set theory. *J.S.L.* 16, 161–190 (1951); 17, 225–237 (1952); 18, 145–167 (1953).

SHOENFIELD, J. R. (1954) A relative consistency proof. *J.S.L.* 19, 21–28.

SOLOVAY, R. M. (1966) On the consistency of Takeuti's TT (abstract). *J.S.L.* 31, 691.

STEGMÜLLER, W. (1962) Eine Axiomatisierung der Mengenlehre beruhend auf den Systemen von Bernays und Quine. In Käsbauer et al. (Eds.), *Logik und Logikkalkül*, pp. 57–103. K. Alber, Freiburg.

TAKEUTI, G. (1961) Axioms of infinity of set theory. *J. Math. Soc. Japan.* 13, 220–233.

TAKEUTI, G. (1969) *The universe of set theory*, pp. 74–128. In BULOFF et al. (1969).

THARP, L. H. (1966) Bernays' set theory and the continuum hypothesis (abstract). *Notices A.M.S.* 13, 138.

WANG, H. (1949) On Zermelo's and von Neumann's axioms for set theory. *Acad. Sci. U.S.A.* 35, 150–155.

SETS AND CLASSES; On the work by Paul Bernays
© North-Holland Publishing Company (1976) pp. 217–255.

# CHOICE FUNCTIONS ON SETS AND CLASSES

Ulrich FELGNER

*Tübingen, West Germany*

## 1. Introduction

The axiomatic set theory of Zermelo–Fraenkel ZF is based on the idea of limitation of size. In ZF a list of principles for set formation is given like union, power set, and replacement, and the universe V of all sets is built up in stages $V_\alpha$. A general axiom-schema of comprehension is not given in the axiomatic system ZF. Bernays has extended set theory to class theory by modifying some ideas of VON NEUMANN [1928]. In this theory we have the advantage that the operation of forming a class $\{x ; \Phi(x)\} = C$ from a predicate $\Phi(x)$ (of the ZF-language) is unrestricted. Bernays obtained his axiom system in 1929. He published this system together with a development of the main parts of set theory within that system in the famous sequence of seven papers in *The Journal of Symbolic Logic* (vol. 2 (1937)— vol. 19 (1954)). A modified version appeared in 1958 in his book. In stating the axioms, Bernays avoided the existential form by using primitive symbols. However, the axiom of choice is the only axiom stated in existential form. At the end of his book, p. 196, Bernays introduces the Hilbert $\epsilon$-operator and the similar $\sigma$-operator. Using these operators, strong versions of the axiom of choice $A_\sigma$ and $A'_\sigma$ are given which avoid the existential form.

It is the purpose of this article to discuss these axioms of choice and related versions of choice, and to investigate their relative strength. Some of the results presented here are known from the literature, others are known, but have never appeared in print and several results are new. I believe that in particular all results presented in §5 are new.[1]

We are concerned mainly with the following two versions of the axiom of choice:

AC (the local version of the axiom of choice). *"On every set of non-empty sets there is a choice function"*.

---

[1] I am grateful to T. Flannagan and W. Guzicki for their valuable comments during the preparation of this paper.

217

**E**   (the global version of the axiom of choice). *"There is a function F which is a class such that* $F(x) \in x$ *for every non-empty set x".*

Here $F(x)$ is the image of $x$ under the function $F$. In §4 we shall deal with the axiom $\mathbf{A}_\sigma$.

The paper is organized as follows. In §2 we give a proof of the independence of the axiom of choice **AC**. The model $\mathfrak{N}$ of $\to$ **AC** which is constructed is a Cohen-extension of a countable model $\mathfrak{M}$, but $\mathfrak{N}$ is uncountable! This is a rather unusual phenomenon. We shall use $\mathfrak{N}$ in order to obtain the result, which is, that not all models of **ZF** are extendable to models of **ZF**+**AC** without adding ordinals. In §3 we present a theorem of Easton which states that the global version **E** of the axiom of choice is not implied by the local version **AC**. Section 4 contains a proof that von Neumann–Bernays set theory plus **E** is a conservative extension of von Neumann–Bernays set theory plus **AC**. Let **NB** denote von Neumann–Bernays set theory. Thus, although **NB**+**E** is strictly stronger than **NB**+**AC** by Easton's result, both theories have precisely the same provable statements about sets. A similar result holds for the impredicative class theory of Wang and Morse. Finally, §5 discusses the status of the axioms of choice in set theories without the axiom of foundation.

Since we are dealing with provability and independence, we have to be definite about our choice of axioms. The language $\mathcal{L}_{\text{ZF}}$ contains one sort of variable $x$, $y$, $z$, $x_0$, $y_0$,..., (set variables), a binary predicate $\in$, logical symbols $\wedge$, $\vee$, $\forall$, $\exists$, $\to$, $\to$, $\leftrightarrow$, $=$ (and, or, for all, there exists, not, implies, equivalence, equality) and brackets. The language $\mathcal{L}_{\text{NB}}$ of class theory contains one sort of variable $X$, $Y$, $Z$, $X_0$,... (class variables), a binary predicate $\in$ and logical symbols $\wedge$, $\vee$, $\forall$, $\exists$, $\to$, $\to$, $\leftrightarrow$, $=$, and brackets.

Let $\mathbf{ZF}^0$ denote the system of axioms consisting of the axioms of extensionality, empty set, pairs, unions, power set, infinity, and replacement (Ersetzung). The system **ZF** results from $\mathbf{ZF}^0$ by adding the axiom of foundation to $\mathbf{ZF}^0$. The axioms of **ZF** are all formulated in the language $\mathcal{L}_{\text{ZF}}$. Thus **ZF** is Zermelo–Fraenkel set theory. The axiom of choice **AC** is *not* an axiom of **ZF**.

As usual, we introduce lowercase letters $x$, $y$, $z$, $x_0$, $x_1$,..., in the language $\mathcal{L}_{\text{NB}}$. Let $\mathfrak{M}(X)$ be an abbreviation for $\exists Y\,(X \in Y)$. Now let $\forall x\,\Phi(x)$ stand for $\forall X\,(\mathfrak{M}(X) \to \Phi(X))$ and let $\exists x\,\Phi(x)$ stand for $\exists X\,(\mathfrak{M}(X) \wedge \Phi(X))$, where $\Phi(X)$ is a formula of $\mathcal{L}_{\text{NB}}$. Note that the variable $X$ used in this definition is not supposed to occur in $\Phi(x)$. Thus we may consider $\mathcal{L}_{\text{ZF}}$ as a sublanguage of $\mathcal{L}_{\text{NB}}$. Read $\mathfrak{M}(X)$ as "$X$ is a set" ("Menge").

Let $\mathbf{NB}^0$ denote the system of axioms I (extensionality), II (axioms of direct construction of sets), III (axioms for direct construction of classes),

V (subclass axiom, replacement, sum axiom, and power set axiom) and VI (infinity) of BERNAYS [1937, 1941], parts I and II (identify however $\in$ and $\eta$). The addition of the axiom of foundation (restriction) VII to $NB^0$ yields the system NB. Note that the axiom of choice (axiom IV in BERNAYS [1941]) is not an axiom of the system NB. The axiom system $NB^0$ is equivalent to the system of axioms of groups $A$, $B$, $C$ of GÖDEL [1940], and hence NB is the system of axioms of groups $A$, $B$, $C$, $D$ of GÖDEL [1940]. Hence, the axioms of NB are understood to be formulated in the language $\mathscr{L}_{NB}$ and NB is called the von Neumann–Bernays set theory.

We have the usual set theoretic notation. $X \subseteq Y$ denotes inclusion, $X \cap Y$ denotes intersection, $X \cup Y$ union, $P(x) = \{y \, ; \, y \subseteq x\}$ is the power set of the set $x$. $\{x,y\}$ is the unordered pair and $\langle x,y \rangle = \{\{x\},\{x,y\}\}$ is the ordered pair. A function $F$ is a class of ordered pairs, such that for each $x$ in the domain $\mathrm{dom}\,(F) = \mathrm{Pr}_1(F) = \{y \, ; \, \exists z : \langle y,z \rangle \in F\}$ of $F$ there is a unique $u$ such that $\langle x,u \rangle \in F$ and we put $u = F(x)$. Ordinals are defined à la von Neumann and they are denoted by lowercase Greek letters.

## 2. The independence of the Axiom of Choice AC

Using the method of permutations models, Fraenkel proved in 1922 that the axiom of choice AC is not provable in the axiom system ZFU (ZF with "Urelements"—see FRAENKEL [1922] and [1937]). In ZFU the axiom of extensionality is not valid. SPECKER [1957] and MENDELSON [1956] generalized Fraenkel's results. They showed that AC cannot be proved in the system $ZF^0$. (In contrast to ZFU the axiom of extensionality is valid in $ZF^0$.) For a presentation of these results the reader is referred to JECH [1973], or to FELGNER [1971a]. We note that similarly neither AC nor E are provable in $NB^0$.

The consistency of AC with the ZF-axioms was proved by Gödel in 1936 in lectures given at the University of Wien (see Footnote 15 in MOSTOWSKI [1939], and GÖDEL [1938], [1939]). Gödel slightly extended this result in 1940 by proving that E is consistent with NB (see GÖDEL [1940]).

The independence of AC from the system ZF of *all* Zermelo–Fraenkel axioms was not proved until 1963. Using his method of forcing, Cohen constructed a countable model $\mathfrak{N}$ of $ZF + \neg AC$, where $\mathfrak{N}$ is an extension of a given countable standard model of $ZF + AC$. Since 1963 the forcing method was applied by numerous authors for solving independence problems in set theory. In all these applications of the forcing method one starts with a given countable model $\mathfrak{M}$ of ZF (or $ZF + V = L$), defines a ramified language $\mathfrak{L}$ in $\mathfrak{M}$, a forcing relation $p \Vdash \Phi$, and as soon as a complete sequence of conditions is chosen, $\mathscr{P}$ say, the extension $\mathfrak{N}$ of $\mathfrak{M}$

can be defined in dependence of $\mathscr{P}$. The sets of $\mathfrak{N}$ are valuations of constant terms $t$ of $\mathfrak{L}$. Thus the countability of $\mathfrak{M}$ implies the countability of $\mathfrak{N}$.

However, it is remarkable, that by a modification of Cohen's method, it is possible to obtain *uncountable* generic extensions of countable models. This device is due to Solovay, but is so far unpublished. We present here Solovay's construction.

NOTATION. Let $\mathfrak{M}$ be any model of ZF. Notions and operations which are meant in the sense of $\mathfrak{M}$ are written with a superscript $\mathfrak{M}$. Thus $\mathsf{P}^{\mathfrak{M}}(x)$ is the power set of $x$ in the sense of $\mathfrak{M}$, $\mathbf{On}^{\mathfrak{M}}$ is the $\mathfrak{M}$-class of all ordinals in the $\mathfrak{M}$-sense, and $\omega_1^{\mathfrak{M}}$ is the first uncountable ordinal in the sense of $\mathfrak{M}$. In contrast to this, $\omega_1$ is the actual first uncountable ordinal (in the sense of the metalanguage). As usual $\mathfrak{M}$ is a standard model if the membership relation $\in^{\mathfrak{M}}$ of $\mathfrak{M}$ coincides with the actual $\in$-relation and if $\mathfrak{M}$ is transitive with respect to $\in$. If $\mathfrak{M}$ is standard, then $\omega = \omega_0 = \omega_0^{\mathfrak{M}}$.

*Weakly generic sequences.* If $\langle S, \leqslant \rangle$ is a partially ordered set and $A \subseteq S$, then $A$ is called *cofinal* in $S$ if for each $p \in S$ there exists $q \in A$ such that $p \leqslant q$. If $\mathfrak{M}$ is a standard model of ZF and if $\langle s, \leqslant \rangle = \mathfrak{S}$ is a partially ordered set in $\mathfrak{M}$, then a subset $G$ of $s$ is called $\mathfrak{S}$-*generic* over $\mathfrak{M}$ if the following three conditions are satisfied:

(i) $\forall p_1 \in G \ \forall p_2 \in G \ \exists q \in G \ [p_1 \leqslant q \ \& \ p_2 \leqslant q]$,

(ii) $\forall p \in G \ \forall q \in s \ [q \leqslant p \rightarrow q \in G]$,

(iii) $\forall B \ [if \ B \ is \ cofinal \ in \ \mathfrak{S} \ and \ B \in \mathfrak{M}, \ then \ B \cap G \neq \emptyset]$.

DEFINITION. Let $\mathfrak{M}$ be a countable standard model of ZF and let $E = \{a_0, \ldots, a_n\}$ be a finite set of subsets $a_i$ of $\omega$, $a_i \notin \mathfrak{M}$. $E$ is said to be *Cohen-generic over* $\mathfrak{M}$, if for the $\mathfrak{M}$-set $C_n = \{p \, ; \, p$ is a function from a finite subset of $(n+1) \times \omega$ into $2\}$, partially ordered by inclusion there exists a subset $G \subseteq C_n$ which is $C_n$-generic over $\mathfrak{M}$ such that for each $j \leqslant n$ and all $k \in \omega$: $k \in a_j \Leftrightarrow \exists p \in G \colon p(j,k) = 1$.

Here $2 = \{0,1\}$ and $n+1 = \{0,1,\ldots, n\}$ since the ordinals are defined à la von Neumann.

DEFINITION (Solovay). Let $\mathfrak{M}$ be a countable standard model of ZF and let $A$ be any set of subsets of $\omega$. Then $A$ is called *weakly Cohen-generic over* $\mathfrak{M}$ iff each finite subset $E$ of $A$ is Cohen-generic over $\mathfrak{M}$.

Cohen showed that if $E = \{a_0, \ldots, a_n\}$ is Cohen-generic over the countable standard model $\mathfrak{M}$ of ZF and if $\mathfrak{M}[a_0, \ldots, a_n] = \mathfrak{N}$ denotes the collection of all sets constructible in $\mathbf{On}^{\mathfrak{M}} \cup \{a_0, \ldots, a_n\}$, then $\mathfrak{N}$ is a (countable standard) model of ZF. Thus the sets $a_0, \ldots, a_n$ "generate" a

ZF-model $\mathfrak{N}$ such that $\mathbf{On}^{\mathfrak{M}} = \mathbf{On}^{\mathfrak{N}}$. We shall show similarly that weakly Cohen-generic sequences generate ZF-models. To do so we shall introduce a ramified language and a forcing relation which gives a detailed description of the extension $\mathfrak{M}[a_0, \ldots, a_n, \ldots]$.

*The forcing relation.* Let $\mathfrak{L}^\omega$ be the ramified language (defined in $\mathfrak{M}$), which contains, besides the usual ZF-symbols (variables, $\in$, logical symbols), constants $x$ (for each set $x$ of $\mathfrak{M}$), limited quantifiers $\mathsf{V}^\alpha$, $\mathsf{\Lambda}^\alpha$ and limited comprehension operators $E^\alpha$ (for each ordinal $\alpha$ of $\mathfrak{M}$) and constants $\dot{a}_n$ for $n \in \omega$.

Let $C_\omega$ be in $\mathfrak{M}$ the set of all functions $p$ from a finite subset of $\omega \times \omega$ into $2 = \{0,1\}$. The elements of $C_\omega$ are called *conditions* and $p, p', q, q', \ldots$ will be used to denote conditions. Define a *weak forcing relation* $\Vdash_\omega$ between conditions $p$ and $\mathfrak{L}^\omega$-sentences, $\Phi$ as usual containing the following key-clause

$$p \Vdash_\omega m \in \dot{a}_n \Leftrightarrow p(m,n) = 1$$

(See FELGNER [1971a] e.g. for all details.) If $\Phi$ is a sentence of $\mathfrak{L}^\omega$, then put $\mathrm{occ}\,(\Phi) = \{n \in \omega \,;\, \dot{a}_n \text{ occurs in } \Phi\}$. The following Lemma is easily established (see e.g. FELGNER [1971a], p. 132).

RESTRICTION LEMMA. *If* $p \Vdash_\omega \Phi$ *and* $p_0 = \{\langle m,n,e\rangle \in p \,;\, n \in \mathrm{occ}\,(\Phi)\}$, *then* $p_0 \Vdash_\omega \Phi$.

DEFINITION. Let $\langle a_n \,;\, n \in \omega \rangle$ be a sequence of subsets of $\omega$, $a_n \notin \mathfrak{M}$, and let $p$ be a condition. Then $p$ is called *compatible* with $\langle a_n \,; n \in \omega \rangle$ if $p \subseteq \{\langle m,n,e\rangle ; (m \notin a_n \wedge e = 0) \vee (m \in a_n \wedge e = 1)\}$.

If $\mathfrak{M}$ is a standard model of ZF and if $\langle a_n \,; n \in \omega \rangle$ is any sequence of subsets of $\omega$, then $\mathfrak{M}[a_0, \ldots, a_n, \ldots]$ denotes the constructible closure of $\mathfrak{M} \cup \{a_n \,; n \in \omega\}$. More precisely, the structure $\mathfrak{M}^* = \mathfrak{M}[a_0, \ldots, a_n, \ldots]$ is defined as follows.

Let $T$ be in $\mathfrak{M}$ the class of all constant terms of $\mathfrak{L}^\omega$ (see FELGNER [1971a], p. 79 for the definition, where $\lambda$ has to be taken as $\omega$). Define an interpretation $\Omega$ of the constant terms $t \in T$ inductively by setting $\Omega(x) = x$ (for all $x \in \mathfrak{M}$), $\Omega(\dot{a}_n) = a_n$ (for $n \in \omega$) and then extending to all limited comprehension terms $E^\alpha x \Phi(x)$ of $T$ ($\alpha \in \mathbf{On}^{\mathfrak{M}}$). Thus $\mathfrak{M}^* = \{\Omega(t); t \in T\}$.

Clearly the structure $\mathfrak{M}^* = \mathfrak{M}[a_0, \ldots, a_n, \ldots]$ need not be a model of ZF for arbitrary sequences $\langle a_n \,; n \in \omega \rangle$. We shall prove that if $\langle a_n \,; n \in \omega \rangle$ is weakly Cohen-generic over the countable standard model $\mathfrak{M}$ of ZF, then $\mathfrak{M}^* = \mathfrak{M}[a_0, \ldots, a_n, \ldots]$ is also a countable standard model of ZF. This will be a consequence of the following main lemma.

REDUCTION LEMMA. *Let $\mathfrak{M}$ be a countable standard model of* **ZF** *and let $\langle a_n ; n \in \omega \rangle$ be weakly-Cohen-generic over $\mathfrak{M}$. For any sentence $\Phi$ of $\mathfrak{L}^\omega$ the following two conditions are equivalent:* [1]
  (i) $\mathfrak{M}^* = \mathfrak{M}[a_0, \ldots, a_n, \ldots] \models \Phi$,
  (ii) *there is a condition $p \in C_\omega$ compatible with $\langle a_n ; n \in \omega \rangle$ such that $p \Vdash_\omega \Phi$.*

PROOF by induction on the length of $\Phi$.

*Case* 1.  $\Phi$ is atomic. If (for example), $\Phi$ is $m \in a_n$, then $\mathfrak{M}^* = \Phi$ implies $m \in a_n$. Thus $p = \{\langle m,n,1 \rangle\}$ is compatible with $\langle a_n ; n \in \omega \rangle$ and clearly this $p$ forces $m \in \dot{a}_n$. Conversely, if $p \Vdash_\omega m \in \dot{a}_n$, where $p$ is compatible with $\langle a_n ; n \in \omega \rangle$, then $\langle m,n,1 \rangle \in p$ and hence $m \in a_n$ by the compatibility. This proves $\mathfrak{M}^* \models \Phi$.

*Case* 2.  $\Phi$ is $\Psi_1 \wedge \Psi_2$ or $\Phi$ is $\Psi_1 \vee \Psi_2$: obvious.

*Case* 3.  $\Phi$ is $\rightarrow \Psi$. Assume that $p \Vdash_\omega \rightarrow \Psi$ for some $p$ is compatible with $\langle a_n ; n \in \omega \rangle$. Then $\mathfrak{M}^*$ cannot satisfy $\Psi$, for otherwise, by the induction hypothesis, a condition $q \in C_\omega$ which is compatible with $\langle a_n ; n \in \omega \rangle$ would force $\Psi$. But both conditions are compatible with $\langle a_n ; n \in \omega \rangle$. Hence $p \cup q$ is a condition and we infer $p \cup q \Vdash_\omega \Psi \wedge \rightarrow \Psi$, a contradiction! Thus we have shown that $\mathfrak{M}^* \models \rightarrow \Psi$.

Assume now that conversely $\mathfrak{M}^* \models \rightarrow \Psi$ holds. Hence $\Psi$ does not hold in $\mathfrak{M}^*$ and it follows from the induction hypothesis that no condition $p$ compatible with $\langle a_n ; n \in \omega \rangle$ can force $\Psi$. By the weak genericity of $\langle a_n ; n \in \omega \rangle$ the set $E = \{a_j ; j \in \mathrm{occ}\,(\Psi)\}$ is Cohen-generic over $\mathfrak{M}$. (Notice that occ $(\Psi)$ is $\mathfrak{M}$-finite and hence actually finite since $\mathfrak{M}$ is a standard model.) Suppose that $E = \{a_0, \ldots, a_k\}$. Hence there is a set $G$ which is $C_k$-generic over $\mathfrak{M}$, and $i \in a_j \Leftrightarrow \exists p \in G: p(i,j) = 1$ for $j \leq k$, $i \in \omega$. In particular every element of $G$ is compatible with $\langle a_n ; n \in \omega \rangle$. Consider $\Delta = \{p \in C_k ; p \models_\omega \Psi \text{ or } p \Vdash_\omega \rightarrow \Psi\}$. Since every condition can be extended to a condition which decides $\Psi$, the restriction lemma entails that $\Delta$ is cofinal in $C_k$. Hence $\Delta \cap G \neq \emptyset$. It now follows that there is a condition $q \in G \cap \Delta$ which forces $\rightarrow \Psi$.

*Case* 4.  $\Phi$ is $\mathsf{V}_x \Psi(x)$. Assume first that $\mathfrak{M}^* \models \Phi$. It follows from the definition of $\mathfrak{M}^*$ that $\mathfrak{M}^* \models \Psi(t)$ for some term $t \in T$ of $\mathfrak{L}^\omega$. Therefore, by the induction hypothesis, $\Psi(t)$ is forced by some condition $p$ which is compatible with $\langle a_n ; n \in \omega \rangle$. This clearly gives us that $p$ also forces $\mathsf{V}_x \Psi(x)$.

---

[1] The symbol $\models$ represents the satisfaction relation. Thus $\mathfrak{M} \models \Phi$ means that the sentence $\Phi$ holds in the structure $\mathfrak{M}$.

Assume now that conversly $p \Vdash_\omega \mathbf{V}_x \Psi(x)$ for some $p$ is compatible with $\langle a_n ; n \in \omega \rangle$. Put $E = \{a_j ; j \in \mathrm{occ}\,(\Psi(x))\}$ and assume for notational simplicity that $E = \{a_0, \ldots, a_k\}$. As before let $C_k$ be in $\mathfrak{M}$ the set of all functions from a finite subset of $\{0, 1, \ldots, k\} \times \omega$ into $2 = \{0,1\}$. Let $C^k$ be in $\mathfrak{M}$ the set of all functions from a finite subset of $\{n \in \omega ; n > k\} \times \omega$ into 2. According to the definition of weak forcing $p \Vdash_\omega \mathbf{V}_x \Psi(x)$ holds iff $\forall p' \supseteq p\ \exists q \supseteq p'\ \exists t \in T : q \Vdash_\omega \Psi(t)$, where $T$ is the $\mathfrak{M}$-set of all constant terms of $\mathfrak{L}^\omega$. The restriction lemma allows us to assume that $p \in C_k$. We claim that we can find conditions $q_0 \in C_k$, $q_1 \in C^k$ and a term $t \in T$ such that $p \subseteq q_0$, $q_0 \cup q_1 \Vdash_\omega \Psi(t)$, where $q_0$ is even compatible with $\langle a_n ; n \in \omega \rangle$.

In fact, consider in $\mathfrak{M}$:

$$\Delta = \{p' \in C_k ; p \cup p' \in C_k \Rightarrow \exists p'' \in C^k\ \exists t \in T : p' \cup p'' \Vdash_\omega \Psi(t)\}.$$

If $p' \in C_k$ and if $p$ is not compatible with $p'$, then $p' \in \Delta$. If $p' \cup p$ is a condition, then $p \Vdash_\omega \mathbf{V}_x \Psi(x)$ implies that some extension of $p \cup p'$ forces $\Psi(t)$ for some $t \in T$. Hence $\Delta$ is cofinal in $C_k$.

The set $E$ is Cohen-generic over $\mathfrak{M}$. Hence there exists a set $G$ which is $C_k$-generic over $\mathfrak{M}$ such that $i \in a_j \Leftrightarrow \exists q \in G : p(i,j) = 1$ for all $j \leq k$, $i \in \omega$. Thus $G$ intersects $\Delta$. Let $q_0$ be an arbitrary member of $G \cap \Delta$. Clearly all members of $G$ are compatible with $\langle a_n ; n \in \omega \rangle$. Hence $p \cup q_0$ is a function, and by the definition of $\Delta$ there is a condition $q_1 \in C^k$ and a term $\hat{t} \in T$ such that

$$(\#) \qquad\qquad q_0 \cup q_1 \Vdash_\omega \Psi(\hat{t}),$$

where $q_0$ (as a member of $G$) is compatible with $\langle a_n ; n \in \omega \rangle$. Choose $m$ such that $\hat{t}$ does not contain any constant $\dot{a}_j$ with $j > m$. We write $\hat{t} = \hat{t}(\dot{a}_0, \ldots, \dot{a}_m)$.

If $m \leq k$, then by means of the restriction lemma, $(\#)$ implies $q_0 \Vdash_\omega \Psi(\hat{t})$. We conclude by the induction hypothesis that $\mathfrak{M}^* \models \Psi(\hat{t})$ and hence $\mathfrak{M}^* \models \mathbf{V}_x \Psi(x)$, which is what we wanted to prove.

If $k < m$, then we proceed as follows. Define

$$\mu = \max \{i \in \omega ; \exists j \in \omega : \langle i,j,0 \rangle \in q_1 \vee \langle i,j,1 \rangle \in q_1\},$$

where $\max(X)$ is the maximal element of $X$. As usual, we write $a \equiv b \pmod{u}$ for $\exists x\,(a - b = x \cdot u)$. We define a new sequence of subsets $a_j^*$ of $\omega$ as follows:

$$a_j^* = a_j \quad \text{if } 0 \leq j \leq k,$$
$$a_j^* = \{i \in \omega ; \langle i,j,1 \rangle \in q_1 \vee [i > \mu \wedge i \in a_{k+1} \wedge$$
$$\wedge\ i \equiv j - k - 1 \bmod m + 1 - k]\} \quad \text{if } k + 1 \leq j \leq m,$$

$$a^*_{m+1} = a_{k+1} - \bigcup_{j=k+1}^{m} a^*_j,$$

$$a^*_{m+\nu} = a_{k+\nu} \text{ for } \nu \geq 2.$$

Thus $a_{k+1}$ is split into $m + 1 - k$ subsets of $\omega$: we have taken some (but not all) elements out of $a_{k+1}$ and have added these elements to the finite sets $\{i; \langle i,j,1 \rangle \in q_1\} = b_j \cdot (k + 1 \leq j \leq m)$. A splitting of Cohen-generic sets yields Cohen-generic sets. Hence the sequence $\langle a^*_j; j \in \omega \rangle$ is weakly Cohen-generic over $\mathfrak{M}$ and obviously $\mathfrak{M}[a_0, \ldots, a_n, \ldots] = \mathfrak{M}[a^*_0, \ldots, a^*_n, \ldots]$. By definition, $q_0$ and $q_1$ are compatible with $\langle a^*_n; n \in \omega \rangle$. Hence from ($\#$) it follows by the induction hypothesis that $\mathfrak{M}[a^*_0, \ldots, a^*_n, \ldots] \models \Psi(\hat{t})$, and therefore $\mathfrak{M}^* = \mathfrak{M}[a_0, \ldots, a_n, \ldots] \models \Psi(\hat{t})$. By definition, $\Omega(\hat{t})$ is an element of $\mathfrak{M}^*$, hence $\mathfrak{M}^* \models V_x \Psi(x)$.

The case in which $\Phi$ is $V^{\alpha}_x \Psi(x)$ can be treated similarly as above. The reduction lemma is thus proved.

THEOREM 2.1. *Let $\mathfrak{M}$ be a countable standard model of* ZF. *If $\langle a_n; n \in \omega \rangle$ is weakly Cohen-generic over $\mathfrak{M}$, then $\mathfrak{M}[a_0, \ldots, a_n, \ldots]$ is a countable standard model of* ZF.

PROOF. Since $\mathfrak{M} \subseteq \mathfrak{M}[a_0, \ldots, a_n, \ldots] = \mathfrak{M}^*$ and $\mathfrak{M}^*$ is transitive, it is obvious that the axioms of extensionality, null set, pair, union, and infinity hold in $\mathfrak{M}^*$. By virtue of the reduction lemma, one proves, as in the case of a classical Cohen extension, that the axioms of power set and replacement are true in $\mathfrak{M}^*$. In addition, $\mathfrak{M}^*$ clearly satisfies the axiom of foundation, Q.E.D.

LEMMA 2.1. *Let $\mathfrak{M}$ be a countable standard model of* ZF. *Then there exists a sequence $\sigma = \langle a_\nu; \nu < \omega_1 \rangle$ of length $\omega_1$ such that $\sigma$ is weakly Cohen-generic over $\mathfrak{M}$.*

PROOF. We define by simultaneous induction a sequence of ZF-models $\mathfrak{M}_\alpha$ and a sequence $\sigma$ of subsets $a_\alpha$ of $\omega$. Put $\mathfrak{M}_0 = \mathfrak{M}$, and let $a_0$ be any subset of $\omega$ which is Cohen-generic over $\mathfrak{M}_0$. Let $\alpha$ be a countable ordinal and suppose that models $\mathfrak{M}_\beta$ and subsets $a_\beta \subseteq \omega$ are defined for all ordinals $\beta < \alpha$, such that

(i) $\langle a_\nu; \nu < \beta \rangle$ is weakly Cohen-generic over $\mathfrak{M}_0$,

(ii) $\mathfrak{M}_\beta = \mathfrak{M}[a_0, \ldots, a_\nu, \ldots]_{\nu < \beta}$ is the constructible closure of $\mathfrak{M}_0 \cup \{a_\nu; \nu < \beta\}$ and $\mathfrak{M}_\beta$ is a model of ZF,

(iii) if $\nu < \beta < \alpha$, then $a_\beta$ is Cohen-generic over $\mathfrak{M}_\nu$.

Define $\mathfrak{M}_\alpha$ to be the constructible closure of $\mathfrak{M}_0 \cup \{a_\nu; \nu < \alpha\}$. Since $\langle a_\nu; \nu < \alpha \rangle$ is weakly Cohen-generic over $\mathfrak{M}_0$, it follows from Theorem 2.1 that $\mathfrak{M}_\alpha$ is a model of ZF. Let $a_\alpha$ be any subset of $\omega$ which is Cohen-generic over $\mathfrak{M}_\alpha$. It follows from (i) and (iii) that $\langle a_\nu; \nu \leq \alpha \rangle$ is weakly Cohen-generic over $\mathfrak{M}_0$. Thus we obtain by induction an uncountable sequence $\sigma = \langle a_\nu ; \nu < \omega_1 \rangle$ of reals, such that $\sigma$ is weakly Cohen-generic over $\mathfrak{M}$, Q.E.D.

We emphasize the fact that in Lemma 1, $\omega_1$ is the actual first uncountable ordinal, $\omega_1 \neq \omega_1^{\mathfrak{M}}$. Notice that the models $\mathfrak{M}_\alpha$ do not form a chain with respect to $\subseteq$.

THEOREM 2.2 (Solovay). *Let $\mathfrak{M}$ be a countable standard model of* ZF + V = L. *Then $\mathfrak{M}$ can be extended to a standard model $\mathfrak{N}$ of* ZF *such that $\mathfrak{N}$ is uncountable and both $\mathfrak{M}$ and $\mathfrak{N}$ have precisely the same ordinals:* $\mathbf{On}^{\mathfrak{M}} = \mathbf{On}^{\mathfrak{N}}$. *In addition* $\mathfrak{N} \models \rightarrow$ AC.

PROOF.[1] Let $\mathfrak{M}$ be given. By Lemma 2.1 there is a sequence $\sigma = \langle a_\nu ; \nu < \omega_1 \rangle$ of subsets of $\omega$ such that $\sigma$ is weakly Cohen-generic over $\mathfrak{M}$. Let $\zeta$ be the least ordinal not in $\mathfrak{M}$, thus $\zeta = \mathbf{On}^{\mathfrak{M}}$. For an ordinal $\alpha \in \mathfrak{M}$ let $M_\alpha$ be in $\mathfrak{M}$ the set of all sets $x$ in $\mathfrak{M}$ of rank $< \alpha$. Let $\mathscr{L}$ be the language, which has besides the usual ZF-symbols (variables, $\in$ and logical symbols) and unary predicates $\dot{a}_\nu$ (for each $\nu < \omega_1$). A sequence of $\mathscr{L}$-structures $\mathfrak{N}_\alpha = \langle N_\alpha, \in, b_0^\alpha, b_1^\alpha, \ldots, b_\nu^\alpha, \ldots \rangle_{\nu < \omega_1}$ is defined by induction as follows: $\mathfrak{N}_0 = \langle \emptyset, \in, \emptyset, \emptyset, \ldots \rangle$ and

$$N_{\alpha+1} = M_{\alpha+1} \cup \{z ; z \subseteq N_\alpha \text{ and } z \text{ is first-order definable}$$
$$\text{over } \mathfrak{N}_\alpha \text{ with parameters allowed}\},$$

$$b_\nu^{\alpha+1} = M_{\alpha+1} \cap a_\nu,$$

$$N_\lambda = \cup \{N_\alpha ; \alpha < \lambda\}, \qquad b_\nu^\lambda = M_\lambda \cap a_\nu \quad \text{for } \lambda \text{ a limit number.}$$

Finally, put $\mathfrak{N}^* = \cup \{\mathfrak{N}_\alpha ; \alpha < \zeta\}$, thus

$$\mathfrak{N}^* = \langle \bigcup_{\alpha < \zeta} N_\alpha, \in, a_0, a_1, \ldots, a_\nu, \ldots \rangle_{\nu < \omega_1}.$$

Since $\omega \in \mathfrak{M}$ it follows that $a_\nu = \omega \cap a_\nu \in N = \cup_{\alpha < \zeta} N_\alpha$. $\mathfrak{N} = \langle N, \in \rangle$ is the desired model and $\mathfrak{N}$ is transitive and uncountable. Further $\zeta \notin N_\alpha$ for all $\alpha < \zeta$ so that $\zeta \neq N$. But $\zeta \subseteq N$ and hence $\zeta = \mathbf{On}^{\mathfrak{N}}$. Notice that we have stopped the construction of the structures $N_\alpha$ at stage $\zeta$ and that it is, hence, not evident whether $\mathfrak{N} = \langle \cup_{\alpha < \zeta} N_\alpha, \in \rangle$ is a model of ZF or not. If we had defined $\mathfrak{N}$ as the union of structures $\mathfrak{N}_\alpha$ for *all* ordinals, then standard arguments would have shown that $\langle \cup \{\mathfrak{N}_\alpha ; \alpha \in \mathbf{On}\}, \in \rangle$ is a transitive ZF-model containing all ordinals (see TAKEUTI–ZARING [1973], p. 76). However, it can also be shown that $\mathfrak{N} = \langle \cup_{\alpha < \zeta} N_\alpha, \in \rangle$ is a ZF-model, as follows.

Let $\mathscr{L}(\dot{A})$ be the first-order language which contains the usual ZF-symbols (variables, $\in$ and logical symbols) a unary predicate $\dot{A}$. Put

---

[1] A related result was obtained recently by P. E. Cohen. See Cohen (1974).

$A = \{a_\nu ; \nu < \omega_1\}$. Then $\langle N, \in, A \rangle$ is a structure for the language $\mathscr{L}(\dot{A})$, where $N = \cup\{N_\alpha ; \alpha < \zeta\}$. In this way $A = \{x \in N ; \langle N, \in, A \rangle \models \dot{A}(x)\}$ is a definable class but not an element of $N$. By the Löwenheim–Skolem theorem there is a countable elementary substructure $\mathfrak{B} = \langle B, \in, A \cap B \rangle < \langle N, \in, A \rangle$ such that $\zeta \subseteq B$ (and hence $\mathfrak{M} \subseteq B$ since $\mathfrak{M} \models V = L$).

Assume that $\mathfrak{B}$ is transitive and let $c$ denote in $\mathfrak{B}$ the power set of $\omega$. Hence $\mathfrak{B} \models "c = P(\omega)"$ and $\mathfrak{B} < \langle N, \in, A \rangle$ implies that also $\langle N, \in, A \rangle \models \forall x (x \in c \leftrightarrow x \subseteq \omega)$. Hence $a_\nu \in c$ holds in $\langle N, \in, A \rangle$ for all $\nu < \omega_1$. It follows that $a_\nu \in B$ by the transitivity of $B$ and thus that $B$ is uncountable, a contradiction. This proves that $\mathfrak{B}$ cannot be transitive.

By Mostowski's isomorphism theorem (see JECH [1973], p. 34, SHOEN-FIELD [1967], p. 262) there is a transitive set $C$ and a function $F$ such that $F$ is an isomorphism from $\langle B, \in \rangle$ onto $\langle C, \in \rangle$. Consider the set $D = \{F(x); x \in A \cap B\}$ and let $E = \{d_0, d_1, \ldots, d_n\}$ be a finite subset of $D$. We claim that $E$ is Cohen-generic over $\mathfrak{M}$. Note that $\mathfrak{M}$ is definable in $\mathfrak{C} = \langle C, \in \rangle$ as the class of all constructible sets. Also, since $\mathfrak{M}$ is transitive and $\mathfrak{M} \subseteq B$ it follows that $F$ leaves $\mathfrak{M}$ pointwise fixed. Hence, if $\text{cond}_n$ denotes the set of all functions $p$ from a finite subset of $(n + 1) \times \omega$ into $2 = \{0,1\}$, then $\text{cond}_n^{\mathfrak{M}} = \text{cond}_n^{\mathfrak{B}} = \text{cond}_n^{\mathfrak{C}} = \text{cond}_n^{\mathfrak{N}}$. It thus follows from $\mathfrak{C} \simeq \mathfrak{B} < \mathfrak{N}$ that if $G \in \mathfrak{M}$ and $G$ is cofinal in $\text{cond}_n^{\mathfrak{M}}$, then $E$ meets $G$. Hence $D$ is weakly Cohen-generic over $\mathfrak{M}$. Put $D = \{d_i ; i \in \omega\}$ and it turns out that $\mathfrak{C} = \mathfrak{M}[d_0, d_1, \ldots, d_i, \ldots]_{i \in \omega}$. By Theorem 2.1 $\mathfrak{C}$ is a model of ZF. Now $\mathfrak{C} \simeq \mathfrak{B} < \mathfrak{N}$ implies that $\mathfrak{N}$ is also a model of ZF.

By the construction of $\mathfrak{N}$, both models $\mathfrak{M}$ and $\mathfrak{N}$ have the same ordinals. Thus $\mathbf{On}^{\mathfrak{M}} = \mathbf{On}^{\mathfrak{N}}$ is countable in the metalanguage. But $a_\nu \in P^{\mathfrak{N}}(\omega)$ for all $\nu < \omega_1$ and hence $P^{\mathfrak{N}}(\omega)$ is uncountable in the metalanguage. $P^{\mathfrak{N}}(\omega)$ cannot have a well ordering in $\mathfrak{N}$, since otherwise the well ordering of $P^{\mathfrak{N}}(\omega)$ could be injected into the ordinals of $\mathfrak{N}$. The different cardinalities show that this is clearly impossible. Thus $\mathfrak{N} \models \neg AC$, Q.E.D.

COROLLARY 2.1 (Cohen). *If* ZF *is consistent, then the axiom of choice* AC *is not provable in* ZF.

If one is only interested in Corollary 2.1, then a simple Cohen-extension $\mathfrak{M}[a_0, \ldots, a_n, \ldots]_{n \in \omega}$ gives the independence result almost immediately: $\mathfrak{M}[a_0, \ldots, a_n, \ldots]_{n \in \omega} \models ZF + \neg AC$. The proof that AC fails in this model is a symmetry argument (cf. FEFERMAN [1965]). In contrast to this we could prove $\mathfrak{N} \models \neg AC$ by a simple *cardinality argument*. (*Symmetry arguments have not been used!*)

However, we have proved Theorem 2.2, mainly in order to obtain the following highly interesting consequence. (We presuppose existence of a countable standard model of ZF.)

COROLLARY 2.2 (Solovay).    *There exists a standard model $\mathfrak{N}$ of* ZF $+$ $\rightarrow$ AC *such that every* ZF*-model $\mathfrak{A}$ which extends $\mathfrak{N}$ and has the same ordinals also violates the axiom of choice.*

The same cardinality argument as in the proof of Theorem 2.2 shows that if $\mathfrak{N} \subseteq \mathfrak{A}$, $\mathbf{On}^{\mathfrak{N}} = \mathbf{On}^{\mathfrak{A}}$, where $\mathfrak{N}$ is the model constructed in Theorem 2.2, then card $(\mathbf{On}^{\mathfrak{A}}) = \omega < \omega_1 \leqslant$ card $(\mathsf{P}^{\mathfrak{A}}(\omega))$. Thus $\mathsf{P}^{\mathfrak{A}}(\omega)$ cannot have a well ordering in $\mathfrak{A}$, and so $\mathfrak{A} = \rightarrow$ AC

The model $\mathfrak{N}$ in Corollary 2.2 is uncountable. A considerable strengthening of Corollary 2.2 was obtained by MORRIS [1970] when he proved the following theorem:

(∗)     *Every countable standard model $\mathfrak{M}$ of* ZF $+$ AC *can be extended to a countable standard model $\mathfrak{N}$ of* ZF $+ \rightarrow$ AC *such that the following occurs: if $\mathfrak{N}^*$ is a standard model of* ZF $+$ AC *and $\mathfrak{N}^*$ is an extension of $\mathfrak{N}$, then $\mathfrak{N}^*$ has an ordinal which is greater than every ordinal of $\mathfrak{N}$.*

In fact, Morris considers the following ZF-sentence:

NE     $\forall \alpha \, \exists x \,$ [*x is a union of countably many countable sets and* $\mathsf{P}(x)$ *can be partitioned into* $\aleph_\alpha$ *non-empty sets*].

The model $\mathfrak{N}$ in (∗) is constructed as a certain generic extension of $\mathfrak{M}$ such that $\mathfrak{N} \models$ NE. In contrast to (∗), we mention the following theorem of BARWISE [1971]:

(∗∗)     *If $\mathfrak{M} = \langle M, E \rangle$ is any countable model of* ZF, *then there is an end extension $\mathfrak{N}$ of $\mathfrak{M}$ such that $\mathfrak{N} \models$* ZF $+$ V $=$ L *(and so $\mathfrak{N} \models$* AC*).*

It is interesting to compare AC with the generalized continuum hypothesis GCH ($\forall \alpha \, [2^{\aleph_\alpha} = \aleph_{\alpha+1}]$) from the point of view of extending models. Here, Jensen has shown that every countable standard model $\mathfrak{M}$ of ZF $+$ AC can be extended to a model $\mathfrak{N}$ of ZF $+$ GCH such that both $\mathfrak{M}$ and $\mathfrak{N}$ have the same ordinals.

An application of the two-cardinal theorems from model theory will yield further generalizations of Corollary 2.2. We consider in ZF the one-place predicate ord $(x) \Leftrightarrow$ "*x is an ordinal number*". If $\sigma$ and $\tau$ are cardinals, then we say that the ZF-model $\mathfrak{M}$ admits the pair $\langle \sigma, \tau \rangle$ iff $\sigma$ is the cardinality of the whole model and $\tau$ is the cardinality of the $\mathfrak{M}$-class of ordinals: $\tau =$ card $(\mathbf{On}^{\mathfrak{M}}) =$ card $(\{x \in \mathfrak{M}; \mathfrak{M} \models$ ord $(x)\})$. Corollary 2.2 shows that there is a ZF-model $\mathfrak{N}$ which admits the pair $\langle \omega_1, \omega \rangle$. Under the assumption of the existence of one countable standard model of ZF we claim the following:[1]

COROLLARY 2.3.　*Assume that* $V = L$ *holds in the metatheory. If* $\kappa$ *is any infinite cardinal number, there is a* ZF*-model* $\mathfrak{M}$ *which admits the pair* $\langle \kappa^+, \kappa \rangle$, *that is,* card $(\mathfrak{M}) = \kappa^+$ *and* card $(\mathbf{On}^{\mathfrak{M}}) = \kappa$.

Under the assumption of the GCH in the metatheory, the claim results from Chang's two-cardinal theorem for $\kappa$ regular. For $\kappa$ singular, the claim follows from Jensen's two-cardinal theorem, where it is assumed that $V = L$ holds in the metalanguage (see SACKS [1972], p. 141–143, CHANG–KEISLER [1973], p. 438–443).

A considerable strengthening of Theorem 2.2 has recently been obtained by FRIEDMAN [∞] when he proved the following theorem:

*If* $\mathfrak{M}$ *is a countable standard model of* ZF *and* $\zeta = \mathbf{On}^{\mathfrak{M}}$ *then there is an extension* $\mathfrak{N}$ *of* $\mathfrak{M}$ *such that* $\mathbf{On}^{\mathfrak{M}} = \mathbf{On}^{\mathfrak{N}} = \zeta$ *and* $\mathfrak{N}$ *has power* $\beth_\zeta$, *where* $\mathfrak{N} \models$ ZF$+$AC.

Here $\beth_0 = \aleph_0$, $\beth_{\alpha+1} = $ card $(2^{\beth_\alpha})$ and $\beth_\lambda = \sup_{\alpha < \lambda} \beth_\alpha$ for $0 \neq \lambda = \cup \lambda$. Friedman shows that this result has consequences concerning the Hanf number of certain infinitary languages.

## 3. E is not implied by AC

It is obvious that in NB-set theory the local axiom of choice AC follows from the global axiom of choice E. Specker showed that in set theory with urelements, E is not implied by AC (see BERNAYS [1958], p. 196). For NB-set theory (which includes the axiom of foundation), the independence of E from AC was first proved by EASTON [1964].[2] We assume that the reader is familiar with Cohen's method of forcing via ramified languages (cf. EASTON [1970] and FELGNER [1971a]).

THEOREM 3.1 (Easton).　*The global form of the axiom of choice cannot be proved in the system* NB $+$ AC $+$ GCH.

PROOF.　Let $\mathfrak{M}$ be any countable model of NB $+$ GCH. Clearly $\mathfrak{M}$ is also a model of AC since GCH $\Rightarrow$ AC. We extend $\mathfrak{M}$ to a model $\mathfrak{N}$ of NB $+$ GCH by adding a proper class of generic sets $a_\gamma^\alpha \subseteq \aleph_\alpha^{\mathfrak{M}}$ and then defining a certain submodel $\mathfrak{N}^*$ of $\mathfrak{N}$. The relation between $\mathfrak{N}^*$ and $\mathfrak{N}$ is similar to the relation between Feferman's model $\mathfrak{M}[a_0, \ldots, a_n, \ldots]$ and the Halpern–

---

[1] $\kappa^+$ is the next cardinal number after $\kappa$.

[2] This result of W. B. Easton is contained in §6 of his dissertation (Princeton, 1964) and is not yet published. It is presented here with his kind permission.

Lévy model $\mathfrak{M}[a_0,\ldots, a_n,\ldots, A]$. (See e.g. FELGNER [1971a], p. 131 and p. 160.)

DEFINITION OF $\mathfrak{N}$. Define in $\mathfrak{M}$ a ramified language $\mathcal{L}$ as follows: the alphabet of $\mathcal{L}$ has one sort of variable $v_0, v_1,\ldots, v_n,\ldots$ $(n \in {}^{\mathfrak{M}}\omega^{\mathfrak{M}})$, a constant $S$ for each class $S$ of $\mathfrak{M}$, the membership predicate $\in$, logical symbols $\vee$, $V$, $\rightarrow$ (or, there exists, not), limited existential quantifiers $V^\alpha$ and limited comprehension operators $E^\alpha$ for each ordinal $\alpha$ of $\mathfrak{M}$, and a ternary predicate $\hat{A}$. The other logical symbols ($\wedge$, $\Lambda$, $\rightarrow$, $\leftrightarrow$, $\Lambda_x^\alpha$: and, for all, implies, is equivalent to, for all $x$ of degree $<\alpha$) are introduced by definition—their use can be eliminated.

Let $\delta(t)$ denote the degree (or: rank) of the constant term $t$ of $\mathcal{L}$ (see, FELGNER [1971a], p. 79 or EASTON [1970], p. 146, where the notation $\rho(t)$ is used). In the sequel, $t_1 \simeq t_2$ stands for $\Lambda_v^\sigma$ $(v \in t_1 \leftrightarrow v \in t_2)$, where $\sigma = \max\{\delta(t_1), \delta(t_2)\}$. Let $\Omega$ be the $\mathfrak{M}$-class of all ordinals of $\mathfrak{M}$, $\Omega = \mathbf{On}^{\mathfrak{M}}$, and let Reg be the $\mathfrak{M}$-class of those ordinals $\alpha$ of $\mathfrak{M}$ for which $\aleph_\alpha$ is a regular cardinal in the sense of $\mathfrak{M}$.

DEFINITION (in $\mathfrak{M}$). A *condition* $p$ is a function from a subset $D$ of $\Omega \times \mathrm{Reg} \times \Omega$ into $2 = \{0,1\}$ such that:

  (i) if $\langle \alpha,\beta,\gamma \rangle \in D$, then $\alpha < \aleph_\beta$ and $\gamma < \aleph_{\beta+1}$, and
  (ii) for each regular $\aleph_\xi$: card $(\{\langle \alpha,\beta,\gamma \rangle \in D;\ \beta \leq \xi\}) < \aleph_\xi$.

A forcing relation $\Vdash$ is defined as usual. The definition contains the following key clause, where $t_1$, $t_2$, $t_3$ are constant terms of $\mathcal{L}$:

$$p \Vdash \hat{A}(t_1, t_2, t_3) \Leftrightarrow \exists \alpha,\gamma \in \Omega\, \exists \beta \in \mathrm{Reg}\,[\alpha \leq \delta(t_1),\ \beta \leq \delta(t_2),\ \gamma \leq \delta(t_3),$$
$$p \Vdash t_1 \simeq \alpha,\ p \Vdash t_2 \simeq \beta,\ p \Vdash t_3 \simeq \gamma \text{ and } p(\alpha,\beta,\gamma) = 1].$$

Let $\mathcal{P}$ be a complete sequence of conditions. The model $\mathfrak{N}$ can now be defined as follows:

  (i) If $\Phi(v)$ is any formula of $\mathcal{L}$, the set (defined in the metalanguage) $\mathsf{K}x\ \Phi(x) = \{t \in T;\ \mathcal{P} \Vdash \Phi(t)\}$ is a class of $\mathfrak{N}$. ($T$ is the $\mathfrak{M}$-class of all comprehension terms $E^\alpha x\Phi(x)$ and constants $s$ for *sets* $s$ of $\mathfrak{M}$. $\mathcal{P} \Vdash \Psi$ means $p \Vdash \Psi$ for some $p \in \mathcal{P}$.)
  (ii) Those classes of $\mathfrak{N}$ which have the form $\mathsf{K}x$ $(x \in t)$, with $t \in T$, are called sets of $\mathfrak{N}$.
  (iii) The $\in$-relation is defined in $\mathfrak{N}$ as follows: $\mathsf{K}x\ \Phi(x) \in \mathsf{K}y\ \Psi(y)$ will hold if $\mathsf{K}x\ \Phi(x) = \mathsf{K}x\ (z \in t)$ for some $t \in T$ and $\mathcal{P} \Vdash \Psi(t)$.
  (iv) The relation $\hat{A}(\mathsf{K}x\ \Phi(x), \mathsf{K}y\ \Psi(y), \mathsf{K}z\ \Gamma(z))$ will hold if for some ordinals $\alpha$, $\beta$, $\gamma$ such that $p(\alpha,\beta,\gamma) = 1$ for some $p$ in $\mathcal{P}$, $\mathsf{K}x\ \Phi(x) = \mathsf{K}x\ (x \in \alpha)$, $\mathsf{K}y\ \Psi(y) = \mathsf{K}y\ (y \in \beta)$ and $\mathsf{K}z\ \Gamma(z) = \mathsf{K}z\ (z \in \gamma)$.

(v) If $C$ is any constant or comprehension term of $\mathscr{L}$, then $C$ is interpreted in $\mathfrak{N}$ by the class $\mathbf{K}x$ $(x \in C)$.

(vi) Individual variables $v_0, v_1, \ldots$ range over sets of $\mathfrak{N}$. The limited quantifiers $\mathbf{V}^\alpha$ quantify over sets of the form $\mathbf{K}_x$ $(x \in t)$ where $t \in T$ and $\delta(t) < \alpha$.

We have thus defined how the ramified language $\mathscr{L}$ is interpreted on the domain $\mathfrak{N} = \{\mathbf{K}x\ \Phi(x); \Phi(x) \in \mathscr{L}\}$.

The model $\mathfrak{N}$ is Easton's model of [1970] with $G(\alpha) = \alpha + 1$. Easton showed that $\mathfrak{N}$ is a countable model of **NB**-set theory such that **E** holds in $\mathfrak{N}$. Since we have chosen the function $G(\alpha) = \alpha + 1$, $\mathfrak{N}$ also satisfies the generalized continuum hypothesis (see EASTON [1970], p. 175–177). Thus $\mathfrak{N} \models \mathbf{NB} + \mathbf{E} + \mathbf{GCH}$.

For $\beta \in \mathrm{Reg}$ and $\gamma \in \Omega$ define in $\mathfrak{N}$:

$$a_\gamma^\beta = \mathbf{K}x\ \hat{A}(x, \boldsymbol{\beta}, \boldsymbol{\gamma}).$$

Then $a_\gamma^\beta \subseteq \aleph_\beta^{\mathfrak{M}} = \aleph_\beta^{\mathfrak{N}}$, $a_\gamma^\beta \notin \mathfrak{M}$ and $a_\gamma^\beta$ is generic over $\mathfrak{M}$. Thus $\mathfrak{N}$ is obtained from $\mathfrak{M}$ by adding $\aleph_{\beta+1}^{\mathfrak{M}}$ new subsets of $\aleph_\beta^{\mathfrak{M}}$ for each regular cardinal $\aleph_\beta^{\mathfrak{M}}$ and a class which enumerates all these new sets. The submodel $\mathfrak{N}^*$ of $\mathfrak{N}$ will contain all the sets $a_\gamma^\beta$ but will omit the class

$$A = \mathbf{K}v\ (\mathbf{V}_x \mathbf{V}_y \mathbf{V}_z\ v = \langle x, y, z \rangle \wedge \hat{A}(x, y, z))$$

which induces in $\mathfrak{N}$ a well ordering of $\{a_\gamma^\beta; \beta \in \mathrm{Reg}, \gamma \in \aleph_{\beta+1}\}$. However, $\mathfrak{N}^*$ will contain arbitrarily large initial segments of this well ordering, so that $\mathfrak{N}^* \models \mathbf{AC}$. There will be no class in $\mathfrak{N}^*$ which contains just these initial segments, so **E** will fail in $\mathfrak{N}^*$.

DEFINITION OF $\mathfrak{N}^*$. $X$ is a class of $\mathfrak{N}^*$ iff $X$ is a class of $\mathfrak{N}$ which can be represented in the form $X = \mathbf{K}x\ \Phi(x)$, where $\Phi(x)$ contains no subformula $\hat{A}(u, v, w)$ in which one of the terms $u$, $v$, $w$ is a variable which is *not* in the scope of a limited quantifier.

LEMMA 3.1. $\mathfrak{N}^*$ *is a model of* $\mathbf{NB} + \mathbf{AC} + \mathbf{GCH}$.

PROOF. First notice that $\mathfrak{M} \subseteq \mathfrak{N}^* \subseteq \mathfrak{N}$. Obviously $\mathfrak{N}^*$ and $\mathfrak{N}$ have the same sets. Hence, $\mathfrak{N} \models \Psi$ iff $\mathfrak{N}^* \models \Psi$ for all **ZF**-sentences $\Psi$. Since $\mathfrak{N} \models \mathbf{NB} + \mathbf{GCH} + \mathbf{AC}$, we conclude that $\mathfrak{N}^*$ satisfies: the axioms of extensionality, I(1); of direct construction, II(1) and II(2); subclass, V$a$; power set, V$c$; infinity, VI; foundation, VII; choice, **AC** and **GCH**. If $s$ is a set and $F$ a function in $\mathfrak{N}^*$, then $\{F(x); x \in s\} = F\ ``s$ is a set in $\mathfrak{N}$ since $\mathfrak{N}$ satisfies the replacement axiom V$b$. But a set of $\mathfrak{N}$ is a set in $\mathfrak{N}^*$. Thus, $F\ ``s$ is a set in $\mathfrak{N}^*$; so replacement holds in $\mathfrak{N}^*$. Clearly $\mathfrak{N}^*$ also satisfies axiom I(2), and axioms $a(1)$ and $b(1)$ of group III. Each of the axioms

$a(2)$, $a(3)$, $b(2)$, $b(3)$, $c(1)$, $c(2)$, $c(3)$ of group III is of the form

$$\bigwedge_{X_1} \cdots \bigwedge_{X_n} \bigvee_Y \bigwedge_z [z \in Y \leftrightarrow \Phi(X_1, \ldots, X_n, z)],$$

with $n = 0, 1, 2, \ldots$. For given classes $X_1 = \mathsf{K}x\, \Psi_1(x), \ldots, X_n = \mathsf{K}x\, \Psi_n(x)$, the required class $Y$ is $\mathsf{K}x\, \Phi^0(x)$, where $\Phi^0(x)$ is the formula obtained by replacing each subformula $u \in X_i$ of $\Phi(X_1, \ldots, X_n, z)$ by $\Psi_i(u)$. Thus, if $X_1, \ldots, X_n$ are in $\mathfrak{N}^*$, then $Y$ is in $\mathfrak{N}^*$. Hence, all the axioms of group III are true in $\mathfrak{N}^*$, Q.E.D.

It remains to show that the global axiom of choice $\mathsf{E}$ is not valid in $\mathfrak{N}^*$. The proof will be based on a symmetry argument. If $\aleph_\alpha$ is a regular cardinal in $\mathfrak{M}$, then consider in $\mathfrak{M}$:

$$\hat{b}_\alpha = \mathsf{E}^{\aleph_\alpha + 1} x [\bigvee_y^{\aleph_\alpha} (y \in \aleph_\alpha \wedge \bigwedge_z^{\aleph_\alpha} (z \in y \vee (z \in x \leftrightarrow \hat{A}(z, \alpha, \aleph_\alpha))))]$$

$$\hat{c}_\alpha = \mathsf{E}^{\aleph_\alpha + 1} x [\bigvee_y^{\aleph_\alpha} (y \in \aleph_\alpha \wedge \bigwedge_z^{\aleph_\alpha} (z \in y \vee (z \in x \leftrightarrow - \hat{A}(z, \alpha, \aleph_\alpha))))]$$

Put $b_\alpha = \mathsf{K}x\ (x \in \hat{b}_\alpha)$ and $c_\alpha = \mathsf{K}x\ (x \in \hat{c}_\alpha)$. Then $b_\alpha$ is the set of all those subsets $x$ of $\aleph_\alpha^{\mathfrak{M}}$ which differ from the set $a_{\aleph_\alpha}{}^\alpha = \mathsf{K}z\hat{A}(z, \alpha, \aleph_\alpha)$ only on a set $y$ of cardinality less than $\aleph_\alpha$. The set $c_\alpha$ is the set of complements of elements of $b_\alpha$ with respect to $\aleph_\alpha$. (Notice that $\mathfrak{M}$ and $\mathfrak{N}$ have the same cardinals, EASTON [1970], p. 175, and hence $\aleph_\alpha^{\mathfrak{M}} = \aleph_\alpha^{\mathfrak{N}} = \aleph_\alpha^{\mathfrak{N}^*}$. For simplicity we write $\aleph_\alpha = \aleph_\alpha^{\mathfrak{M}}$.) The expression $\{\{b_\alpha, c_\alpha\}; \alpha \in \mathrm{Reg}\}$ is a class of $\mathfrak{N}$ but not of $\mathfrak{N}^*$. However, we shall prove that the $\mathfrak{N}^*$-class of *all* unordered pairs has no choice function in $\mathfrak{N}^*$. This will be done by a symmetry argument which interchanges $b_\alpha$ and $c_\alpha$.

DEFINITION. Let $\aleph_\alpha$ be a regular cardinal in $\mathfrak{M}$, $s \subseteq \aleph_\alpha$, $s$ a set of $\mathfrak{M}$. We define a mapping $\pi_s^\alpha$ which acts on conditions $p$ and on $\mathscr{L}$-formulas $\Phi$ as follows:

$$\pi_s^\alpha(p) = \{\langle \beta, \gamma, \delta, e \rangle; (\delta = \aleph_\alpha \wedge \gamma = \alpha \wedge \beta \in s \wedge \langle \beta, \gamma, \delta, e - 1 \rangle \in p) \vee$$
$$\vee ((\delta \neq \aleph_\alpha \vee \gamma \neq \alpha \vee \beta \notin s) \wedge \langle \beta, \gamma, \delta, e \rangle \in p)\}.$$

$\pi_s^\alpha(\Phi)$ is the $\mathscr{L}$-formula which results from $\Phi$ by replacing each occurrence (including occurrences within comprehension terms) of a subformula $\hat{A}(t_1, t_2, t_3)$ in which $t_3$ is a constant term of degree $\delta(t_3) \geqslant \aleph_\alpha$, *or* a variable which is either in the scope of an unlimited quantifier or in the scope of a limited quantifier of degree $\geqslant \aleph_\alpha$, by the formula

$$\hat{A}(\pi_s^\alpha(t_1), \pi_s^\alpha(t_2), \pi_s^\alpha(t_3)) \leftrightarrow - (\pi_s^\alpha(t_1) \in s \wedge \pi_s^\alpha(t_2) \simeq \alpha \wedge \pi_s^\alpha(t_3) \simeq \aleph_\alpha).$$

If $T$ is a class of $\mathfrak{M}$, then $\pi_s^\alpha(T) = T$, and in addition $\pi_s^\alpha(\mathsf{E}^\xi x \Psi(x)) = \mathsf{E}^\xi x \pi_s^\alpha(\Psi(x))$.

Here, for limited quantifiers $\mathsf{V}^{\xi},\mathsf{\Lambda}^{\xi}$, the ordinal $\xi$ is called the degree of the quantifier. Thus, the definition of $\pi_s^{\alpha}(\Phi)$ is given by an induction on the order $\mathrm{ord}(\Phi)$ of $\Phi$ (see EASTON [1970], p. 149 for a definition of $\mathrm{ord}(\Phi)$) for limited $\mathscr{L}$-formulas $\Phi$, and by induction on the length of $\Phi$ for unlimited $\mathscr{L}$-formulas. It is clear from this definition that if $\mathrm{ord}(\Phi) = \omega^2 \cdot \eta_1 + \omega \cdot \eta_2 + \eta_3$, then $\mathrm{ord}(\pi_s^{\alpha}(\Phi)) = \omega^2 \cdot \eta_1 + \omega \cdot \eta_2 + \eta_3^*$, with $\eta_3 \leq \eta_3^*$. This follows since $s$ has degree $\delta(s) \leq \aleph_{\alpha}$ ($s \subseteq \aleph_{\alpha}$ and $\delta(s)$ is the set-theoretical rank of $s$ in $\mathfrak{M}$). Thus, $\pi_s^{\alpha}$ takes comprehension terms $\mathsf{E}^{\xi}x\Phi(x)$ into comprehension terms $\mathsf{E}^{\xi}x\pi_s^{\alpha}(\Phi(x))$, and preserves the degree of any term of $\mathscr{L}$.

Let $\Vdash^*$ denote the weak-forcing relation

$$p \Vdash^* \Phi \Leftrightarrow p \Vdash \to (\to \Phi).$$

We say that $p$ decides $\Phi$ (in symbols, $p \parallel \Phi$) iff either $p \Vdash \Phi$ or $p \Vdash \to \Phi$.

SYMMETRY LEMMA.    *Let* $\Phi$ *be an* $\mathscr{L}$-*sentence,* $p$ *a condition and* $s$ *a subset of the regular cardinal* $\aleph_{\alpha}$ *of* $\mathfrak{M}$, *where* $s$ *is a set of* $\mathfrak{M}$. *Then:*

$$p \Vdash^* \Phi \Leftrightarrow \pi_s^{\alpha}(p) \Vdash^* \pi_s^{\alpha}(\Phi).$$

PROOF.    By induction along the inductive definition of forcing. There are only two critical cases to check, namely the cases where $\Phi$ is $\hat{A}(t_1,t_2,t_3)$ or $\mathsf{V}_x^{\beta}\Psi(x)$.

*Case* 1.    $\Phi$ is $\hat{A}(t_1,t_2,t_3)$. Since $\Phi$ is a sentence, $t_1$, $t_2$, $t_3$ are constant terms of $\mathscr{L}$. Let $p'$ be an extension of $p$, $p' \supseteq p$, such that $p'$ decides $\Phi$ (i.e. either $p' \Vdash \Phi$ or $p' \Vdash \to \Phi$), and let $p^*$ be an extension of $p'$ such that $\pi_s^{\alpha}(p^*)$ decides $\pi_s^{\alpha}(\Phi)$. We claim that $p^* \Vdash \Phi \Leftrightarrow \pi_s^{\alpha}(p^*) \Vdash \pi_s^{\alpha}(\Phi)$.

Suppose first that there is an extension $q$ of $p^*$ and ordinals $\beta$, $\gamma$, $\delta$ in $\mathfrak{M}$ such that

$$(\dagger) \qquad q \Vdash t_1 \approx \beta \ \& \ q \Vdash t_2 \approx \gamma \ \& \ q \Vdash t_3 \approx \delta.$$

We consider two subcases:

*Subcase* 1(a).    $\beta \in s$, $\gamma = \alpha$ and $\delta = \aleph_{\alpha}$ (in $\mathfrak{M}$). In this case,

$$(*) \qquad \mathrm{ord}(\hat{A}(t_1,t_2,t_3)) = \omega^2 \cdot [\max\{\delta(t_1),\delta(t_2),\delta(t_3)\} + 1] + \omega + 1,$$

but

$$(**) \qquad \mathrm{ord}(\pi_s^{\alpha}(t_1) \in s \wedge \pi_s^{\alpha}(t_2) \approx \alpha \wedge \pi_s^{\alpha}(t_3) \approx \aleph_{\alpha}) =$$
$$= \omega^2 \cdot [\max\{\delta(t_1),\delta(t_2),\delta(t_3)\} + 1] + n,$$

where $n$ is the $\mathfrak{M}$-finite length of that formula. (Note that $\delta(t_i) = \delta(\pi_s^{\alpha}(t_i))$ and that $q \Vdash t_i \approx x$ (for some set $x$ of $\mathfrak{M}$) implies $\delta(t_i) \geq \delta(x) = $ rank of $x$.) Thus, the formula $\hat{A}(t_1,t_2,t_3)$ in $(*)$ has a greater order than the formula in

(**). Hence, by the induction hypothesis:

(□)     $q \Vdash^* (t_1 \in s \wedge t_2 \simeq \alpha \wedge t_3 \simeq \aleph_\alpha) \Leftrightarrow$
$$\Leftrightarrow \pi_s^\alpha(q) \Vdash^* (\pi_s^\alpha(t_1) \in s \wedge \pi_s^\alpha(t_2) \simeq \alpha \wedge \pi_s^\alpha(t_3) \simeq \aleph_\alpha).$$

But $\langle \beta,\gamma,\delta,1 \rangle \in q \Leftrightarrow \langle \beta,\gamma,\delta,0 \rangle \in \pi_s^\alpha(q)$, since $\langle \beta,\gamma,\delta \rangle = \langle \beta,\alpha,\aleph_\alpha \rangle$ with $\beta \in s$. Hence,

(△)     $q \Vdash^* \hat{A}(t_1,t_2,t_3) \Leftrightarrow q \Vdash^* \hat{A}(\beta,\alpha,\aleph_\alpha) \Leftrightarrow$
$$\Leftrightarrow \pi_s^\alpha(q) \Vdash^* \to \hat{A}(\beta,\alpha,\aleph_\alpha).$$

Since $\operatorname{ord}(t_1 \simeq \beta) = \omega^2 \cdot (\delta(t_1)+1)+1 < \operatorname{ord}(\hat{A}(t_1,t_2,t_3))$, the induction hypothesis applied to (†) yields $\pi_s^\alpha(q) \Vdash^* \pi_s^\alpha(t_1) \simeq \beta$ and similarly $\pi_s^\alpha(q) \Vdash^* \pi_s^\alpha(t_2) \simeq \gamma$, $\pi_s^\alpha(q) \Vdash^* \pi_s^\alpha(t_3) \simeq \delta$. As $\gamma = \alpha$ and $\delta = \aleph_\alpha$ (in $\mathfrak{M}$) we infer

$$\pi_s^\alpha(q) \Vdash^* \to \hat{A}(\beta,\alpha,\aleph_\alpha) \Leftrightarrow \pi_s^\alpha(q) \Vdash^* \to \hat{A}(\pi_s^\alpha(t_1),\pi_s^\alpha(t_2),\pi_s^\alpha(t_3)).$$

This combined with (△) gives

(▽)     $q \Vdash^* \hat{A}(t_1,t_2,t_3) \Leftrightarrow \pi_s^\alpha(q) \Vdash^* \to \hat{A}(\pi_s^\alpha(t_1),\pi_s^\alpha(t_2),\pi_s^\alpha(t_3)).$

As we have seen in (□) that (†) implies

$$\pi_s^\alpha(q) \Vdash^* (\pi_s^\alpha(t_1) \in s \wedge \pi_s^\alpha(t_2) \simeq \alpha \wedge \pi_s^\alpha(t_3) \simeq \aleph_\alpha),$$

it obviously follows that $\pi_s^\alpha(q) \Vdash^* \to \hat{A}(\pi_s^\alpha(t_1),\pi_s^\alpha(t_2),\pi_s^\alpha(t_3))$ is equivalent to

$$\pi_s^\alpha(q) \Vdash^* [\to \hat{A}(\pi_s^\alpha(t_1),\pi_s^\alpha(t_2),\pi_s^\alpha(t_3)) \leftrightarrow$$
$$\leftrightarrow (\pi_s^\alpha(t_1) \in s \wedge \pi_s^\alpha(t_2) \simeq \alpha \wedge \pi_s^\alpha(t_3) \simeq \aleph_\alpha)].$$

This combined with (▽) proves our claim that

$$p^* \Vdash \hat{A}(t_1,t_2,t_3) \Leftrightarrow \pi_s^\alpha(p^*) \Vdash \pi_s^\alpha(\hat{A}(t_1,t_2,t_3)),$$

for $p^* \subseteq q$, $p^* \| \hat{A}(t_1,t_2,t_3)$, and $\pi_s^\alpha(p^*) \| \pi_s^\alpha(\hat{A}(t_1,t_2,t_3))$.

*Subcase* 1(b). Either $\beta \notin s$, $\gamma \neq \alpha$, or $\delta \neq \aleph_\alpha$ (in $\mathfrak{M}$). According to the definition, $\langle \beta,\gamma,\delta,1 \rangle \in q$ iff $\langle \beta,\gamma,\delta,1 \rangle \in \pi_s^\alpha(q)$. Hence, by (†) and the definition of forcing:

$$q \Vdash \hat{A}(t_1,t_2,t_3) \Leftrightarrow \pi_s^\alpha(q) \Vdash \hat{A}(\pi_s^\alpha(t_1),\pi_s^\alpha(t_2),\pi_s^\alpha(t_3)).$$

But $\beta$, $\gamma$, $\alpha$, $\aleph_\alpha$ and $s$ are sets of $\mathfrak{M}$, so every condition forces $\to (\beta \in s \wedge \gamma \simeq \alpha \wedge \delta \simeq \aleph_\alpha)$. In particular, this sentence is forced by $q$, and, by the induction hypothesis, is also forced by $\pi_s^\alpha(q)$. Thus, $q \Vdash \hat{A}(t_1,t_2,t_3)$ is clearly equivalent to

$$\pi_s^\alpha(q) \Vdash (\hat{A}(\pi_s^\alpha(t_1),\pi_s^\alpha(t_2),\pi_s^\alpha(t_3)) \leftrightarrow \to (\pi_s^\alpha(t_1) \in s \wedge$$
$$\wedge \pi_s^\alpha(t_2) \simeq \alpha \wedge \pi_s^\alpha(t_3) \simeq \aleph_\alpha)),$$

ULRICH FELGNER

which in turn is $\pi_s^\alpha(q)\Vdash^* \pi_s^\alpha(\hat{A}(t_1,t_2,t_3))$. This implies that

$$p*\Vdash \hat{A}(t_1,t_2,t_3) \Leftrightarrow \pi_s^\alpha(p*)\Vdash \pi_s^\alpha(A(t_1,t_2,t_3))$$

by the choice of $p*$.

Assume now that (†) does not hold. This implies by the definition of forcing that $p*\Vdash \to \hat{A}(t_1,t_2,t_3)$. Using the induction hypothesis it follows that there cannot be any extension $q$ of $p*$ such that $\pi_s^\alpha(q)\Vdash \pi_s^\alpha(t_1) \simeq \beta$, $\pi_s^\alpha(q)\Vdash \gamma \simeq \pi_s^\alpha(t_2)$, and $\pi_s^\alpha(q)\Vdash \delta \simeq \pi_s^\alpha(t_3)$ for some ordinals $\beta$, $\gamma$, $\delta$ of $\mathfrak{M}$. Thus, $\pi_s^\alpha(p*)\Vdash \to \hat{A}(\pi_s^\alpha(t_1),\pi_s^\alpha(t_2),\pi_s^\alpha(t_3))$ also holds. In particular,

$$\pi_s^\alpha(p*)\Vdash \to (t_1 \in s \wedge t_2 \simeq \alpha \wedge t_3 \simeq \aleph_\alpha).$$

It is now obvious that $p*\Vdash \hat{A}(t_1,t_2,t_3)$ is equivalent to

$$\pi_s^\alpha(p*)\Vdash (\hat{A}(\pi_s^\alpha(t_1),\pi_s^\alpha(t_2),\pi_s^\alpha(t_3)) \leftrightarrow \to (\pi_s^\alpha(t_1)\in s \wedge$$
$$\wedge \pi_s^\alpha(t_2) \simeq \alpha \wedge \pi_s^\alpha(t_3) \simeq \aleph_\alpha)).$$

Thus, we have shown that in all cases, $p*\Vdash \hat{A}(t_1,t_2,t_3)$ iff $\pi_s^\alpha(p*)\Vdash \pi_s^\alpha(\hat{A}(t_1,t_2,t_3))$. This is true for any extension $p*$ of $p$ such that $p*\Vert \hat{A}(t_1,t_2,t_3)$ and $\pi_s^\alpha(p*)\Vert \pi_s^\alpha(\hat{A}(t_1,t_2,t_3))$. But "not $p\Vdash^* \Phi$" is equivalent to "$\exists p' \supseteq p : p'\Vdash \to \Phi$" (see FELGNER (1971a), p. 83, Lemma A(i)). Therefore, our claim

$$p\Vdash^* \hat{A}(t_1,t_2,t_3) \Leftrightarrow \pi_s^\alpha(p)\Vdash^* \pi_s^\alpha(\hat{A}(t_1,t_2,t_3))$$

follows.

*Case* 2.  $\Phi$ is $V_x^\tau \Psi(x)$. Let $p*$ be an extension of $p$ such that $p*\Vert \Phi$ and $\pi_s^\alpha(p*)\Vert \pi_s^\alpha(\Phi)$. As in Case 1, it is sufficient to prove that $p*\Vdash \Phi$ iff $\pi_s^\alpha(p*)\Vdash \pi_s^\alpha(\Phi)$.

For some term $t$ of degree $\delta(t)<\tau$, $p*\Vdash V_x^\tau \Psi(x) \Leftrightarrow p*\Vdash \Psi(t)$. Hence, if $p*\Vdash V_x^\tau \Psi(x)$, then there is a constant term $t$ of degree $\delta(t)<\tau$ such that $\pi_s^\alpha(p*)\Vdash^* \pi_s^\alpha(\Psi(t))$ (by the induction hypothesis). If we can show that

(‡)     $\pi_s^\alpha(p*)\Vdash^* \pi_s^\alpha(\Psi(t)) \Leftrightarrow \pi_s^\alpha(p*)\Vdash^* \pi_s^\alpha(\Psi(x))[x/\pi_s^\alpha(t)],$

where $\pi_s^\alpha(\Psi(x))[x/\pi_s^\alpha(t)]$ is the result of substituting $\pi_s^\alpha(t)$ for $x$ in the $\mathcal{L}$-formula $\pi_s^\alpha(\Psi(x))$, it will follow that $\pi_s^\alpha(p*)\Vdash^* V_x^\tau \pi_s^\alpha(\Psi(x))$, i.e. $\pi_s^\alpha(p*)\Vdash^* \pi_s^\alpha(\Phi)$.

Conversely, if $\pi_s^\alpha(p*)\Vdash \pi_s^\alpha(\Phi)$, then by a similar argument, it follows from (‡) and the induction hypothesis that $p*\Vdash^* \Phi$. Thus, all we have to do is prove (‡).

If the formulas $\pi_s^\alpha(\Psi(t))$ and $\pi_s^\alpha(\Psi(x))[x/\pi_s^\alpha(t)]$ are at all different, then $\pi_s^\alpha(\Psi(x))[x/\pi_s^\alpha(t)]$ can be obtained from $\pi_s^\alpha(\Psi(t))$ by finitely many replacements of a subformula of the form $\hat{A}(t'_1,t'_2,t)$ by the formula

$$\hat{A}(t'_1,t'_2,\pi_s^\alpha(t)) \leftrightarrow \,\rightarrow (t'_1 \in s \wedge t'_2 \simeq \alpha \wedge \pi_s^\alpha(t) \simeq \aleph_\alpha).$$

It suffices to show that if $\Gamma^*$ is obtained from $\Gamma$ by a single replacement of this kind, then $p \parallel^* \Gamma^* \leftrightarrow \Gamma$. We prove this by induction on the length of the formula $\Gamma$. There are two cases to consider.

*Case* 2(a).   $\Gamma$ is $\hat{A}(t'_1,t'_2,\pi_s^\alpha(t))$. Note that by the definition of $\pi_s^\alpha(\Phi)$, the constant term $t$ must have degree less than $\aleph_\alpha$ since otherwise the formulas $\pi_s^\alpha(\Psi(t))$ and $\pi_s^\alpha(\Psi(x))[x/\pi_s^\alpha(t)]$ would not be different. But then $p * \parallel \rightarrow \pi_s^\alpha(t) \simeq \aleph_\alpha$ (see EASTON [1970], Lemma 13). Hence

$$p * \parallel \rightarrow (t'_1 \in s \wedge t'_2 \simeq \alpha \wedge \pi_s^\alpha(t) \simeq \aleph_\alpha).$$

Then, obviously, $p * \parallel^* \Gamma \leftrightarrow (\Gamma \leftrightarrow \rightarrow (t'_1 \in s \wedge t'_2 \simeq \alpha \wedge \pi_s^\alpha(t) \simeq \aleph_\alpha))$, i.e. $p * \parallel^* \Gamma \leftrightarrow \Gamma^*$.

*Case* 2(b).   $\Gamma$ is not of the form $\hat{A}(t'_1,t'_2,\pi_s^\alpha(t))$. Here the claim follows by a straightforward computation. The Symmetry Lemma is thus proved.

LEMMA 3.2.   $\mathfrak{N}^*$ *is a model of* $\rightarrow$E.

PROOF.   Suppose that the global form of the axiom of choice E holds in $\mathfrak{N}^*$. Let $R$ be the $\mathfrak{N}^*$-class of all unordered pairs. By our assumption there is a choice function $G$ on $R$ in $\mathfrak{N}^*$. Define in $\mathfrak{N}^*$:

$$Q = \{\langle x,y\rangle; \{x,y\} \in R \,\&\, G(\{x,y\}) = x\}.$$

By the definition of $\mathfrak{N}^*$ there is an unlimited $\mathscr{L}$-formula $\Psi(x,y)$ which contains no subformula $\hat{A}(u,v,w)$ in which one of the terms $u$, $v$, $w$ is a variable which is not in the scope of a limited quantifier, such that $Q = \mathsf{K}x \,(\mathsf{V}_y \, \mathsf{V}_z \, x = \langle y,z\rangle \wedge \Psi(y,z))$. Here, $x = \langle y,z\rangle$ stands for the unlimited $\mathscr{L}$-formula

$$\bigwedge_a [a \in x \leftrightarrow (\bigwedge_b (b \in a \leftrightarrow b = y) \vee \bigwedge_b (b \in a \leftrightarrow (b = y \vee b = z)))].$$

Since $G$ is a choice function, we conclude in particular that for each $\gamma$ in $\text{Reg} = \{\xi; \aleph_\xi \text{ is regular}\}$ either

$$\mathfrak{N}^* \models \Psi(\hat{b}_\gamma,\hat{c}_\gamma) \wedge \rightarrow \Psi(\hat{c}_\gamma,\hat{b}_\gamma),$$

or

$$\mathfrak{N}^* \models \Psi(\hat{c}_\gamma,\hat{b}_\gamma) \wedge \rightarrow \Psi(\hat{b}_\gamma,\hat{c}_\gamma)$$

holds. Let $\aleph_\alpha$ be (in $\mathfrak{M}$) the least-regular cardinal which is strictly greater than the degree (= rank) of any constant term or limited quantifier which occurs in $\Psi$. The degree of a limited quantifier $\mathsf{V}^\beta$ is defined to be $\beta$. We claim that $\mathfrak{N}^* \models \Psi(\hat{b}_\alpha,\hat{c}_\alpha) \leftrightarrow \Psi(\hat{c}_\alpha,\hat{b}_\alpha)$ holds.

Let $p$ be any condition. Clauses (i) and (ii) of the definition of a condition imply that there is an ordinal $\lambda$ in $\mathfrak{M}$, $\lambda < \aleph_\alpha$, such that $\langle \gamma, \alpha, \eta \rangle$ is in the domain of $p$ only if $\gamma < \lambda$. Put $s = \aleph_\alpha - \lambda$ (set theoretic difference) and $\pi = \pi_s{}^\alpha$. Then, by the choice of $\lambda$, $\pi(p) = p$ and hence by the symmetry lemma:

$$p \Vdash^* \Psi(\hat{b}_\alpha, \hat{c}_\alpha) \Leftrightarrow p \Vdash^* \pi(\Psi(\hat{b}_\alpha, \hat{c}_\alpha)).$$

By the assumption on the degrees of constant terms and limited quantifiers occurring in $\Psi$, the formula $\pi(\Psi(\hat{b}_\alpha, \hat{c}_\alpha))$ is simply $\Psi(\pi(\hat{b}_\alpha), \pi(\hat{c}_\alpha))$. Hence, $p \Vdash^* \Psi(\hat{b}_\alpha, \hat{c}_\alpha) \Leftrightarrow p \Vdash^* \Psi(\pi(\hat{b}_\alpha), \pi(\hat{c}_\alpha))$. Next we show that $p \Vdash^* \pi(\hat{b}_\alpha) = \hat{c}_\alpha$. In fact let $\mathscr{C}$ be any complete sequence of conditions which contains $p$ and let $\mathfrak{M}(\mathscr{C})$ be the resulting **NB**-model. Then in the sense of $\mathfrak{M}(\mathscr{C})$:

$$\mathsf{K}x\, (x \in \pi(\hat{b}_\alpha)) = \{(x \cap \lambda) \cup (s - x); x \in \mathsf{K}y\, (y \in \hat{b}_\alpha)\} = \mathsf{K}x\, (x \in \hat{c}_\alpha).$$

Thus $\mathfrak{M}(\mathscr{C}) \models \pi(b_\alpha) = c_\alpha$. Since this holds for all complete sequences $\mathscr{C}$ containing $p$, it follows that $p \Vdash^* \pi(\hat{b}_\alpha) = c_\alpha$. A similar argument shows that $p \Vdash^* \pi(\hat{c}_\alpha) = \hat{b}_\alpha$. It now follows that $p \Vdash^* \Psi(\hat{b}_\alpha, \hat{c}_\alpha) \Leftrightarrow p \Vdash^* \Psi(\hat{c}_\alpha, \hat{b}_\alpha)$ holds for every condition $p$. Thus $\mathfrak{N}^* \models \Psi(\hat{b}_\alpha, \hat{c}_\alpha) \leftrightarrow \Psi(\hat{c}_\alpha, \hat{b}_\alpha)$, a contradiction. This shows that $\mathsf{E}$ does not hold in the model $\mathfrak{N}^*$.

Thus, we have completed the proof of Theorem 3.1.

*Digression.* For a class $X$ and a set $s$, define

$$X^{(s)} = \{y ; \langle s, y \rangle \in X\},$$
$$\mathrm{Pr}_1(X) = \{y ; \exists z : \langle y, z \rangle \in X\}.$$

Let $\mathsf{V}$ be the class of all sets and $\mathsf{On}$ the class of all ordinals. MAREK and ZBIERSKI [1972] considered the following two strong forms of the axiom of choice, $\mathsf{C_V}$ (choice on the universe $\mathsf{V}$) and $\mathsf{C_{On}}$ (choice on the ordinals):

$\mathsf{C_V}$     $\forall x\, \exists X\, \Phi(x, X) \rightarrow \exists Y\, \forall x\, (\mathrm{Pr}_1(Y) = \mathsf{V} \wedge \Phi(x, Y^{(x)}))$,

$\mathsf{C_{On}}$     $\forall \alpha\, \exists X\, \Phi(\alpha, X) \rightarrow \exists Y\, \forall \alpha \in \mathsf{On}[\mathrm{Pr}_1(Y) = \mathsf{On} \wedge \Phi(\alpha, Y^{(\alpha)})]$.

It is obvious that in **NB**-set theory $\mathsf{C_V}$ implies $\mathsf{E}$ (take in $\mathsf{C_V}$ the formula $x = \emptyset \vee X \in x$) and $\mathsf{C_V}$ implies $\mathsf{C_{On}}$. Furthermore, the conjunction of $\mathsf{C_{On}}$ and $\mathsf{AC}$ implies $\mathsf{E}$ (to see this, consider in $\mathsf{C_{On}}$ the formula, "$X$ is a well ordering of $\mathsf{P}(\alpha) = \{x; x \subseteq \alpha\}$" and use the Proof of Theorem 7.22 in RUBIN–RUBIN [1963], p. 77, or consider the formula "$X$ is a well ordering of $V_\alpha$", where the $V_\alpha = \{x; \rho(x) < \alpha\}$ are the von Neumann–Stufen). On the other hand, $\mathsf{C_V}$ follows from $\mathsf{E} \wedge \mathsf{C_{On}}$ since $\mathsf{E}$ implies that there is a class $G$ which maps $\mathsf{V}$ in a one-to-one fashion onto $\mathsf{On}$. Thus:

(in **NB**):     $\mathsf{C_V} \leftrightarrow (\mathsf{C_{On}} \wedge \mathsf{AC}) \rightarrow \mathsf{E} \rightarrow \mathsf{AC}$.

Theorem 3.1 shows that the last arrow cannot be reversed in **NB**. Marek proved in MAREK (1973), p. 36 that $C_V$ is independent from $E$. Hence (in $NB$) $C_V \to E \to AC$ while none of the converse implications are provable.

## 4. Conservative extensions

In the preceding section we have seen that the global axiom of choice $E$ is not implied by the local axiom of choice $AC$. Thus, $NB + E$ is a strictly stronger theory than $NB + AC$. We shall see in this section that, on the other hand, $NB + E$ is not so much stronger than $NB + AC$: we shall prove that in $NB + E$ one can prove nothing more about sets than one can prove already in $NB + AC$. More precisely, we shall prove the following result:

"$NB + E$ *is a conservative extension of* $NB + AC$ *with respect to* $ZF$*-sentences*".

(See SHOENFIELD [1967], p. 41 for terminology, and notice that $\mathscr{L}_{ZF}$ is a sublanguage of $\mathscr{L}_{NB}$—see §1.) This result appeared in FELGNER [1971]. Here we present a slightly simplified and modified version of that proof. It is convenient to have the following version of the axiom of dependent choices at hand. Let $\alpha$ be a cardinal number:

$DCC^\alpha$:    *Axiom of dependent choices on classes of length* $\alpha$

*If $R$ is a binary relation between subsets and elements of a class $S$ such that*

$$\forall y \subseteq S[\operatorname{card}(y) < \alpha \Rightarrow \exists z \in S: \langle y,z \rangle \in R],$$

*then there is a function $f : \alpha \to S$ such that*

$$\langle \{f(\gamma); \gamma \in \beta\}, f(\beta) \rangle \in R \quad \text{for every } \beta < \alpha.$$

This axiom is a generalization of the axiom $DC$ introduced by BERNAYS (1942), p. 86:

$DC$:    *Axiom of dependent choices*

*If $r$ is a binary relation on the set $s$ such that for every $x \in s$ there is an element $y \in s$ such that $\langle x,y \rangle \in r$, then there is a sequence $\langle x_n ; n \in \omega \rangle$ of* elements $x_n \in s$ such that $\langle x_n, x_{n+1} \rangle \in r$ for all $n \in \omega$.

This axiom $DC$ was rediscovered independently six years later by TARSKI [1948], p. 96. Denote by $DC^\alpha$ the axiom which results from $DCC^\alpha$ by requiring that $R$ and $S$ are sets. These axioms $DC^\alpha$ have been introduced by Lévy in [1964]. Clearly $NC$ and $DC^\omega$ are equivalent. Lévy showed in LÉVY [1964] that

$$(\text{in } NB^0): \quad AC \Leftrightarrow (\forall \alpha : DC^\alpha).$$

The reader is referred to FELGNER [1971a], p. 146–166 for further results concerning the axioms $DC^\alpha$. The $DCC^\alpha$ will be discussed in §5. Here, we confine ourselves to the following result.

LEMMA 4.1. (for every cardinal $\alpha$). *In the axiom system* NB (*which includes the axiom of foundation*), *the axioms* $DC^\alpha$ *and* $DCC^\alpha$ *are equivalent.*

PROOF. Since $DCC^\alpha \Rightarrow DC^\alpha$ is obvious, we have only to prove the converse. Let $R$ and $S$ be given such that the hypothesis of $DCC^\alpha$ is true. Let $\rho(x) = \min\{\gamma; x \in V_{\gamma+1}\}$ be the usual rank of the set $x$. By the axiom of foundation every set $x$ has a rank $\rho(x)$. Let $p$ be an arbitrary element of $S$ and put $G_0 = \{p\}$. We shall define sets $G_\nu$ by induction:

$$G_1 = \{x \in S; \langle\{p\},x\rangle \in R \wedge \forall y \in S(\langle\{p\},y\rangle \in R \Rightarrow \rho(x) \leqslant \rho(y))\}.$$

Suppose $G_\nu \neq \emptyset$ is defined for all $\nu < \lambda$ where $\lambda < \alpha$. Call a sequence $d = \langle u_\nu; \nu < \lambda\rangle$ of elements $u_\nu \in S$ a *regular $\lambda$-chain* iff $u_\nu \in G_\nu$ and $\langle\{u_\gamma; \gamma < \nu\},u_\nu\rangle \in R$ for all $\nu < \lambda$. Let $D_\lambda$ be the set of all regular $\lambda$-chains. For $d \in D_\lambda$ define

$$H_\lambda(d) = \{x \in S; \langle d,x\rangle \in R \wedge \forall y \in S(\langle d,y\rangle \in R \Rightarrow \rho(x) \leqslant \rho(y))\},$$

and finally $G_\lambda = \cup\{H_\lambda(d); d \in D_\lambda\}$. The set $t = \cup\{G_\nu; \nu < \alpha\}$ equipped with the restriction of $R$ to $t$, satisfies the hypothesis of $DC^\alpha$. Hence, by $DC^\alpha$, there is a function $f$ defined on $\alpha$ such that $\langle\{f(\gamma); \gamma < \beta\},f(\beta)\rangle \in R$ for all $\beta < \alpha$. Thus $DCC^\alpha$ holds, Q.E.D.

COROLLARY. *In* NB *the local axiom of choice* AC *is equivalent to* $\forall\alpha$: $DCC^\alpha$.

The result that NB + E is a conservative extension of NB + AC with respect to ZF-sentences, will be a corollary to the following more general theorem.

THEOREM 4.1 (FELGNER [1971]). *Every countable model* $\mathfrak{M}$ *of* NB + AC *can be extended to a countable model* $\mathfrak{N}$ *of* NB + E *such that* $\mathfrak{M}$ *and* $\mathfrak{N}$ *have precisely the same "sets".*

PROOF (outline). Let $\mathfrak{M}$ be given, $\mathfrak{M} \models$ NB + AC, and let $\in^{\mathfrak{M}}$ be the membership relation of $\mathfrak{M}$. We shall extend $\mathfrak{M}$ to a model $\mathfrak{N}$ in such a way that $\mathfrak{N}$ has no new sets but only new classes. In particular, we shall add a universal choice function $F$ to $\mathfrak{M}$. We shall apply Cohen's method of forcing in order to obtain a generic universal choice function $F$. The genericity of $F$ guarantees that the structure $\mathfrak{N} = \mathfrak{M}[F]$ generated by $\mathfrak{M}$ and $F$ is a model of NB-set theory.

We define a language $\mathfrak{L}^F$ which has set variables $v_i$ (for each integer $i$ of

$\mathfrak{M}$, notice that $\mathfrak{M}$ may contain non-standard integers), constants $S$ for each class $S$ of $\mathfrak{M}$, a unary predicate symbol $F$, a binary predicate symbol $\in$, the sentential connectives $\rightarrow$, $\vee$ ("not", "or"), a quantifier $\mathsf{V}$ ("there exists"), and brackets. If $s$ is a set in the sense of $\mathfrak{M}$, then the constant $s$ will be called a set constant.

The formulas of $\mathfrak{L}^F$ are defined in the metalanguage, so that the length of a formula will be finite in the usual sense:

(i) If $a$ and $b$ are variables or set constants, then $F(a)$ and $a \in b$ are formulas of $\mathfrak{L}^F$,

(ii) If $a$ is a variable or a set constant, and if $S$ is any constant, then $a \in S$ is a formula of $\mathfrak{L}^F$,

(iii) If $\Phi$ and $\Psi$ are formulas of $\mathfrak{L}^F$, and if $x$ is a variable, then $\rightarrow \Phi$, $\Phi \vee \Psi$, and $\mathsf{V}_x \Phi$ are formulas of $\mathfrak{L}^F$.

We introduce the other logical symbols $\wedge$, $\rightarrow$, $\leftrightarrow$, and $\bigwedge$ (conjunction, implication, equivalence, and universal quantification) into $\mathfrak{L}^F$ as usual by definition. Their use can be eliminated.

DEFINITION (in $\mathfrak{M}$). A *condition* is a set $p$ such that $p$ is a function and $p(x) \in x$ for all $x$ in the domain of $p$. Let **cond** be in $\mathfrak{M}$ the class of all conditions.

By a simple induction on the length of the $\mathfrak{L}^F$-formula $\Phi$ we define in the metalanguage the forcing relation $p \Vdash \Phi$ ($p$ forces $\Phi$) as follows:

(1) $\qquad p \Vdash t \in S \Leftrightarrow t \in^{\mathfrak{M}} S,$

(2) $\qquad p \Vdash F(s) \Leftrightarrow s \in^{\mathfrak{M}} p,$

(3) $\qquad p \Vdash \rightarrow \Phi \Leftrightarrow \mathsf{V} q \in^{\mathfrak{M}} \mathbf{cond}\, [p \subseteq^{\mathfrak{M}} q \Rightarrow \text{not } q \Vdash \Phi],$

(4) $\qquad p \Vdash \Phi \vee \Psi \Leftrightarrow (p \Vdash \Phi \text{ or } p \Vdash \Psi),$

(5) $\qquad p \Vdash \mathsf{V}_x \Phi(x) \Leftrightarrow \exists s\, [s \text{ is a set of } \mathfrak{M} \text{ and } p \Vdash \Phi(s)].$

Here $\subseteq^{\mathfrak{M}}$ denotes inclusion in the sense of $\mathfrak{M}$, i.e.

$$x \subseteq^{\mathfrak{M}} y \Leftrightarrow \mathsf{V}z\, (z \in^{\mathfrak{M}} x \Rightarrow z \in^{\mathfrak{M}} y),$$

and $\mathsf{V}, \exists, \Rightarrow$, & are the logical symbols of our metalanguage. A sequence $\mathscr{C} = \langle p^{(n)}; n \in \omega \rangle$ of conditions is called complete, if $\mathscr{C}$ is well ordered by $\subseteq^{\mathfrak{M}}$ and of order type $\omega$ and, if for every class $C$ of conditions, $C$ in $\mathfrak{M}$, which is cofinal in **cond**, there is some $p^{(k)}$ in $\mathscr{C}$ such that $p^{(k)} \in^{\mathfrak{M}} C$.

Let $\mathscr{P}$ be a complete sequence of conditions. The model $\mathfrak{N}$ can now be defined:

(i) If $\Phi(x)$ is a formula of $\mathfrak{L}^F$, then the collection of all set constants $s$ such that $\mathscr{P} \Vdash \Phi(s)$ is called a class of $\mathfrak{N}$, and will be denoted by $\mathsf{K}x\, \Phi(x)$.

(ii) Sets of $\mathfrak{N}$ are classes of the form $\mathsf{K}x\, (x \in s)$, where $s$ is a set constant of $\mathfrak{L}^F$.

(iii) The membership relation $\in^{\mathfrak{N}}$ is defined as follows: $\mathsf{K}x\,\Phi(x)\in^{\mathfrak{N}}\mathsf{K}y\,\Psi(y)$ holds iff there is some set $s$ in $\mathfrak{M}$ such that $s\in\mathsf{K}y\,\Psi(y)$ and $\mathsf{K}x\,\Phi(x)=\mathsf{K}x\,(x\in s)$ (equality of these collections in the sense of the metatheory!).

(iv) A class $\mathsf{K}x\,\Phi(x)$ of $\mathfrak{N}$ satisfies the predicate $F$ in $\mathfrak{N}$ iff $\mathsf{K}x\,\Phi(x)\in^{\mathfrak{N}}\mathsf{K}y\,F(y)$.

(v) A constant $S$ (where $S$ is a class of $\mathfrak{M}$) is interpreted in $\mathfrak{N}$ by the class $\mathsf{K}x\,(x\in s)$.

Thus, we have defined how the language $\mathfrak{L}^F$ is interpreted in $\mathfrak{N}=\{\mathsf{K}x\,\Phi(x); \Phi(x)$ is a formula of $\mathfrak{L}^F$ which has $x$ as its only free variable$\}$. The mapping $\tau: \mathfrak{M}\to\mathfrak{N}$ which is given by $\tau(S)=\mathsf{K}x\,(x\in S)$, is an isomorphism from $\mathfrak{M}$ into $\mathfrak{N}$ such that $S_1\in^{\mathfrak{M}}S_2\Leftrightarrow\tau(S_1)\in^{\mathfrak{N}}\tau(S_2)$. This follows immediately from the fact $\mathsf{K}x\,(x\in S_1)=\mathsf{K}y\,(y\in S_2)\leftrightarrow\mathcal{P}\Vdash S_1=S_2$. In particular $\tau$ maps the class of all sets of $\mathfrak{M}$ onto the class of all sets of $\mathfrak{N}$. Thus, if we identify $\mathfrak{M}$ with its isomorphic image in $\mathfrak{N}$, then $\mathfrak{M}$ and $\mathfrak{N}$ have precisely the same sets. It can now be easily shown that $\mathfrak{N}$ satisfies all the axioms of groups I (extensionality), II (direct construction of sets), III (construction of classes), VI (infinity), VII (foundation), and axioms $a$, $b$, $d$ of group V (subclass, sum and power set). We refer to FELGNER [1971] where all necessary details are given.

LEMMA 4.2. *The global axiom of choice* $\mathsf{E}$ *holds in* $\mathfrak{N}$.

PROOF. It is clear that $\mathbf{F}=\mathsf{K}x\,F(x)$ is a function in $\mathfrak{N}$ such that $\mathbf{F}(a)\in^{\mathfrak{N}}a$ for all non-empty sets $a$ of $\mathfrak{N}$. We have to show that $\mathbf{F}$ is defined for all non-empty sets of $\mathfrak{N}$. In fact let $a$ be a given non-empty set of $\mathfrak{N}$. By the definition of $\mathfrak{N}$, there is a set $s$ in $\mathfrak{M}$ such that $a=\mathsf{K}x\,(x\in s)$. But $\tau$ is an $\in$-isomorphism from $\mathfrak{M}$ into $\mathfrak{N}$, $\tau(s)=a$, and hence, $s$ must be non-empty in $\mathfrak{M}$. Therefore

$$D=\{p\,;\,p\in^{\mathfrak{M}}\mathbf{cond}\ \&\ \exists t\,(t\in^{\mathfrak{M}}s\ \&\ \langle s,t\rangle\in^{\mathfrak{M}}p)\}^{\mathfrak{M}}$$

is a class (defined in $\mathfrak{M}$) which is cofinal in $\mathbf{cond}$. Since $\mathcal{P}$ is a complete sequence of conditions, there must be a member of $\mathcal{P}$, say $p^{(k)}$, such that $p^{(k)}\in^{\mathfrak{M}}D$. Hence $p^{(k)}\Vdash F(\langle s,t\rangle)$ by the definition of forcing. This gives us

$$\langle\mathsf{K}x\,(x\in s),\mathsf{K}y\,(y\in t)\rangle\in^{\mathfrak{M}}\mathbf{F}\quad\text{and}\quad\mathsf{K}y\,(y\in t)\in^{\mathfrak{N}}\mathsf{K}x\,(x\in s).$$

It follows that $\mathbf{F}$ is defined for every non-empty set of $\mathfrak{N}$, Q.E.D.

Let $\Phi(x_0,x_1,\ldots,x_n)$ be a formula of $\mathfrak{L}^F$ with no free variables other than $x_0,\ldots,x_n$, let $s$ be a set constant and $y$ a variable not occurring in $\Phi$. Define $\mathrm{Res}\,(\Phi,s,y)$ (restriction of $\Phi$ to $s$ and $y$) as the following formula:

$$\bigwedge_{x_1}\cdots\bigwedge_{x_n}[(x_1\in s\wedge\cdots\wedge x_n\in s)\to(\bigvee_{x_0}\Phi(x_0,\ldots,x_n)\leftrightarrow\bigvee_{x_0\in y}\Phi(x_0,\ldots,x_n))].$$

The next lemma will show that for every set constant $s$, the class $\{q \in^{\mathfrak{M}} \text{cond}; q \Vdash V_y \text{ Res } (\Phi,s,y)\}$ is cofinal in **cond**.

LEMMA 4.3.  *Let $s$ be a set of $\mathfrak{M}$, $p$ a condition and $\Phi(x_0,\ldots, x_n)$ a formula of $\mathfrak{L}^F$ with no free variable other than $x_0,\ldots, x_n$. There exists an extension $q$ of $p$ such that*

$$q \Vdash \underset{y}{V} \text{ Res } (\Phi,s,y).$$

PROOF.    Let $s^n$ be in $\mathfrak{M}$ the set of all $n$-tuples of elements of $s$. Since $\mathfrak{M}$ satisfies the local axiom of choice **AC** there is a well ordering of $s^n$ in $\mathfrak{M}$. Hence, we can index the elements of $s^n$ by ordinals $\alpha$, $s^n = \{u_\alpha ; \alpha < \lambda\}^{\mathfrak{M}}$, where $\lambda$ is a cardinal of $\mathfrak{M}$. If $u_\alpha$ is the $n$-tuple $\langle z_1,\ldots, z_n \rangle$ in $\mathfrak{M}$, then we shall write $\Phi(y,u_\alpha)$ instead of $\Phi(y, z_1,\ldots, z_n)$. Now define in $\mathfrak{M}$:

$$K = \{\langle q,u_\alpha,e,v\rangle; p \subseteq q \,\&\, q \in \text{cond} \,\&\, \alpha < \lambda \,\&\, e \in \{0,1\} \,\&$$
$$\&\, [(e = 1 \,\&\, q \Vdash \Phi(v,u_\alpha))$$
$$\text{or } (e = 0 \,\&\, \rightarrow \exists q' \supseteq q \, \exists w : q' \Vdash \Phi(w,u_\alpha))]\}.$$

A partial ordering $<$ can be defined on $K$ as follows:

$$\langle q_1,u_\alpha,e_1,v_1\rangle < \langle q_2,u_\beta,e_2,v_2\rangle \Leftrightarrow q_1 \subseteq q_2 \,\&\, \alpha < \beta.$$

If $a \in K$, then put $\varphi(a) = \beta \Leftrightarrow \exists q \, \exists e \, \exists v : a = \langle q,u_\beta,e,v\rangle$. We call $\varphi(a)$ the order of $a$. A subset $t$ of $K$ is called a thread, if $t$ is totally ordered by $<$ and

$$\forall a \in t \, \forall \gamma \, [\gamma < \varphi(a) \Rightarrow \exists b \in t : \varphi(b) = \gamma]$$

holds. As usual $\text{Pr}_1 (\langle q,u_\alpha,e,v\rangle) = q$ is the projection to the first coordinate. We are now in a position to define a relation $R$ between subsets and elements of $K$ as follows:

$$\langle t,a\rangle \in R \Leftrightarrow \begin{cases} t \text{ is a thread } \& \ a \in K \ \& \\ \varphi(a) = \sup \{\gamma + 1; \exists b \in t : \varphi(b) = \gamma\} \ \& \\ \text{Pr}_1 (a) \supseteq \cup \{\text{Pr}_1 (b); b \in t\}. \end{cases}$$

By the Corollary of Lemma 4.1, the axiom $\text{DCC}^\lambda$ holds in $\mathfrak{M}$. Hence, there is a function $f$ from $\lambda$ into $K$ such that

$$\langle \{f(\gamma); \gamma < \alpha\},f(\alpha)\rangle \in R$$

for all $\alpha < \lambda$. Put $p^* = \cup\{\text{Pr}_1(f(\alpha)); \alpha < \lambda\}$ and $r = \{v; \exists \alpha < \lambda \, \exists q \, \exists e : f(\alpha) = \langle q,u_\alpha,e,v\rangle\}$ (notice that $\varphi(f(\alpha)) = \alpha$ always holds). It follows that $p^* \Vdash \text{Res} (\Phi,s,r)$, and hence $p^* \Vdash V_y \text{ Res } (\Phi,s,y)$, Q.E.D.

It follows from Lemma 4.3 that for every $\mathfrak{L}^F$-formula $\Phi(x_0,\ldots, x_n)$ and every set $s$ of $\mathfrak{M}$ there is a set $r$ in $\mathfrak{M}$ such that $\mathfrak{N} \models \text{Res} (\Phi,s,r)$ holds.

It is now a routine matter to show that this implies that the axiom of replacement holds in $\mathfrak{N}$ (see FELGNER [1971] for all details). Theorem 4.1 is thus proved.

REMARK. In contrast to the result of Morris, which says that not every countable model $\mathfrak{M}$ of NB-set theory can be extended to a countable model $\mathfrak{N}$ of NB + AC without adding ordinals (see §2), Theorem 4.1 says that every countable model $\mathfrak{M}$ of NB + AC can be extended to a countable model of NB + E without adding ordinals! One reason for the extendibility of models $\mathfrak{M}$ satisfying AC is that the axioms DCC$^\alpha$ provide choices from "sets of classes". The importance of DCC$^\alpha$ in this context will become clearer as soon as the question of extendibility is discussed in the absence of the axiom of foundation.

The axiom of choice AC is sometimes considered as an axiom which enlarges the universe of sets, since it provides to every collection of non-empty sets a further set, namely a choice function. I think that AC has more the character of an axiom which restricts the universe of sets: only those collections are sets which have choice functions. It follows from Gödel's work that the minimal model of constructible sets satisfies AC. The result of Morris shows that models of NB + AC are not arbitrarily large (if one fixes the ordinals). However, Theorem 4.1 shows that E restricts the universe of sets no more than AC.

By results of Cohen and Jensen (see §2) the same is true for the general continuum hypothesis GCH. In contrast to this, Gödel's axiom of constructibility V = L is definitely a restrictive axiom.

Let $\mathscr{A}$ be the class of models of NB + AC + $\rightarrow$ E and let $\mathscr{B}$ be the class of models of NB + E. Theorems 3.1 and 4.1 show that there is a chain of countable models $\mathfrak{M}_0 \subseteq \mathfrak{M}_1 \subseteq \cdots \subseteq \mathfrak{M}_n \subseteq \mathfrak{M}_{n+1} \subseteq \cdots$ such that $\mathfrak{M}_{2n} \in \mathscr{A}$ and $\mathfrak{M}_{2n+1} \in \mathscr{B}$ for all $n \in \omega$. The existence of this alternating chain shows that the disjoint classes $\mathscr{A}$ and $\mathscr{B}$ cannot be separated by an $V_2^0 \cap \Lambda_2^0$-class (see ADDISON [1965]). However, not much more is known about such separability questions.

The following theorem was obtained independently by several people, COHEN [1966], p. 77, FELGNER [1971], GRIŠIN [1972], Jensen, Kripke, and Solovay. A forcing-free proof was obtained by GAIFMAN [1968].

THEOREM 4.2. *If $\Phi$ is a sentence of the* ZF-*language $\mathscr{L}_{\mathrm{ZF}}$, then $\Phi$ is provable in* NB + E *iff $\Phi$ is provable in* NB + AC.

PROOF. If NB + AC $\vdash \Phi$ then clearly also NB + E $\vdash \Phi$, since AC follows from E.[1] Conversely, suppose that NB + E $\vdash \Phi$, where $\Phi$ is a sentence in

---

[1] The symbol $\vdash$ denotes provability. Thus $T \vdash \Phi$ means that $\Phi$ is provable in the theory $T$.

the ZF-language, i.e. $\Phi$ contains no class variables. Assume that $\Phi$ is not provable in NB + AC. Then NB + AC + $(\rightarrow \Phi)$ is consistent and has a model $\mathfrak{A}$. By the Löwenheim–Skolem theorem NB + AC + $\rightarrow \Phi$ has a countable model $\mathfrak{M}$. By theorem 4.1, $\mathfrak{M}$ can be extended to a model $\mathfrak{N}$ of NB + E such that both $\mathfrak{M}$ and $\mathfrak{N}$ have the same sets. Since $\Phi$ speaks only about sets, it thus follows that $\mathfrak{N}$ must also satisfy $\rightarrow \Phi$. Hence $\mathfrak{N} \models$ NB + E + $\rightarrow \Phi$. But by our assumption, $\Phi$ is provable in NB + E, thus $\mathfrak{N} \models \Phi$, a contradiction. This shows that $\Phi$ must be a theorem of the theory NB + AC, Q.E.D.

COROLLARY 4.1. *If $\Phi$ is a sentence of the ZF-language. Then $\Phi$ is provable in ZF + AC iff $\Phi$ is provable in NB + E.*

PROOF. It is well known that ZF $\vdash \Phi$ iff NB $\vdash \Phi$ for every ZF-sentence $\Phi$ (see COHEN [1966], p. 77, FRAENKEL–BAR–HILLEL–LÉVY–VAN DALEN [1973], pp. 131–132). Hence, if NB + E $\vdash \Phi$, then NB + AC $\vdash \Phi$ by Theorem 4.2, and therefore NB $\vdash$ (AC $\Rightarrow \Phi$). We conclude that ZF $\vdash$ (AC $\Rightarrow \Phi$), and hence ZF + AC $\vdash \Phi$, Q.E.D.

Let $\mathscr{L}_{ZF}^{\sigma}$ be the first-order language which results from $\mathscr{L}_{ZF}$ by adding the unary function symbol $\sigma$. The terms of $\mathscr{L}_{ZF}^{\sigma}$ are defined inductively: the variables $x, y, z, x_0, x_1, \ldots$ are terms, and if $t$ is a term, then $\sigma(t)$ is a term. The formulas of $\mathscr{L}_{ZF}^{\sigma}$ are also defined inductively: if $t_1$ and $t_2$ are terms, then $t_1 \in t_2$ and $t_1 = t_2$ are formulas, and if $\Phi$ and $\Psi$ are formulas, then $\rightarrow \Phi$, $\Phi \wedge \Psi$, $\Phi \vee \Psi$, $\Phi \rightarrow \Psi$, $\Phi \leftrightarrow \Psi$, $\forall x\, \Phi$, and $\exists x\, \Phi$ are also formulas (where $x$ is a variable).

The system ZF$_{\sigma}^0$ consists of the axioms of extensionality, empty set, pairs, unions, power set, infinity, replacement (where all formulas $\Phi(x,y)$ from $\mathscr{L}_{ZF}^{\epsilon}$ are allowed to appear in the schema of replacement), and the axiom

A$_{\sigma}$ $\qquad\qquad \forall x\, (x \neq \emptyset \Rightarrow \sigma(x) \in x).$

It follows from the axioms of the predicate calculus that

$$\forall x\, \forall y\, [x = y \rightarrow \sigma(x) = \sigma(y)];$$

$$\text{ZF}_{\sigma} = \text{ZF}_{\sigma}^0 + \textit{Axiom of foundation}.$$

The language $\mathscr{L}_{ZF}^{\epsilon}$ is defined similarly: $\mathscr{L}_{ZF}^{\epsilon}$ results from $\mathscr{L}_{ZF}$ by adding Hilbert's $\epsilon$-symbol. The formulas and terms of $\mathscr{L}_{ZF}^{\epsilon}$ are defined by a simultaneous induction: all variables $x, y, z, \ldots$ are terms; if $t_1$ and $t_2$ are terms than $t_1 \in t_2$ and $t_1 = t_2$ are formulas. If $\Phi$ is a formula which contains at least one free variable $x$, then $\epsilon_x \Phi$ is a term; if $\Phi$ and $\Psi$ are formulas, then $\rightarrow \Phi$, $\Phi \wedge \Psi$, $\Phi \vee \Psi$, $\Phi \rightarrow \Psi$, $\Phi \leftrightarrow \Psi$, $\forall x\, \Phi$ and $\exists x\, \Phi$ are formulas.

The system $\mathsf{ZF}_\epsilon^0$ consists of the axioms of extensionality, empty set, pairs, unions, power set, infinity, and replacement (where all formulas $\Phi(x,y)$ from $\mathscr{L}_{\mathsf{ZF}}^\epsilon$ are allowed to appear in the schema of replacement). Besides the usual logical axioms the system $\mathsf{ZF}_\epsilon^0$ also contains Hilbert's axiom

$$\exists x \ \Phi(x) \to \Phi(\epsilon_x \Phi)$$

and Ackermann's axiom

$$\forall x \ (\Phi(x) \leftrightarrow \Psi(x)) \to \epsilon_x \Phi = \epsilon_x \Psi$$

as logical axioms. The system which is obtained from $\mathsf{ZF}_\epsilon^0$ by adding the axiom of foundation is called $\mathsf{ZF}_\epsilon$.

It is obvious that the axiom of choice $\mathsf{AC}$ is provable in both systems $\mathsf{ZF}_\sigma^0$ and $\mathsf{ZF}_\epsilon^0$. As a corollary to Theorem 4.2 we now obtain:

COROLLARY 4.2. *Let $\Phi$ be a sentence of the ordinary $\mathsf{ZF}$-language $(\Phi \in \mathscr{L}_{\mathsf{ZF}})$. Then the following three conditions are equivalent*:

   (i) $\mathsf{ZF} + \mathsf{AC} \vdash \Phi$,
   (ii) $\mathsf{ZF}_\sigma \vdash \Phi$,
   (iii) $\mathsf{ZF}_\epsilon \vdash \Phi$.

PROOF. Since $\mathsf{ZF}_\sigma \vdash \mathsf{AC}$, it is obvious that (i) implies (ii). Since the symbol $\sigma$ can be interpreted in $\mathscr{L}_{\mathsf{ZF}}^\epsilon$ by the stipulation $\sigma(x) = \epsilon_y(y \in x)$ so that Hilbert's axiom gives $\sigma(x) \in x$ for all $x$ such that $\exists y \ (y \in x)$, we see immediately that (ii) implies (iii). Now suppose that (iii) holds: $\mathsf{ZF}_\epsilon \vdash \Phi$. Let $\rho$ be the ordinary rank function: $\rho(z) = \min \{\alpha ; z \in V_{\alpha+1}\}$. The $\epsilon$-terms have an interpretation in $\mathsf{ZF}_\sigma$ by defining for an arbitrary formula $\Psi(x)$,

$$\epsilon_x \Psi = \sigma(\{x ; \Psi(x) \wedge \forall y \ (\Psi(y) \to \rho(x) \leqslant \rho(y))\}).$$

Thus (iii) implies (ii). It follows easily from Theorem 4.1 that (ii) implies (i): if $\mathfrak{M}$ is any model of $\mathsf{ZF} + \mathsf{AC}$, then $\mathfrak{M}$ can be extended to a model $\mathfrak{M}^*$ of $\mathsf{NB} + \mathsf{AC}$ just by adding predicative classes (see FRAENKEL–BAR-HILLEL–LÉVY–VAN DALEN [1973], pp. 131–132 for all details). $\mathfrak{M}$ and $\mathfrak{M}^*$ have the same "sets". Thus, Theorem 4.1 gives an extension $\mathfrak{N}$ of $\mathfrak{M}^*$ such that $\mathfrak{N} \models \mathsf{NB} + \mathsf{E}$ and such that $\mathfrak{N}$ and $\mathfrak{M}$ have the same "sets". If we interpret $\sigma$ by the global choice function which exists in $\mathfrak{N}$, it then follows, that every model $\mathfrak{M}$ of $\mathsf{ZF} + \mathsf{AC}$ can be expanded to a model of $\mathsf{ZF}_\sigma$ (without adding new sets). Thus (i) follows from (ii) in the same way as we proved Theorem 4.2, Q.E.D.

Theorem 4.2 and its two corollaries follow almost immediately from Theorem 4.1 which was proved by means of forcing. Gaifman obtained a forcing-free proof of Theorem 4.1 and obtained thereby an even stronger result. Gaifman's result is as follows:

(•) *Let $\mathfrak{M}$ be a model of* ZF + AC *such that the ordinals of $\mathfrak{M}$ are cofinal with $\omega$. Then $\mathfrak{M}$ can be expanded to a model $\mathfrak{N} = \langle \mathfrak{M}, F \rangle$ of* ZF$_\sigma$.

In fact, let $\mathfrak{M}$ be a given model of ZF + AC such that there is a countable increasing sequence of ordinals $\alpha_n$ (of $\mathfrak{M}$) with the property that every ordinal in the sense of $\mathfrak{M}$ is less than some $\alpha_n$. Notice that $\mathfrak{M}$ need not be countable! Denote the $\mathfrak{M}$-set of those sets of $\mathfrak{M}$ whose ranks are less than $\gamma$ by $V_\gamma^{\mathfrak{M}}$. Construct a tree $T$ such that the $n^{\text{th}}$ level of $T$ consists of all linear orderings of some $V_\gamma^{\mathfrak{M}}$ for $\gamma \geq \alpha_n$ which are in $\mathfrak{M}$ and which are inside $\mathfrak{M}$ well orderings of $V_{\alpha_n}^{\mathfrak{M}}$. Put $W_1 \trianglelefteq W_2$ iff $W_1$ is an initial segment of $W_2$. Thus $\langle T, \trianglelefteq \rangle$ is a tree. Let $\mathscr{L}_{\text{ZF}}^w$ be the language which results from $\mathscr{L}_{\text{ZF}}$ by adding a binary predicate $w(,)$. In a structure $\langle V_\alpha, W \rangle$, where $W \in T$, the predicate $w$ is interpreted by the ordering relation $W$. Let $\langle V_\alpha^{\mathfrak{M}}, W_1 \rangle <_n \langle V_\beta^{\mathfrak{M}}, W_2 \rangle$ mean that $\langle V_\alpha^{\mathfrak{M}}, W_1 \rangle$ is an $n$-elementary substructure of $\langle V_\beta^{\mathfrak{M}}, W_2 \rangle$, i.e. $\langle V_\alpha^{\mathfrak{M}}, W_1 \rangle \models \Phi$ iff $\langle V_\beta^{\mathfrak{M}}, W_2 \rangle \models \Phi$ for all sentences $\Phi \in \mathscr{L}_{\text{ZF}}^w$ in prenex form containing names for elements of $V_\alpha^{\mathfrak{M}}$ such that $\Phi$ contains at most $n$ alternating blocks of quantifiers. Using reflection inside $\mathfrak{M}$ one can prove the existence of a branch $W_0 < W_1 \triangleleft \cdots \triangleleft W_n \triangleleft \cdots$ in the tree $\langle T, \trianglelefteq \rangle$ such that inside $\mathfrak{M}$, $W_n$ is a well ordering of $V_{\gamma_n}^{\mathfrak{M}}$ and $\langle V_{\gamma_n}^{\mathfrak{M}}, W_n \rangle <_n \langle V_{\gamma_{n+1}}^{\mathfrak{M}}, W_{n+1} \rangle$ for all $n \in \omega$. Since $\langle \alpha_n ; n \in \omega \rangle$ is cofinal in the $\mathfrak{M}$-class of all ordinals, the union over all these $V_{\gamma_n}^{\mathfrak{M}}$ is equal to the universe of $\mathfrak{M}$ and $W = \cup \{ W_n ; n \in \omega \}$ is a well ordering of the universe of $\mathfrak{M}$. Thus $\mathscr{L}_{\text{ZF}}^\sigma$ can be interpreted in $\langle \mathfrak{M}, W \rangle$. Using the relation $<_n$ one can show that $\langle \mathfrak{M}, W \rangle$ is a model of ZF$_\sigma$, Q.E.D.

*An open problem.* Mostowski has shown that ZF $\vdash \Phi$ iff NB $\vdash \Phi$ for all ZF-sentences $\Phi$. SHOENFIELD [1954] showed that there is a primitive recursive function $f$ such that, if $p$ is the Gödel number of a proof of $\Phi$ in NB then $f(p)$ is the Gödel number of a proof of $\Phi$ in ZF (see also DOETS [1969] and FLANNAGAN [1975]). It is not known whether a similar result holds for NB + E and ZF + AC.

In closing this section we mention that Theorems 4.1 and 4.2 also hold for the impredicative theory of classes M of Wang and Morse (sometimes also called Morse–Kelley set theory). The language $\mathscr{L}_M$ has $\in$ and only one sort of variables: capital letters $X, Y, Z, \ldots$ which range over classes. The axioms of M are extensionality, empty set, pairs, union, power set, replacement, infinity, foundation, and the class-existence schema (i.e. Axioms I–VII and VIII$_\Phi$ in MAREK [1973]). In 1970, the author proved the following result (see MAREK [1973], p. 10):

($\diamond$)    *Every countable model $\mathfrak{M}$ of M + AC can be extended to a*
    *countable model $\mathfrak{N}$ of M + E such that $\mathfrak{M}$ and $\mathfrak{N}$ have the*
    *same "sets".*

As a corollary we obtain:

($\diamond\diamond$)    *If $\Phi$ is any ZF-sentence, then* M + AC $\vdash \Phi$ *iff* M + E $\vdash \Phi$.

This can be proved in a quite similar way as we have proved Theorems 4.1 and 4.2. In order to prove ($\diamond$), define the class of conditions to consist of all local choice functions $f$ which are in $\mathfrak{M}$ and obtain a generic filter $G$. Using techniques developed by CHUAQUI [1972], one shows that $G$ is strongly generic and that hence the resulting extension is a model of M + E. We refer to MAREK–ZBIERSKI [1972] for a discussion of further axioms of choice in M.

## 5. Axioms of choice in set theory with atoms

It is the aim of this section to discuss the question of whether the results obtained in §4 remain true if we drop the axiom of foundation. We shall discuss for example whether $ZF_\sigma^0$ is a conservative extension of $ZF^0$ + AC or not.

The axiom of extensionality excludes the existence of urelements, i.e. objects $u$ such that $u \neq \emptyset$ and $\forall x \, (x \notin u)$. The axiom of foundation $\forall x \, [x \neq \emptyset \rightarrow \exists y \in x (x \cap y = \emptyset)]$ excludes the existence of ungrounded sets like reflexive sets $x = \{x\}$. If $\mathfrak{U}$ is a set of urelements, then define by induction

$$R(\alpha,\mathfrak{U}) = \mathfrak{U} \cup P(\bigcup_{\beta < \alpha} R(\beta,\mathfrak{U})),$$

where $\alpha$ is an ordinal number. The assumption that $\bigcup \{R(\alpha,\mathfrak{U}); \alpha$ is an ordinal$\}$ is equal to the universe $V$ of all sets, corresponds to our intuitive understanding of the notion of set: the universe of sets is built up in stages $R(\alpha,\mathfrak{U})$ and every set is well founded relative to the given class $\mathfrak{U}$ of urelements. The urelements correspond to what Cantor called "Objekte der Anschauung". Urelements appear as soon as we use our set-theoretical formalism in connection with the axioms of some other field of science, e.g. in connection with the axioms for euclidean geometry. In the latter case the "points" are to be considered as urelements since their set-theoretical nature is not specified.

In the case of the theories $ZF^0$ and $NB^0$ the situation is different. The existence of urelements is excluded but it is consistent with $ZF^0$ and $NB^0$ to assume the existence of ungrounded sets, e.g. sets $x$ such that

$x \ni x_1 \ni x_2 \ni \cdots \ni x_n \ni \cdots$ (for all $n \in \omega$). The theories $\mathbf{ZF}^0$ and $\mathbf{NB}^0$ became important in connection with the Fraenkel–Mostowski–Specker method for obtaining independence results (see e.g. FELGNER [1971a], pp. 46–75). Even after the appearance of Cohen's forcing method, the method of Fraenkel–Mostowski–Specker remained of interest, since (i) the permutation models constructed by that method are much easier to handle than generic extensions, and (ii) independence results obtained by means of permutation models can be carried over in many cases to independence results for set theories including the axiom of foundation. This is accomplished by the Jech–Sochor–Pincus theorem (see JECH [1973], pp. 85–117).

If we now try to generalize the results of §4 to set theories not containing the axiom of foundation, then this is done, not only to see whether these results depend on the axiom of foundation or not, but also to overcome some fascinating combinatorial problems which arise in this connection. In doing so we hope to throw some more light on the results of §4.

Further, the axiom of foundation has also the flavour of choice, since by the axiom of foundation there is a function which selects subsets from classes. Hence the combinatorial power of various axioms of choice is best seen in the absence of foundation.

*First observation.* Statements $\Psi$ which are equivalent to $\mathbf{AC}$ or to $\mathbf{E}$ on the basis of the axioms of $\mathbf{ZF}$ or $\mathbf{NB}$ need not be equivalent to $\mathbf{AC}$ respectively to $\mathbf{E}$ on the basis of the weaker systems $\mathbf{ZF}^0$ and $\mathbf{NB}^0$. As an example consider:

Inj  (The injection principle): *Every set can be injected into every proper class.*

PW  *The power set of every well-orderable set is well orderable.*

It is proved in FELGNER–JECH [1973] that in $\mathbf{NB}^0$: Inj $\to$ AC $\to$ PW, while none of the converse implications is provable. In $\mathbf{NB}$, however, all these three statements are equivalent. Consider also:

N  (Von Neumann's axiom): *If $X$ is a proper class, then there is a one-to-one mapping from $X$ onto the class $V$ of all sets.*

Obviously in $\mathbf{NB}^0$: $\mathbf{N} \to$ "$V$ *is well orderable*" $\to \mathbf{E}$. We shall see below that in $\mathbf{NB}^0$ none of the converse implications are provable. However, in $\mathbf{NB}$ all these statements $\mathbf{N}$, $\mathbf{E}$, and "$V$ is well orderable" are equivalent.

This suggests that if we drop the axiom of foundation in Theorem 4.2, we must choose carefully between certain forms of local and global choice in order to obtain a true theorem.

LEMMA 5.1.   *In* $\mathbf{NB}^0$, $(\forall \alpha \ \mathbf{DCC}^\alpha) \Rightarrow \mathsf{Inj}$ *holds. The converse implication is not provable in* $\mathbf{NB}^0$.

PROOF.   First, we show that $\forall \alpha : \mathbf{DCC}^\alpha$ implies $\mathsf{Inj}$. Let $s$ be a set and $T$ a proper class. Since $\mathbf{DCC}^\alpha \Rightarrow \mathbf{DC}^\alpha$, it follows that $s$ can be well ordered. Let $\lambda$ be a cardinal such that $s = \{r_\beta ; \beta < \lambda\}$, where the $\beta$ are ordinals. Define a tree $D$ such that the $\beta^{\mathrm{th}}$-level of $D$ consists of all injections from $\{r_\gamma ; \gamma < \beta\}$ into $T$. Since the elements $f$ of $D$ are defined on initial segments of $s$, it is obvious that $D$ is a tree with respect to the inclusion relation $\subseteq$. By $\mathbf{DCC}^\lambda$ there is a chain $\langle f_\nu ; \nu < \lambda \rangle$ of length $\lambda$ in $\langle D, \subseteq \rangle$. Then $\cup \{f_\nu ; \nu < \lambda\}$ is the required injection from $s$ into $T$.

In order to show that $\mathsf{Inj}$ does not imply $\forall \alpha : \mathbf{DCC}^\alpha$ in $\mathbf{NB}^0$, we construct a Fraenkel–Mostowski–Specker model $\mathfrak{M}$ in which $\mathsf{Inj}$ holds, but $\mathbf{DCC}^\omega$ will fail in $\mathfrak{M}$. Let $\mathbf{On}$ be the class of all ordinals and let $\mathbf{On}^m$ be the class of all functions from $m$ into $\mathbf{On}$. Let $A$ be a proper class of atoms (reflexive sets $a = \{a\}$) which are indexed by the elements of $\cup \{\mathbf{On}^m ; 1 \leq m \in \omega\}$, $A = \{a_f ; \exists m \ (1 \leq m \ \& \ f \in \mathbf{On}^m)\}$. Define $a_f \lhd a_g \Leftrightarrow f \subset g$, then $\langle A, \trianglelefteq \rangle$ is a tree. If $B \subseteq A$, then $B$ is called a *small subtree*, if $B$ is a set such that $B$ contains no branch of length $\omega$ and $\forall x \in B \ \forall y \ [y \lhd x \Rightarrow y \in B]$ holds. Consider

$$G = \{\tau ; \tau \text{ is a permutation of a subset of } A \text{ which preserves } \trianglelefteq\}.$$

Let $\mathrm{dom}\,(\tau)$ be the domain of the permutation $\tau$. For $\tau \in G$ let $\hat{\tau}$ be the mapping[1] defined by $\hat{\tau}(x) = \tau(x)$ for $x \in \mathrm{dom}\,(\tau)$ and $\hat{\tau}(x) = x$ for $x \notin \mathrm{dom}\,(\tau)$, $x \in A$. A subgroup $H$ of $G$ is called *nice* if there is a small subtree $T$ of $\langle A, \trianglelefteq \rangle$ such that

$$H = \{\tau \in G ; \tau \text{ leaves } T \text{ pointwise fixed}\}.$$

For groups $H_1$ and $H_2$, let $H_1 \leq H_2$ mean that $H_1$ is a subgroup of $H_2$. Define

$$\mathscr{F} = \{H ; H \leq G \ \& \ \exists K \ [K \leq H \ \& \ K \text{ is a nice subgroup of } G]\}.$$

If $s$ is a subset of the class $A$, then define by transfinite induction $R_0(s) = s$, $R_\alpha(s) = \cup \{\mathbf{P}(R_\beta(s)); \beta < \alpha\}$. Since $a_f \in A$ implies $a_f = \{a_f\}$, it is obvious that $\beta < \alpha$ implies $R_\beta(s) \subseteq R_\alpha(s)$. Finally, we put $W(A) = \{x ; \exists s \subseteq A \ \exists \alpha \in \mathbf{On}[s \text{ is a set } \& \ x \in R_\alpha(s)]\}$. For $x \in W(A)$ let $TC(x) = \{x\} \cup x \cup \cup x \cup \cup(\cup x) \cup \cdots$ be the transitive closure of $x$. Following Mirimanoff, we call

$$\ker(x) = TC(x) \cap A$$

the kernel of the set $x \in W(A)$. We are now in the position to define the model $\mathfrak{M}$. Define

---

[1] Every $\hat{\tau}$ extends uniquely to an $\in$-automorphism of $W(A)$. This extension will be denoted again by $\hat{\tau}$.

$M = \{x \in W(A); \ker(x) \text{ is a small subtree of } \langle A, \trianglelefteq \rangle\}.$

We say that $x$ is a set of $\mathfrak{M}$ iff $x \in M$. We say that $X$ is a class of $\mathfrak{M}$ iff $X \subseteq M$ and there is a group $H \in \mathcal{F}$ such that $\hat{\tau}(y) \in X \Leftrightarrow y \in X$ for all $\tau \in H$. The membership relation of $\mathfrak{M}$ is the actual $\in$-relation. It is a matter of routine to show that $\mathfrak{M}$ is a model of $\mathbf{NB}^0$-set theory. The local axiom of choice $\mathbf{AC}$ holds in $\mathfrak{M}$, since for every set $x$ of $\mathfrak{M}$ the kernel $\ker(x)$ is a small subtree and all small subtrees $T$ have a well ordering in $\mathfrak{M}$ (see e.g. FELGNER [1971a], p. 75). Moreover, $\mathfrak{M}$ is a model of the injection principle Inj. $\langle A, \trianglelefteq \rangle$ is in $\mathfrak{M}$, but $\langle A, \trianglelefteq \rangle$ has no branch of length $\omega$ in $\mathfrak{M}$. Thus $\mathbf{DCC}^\omega$ fails in $\mathfrak{M}$. Lemma 5.1 is thus proved.

COROLLARY. $\mathbf{NB}^0 \vdash (\forall \alpha \, \mathbf{DCC}^\alpha) \Rightarrow \mathsf{Inj} \Rightarrow \mathbf{AC}$, $\mathbf{NB} \vdash \mathbf{AC} \Rightarrow (\forall \alpha \ \mathbf{DCC}^\alpha)$, but neither $\mathbf{AC} \Rightarrow \mathsf{Inj}$ nor $\mathsf{Inj} \Rightarrow (\forall \alpha \, \mathbf{DCC}^\alpha)$ are provable in $\mathbf{NB}^0$.

LEMMA 5.2.   The implication $\mathbf{E} \Rightarrow$ "$V$ is well orderable" is provable in $\mathbf{NB}$ but not in $\mathbf{NB}^0$.

PROOF.   In $\mathbf{NB}$ every set $x$ has a unique rank $\rho(x)$. By $\mathbf{E}$ there is a function $F$ such that for each ordinal $\alpha$, $F(\alpha)$ is a well ordering of $V_\alpha = \{x; \rho(x) < \alpha\}$. By the axiom of foundation $\cup \{V_\alpha; \alpha \in \mathbf{On}\} = V = \{x; x \text{ is a set}\}$ holds. It follows that

$$x \leq y \Leftrightarrow \rho(x) < \rho(y) \quad \text{or} \quad [\rho(x) = \rho(y) \wedge \langle x, y \rangle \in F(\rho(x))]$$

is a well ordering on $V$.

We now prove that $\mathbf{E}$ does not imply on the basis of the axioms of $\mathbf{NB}^0$ that the universe of sets can be well ordered. Let $A$ be a countably infinite set of reflexive sets, $A = \{a_r; r \in \mathbf{Q}\}$, indexed by the set $\mathbf{Q}$ of all rational numbers. If $\leq$ denotes the usual linear ordering of $\mathbf{Q}$, then put $a_r \lhd a_s \Leftrightarrow r < s$ (for $r, s \in \mathbf{Q}$). Define

$$R_0(A) = A,$$

and
$$R_\alpha(A) = \cup \{\mathbf{P}(R_\beta(A)); \beta < \alpha\}$$

$$W(A) = \cup \{R_\alpha(A); \alpha \in \mathbf{On}\}.$$

Let $G$ be the group of all permutations of $A$ (i.e. one-to-one mappings from $A$ onto $A$) which preserve the linear ordering $\trianglelefteq$. If $H$ is a subgroup of $G$, then $H$ is called a finite-support subgroup, if there is a finite subset $e$ of $A$ such that $H = \{\tau \in G; \tau \text{ leaves } e \text{ pointwise fixed}\}$. Let $\mathcal{F}$ be the filter of subgroups such that the set of all finite-support subgroups is a filter base of $\mathcal{F}$. Again let $TC(x)$ be the transitive closure of $x$ and $\ker(x) = A \cap TC(x)$ be the kernel of $x$. Put $M = \{x \in W(A); \ker(x) \text{ is finite}\}$. The elements of $M$ are the "sets" of $\mathfrak{M}$. A class $X$ is called a "class of $\mathfrak{M}$" iff $X \subseteq M$ and

$$\exists H \in \mathcal{F} \, \forall y \in X \, \forall \tau \in H \, [y \in X \Leftrightarrow \tau(y) \in H].$$

The epsilon relation is interpreted in $\mathfrak{M}$ by the usual $\in$-relation. The standard arguments show that $\mathfrak{M}$ is a model of $\mathbf{NB}^0$. Since $A$ is a proper class in $\mathfrak{M}$ and there is no well ordering of $A$ in $\mathfrak{M}$, it follows that the universe of sets has no well ordering in $\mathfrak{M}$. It remains to show that $\mathfrak{M}$ is a model of the global axiom of choice.

Let $\mathbf{Q} = \{r_n ; n \in \omega\}$ be the standard enumeration of $\mathbf{Q}$ and define:

$$M_n = \{x \in M ; \ker (x) = \{a_{r_0}, a_{r_1}, \ldots, a_{r_{n-1}}\}\},$$
$$M_n^* = \{x \in M ; \ker (x) \text{ has cardinality } n\}.$$

$M_n$ and $M_n^*$ are both classes of $\mathfrak{M}$ and $M_n^* = \{\tau(x); x \in M_n, \tau \in G\}$. Since we assume that the model $\mathfrak{M}$ is constructed within a universe of sets which is well ordered, it follows that for each particular $n$ there is a well ordering $\Gamma_n$ of $M_n$ in $\mathfrak{M}$. Since $\trianglelefteq$ is preserved by all $\tau \in G$, it follows that $\trianglelefteq$ is in $\mathfrak{M}$. Let $S(A)$ be the class of all finite subsets of $A$ and let $L$ be the lexicographic linear ordering on $S(A)$. Both $S(A)$ and $L$ are classes of $\mathfrak{M}$. For $x \in M_n^*$, $y \in M_n^*$, $x \neq y$ define

$$x \underset{n}{\leq} y \Leftrightarrow \begin{cases} \ker (x) \neq \ker (y) \ \& \ \langle \ker (x), \ker (y) \rangle \in L, & \text{or} \\ \ker (x) = \ker (y) \ \& \ \exists \tau \in G \ [\tau(x) \in M_n \ \& \ \langle \tau(x), \tau(y) \rangle \in \Gamma_n]. \end{cases}$$

It follows that $<_n$ is a linear ordering on $M_n^*$ and that $<_n$ is in the model $\mathfrak{M}$. Let $<$ be the union of the relations $<_n$ (for $n \in \omega$). Since $<$ is $\mathscr{F}$-symmetric, it is in $\mathfrak{M}$. A global choice function $F$ can now be defined in $\mathfrak{M}$ by the stipulation

$$F(x) = \min \{y ; y \in x\},$$

where the minimum is meant in the sense of $\trianglelefteq$. Note that if $x$ is a set of $\mathfrak{M}$, $y \in x$, then $\ker (y) \subseteq \ker (x)$ and $\trianglelefteq$ induces a well ordering on $\{z \in M ; \ker (z) \subseteq \ker (x)\}$. Thus $F(x)$ is well defined and Lemma 5.2 is thus proved.

LEMMA 5.3. *The implication "$V$ is well orderable" $\Rightarrow \mathbf{N}$ is provable in* $\mathbf{NB}$ *but not in* $\mathbf{NB}^0$.

PROOF. Let $\dot{W}$ be a well ordering of $V$ and define a new ordering $\leq$ on $V$ by the stipulation

$$x < y \Leftrightarrow [\rho(x) < \rho(y) \lor (\rho(x) = \rho(y) \land \langle x,y \rangle \in W)],$$

where $\rho(x)$ is the rank of $x$. Thus in the presence of the axiom of foundation, $V$ has a well ordering which is isomorphic with the class of all ordinals. From this von Neumann's axiom $\mathbf{N}$ readily follows.

In order to see that $\mathbf{N}$ is not implied by the statement that $V$ is well orderable in $\mathbf{NB}^0$, one simply produces a model $\mathfrak{M}$ of $\mathbf{NB}^0$ whose universe of sets is well ordered such that $\mathfrak{M}$ contains a class $A$ of reflexive sets such that in the metalanguage card $(\mathbf{On}^{\mathfrak{M}}) <$ card $(A)$, where $\mathbf{On}^{\mathfrak{M}}$ is the $\mathfrak{M}$-class of all ordinals of $\mathfrak{M}$, Q.E.D.

We now return to our question of whether we can find a theorem like Theorem 4.2 which concerns set theories not containing the axiom of foundation. The proof of Theorem 4.1, as it is given in §4, immediately gives the following result: Every countable model $\mathfrak{M}$ of $\mathsf{NB}^0 + \forall\alpha : \mathsf{DCC}^\alpha$ can be extended to a model $\mathfrak{N}$ of $\mathsf{NB}^0 + \mathsf{E}$ such that both $\mathfrak{M}$ and $\mathfrak{N}$ have the same sets. In fact it was for the sake of this result that we have introduced the axioms $\mathsf{DCC}^\alpha$ and have presented the proof of Theorem 4.1 using these axioms $\mathsf{DCC}^\alpha$. Hence $\mathsf{NB}^0 + \mathsf{E} \vdash \Phi$ implies $\mathsf{NB}^0 + \forall\alpha : \mathsf{DCC}^\alpha \vdash \Phi$ for every $\mathsf{ZF}$-sentence $\Phi$. But $\mathsf{NB}^0 + \mathsf{E}$ is not an extension of the theory $\mathsf{NB}^0 + \forall\alpha : \mathsf{DCC}^\alpha$ (in fact the model constructed in the proof of Lemma 5.2 satisfies $\mathsf{E}$ but not $\mathsf{Inj}$ and in particular not $\mathsf{DCC}^\omega$). Flannagan suggested that if one uses well orderings instead of choice functions as conditions in the proof of Theorem 4.1, one would get models of $\mathsf{NB}^0 + \mathsf{N}$. Hence

THEOREM 5.1. $\mathsf{NB}^0 + \mathsf{N}$ *is a conservative extension of* $\mathsf{NB}^0 + \forall\alpha : \mathsf{DCC}^\alpha$ *with respect to* $\mathsf{ZF}$*-sentences.*

PROOF. Let $\Phi$ be a $\mathsf{ZF}$-sentence such that $\mathsf{NB}^0 + \mathsf{N} \vdash \Phi$ and suppose that $\Phi$ is not provable in $\mathsf{NB}^0 + \forall\alpha : \mathsf{DCC}^\alpha$. Then $\mathsf{NB}^0 + \forall\alpha : \mathsf{DCC}^\alpha + \rightarrow \Phi$ is consistent and has a countable model $\mathfrak{M}$. Use a forcing language $\mathfrak{L}^w$ which is the same as the language $\mathfrak{L}^F$ used in the proof of Theorem 4.1 but contains a binary predicate $W(-,-)$ instead of the unary predicate $F(-)$. If $R$ is a set of ordered pairs, then $\mathrm{Pr}_1(R) = \{x ; \exists y : \langle x,y \rangle \in R\}$, $\mathrm{Pr}_2(R) = \{y ; \exists x : \langle x,y \rangle \in R\}$, and $\mathrm{Fd}(R) = \mathrm{Pr}_1(R) \cup \mathrm{Pr}_2(R)$ is called the *field* of $R$. We say that $p$ is a condition if $p$ is, in $\mathfrak{M}$, a well-ordering relation on its field. If $p$ and $q$ are conditions, then we say that $q$ extends $p$ iff the well ordering $p$ is an initial segment of the well ordering $q$. Now obtain a complete sequence of conditions and define the extension $\mathfrak{N}$ similarly as in the proof of Theorem 4.1. It turns out that $\mathfrak{N}$ is a model of $\mathsf{NB}^0 +$ "the universe of all sets has a well ordering such that all initial segments are sets". Thus $\mathfrak{N}$ satisfies von Neumann's axiom $\mathsf{N}$. Since $\Phi$ follows from $\mathsf{N}$ in $\mathsf{NB}^0$, $\mathfrak{N}$ is a model of $\Phi$. But $\mathfrak{M}$ satisfies $\rightarrow \Phi$. Since $\Phi$ speaks only about sets and $\mathfrak{M}$ and $\mathfrak{N}$ have the same sets, also $\mathfrak{N}$ must satisfy $\rightarrow \Phi$, a contradiction, Q.E.D.

REMARK. The proof of Theorem 5.1 shows that in some cases it is possible to apply Cohen's forcing method to models which do not satisfy the axiom of foundation. We do not know whether this is always possible. In the proof of Theorem 5.1, we succeeded in applying Cohen's forcing method, since no new sets had been added to the ground model $\mathfrak{M}$. We could thus define the extension $\mathfrak{N}$ without any $\in$-induction.

It is not known whether $\mathsf{NB}^0 + \mathsf{E}$ is a conservative extension of $\mathsf{NB}^0 + \mathsf{AC}$ with respect to $\mathsf{ZF}$-sentences, or similarly, whether $\mathsf{ZF}_\sigma^0$ is a conservative extension of $\mathsf{ZF}^0 + \mathsf{AC}$. This question was raised independently by Flannagan in his thesis and by GRISHIN [1972]. However, it was proved independently by GRISHIN [1972] and simultaneously by us that $\mathsf{ZF}_\epsilon^0$ is not a conservative extension of $\mathsf{ZF}^0 + \mathsf{AC}$.

LEMMA 5.4.    *There is a $\mathsf{ZF}$-sentence $\Phi$ such that $\Phi$ is provable in $\mathsf{ZF}_\epsilon^0$, but $\Phi$ is not provable in $\mathsf{ZF}^0 + \mathsf{AC}$.*

PROOF.    We call a set $x$ an $n$-cycle if there are sets $y_1, y_2, \ldots, y_n$ such that $x = y_1 \in y_2 \in y_3 \in \cdots \in y_{n-1} \in y_n \in x$ and $y_i$ is the only element of $y_{i+1}$ (for all $1 \le i < n$) and $y_n$ is the only element of $x$. Now let $\Phi$ be the following sentence:

> *"If for every $n \in \omega$, $1 \le n$, there is an $n$-cyclic set, then there is a set $C$ such that $C$ contains precisely one $n$-cyclic set for each $1 \le n \in \omega$".*

If we apply the axiom schema of replacement

$$\forall x \, \exists! y \, \Psi(x,y) \to \forall a \, \exists b \, \forall y \, [y \in b \leftrightarrow \exists x \, (x \in a \wedge \Psi(x,y))]$$

to the formula $y = \epsilon_z$ ($z$ is an $x$-cyclic set), then for $a = \omega$ we obtain the choice set $b = C$ as required. Thus $\mathsf{ZF}_\epsilon^0 \vdash \Phi$.

It can be shown by means of permutation models that $\Phi$ is not provable in $\mathsf{ZF}^0 + \mathsf{AC}$. The consistency of the existence of $n$-cyclic sets with $\mathsf{NB}^0$ was shown by HÁJEK [1965], p. 109 and BOFFA [1968], [1968a]. Let $A_n$ be a countably infinite set of $n$-cyclic sets for each $1 \le n \in \omega$, and put $A = \cup \{A_n ; 1 \le n \in \omega\}$. Define $R_0(A) = A$,

$$R_\alpha(A) = \cup \{\mathsf{P}(R_\beta(A)); \beta < \alpha\}, \qquad W(A) = \cup \{R_\alpha(A); \alpha \in \mathbf{On}\}$$

and finally

$$M = \{x \in W(A); \ker(x) = A \cap TC(x) \text{ is finite}\}.$$

Let $G$ be the group of those permutations $\tau$ of $A$ which map $A_n$ onto $A_n$ (for all $1 \le n \in \omega$). A subgroup $H$ of $G$ is called a finite-support subgroup if there is a finite set $e \subseteq A$ such that $H = \{\tau \in G ; \tau$ leaves $e$ pointwise fixed$\}$. Let $\mathscr{F}$ be the filter of subgroups generated by the finite-support subgroups. A class $X$ is in the model $\mathfrak{M}$ if $X \subseteq M$ and

$$\exists H \in \mathscr{F} \, \forall y \in X \, \forall \tau \in H \, [y \in X \leftrightarrow \tau(y) \in X].$$

The elements of $M$ are called the sets of $\mathfrak{M}$. It is easily seen that $\mathfrak{M}$ is a model of $\mathsf{ZF}^0 + \mathsf{AC}$ such that $\mathfrak{M} \models \to \Phi$. Thus Lemma 5.4 is proved.

# References

ADDISON, J. W., HENKIN, L., and TARSKI, A. (Eds.) (1965) *The theory of models*. Proc. of the 1963 international symposium at Berkeley. North-Holland, Amsterdam. 494 pp. (2nd printing (1972), 509 pp.)

ADDISON, J. W. (1965a) *The method of alternating chains*, pp. 1–16. In ADDISON et al. (1965).

BARWISE, J. (1971) *Infinitary methods in the model theory of set theory*, pp. 53–56. In GANDY and YATES (1971).

BELL, J. L. and SLOMSON, A. (1969) *Models and ultraproducts: An introduction*. North-Holland, Amsterdam. 322 pp. (1st revised reprint (1971)).

BERNAYS, P. (1937–1954) A system of axiomatic set theory; I–VII. *J.S.L.* I: **2**, 65–77 (1937); II: **6**, 1–17 (1941); III: **7**, 65–89 (1942); IV: **7**, 133–145 (1942); V: **8**, 89–106 (1943); VI: **13**, 65–79 (1948); VII: **19**, 81–96 (1954). This volume.

BERNAYS, P. (1958) *Axiomatic set theory* (with a historical introduction by A. A. Fraenkel). North-Holland, Amsterdam. 226 pp. (2nd ed. (1968), 235 pp.).

BOFFA, M. (1968) Les ensembles extraordinaire. *Bull. Soc. Math. Belgique* **20**, 3–15.

BOFFA, M. (1968a) Elimination de cycles d'appartenance par permutation de l'univers. *C.R. Acad. Sci. Paris* **266**, 545–546.

BOFFA, M. (1971) Forcing and reflection. *Bull. Acad. Polon. Sc.* **19**, 181–183.

CHANG, C. C. and KEISLER, H. J. (1973) *Model theory*. North-Holland, Amsterdam, 550 pp.

CHUAQUI, R. (1972) Forcing for the impredicative theory of classes. *J.S.L.* **37**, 1–18.

COHEN, P. J. (1966) *Set theory and the continuum hypothesis*. Benjamin, New York, 160 pp.

COHEN, P. J. (1974). Models of set theory with more real numbers than ordinals. *J.S.L.* **39**, 579–583.

DOETS, H. C. (1969) Novak's result by Henkin's method. *Fund. Math.* **64**, 329–333.

EASTON, W. B. (1970) Powers of regular cardinals. *Ann. of Math. Logic* **1**, 139–178.

FEFERMAN, S. (1965) Some applications of the notions of forcing and generic sets. *Fund. Math.* **56**, 325–345. (Summary in ADDISON et al. (1965), pp. 89–95.)

FELGNER, U. (1971) Comparison of the axioms of local and universal choice. *Fund. Math.* **71**, 43–62.

FELGNER, U. (1971a) *Models of ZF-set theory*. Springer Lecture Notes in Mathematics, Vol. 223. Springer, Berlin, 173 pp.

FELGNER, U. and JECH, Th. J. (1973) Variants of the axiom of choice in set theory with atoms. *Fund. Math.* **79**, 79–85.

FLANNAGAN, T. B. (1976) A new finitary proof of a theorem of Mostowski. This volume.

FRAENKEL, A. A. (1922) Über den Begriff "definit" und die Unabhängigkeit des Auswahlaxioms. *Sitzungsberichte der Preuss. Akademie d. Wiss.*, Phys.–Math. Klasse, pp. 253–257.

FRAENKEL, A. A. (1937) Über eine abgeschwächte Fassung des Auswahlaxioms. *J.S.L.* **2**, 1–25.

FRAENKEL, A. A., BAR-HILLEL, Y., LÉVY, A. and DALEN, D. VAN (1973) *Foundations of set theory*. North-Holland, Amsterdam, 404 pp.

FRIEDMAN, H. (∞). Large models with countable height. *J.S.L.*, to appear.

GAIFMAN, H. (1968) Two results concerning extensions of models of set theory (abstract). *Notices A.M.S.* **15**, 947 pp.

GANDY, R. O. and YATES, C. E. M. (Eds.) (1971) *Logic colloquium '69*. Proceedings of the summer school and colloquium in mathematical logic, Manchester, August 1969. North-Holland, Amsterdam. 451 pp.

GÖDEL, K. (1938) The consistency of the axiom of choice and of the generalized continuum hypothesis. *Acad. U.S.A.* **24**, 556–567.

GÖDEL, K. (1939) Consistency proof for the generalized continuum hypothesis. *Ibid.* **25**, 220–224.

GÖDEL, K. (1940) *The consistency of the axiom of choice and of the generalized continuum hypothesis with the axioms of set theory*. Annals of Math. Studies, Vol. 3. Princeton University Press, Princeton, N.J., 66 pp. (7th printing (1966).)

GRIŠIN, V. N. (1972) The theory of Zermelo–Fraenkel sets with Hilbert $\epsilon$-terms. *Math. Notes Acad. Sci. U.S.S.R.* **12**, 779–783.

HÁJEK, P. (1965) Modelle der Mengenlehre in denen Mengen gegebener Gestalt existieren. *Zeitschr. f. math. Logik* **11**, 103–115.

JECH, TH. J. (1973) *The axiom of choice*. North-Holland, Amsterdam. 203 pp.

LÉVY, A. (1964) The interdependence of certain consequences of the axiom of choice. *Fund. Math.* **54**, 135–157.

MAREK, W. (1973) On the metamathematics of impredicative set theory. *Dissertationes Math.* Vol. 98. Warszaw.

MAREK, W. and ZBIERSKI, P. (1972) Axioms of choice in impredicative set theory. *Bull. Acad. Polon. Sci.* **20**, 255–258.

MENDELSON, E. (1956) The independence of a weak axiom of choice. *J.S.L.* **21**, 350–366.

MORRIS, D. B. (1970) Adding total indiscernibles to models of set theory. Dissertation, Wisconsin.

MOSTOWSKI, A. (1939) Über die Unabhängigkeit des Wohlordnungssatzes vom Ordnungsprinzip. *Fund. Math.* **32**, 201–252.

NEUMANN, J. VON (1928) Die Axiomatisierung der Mengenlehre. *Math. Zeitschr.* **27**, 669–752. Also in VON NEUMANN (1961), pp. 339–422.

NEUMANN, J. VON (1961) *Collected Works*. Vol. I. Pergamon, New York, 654 pp.

RUBIN, H. and RUBIN, J. E. (1963) *Equivalents of the axiom of choice*. North-Holland, Amsterdam, 134 pp. (2nd ed. (1970).)

SACKS, G. E. (1972) *Saturated model theory*. Benjamin, New York, 335 pp.

SHOENFIELD, J. R. (1954) A relative consistency proof. *J.S.L.* **19**, 21–28.

SHOENFIELD, J. R. (1967) *Mathematical logic.* Addison-Wesley, Reading, Mass. 344 pp.

SPECKER, E. (1957) Zur Axiomatik der Mengenlehre (Fundierungs- und Auswahlaxiom). *Zeitschr. f. math. Logik* **3**, 173–210.

TAKEUTI, G. and ZARING, W. M. (1973) *Axiomatic set theory.* Springer, Berlin. 238 pp.

TARSKI, A. (1948) Axiomatic and algebraic aspects of two theorems on sums of cardinals. *Fund. Math.* **35**, 79–104.

SETS AND CLASSES; On the work by Paul Bernays
© North-Holland Publishing Company (1976) pp. 257-275.

# A NEW FINITARY PROOF OF A THEOREM
# OF MOSTOWSKI

Timothy B. FLANNAGAN[1]

*Heidelberg, West Germany*

## 0. Historical introduction

In NOVAK [1948], [1951], it was shown that if $\mathfrak{C}$ is a consistent theory formalized in the first-order predicate calculus, and if $\mathfrak{C}'$ is a theory related to $\mathfrak{C}$ in much the same way as von Neumann–Bernays–Gödel set theory is related to Zermelo–Fraenkel set theory ZF, then $\mathfrak{C}'$ is also consistent. Novak's method was to construct a model of $\mathfrak{C}'$ within the formal syntax of $\mathfrak{C}$. In 1949 in a talk at Princeton, Mostowski showed by an elementary argument that Novak's proof could be adapted to prove the stronger result that $\mathfrak{C}'$ is a conservative extension of $\mathfrak{C}$. The argument is given in outline at the bottom of p. 112 of MOSTOWSKI [1951]. Later, ROSSER and WANG [1950] gave another proof of the same result using Mostowski's method. More recently, DOETS [1969] gave another proof by constructing a Henkin-type canonical model of $\mathfrak{C}'$. All these proofs have the property of being non-finitary, where "finitary" is taken in the sense of HILBERT and BERNAYS [1934], [1968], p. 32; but SHOENFIELD [1954], gave a finitary proof.

In §1 of this paper we give another finitary proof of this result. In fact, by slightly relaxing the usual definition of normality in the class comprehension schema (see A3, p. 259 below) we obtain a correspondingly stronger result than Mostowski's. The central idea in the proof is due to Shoenfield, viz, replacing abstraction terms by their definitions; but for the following reasons, our proof is slightly more natural and direct:

(1) We do not avoid bound-class variables in the manner of SHOEN-FIELD [1954] and we use ε-terms of the form $\epsilon XA$ for abstraction terms ($X$ being a class variable) since these are available anyway.

(2) Shoenfield's use of Hilbert and Bernays' method of proof of the first ε-theorem results in the unnecessary removal of bound individual (set) variables, and these must be restored.

[1] The author is grateful to the Alexander von Humboldt Stiftung for financial support.

257

(3) We do not introduce Hilbert's full $\epsilon$-calculus where the "subordination" of $\epsilon$-terms to other expressions may occur in logical axioms.

In §2 we give some applications of the metatheorem proved in §1, and in §3 we ask some questions and make some remarks.

## 1. The theories $\mathfrak{C}$ and $\mathfrak{C}''$

Let $\mathscr{L}$ be a first-order language determined by:

(i) a vocabulary $\mathscr{V}$ consisting of sets of function and predicate symbols of finite order,

(ii) a denumerably infinite set of *individual* variables $x_1, x_2, \ldots$, denoted syntactically by the letters $u, v, w, x, y, z$ with or without subscripts, and

(iii) logical constants $\rightarrow$, $\vee$, $\wedge$, $\rightarrow$, $\exists$, $\forall$ and = (identity).

$\mathfrak{C}$ is a theory formalized in $\mathscr{L}$ and $\mathfrak{C}''$ is a theory formalized in the language $\mathscr{L}''$ which is obtained from $\mathscr{L}$ by adding the two-place predicate $\eta$ (which must not be contained in $\mathscr{L}$) and a denumerably infinite set of *class* variables $X_1, X_2, \ldots$

The letters $U, V, W, X, Y, Z$, with or without subscripts, will be used syntactically to denote arbitrary class variables or individual variables. The letters $Q, Q'$ will denote either of the quantifiers $\exists$ or $\forall$.

Before defining $\mathfrak{C}''$, we define a slightly less restrictive notion of a "normal" formula than the one used in Wang [1949], Gödel [1940], and consequently in Shoenfield [1954].

We say that a formula $QXA$ of $\mathfrak{C}''$ is *immediately subordinate* to a formula $Q'YB$ of $\mathfrak{C}''$ if it occurs in $B$ and a free occurrence of $Y$ in $B$ occurs within an occurrence of $QXA$. We also say that $QXA$ is *subordinate* to $Q'YB$, if there is a finite sequence of formulas $F_1, F_2, \ldots, F_n$, with $n > 1$, such that $F_1$ is $Q'YB$, $F_n$ is $QXA$ and for each $i = 2, \ldots, n$, $F_i$ is immediately subordinate to $F_{i-1}$. The expression $F_1, \ldots, F_n$ is called a *subordination chain*.

A formula $QxA$ of $\mathfrak{C}''$ is called a (\*)-*formula*, if there is a formula $Q'YB$ and a subordination chain $F_1, \ldots, F_n$ ($n > 1$) such that $F_1$ is $QxA$ and $F_n$ is $Q'YB$. An $\mathscr{L}''$-formula (i.e. a formula of $\mathscr{L}''$) is called a (\*\*)-*formula*, if it is either a (\*)-formula or a formula of the form $QXA$. An $\mathscr{L}''$-formula $QxA$ is called *normal* if it is not a (\*)-formula.

The non-logical axioms of $\mathfrak{C}''$ are those of $\mathfrak{C}$ together with those $\mathscr{L}''$-formulas of the form:

A1      $\forall U, V\ (\forall x\ (x\ \eta\ U \leftrightarrow x\ \eta\ V) \rightarrow U = V)$

A2      $\forall U, V\ (U\ \eta\ V \rightarrow \exists x\ (x = U))$

A3      $\forall X_1 \cdots X_n \exists X \forall z (z \,\eta\, X \leftrightarrow F(z, X_1, \ldots, X_n))$,

where $\forall z (z \,\eta\, X \leftrightarrow F(z, X_1, \ldots, X_n))$ is normal in the sense above.

Showing that $\mathfrak{C}''$ is a conservative extension of $\mathfrak{C}$ clearly involves, *inter alia*, the elimination of class variables and instances of A1–A3 from deductions from $\mathfrak{C}''$ of an $\mathscr{L}$-formula $\theta$. The way in which it is done is similar to the method of proof in FLANNAGAN [1973] of Hilbert's first $\epsilon$-theorem in HILBERT and BERNAYS [1939]. The calculus used is a weakened form of the $\epsilon$-calculus of Hilbert and Bernays, called the $\epsilon*$-calculus. This is described in LEISENRING [1969]. Its axioms are the *proper* axioms of the $\epsilon$-calculus (see below). The effect of this is that our method is more discriminating than the method in SHOENFIELD [1954] in that it necessitates only the elimination of $(**)$-formulas from deductions from $\mathfrak{C}''$ of $\mathscr{L}$-formulas and does not involve the elimination of all bound variables.

## 2. The $\epsilon*$-calculus

Let $\mathscr{L}_\epsilon$ and $\mathscr{L}''_\epsilon$ be the $\epsilon$-languages obtained from $\mathscr{L}$ and $\mathscr{L}''$ respectively by adjoining Hibert's $\epsilon$-symbol. The well-formed expressions of $\mathscr{L}''_\epsilon$ (see ASSER [1957] or LEISENRING [1969]) include $\epsilon$-terms $\epsilon xA$, which we call *individual $\epsilon$-terms*, and $\epsilon YB$ (called *class $\epsilon$-terms*), where $A$ and $B$ are formulas of $\mathscr{L}''_\epsilon$. Of course the only $\epsilon$-terms in $\mathscr{L}_\epsilon$ are individual $\epsilon$-terms. The lowercase letters $r$, $s$, and $t$ denote arbitrary individual terms of $\mathscr{L}''_\epsilon$ (i.e. individual variables or $\epsilon$-terms) and $R$, $S$, and $T$ denote arbitrary terms of $\mathscr{L}''_\epsilon$.

Before defining the notion of a proper formula, we define the *skeleton* of a formula.

Let $A$ be a formula of $\mathscr{L}''_\epsilon$ and $t$ (resp. $T$) have maximal length amongst the individual $\epsilon$-terms (resp. the class $\epsilon$-terms) in $A$ which do not have a free variable bound by a quantifier in $A$. Replace $t$ (resp. $T$) by the first individual variable $x$ (resp. class variable $X$) which does not already appear in $A$. Repeating this procedure, we find after finitely many steps that no more $\epsilon$-terms can be replaced. The resulting formula $A^+$ is called the *skeleton* of $A$.

If $A^+$ is $\epsilon$-free (i.e. does not contain the $\epsilon$-symbol) we say that $A$ is *proper*. Otherwise we say it is *improper*. For example, if $A$ is the formula

$$\exists X (X \,\eta\, Y \wedge \epsilon z(z \,\eta\, Y) \,\eta\, \epsilon U(U \,\eta\, Y \vee U \,\eta\, \epsilon V(Y \,\eta\, V)))),$$

then $A^+$ has the form

$$\exists X (X \,\eta\, Y \wedge x \,\eta\, Z),$$

so $A$ is proper. If $A$ is the Q3₁-axiom (see below)

$$\to \exists x \; (x = Y \wedge x = \epsilon z(z \; \eta \; Y \vee z = x)) \to$$
$$\to (u = Y \wedge u = \epsilon z(z \; \eta \; Y \vee z = u)),$$

then $A^+$ has the form

$$\to \exists x \; (x = Y \wedge x = \epsilon z(z \; \eta \; Y \vee z = x)) \to \to (u = Y) \wedge u = v)),$$

so $A$ is improper.

We now define the $\epsilon *$-calculus for $\mathscr{L}''_\epsilon$ (which we abbreviate as $\epsilon *''$) as follows (see LEISENRING [1969], p. 66): its only rule of inference is Modus Ponens and its axioms are all the proper $\mathscr{L}''_\epsilon$-formulas which are instances of the following schemata:

(1) A certain list of tautologies called $P$-axioms:
(2) The quantification axioms:

| Q1 | $\forall X A \to \to \exists X \to A,$ |
|---|---|
| Q2 | $\to \forall X A \to \exists X \to A,$ |
| Q3₁ | $\to \exists x A \to \to A(t),$ |
| Q3₂ | $\to \exists X A \to \to A(T),$ |
| Q4 | $\exists X A \to A(\epsilon X A).$ |

(3) The identity axioms:

| E1 | $S = T \wedge [A]^X_S \to [A]^X_T,$ |
|---|---|
| E2 | $T = T.$ |

As usual, $[A]^X_S$ denotes the result of replacing every free occurrence of $X$ in $A$ by $S$.

In axiom schema E1, $A$ is required to be an atom (i.e. a formula of the form $S_1 \eta \; T_1$ or $S_1 = T_1$) in which $X$ does not appear free within the scope of an $\epsilon$-symbol.

A deduction in the $\epsilon *$-calculus is defined in the obvious way and is called an $\epsilon *$-deduction.

REMARKS. (1) Instances of Ackermann's schema

$$\forall Z([A]^X_Z \leftrightarrow [B]^Y_Z) \to \epsilon X A = \epsilon Y B$$

are not included in $\epsilon *''$.

(2) The axioms of the $\epsilon *$-calculus for $\mathscr{L}_\epsilon$ (which we call $\epsilon *_0$) are just the axioms of $\epsilon *''$ which contain no class variables. For example, it is only Q3- and Q4-axioms are proper axioms of the form $\to \exists x A \to \to A(t)$ and $\exists x A \to A(\epsilon x A)$ respectively.

(3) In view of axiom A1 of $\mathfrak{C}''$, it is clear that in a deduction in $\epsilon *''$ of a

formula $A$ from $\mathfrak{C}''$, E3-axioms are redundant, but this fact is not used in the sequel.

The axioms of the predicate calculus for $\mathcal{L}''$ (which we call $\mathsf{PC}''$) are just the $\epsilon$-free axioms of $\epsilon *''$ and its rules of inference are:

(i) Modus Ponens,

(ii) the $\exists$-rule: from $A(x) \to B$ infer $\exists x\, A \to B$ provided $x$ does not occur free in $B$; and from $A(X) \to B$ infer $\exists X\, A \to B$ provided $X$ does not occur free in $B$.

The axioms and rules of the predicate calculus for $\mathcal{L}$ (which we call $\mathsf{PC}_0$) are defined in the obvious way. We write $\mathfrak{A} \vdash_{\mathsf{PC}_0} A$, $\mathfrak{A} \vdash_{\mathsf{PC}''} A$, $\mathfrak{A} \vdash_{\epsilon *_0} A$, $\mathfrak{A} \vdash_{\epsilon *''} A$ to denote that there is a deduction of $A$ from $\mathfrak{A}$ in $\mathsf{PC}_0$, $\mathsf{PC}''$, $\epsilon *_0$, $\epsilon *''$ respectively. As usual, $\emptyset \vdash_{\mathsf{PC}_0} A$, $\emptyset \vdash_{\mathsf{PC}''} A$ etc. mean that $A$ is derivable just from the logical axioms and rules of $\mathsf{PC}_0$, $\mathsf{PC}''$ etc.

Our aim in this section is to prove the following metatheorem:

METATHEOREM 2.1.    *There is a finitary proof that $\mathfrak{C}''$ is a conservative extension of $\mathfrak{C}$. That is, if $\theta$ is an $\mathcal{L}$-formula and $\mathfrak{C}'' \vdash_{\mathsf{PC}''} \theta$, then $\mathfrak{C} \vdash_{\mathsf{PC}_0} \theta$.*

## 3. $(\epsilon *, r, T_r)$-deductions

As a measure of the degree of subordination of formulas to other formulas, we need the following notion of the *rank* of an $\mathcal{L}''$-formula $QXA$, $\mathrm{rk}\,(QXA)$:

$$\mathrm{rk}\,(QXA) = \begin{cases} 1 & \text{if there is no formula } Q'YB \text{ subordinate to it.} \\ 1 + \text{the maximal rank of the formulas } Q'YB \text{ which} \\ \text{are subordinate to it} & \text{if there is such a formula.} \end{cases}$$

Let $\mathcal{D}$ be a deduction in $\epsilon *''$.[1] If the axiom $\exists X\, A \to A(\epsilon XA)$ or $\to \exists X\, A \to \to A(T)$ for some term $T$ is used as a logical axiom in $\mathcal{D}$, then $\exists X\, A$ will be called a *class-Q-formula* in $\mathcal{D}$. Similarly, if a $(*)$-formula $\exists y\, B$ is the specified existential formula in the antecedent of a Q3- or Q4-axiom in $\mathcal{D}$, then it will be called a $(*)$-Q-formula in $\mathcal{D}$. Of course, a $(**)$-Q-formula in $\mathcal{D}$ is either a class-Q-formula or a $(*)$-Q-formula. (See p. 258 above for the definition of a $(**)$-formula.)

If all the $(**)$-Q-formulas in $\mathcal{D}$ have rank $\leq r$, then $\mathcal{D}$ will be called an $(\epsilon *, r)$-*deduction*. If in addition, all the $(**)$-Q-formulas in $\mathcal{D}$ are in some finite set $T_r$ of $(**)$-formulas of rank $r$, then $\mathcal{D}$ will be called an $(\epsilon *, r, T_r)$-*deduction*.

We write $\mathfrak{A} \vdash^r A$ and $\mathfrak{A} \vdash^{r, T_r} A$ to denote respectively that there is an $(\epsilon *, r)$-deduction and an $(\epsilon *, r, T_r)$-deduction of $A$ from $\mathfrak{A}$.

Since every class-Q-formula has rank $\geq 1$ and every $(*)$-Q-formula has

---

[1] Note that a deduction in $\epsilon *_0$ is trivially a deduction in $\epsilon *''$.

rank $\geq 2$, it is clear that an $(\epsilon*,1)$-deduction contains no $(*)$-Q-formulas—that its only $(**)$-Q-formulas are class-Q-formulas. It is also clear that an $(\epsilon*,1,\emptyset)$-deduction is an $(\epsilon*,0)$-deduction which in turn contains no $(**)$-Q-formulas, although it might well contain Q3- or Q4-axioms of the form $\rightarrow \exists x A \rightarrow \rightarrow A(t)$ or $\exists x A \rightarrow A(\epsilon x A)$, where $\exists x A$ is normal in the sense of p. 258 above.

The proof of Metatheorem 2.1 involves the replacement of certain formulas by other formulas and $\epsilon$-terms by other terms, so we rely heavily on the following lemmata:

LEMMA 3.1.   *The following properties of the rank function are all trivial consequences of its definition and the notion of subordination:*

R1.   *If* $QXA$ *is subordinate to* $Q'YB$, *then*  $\mathrm{rk}\,(QXA) < \mathrm{rk}\,(Q'YB)$.

R2.   *If* $QXA'$ *is obtained from* $QXA$ *by replacing every occurrence of some $\epsilon$-term $T$ by some other term, then*  $\mathrm{rk}\,(QXA') = \mathrm{rk}\,(QXA)$.

R3.   *If $X$ is any variable which appears free in $QYB$ and $T$ is any term, then*  $\mathrm{rk}\,(QY\,[B]_T{}^X) = \mathrm{rk}\,(QYB)$.

R4.   $\mathrm{rk}\,(QXA) = \mathrm{rk}\,(QX \rightarrow A)$.

R5.   *If*  $\mathrm{rk}\,(QXA) \geq \mathrm{rk}\,(Q'YB)$  *and if*  $QXA$  *is not*  $Q'YB$, *and if* $*$ *denotes the operation of replacing every occurrence of $QXA$ in $Q'YB$ by*  $\mathrm{rk}\,(Q'\,YB)$. *This apparently motiveless statement is used in Lemma 3.7 below.*

LEMMA 3.2 (cf. LEISENRING [1969], Theorem III.1).   *If A is an axiom of $\epsilon*''$ other than a Q4-axiom and if A' is obtained from A by replacing every occurrence of some individual $\epsilon$-term (resp. class $\epsilon$-term) by some other individual term (resp. term), then A' is an axiom of $\epsilon*''$ of the same form as A.*

PROOF.   The lemma is trivial if $A$ is a P-, Q1-, Q2-, E1- or E3-axiom. Notice that the restriction on E1-axioms is used here. Suppose that $A$ is a $Q3_1$-axiom. Clearly, the only way in which $A$ can be damaged by the replacement of an $\epsilon$-term $T$ by another term $S$, i.e. converted into a formula which is no longer a $Q3_1$-axiom, is if it has the form

$$\rightarrow \exists x\, (\cdots \epsilon YB(Y,x) \cdots) \rightarrow \rightarrow (\cdots \epsilon YB(Y,t) \cdots)$$

where $T$ is either $\epsilon YB(Y,x)$ or $\epsilon YB(Y,t)$. However, in this case an $\epsilon$-term will appear in the antecedent of the skeleton of $A$, contrary to the assumption that $A$ is proper. A similar argument holds if $A$ is a $Q3_2$- or $Q4$-axiom, Q.E.D.

LEMMA 3.3 (cf. LEISENRING [1969], Theorem III.3).    *Let $\mathfrak{A} \cup \{A\}$ be any collection of $\mathscr{L}$-formulas. If there is a deduction of $A$ from $\mathfrak{A}$ in $\epsilon *_0$, then there is a deduction of $A$ from $\mathfrak{A}$ in* $\mathsf{PC}_0$.

PROOF.    Let $\mathscr{D}$ be a deduction of $A$ from $\mathfrak{A}$ in $\epsilon *_0$. The proof is by induction on the number $n$ of $\epsilon$-terms in $\mathscr{D}$, all of which are individual $\epsilon$-terms. If $n = 0$, then $\mathscr{D}$ is already a deduction in $\mathsf{PC}_0$. Suppose $n > 0$. Let $\epsilon y B$ have minimal length amongst the $\epsilon$-terms in $\mathscr{D}$. Then no $\epsilon$-terms occur in $\epsilon y B$. Let $x$ be some individual variable which does not occur in $B$ or $A$ and let $\mathscr{D}'$ be the sequence of formulas obtained from $\mathscr{D}$ by replacing every occurrence of $\epsilon y B$ by $x$. If the axiom

(1)                           $\exists y\, B \to B(\epsilon y B)$

is not used in $\mathscr{D}$, then by Lemma 3.2 and since $A$ and $\mathfrak{A}$ are $\epsilon$-free, $\mathscr{D}'$ is a deduction of $A$ from $\mathfrak{A}$ in $\epsilon *_0$ in which only $n - 1$ $\epsilon$-terms are used. Hence, by the induction hypothesis, $\mathfrak{A} \vdash_{\mathsf{PC}_0} A$.

If (1) is used in $\mathscr{D}$, then $\mathscr{D}'$ is a deduction of $A$ from $\exists y\, B \to B(x)$ in $\epsilon *_0$ in which only $n - 1$ $\epsilon$-terms are used. Since the deduction theorem holds in full generality in the $\epsilon *$-calculus,[1] we can therefore find a deduction $\mathscr{D}''$ of

(2)                       $(\exists y\, B \to B(x)) \to A$

from $\mathfrak{A}$ in $\epsilon *_0$ which contains only $n - 1$ $\epsilon$-terms. Since (2) is $\epsilon$-free it follows from the induction hypothesis that $\mathfrak{A} \vdash_{\mathsf{PC}_0} (\exists y\, B \to B(x)) \to A$. Now $B(x) \to A$ follows tautologically from $(\exists y\, B \to B(x)) \to A$, so $\mathfrak{A} \vdash_{\mathsf{PC}_0} B(x) \to A$ and hence $\mathfrak{A} \vdash_{\mathsf{PC}_0} \exists y\, B \to A$ by an application of the $\exists$-rule. Now $A$ is a tautological consequence of $((\exists y\, B \to B(x)) \to A) \wedge (\exists y\, B \to A)$, so $\mathfrak{A} \vdash_{\mathsf{PC}_0} A$, Q.E.D.

LEMMA 3.4.    *Let $\mathfrak{A} \cup \{A\}$ be any collection of $\mathscr{L}''$-formulas and $\mathfrak{A}'$ be the collection of $\mathscr{L}''_\epsilon$-formulas which are substitution instances of the members of $\mathfrak{A}$ formed by allowing $\epsilon$-terms of $\mathscr{L}''_\epsilon$ in place of free variables. If $\mathfrak{A} \vdash_{\mathsf{PC}''} A$, then $\mathfrak{A}' \vdash_{\epsilon *''} A$. In particular, if the members of $\mathfrak{A}$ contain no free variables and if $\mathfrak{A} \vdash_{\mathsf{PC}''} A$, then $\mathfrak{A} \vdash_{\epsilon *''} A$.*

PROOF.    Let $\langle A_1, \ldots, A_n \rangle$, denoted by $\mathscr{D}$, be a deduction of $A$ from $\mathfrak{A}$ in $\mathsf{PC}''$. One shows by an elementary induction on $i$ that $\mathfrak{A}' \vdash_{\epsilon *''} A_i$.

LEMMA 3.5.    *Let $r \geq 1$ and $\exists Y\, B$ be a $(**)$-formula of rank $r$. Let $A$ be an axiom of $\epsilon *''$ and $'$ denote the operation of replacing every occurrence of $\exists Y\, B$ by $B(\epsilon Y B)$ and if $B$ has the form $\to C$, by simultaneously replacing*

---

[1] That is, if there is an $\epsilon *$-deduction of $B$ from $\mathfrak{A} \cup \{A\}$, then there is an $\epsilon *$-deduction of $A \to B$ from $\mathfrak{A}$.

*every occurrence of* $\forall Y C$ *by* $C(\epsilon YB)$. *Then:*

(i) *If A is a* P-, E1- *or* E3-*axiom, then A' is an axiom of the same form.*

(ii) *If A is a* Q1- *or* Q2-*axiom other than* $\forall Y C \rightarrow \rightarrow \exists Y \rightarrow C$ *or* $\rightarrow \forall Y C \rightarrow \exists Y \rightarrow C$, *then A' is an axiom of the same form.*

(iii) *If A is a* Q3$_1$-*axiom* $\rightarrow \exists x D \rightarrow \rightarrow D(t)$ *or a* Q4-*axiom* $\exists x D \rightarrow D(\epsilon x D)$, *where* $\exists x D$ *is normal, then A' is an axiom of the same form.*

(iv) *If A is a* Q3$_1$-*axiom* $\rightarrow \exists x D \rightarrow \rightarrow D(t)$ *or a* Q4-*axiom* $\exists x D \rightarrow D(\epsilon x D)$, *where* $\exists x D$ *has rank* $\leq r$ *and* $\exists x D$ *is not* $\exists Y B$, *then A' is an axiom of the same form. Furthermore, by rank property* R5, rk $(\exists x D) =$ rk $(\exists x D')$.

(v) *If A is a* Q3$_2$-*axiom* $\rightarrow \exists X D \rightarrow \rightarrow D(T)$ *or a* Q4-*axiom* $\exists X D \rightarrow D(\epsilon X D)$, *where* $\exists X D$ *has rank* $\leq r$ *and* $\exists X D$ *is not* $\exists Y B$, *then A' is an axiom of the same form and* rk $(\exists X D) =$ rk $(\exists X D')$.

PROOF.    Cases (i) and (ii) are trivial and the proofs of (iii)–(v) are similar to the proof of Lemma 3.2. We give only one example: Let $A$ be the Q3$_2$-axiom $\rightarrow \exists X D \rightarrow \rightarrow D(T)$ and suppose that $A'$ is not the Q3$_2$-axiom $\rightarrow \exists X D' \rightarrow \rightarrow D'(T')$. Clearly, one of the following cases must hold:

(1) $\exists Y B$ is $\exists X D$, but this is ruled out by the hypothesis of (v).

(2) $\exists Y B$ or $\forall Y C$ is immediately subordinate to $\exists X D$, in which case, e.g. $A$ has the form

(1) $\qquad \rightarrow \exists X (\cdots \exists Y H(Y,X) \cdots) \rightarrow \rightarrow (\cdots \exists Y H(Y,T) \cdots)$,

where $\exists Y H(Y,X)$ is $\exists Y B$, and $A'$ is

$\qquad \rightarrow \exists X (\cdots H(\epsilon YH(Y,X),X \cdots) \rightarrow \rightarrow (\cdots \exists Y H(Y,T) \cdots)$,

which is not a Q3$_2$-axiom.

(3) $\exists Y B$ or $\forall Y C$ has the form $Q Y H(Y,T)$, where $Q Y H(Y,X)$ is immediately subordinate to $\exists X D$. In this case, $A$ has the form (1) for example, and $A'$ has the form

$$\rightarrow \exists X (\cdots \exists Y H(Y,X) \cdots) \rightarrow$$
$$\rightarrow (\cdots H(\epsilon YH(Y,T),T) \cdots).$$

It follows immediately from the rank properties R1 and R3 that if either (2) or (3) holds, then rk $(\exists X D) > r$, contrary to assumption, Q.E.D.

LEMMA 3.6.    *If* $Q X_1 \cdots Q' X_n A$ *is any proper* $\mathscr{L}''_\epsilon$-*formula, then there are* $\epsilon$-*terms* $T_1, \ldots, T_n$ *such that*

(i) *for each* $i = 1 \cdots n$, $T_i$ *is an individual* $\epsilon$-*term if* $X_i$ *is an individual variable and a class* $\epsilon$-*term if* $X_i$ *is a class variable,*

(ii) $\emptyset \vdash_{\epsilon^{*''}} Q X_1 \cdots Q' x_n A \leftrightarrow [A]^{X_1 \cdots X_n}_{T_1 \cdots T_n}$.

PROOF. The proof is by repeated application of the well-known and easily-established facts that if $\exists Y B$ and $\forall Y C$ are proper, then

(1) $$\emptyset \vdash_{\epsilon *''} \exists Y B \leftrightarrow B(\epsilon Y B)$$

and

(2) $$\emptyset \vdash_{\epsilon *''} \forall Y C \leftrightarrow C(\epsilon Y \to C).$$

COROLLARY (Immediate). *If $A$ is any $\mathscr{L}''_{\epsilon}$-formula and $\mathfrak{S}'' \vdash_{\epsilon *''} A$, then $\mathfrak{S}* \vdash_{\epsilon *''} A$, where $\mathfrak{S}*$ is $\mathfrak{S}''$ with axioms* A1–A3 *replaced by*

A1* $\qquad \forall x\, (x \,\eta\, S \leftrightarrow x \,\eta\, T) \to S = T,$

A2* $\qquad S \,\eta\, T \to \exists x\, (x = S),$

A3* $\qquad \forall z\, (z \,\eta\, T^* \leftrightarrow F(z, T_1, \ldots, T_n)), \quad where\, T^*\, is$
$\qquad \epsilon X \,\forall z\, (z \,\eta\, X \leftrightarrow F(z, T_1, \ldots, T_n))\, for\, some\, variable\, X.$

We are now ready to prove the main lemmas in support of Metatheorem 2.1, but at this point we break off to briefly discuss the problems in proving it and to sketch the plan of the proof. Henceforth, $\theta$ will denote a fixed $\mathscr{L}$-formula with no free variables.

Consider an $\epsilon *$-deduction $\mathscr{D}$ of $\theta$ from $\mathfrak{S}*$. If $\mathscr{D}$ contains no instances of axiom A3*, then the problem is fairly trivial (see Lemma 3.9). Suppose $\mathscr{D}$ does contain instances of A3*. One's first inclination would probably be to replace every expression $s \,\eta\, T^*$ by $F(s)$ (see the definition of A3* above). This would be a perfectly safe procedure were it not for the fact that (and this is the central problem in the proof) $\mathscr{D}$ must be assumed to contain Q3$_2$-axioms

(1) $$\to \exists X A \to A(T^*).$$

To replace the formulas $s \,\eta\, T^*$ would clearly damage Q3$_2$-axioms of the form

$$\to \exists X\, (\cdots s \,\eta\, X \cdots) \to \to (\cdots s \,\eta\, T^* \cdots).$$

Now, this in itself is not a problem, for a manoeuvre similar to one used in the following lemma could overcome this difficulty if the only Q3$_2$-axioms in $\mathscr{D}$ of the form (1) are those in which $A$ is not of the form

(2) $$\cdots s_1 \,\eta\, X \cdots s_2 \,\eta\, X \cdots s_n \,\eta\, X \cdots,$$

where $n > 1$. Broadly speaking, the reason for this is as follows: Suppose that $A$ has the form (2) and $\exists X A$ has low rank. Replacing all formulas $s \,\eta\, T^*$ by $F(s)$ converts (1) into

(3) $$\to \exists X A \to \to (\cdots F(s_1) \cdots F(s_n) \cdots).$$

In the course of Lemma 3.7 we then want to replace some formula of the form $\exists Y B$ by $B(\epsilon YB)$, where $\exists Y B$ might have greater rank than $\exists X A$ but might nevertheless appear in one of the formulas $F(s_i)$, $i = 1 \cdots n$, say $F(s_1)$, and contain $s_1$. In this case, let us write $B$ as $B'(Y,s_1)$. In order to avoid damaging (3) beyond repair, we then need to replace not only $\exists Y B'(Y,s_1)$ by $B'(\epsilon YB'(Y,s_1),s_1)$, but for each $i = 2 \cdots n$, $\exists Y B'(Y,s_i)$ by $B'(\epsilon YB'(Y,s_i),s_i)$. However, this leads to complications which we are unable to overcome.

Hence, in order to replace all formulas $s \; \eta \; T^*$ by $F(s)$ we first need to eliminate all Q3$_2$-axioms from $\mathcal{D}$. The first step in this elimination is the replacement of certain formulas $\exists X A$ by $A(\epsilon x A)$. However, this procedure could damage Q3$_1$-axioms

(4)                         $\rightarrow \exists y B \rightarrow \rightarrow B(t)$,

for example, if $\exists X A$ is immediately subordinate to $\exists y B$ or if $\exists X A$ has the form $\exists X [H(X,y)]_i^y$, where $\exists X H(X,y)$ is immediately subordinate to $\exists y B$. But in this case, $\exists y B$ is a $(*)$-Q-formula.

Hence, we must not only eliminate all Q3$_2$-axioms, but all Q3$_1$-axioms (4) where $\exists y B$ is a $(*)$-formula. We do this in fact by eliminating all $(**)$-Q-formulas from $\mathcal{D}$. We start with those of maximal rank.

Once the above eliminations have been carried out, we replace $s \; \eta \; T^*$ by $F(s)$ etc. The rest is easy.

LEMMA 3.7.   *For any $r \geq 1$ and any finite set $T_r$ of $(**)$-formulas of rank $r$, if $\mathfrak{C}^* \vdash^{r,T_r} \theta$, then $\mathfrak{C}^* \vdash^{r,\emptyset} \theta$.*

PROOF.   Let $\langle A_1, \ldots, A_n \rangle$, denoted by $\mathcal{D}$, be an $(\epsilon *,r,T_r)$-deduction of $\theta$ from $\mathfrak{C}^*$. The proof is by induction on the number of $(**)$-formulas in $T_r$. If $n = 0$, $\mathcal{D}$ is already an $(\epsilon *,r,\emptyset)$-deduction. Suppose $n > 0$. Let $\exists Y B$ have maximal length amongst the $(**)$-formulas in $T_r$. Put $S_r = T_r - \{\exists Y B\}$. We show that $\mathfrak{C}^* \vdash^{r,S_r} \theta$ and then apply the induction hypothesis. The proof is exactly the same as if we had chosen a formula $\exists y B$ of maximal length amongst the $(**)$-formulas in $T_r$.

We may suppose that $\exists Y B$ is a $(**)$-Q-formula in $\mathcal{D}$, for otherwise $\mathcal{D}$ is already an $(\epsilon *,r,S_r)$-deduction.

Let $'$ denote the operation of replacing every occurrence of $\exists Y B$ by $B(\epsilon YB)$, and if $B$ has the form $\rightarrow C$, by simultaneously replacing every occurrence of $\forall Y C$ by $C(\epsilon YB)$.

The formula $\theta'$ is clearly $\theta$ since $\theta$ is an $\mathcal{L}$-formula and $\exists Y B$ and $\forall Y C$ contain class variables.

Since no member of $\mathfrak{C}^{*\,1}$ is a $(**)$-formula, and here we make essential use of the normality of instances of axiom schema A3$^*$, it is trivial to see that if $A_i$ is a member of $\mathfrak{C}^*$, then so is $A_i'$.

---

[1] By a member of $\mathfrak{C}^*$ we mean a non-logical axiom of $\mathfrak{C}^*$.

If $A_i$ is the Q1-axiom $\forall Y C \to \to \exists Y \to C$ or the Q2-axiom $\to \forall Y C \to$ $\exists Y \to C$ or the Q4-axiom $\exists Y B \to B(\epsilon Y B)$, then $A_i$ is clearly one of the tautologies

(1)
$$\begin{cases} C(\epsilon Y B) \to \to B(\epsilon Y B), \\ \to C(\epsilon Y B) \to B(\epsilon Y B), \\ B(\epsilon Y B) \to B(\epsilon Y B). \end{cases}$$

If $A_i$ is a $Q3_2$-axiom $\to \exists Y B \to \to B(T)$ for some term $T$, then $A'_i$ is

$$\to B(\epsilon Y B) \to \to B(T').$$

Since there are no (**)-Q-formulas in $\mathscr{D}$ of rank $> r$, it now follows from Lemma 3.5 by our choice of $\exists Y B$ with maximal rank that if $A_i$ is any other logical axiom in $\mathscr{D}$, then $A'_i$ is an axiom of the same form. If $A_i$ is a Q3- or Q4-axiom, then the rank of the specified existential formula $\exists X D$ in its antecedent is unaltered—in particular, if rk $(\exists X D) = r$ (i.e. $\exists X D$ is in $S_r$), then $\exists X D'$ is $\exists X D$— and we say that members of $S_r$ remain members of $S_r$.

Modus Ponens is clearly preserved under the operation $'$, that is, if $A_i$ follows by modus ponens from $A_j$ and $A_j \to A_i$ for some $j < i$, then $A'_i$ follows by modus ponens from $A'_j$ and $A'_j \to A'_i$. Hence, by augmenting $\langle A'_1, \ldots, A'_n \rangle$, call it $\mathscr{D}'$, with proofs of the tautologies (1), we find that for some terms $T_1 \cdots T_m$

(2)  $\mathfrak{C}^* \cup \{\to B(\epsilon Y B) \to \to B(T_1), \ldots, \to B(\epsilon Y B) \to \to B(T_m)\} \vdash^{r,S_r} \theta.$

We now have two cases to consider.

Case (i).  $C(\epsilon Y B)$ is a member of $\mathfrak{C}^*$. In this case, it is not an instance of A3* since such formulas have the form $D(\epsilon X D)$. Hence, $C(\epsilon Y B)$ must be an instance of A1* or A2*, in which case, the formulas $C(T_i)$, for $i = 1 \cdots m$ are also instances of A1* or A2*; so by virtue of the tautologies

$$C(T_i) \to \to B(\epsilon Y B) \to \to B(T_i)$$

it follows from (1) that $\mathfrak{C}^* \vdash^{r,S_r} \theta.$

Case (ii).  $C(\epsilon Y B)$ is not a member of $\mathfrak{C}^*$. In this case $\mathscr{D}$ must be allowed to contain Q3-axioms $\to \exists Y B \to \to B(T)$; that is, $m$ in (2) must be assumed to be $\geq 1$. We therefore proceed as follows: by (2) and the tautologies

$$\begin{cases} B(\epsilon Y B) \to \to B(\epsilon Y B) \to \to B(T_i) \\ \to B(T_i) \to B(\epsilon Y B) \to \to B(T_i) \end{cases}$$

we obtain

(3)                    $\mathfrak{C}^* \cup \{B(\epsilon Y B)\} \vdash^{r,S_r} \theta$

and

(4)                    $\mathfrak{C}^* \cup \{\rightarrow B(T_1), \ldots, \rightarrow B(T_m)\} \vdash^{r,S_r} \theta.$

Let $\mathscr{C}$ be an $(\epsilon *, r, S_r)$-deduction of $\theta$ from $\mathfrak{C}^* \cup \{B(\epsilon YB)\}$, and for each $i = 1 \cdots m$, let $\mathscr{C}_i$ be obtained from $\mathscr{C}$ by replacing every occurrence of $\epsilon YB$ by $T_i$. Let $''$ denote this operation. By Lemma 3.2 every logical axiom in $\mathscr{C}$ becomes under $''$ an axiom of the same form. Moreover, by rank property R2, the ranks of the $(**)$-Q-formulas are unaltered. In particular, by our choice of $\exists Y B$ with maximal length, $\epsilon YB$ cannot appear in any $(**)$-Q-formula in $\mathscr{C}$ of rank $r$. Hence, members of $S_r$ remain members of $S_r$.

If $\epsilon YB$ is a specified term in an instance $I$ of A1* or A2*, then clearly $I''$ is a formula of the same form. We suppose that $\epsilon YB$ is not the specified class term $T^*$ in an instance of A3* in $\mathscr{C}$, for otherwise $B(\epsilon YB)$ is an instance of A3* and by (3) the required result, namely, $\mathfrak{C}^* \vdash^{r,S_r} \theta$, would follow.

Modus ponens is clearly preserved under $''$, so for each $i = 1 \cdots m$ we obtain
$$\mathfrak{C}^* \cup \{B(T_i)\} \vdash^{r,S_r} \theta,$$

and finally, $\mathfrak{C}^* \vdash^{r,S_r} \theta$, Q.E.D.

LEMMA 3.8.    If $\mathfrak{C}^* \vdash^0 \theta$, then $\mathfrak{C}^*$-A3* $\vdash^0 \theta$.

PROOF.    Let $\langle A_1, \ldots, A_n \rangle$, called $\mathscr{D}$, be an $(\epsilon *, 0)$-deduction of $\theta$ from $\mathfrak{C}^*$ and suppose that for $i = 1 \cdots m$, the formulas

$M_i$:                    $\forall z_i \, (z_i \, \eta \, T_i^* \leftrightarrow F_i(z_i)),$

where $T_i^*$ is $\epsilon X_i \, \forall z_i \, (z_i \, \eta \, X_i \leftrightarrow F_i(z_i))$ are the instances of A3* used in $\mathscr{D}$. We systematically eliminate these formulas in a manner similar to the elimination of abstracts in SHOENFIELD [1954].

We may clearly suppose that $T_1^*$ is at least as long as any other $T_i^*$, $i = 2 \cdots m$. For each $j = 1 \cdots n$, let $A_j'$ be obtained from $A_j$ by performing the following three operations in the order r1–r3:

r1.    Replacing all formulas $T_1^* \, \eta \, S$ by $\exists u \, (u \, \eta \, S \wedge \forall v \, (v \, \eta \, u \leftrightarrow F_1(v)))$, where $u$ and $v$ are new individual variables.

r2.    Replacing all formulas $S = T_1^*$ and $T_1^* = S$ by $\forall v \, (v \, \eta \, S \leftrightarrow F_1(v))$.

r3.    Replacing all formulas $S \, \eta \, T_1^*$ by $\exists w \, (w = S) \wedge F_1(S)$, where $w$ is a new individual variable distinct from $u$ and $v$.

REMARK.    The order r1–r3 is not the only order which ensures that formulas eliminated by one replacement are not restored by another. For example, the order r3, r2, r1 would do. However, the order r2, r3, r1 would not do because r2 eliminates formulas of the form $x = T_1^*$, but these are restored by the application of r3 to the formula $T_1^* = T_1^*$.

Clearly under r1–r3 the formula $M_1$ becomes

(1) $$\forall z_1 (\exists w \ (w = z_1) \wedge F_1(z_1) \leftrightarrow F_1(z_1))$$

and by our choice of $T_1^*$ with maximal length, every other $M_i$, $i = 2 \cdots m$, is unaffected; that is, if $A_j$ is $M_i$ for $i = 2 \cdots m$, then $A_j'$ is $A_j$.

If $A_j$ is an instance of A1*, then either $T_1^*$ is neither of the specified terms in $A_j$, in which case, $A_j'$ has the same form as $A_j$; or $T_1^*$ is one of the specified terms in $A_j$. In this case, $A_j'$ can only be a formula of the form

(2) $$\forall z \ (\exists w \ (w = z) \wedge F_1(z) \leftrightarrow z \ \eta \ S) \rightarrow \forall v \ (v \ \eta \ S \ \leftrightarrow F_1(v)),$$

(3) $$\forall z \ (z \ \eta \ S \leftrightarrow \exists w \ (w = z) \wedge F_1(z)) \rightarrow \forall v \ (v \ \eta \ S \ \leftrightarrow F_1(v)),$$

or

(4) $$\forall z \ (\exists w \ (w = z) \wedge F_1(z) \leftrightarrow \exists w \ (w = z) \wedge F_1(z)) \rightarrow$$
$$\rightarrow \forall v \ (\exists w \ (w = v) \wedge F_1(v) \leftrightarrow F_1(v)).$$

If $A_j$ is an instance of A2*, then $A_j'$ can either be a formula of the same form or a formula of the form

(5) $$\exists u \ (u \ \eta \ S \wedge \forall v \ (v \ \eta \ u \leftrightarrow F_1(v))) \rightarrow \exists x \ \forall v \ (v \ \eta \ x \leftrightarrow F_1(v)),$$

(6) $$\exists u \ (\exists w \ (w = u) \wedge F_1(u) \wedge \forall v \ (v \ \eta \ u \leftrightarrow F_1(v)))$$
$$\rightarrow \exists x \ \forall v \ (v \ \eta \ x \leftrightarrow F_1(v)),$$

or

(7) $$\exists w \ (w = S) \wedge F_1(S) \rightarrow \exists x \ (x = S).$$

If $A_j$ is $\theta$ or a member of $\mathfrak{C}$, then $A_j'$ is $A_j$ since $A_j$ contains no class variables and $T_1^*$ does.

If $A_j$ is a P-, Q1- or Q2-axiom, then $A_j'$ is obviously a formula of the same form.

If $A_j$ is a Q3- or Q4-axiom in $\mathcal{D}$, then $T_1^*$ cannot be the specified term in $A_j$ since, $\mathcal{D}$ being an $(\epsilon^*,0)$-deduction, the only Q3- and Q4-axioms in $\mathcal{D}$ are those whose specified existential formula is normal and hence whose specified term is an individual term. Hence, $A_j'$ is an axiom of the same form. For example, suppose $A_j$ is $\rightarrow \exists z \ B \rightarrow \rightarrow B(t)$ and that " denotes the operation r3—of replacing every formula $S \ \eta \ T_1^*$ by $\exists w \ (w = S) \wedge F_1(S)$. Since $B$ is proper ($\mathcal{D}$ being an $\epsilon^*$-deduction), $t$ can appear in neither $S$ nor $T_1^*$. Hence, either $S$ is not $t$, in which case, $A_j''$ clearly has the form $\rightarrow \exists z \ B'' \rightarrow \rightarrow B''(t'')$, or $S$ is $t$ and $B$ has the form $\cdots z \ \eta \ T_1^* \cdots$. In this latter case, $A_j''$ clearly has the form

$$\rightarrow \exists z \ (\cdots \exists w(w = z) \wedge F_1(z) \cdots) \rightarrow \rightarrow (\cdots \exists w(w = t) \wedge F_1(t) \cdots),$$

so it is a Q3-axiom, and moreover, $\rightarrow \exists z \ (\cdots \exists w(w = z) \wedge F_1(z) \cdots)$ is normal.

An easy check shows that if $A_j$ is any other logical axiom in $\mathcal{D}$, then

$\emptyset \vdash^0 A'_j$. We give one example: if $A_j$ is an E1-axiom

$$T_1^* = S \wedge S \eta R \to T_1^* \eta R,$$

where neither $S$ nor $R$ is $T_1^*$, then $A'_j$ is

(8)  $\forall v \, (v \eta \bar{S} \leftrightarrow F_1(v)) \wedge \bar{S} \eta \bar{R} \to \exists u \, (u \eta \bar{R} \wedge \forall v \, (v \eta u \leftrightarrow F_1(v)))$,

where $\bar{\phantom{x}}$ denotes the result of performing r1 then r2.

Since (1)–(8) are formulas $G$ such that $\emptyset \vdash^0 G$, it follows that

$$\mathfrak{C} \cup A1^* \cup A2^* \cup \{M_2, \dots, M_m\} \vdash^0 \theta.$$

Hence, repeating the above procedure $m - 1$ more times, we finally see that $\mathfrak{C}^*-A3^* \vdash^0 \theta$, Q.E.D.

LEMMA 3.9.  *If* $\mathfrak{C}^*-A3^* \vdash^0 \theta$, *then* $\mathfrak{C} \vdash_{\mathrm{PC}_0} \theta$.

PROOF.  First, note that $\mathfrak{C}^*-A3^*$ is $\mathfrak{C} \cup A1^* \cup A2^*$. Let $\langle A_1, \dots, A_n \rangle$, called $\mathcal{D}$, be an $(\epsilon*,0)$-deduction of $\theta$ from $\mathfrak{C}^*-A3^*$.

Let $\mathcal{D}'$ be obtained from $\mathcal{D}$ by replacing all class variables by suitable new individual variables. It is trivial to verify that $\mathcal{D}'$ is a deduction in $\epsilon*_0$ of $\theta$ from $\mathfrak{C} \cup A1^{*\prime}$, where $A1^{*\prime}$ is the schema

$$\forall z \, (z \eta s \leftrightarrow z \eta t) \to s = t.$$

If there is a two-place predicate $P$ in the vocabulary $\mathcal{V}$ such that

$$\forall z \, (Pzs \leftrightarrow Pzt) \to s = t$$

holds in $\mathfrak{C}$, then by replacing every formula $s \eta t$ in $\mathcal{D}'$ by $Pst$, one easily shows that $\mathfrak{C} \vdash_{\epsilon*_0} \theta$, and hence by Lemma 3.3 that $\mathfrak{C} \vdash_{\mathrm{PC}_0} \theta$. If there is no such predicate $P$ in $\mathcal{V}$, then $P$ may be taken to be the identity, Q.E.D.

REMARK  In the above proof, we made essential use of the requirement that $\eta$ is not a predicate in the vocabulary $\mathcal{V}$.

THE PROOF OF METATHEOREM 2.1.  By Lemma 3.4, if $\mathfrak{C}'' \vdash_{\mathrm{PC}''} \theta$, then $\mathfrak{C}'' \vdash_{\epsilon*''} \theta$. Hence by Lemma 3.6 we have $\mathfrak{C}^* \vdash_{\epsilon*''} \theta$, so for some $r$ and $T_r$, $\mathfrak{C}^* \vdash^{r,T_r} \theta$. Hence by Lemma 3.7, $\mathfrak{C}^* \vdash^{r,\emptyset} \theta$. But an $(\epsilon*,r,\emptyset)$-deduction is an $(\epsilon*,r-1,S_{r-1})$-deduction for some $S_{r-1}$. Hence, by repeated applications of Lemma 3.7, we obtain $\mathfrak{C}^* \vdash^0 \theta$. By Lemmas 3.8 and 3.9, it follows that $\mathfrak{C} \vdash_{\mathrm{PC}_0} \theta$, Q.E.D.

## 4. Applications of Metatheorem 2.1

In view of the replacement operations in Lemma 3.7, it is clear that if $G(T_1, \dots, T_n)$ is a normal $\mathcal{L}''$-formula in the sense of p. 258 above, then in Lemma 3.7 all formulas of the form $G$ may be added to $\mathfrak{C}^*$ as axioms.

However, unless we further stipulate that $G$ contains no class terms, it seems impossible to ensure that it survives the replacement operations in Lemma 3.8; but certainly, any such $\mathscr{L}''$-formula without class terms which is valid in $\mathfrak{C}$, when $\eta$ is replaced by either $=$ or some two-place predicate $P$ of $\mathfrak{C}$, will survive all the replacement operations of Lemmas 3.7–3.9. Hence all such formulas may be added to $\mathfrak{C}$ in the statement of the metatheorem.

It seems that we cannot generalize any further, and unfortunately, the requirement that $G$ contains no class terms is so severe as to be of no apparent value. However, it is easily seen that certain normal $\mathscr{L}''$-formulas which contain class variables do, in a sense, survive the replacement operations of Lemmas 3.8 and 3.9. We give three examples.

**4.1.** Let $\mathfrak{C}$ be Peano Arithmetic $N$ (see SHOENFIELD [1967], p. 204). Let $N''$ be obtained from $N$ as $\mathfrak{C}''$ is obtained from $\mathfrak{C}$ and by allowing the quantified formulas specified in the induction schema

**Ind**  $\qquad A(0) \wedge \forall x\,(A(x) \rightarrow A(x')) \rightarrow \forall x\,A(x),$

where $x'$ is the successor of $x$, and is to be normal in the sense of p. 258. In $N''$, **Ind** is then equivalent to the single axiom

$$\forall X(0 \,\eta\, X \wedge \forall x\,(x \,\eta\, X \rightarrow x' \,\eta\, X) \rightarrow \forall x\,(x \,\eta\, X)).$$

Now consider the schema

**Ind\***  $\qquad 0 \,\eta\, T \wedge \forall x(x \,\eta\, T \rightarrow x' \,\eta\, T) \rightarrow \forall x\,(x \,\eta\, T),$

where $T$ is an arbitrary term, and let $N^*$ be $\mathfrak{C} \cup A1^* \cup A2^* \cup A3^* \cup$ **Ind\***. Since the formulas $\forall x\,(x \,\eta\, T \rightarrow x' \,\eta\, T)$ and $\forall x\,(x \,\eta\, T)$ are normal, **Ind\*** survives the operations of Lemma 3.7; i.e. if $N^* \vdash^{r,T_r} \theta$, then $N^* \vdash^{r,\emptyset} \theta$.

Now under the replacement operations r1–r3 in Lemma 3.8, any instance of **Ind\*** either becomes a formula of the same form or a normal formula of the form

$$F_1(0) \wedge \exists w\,(w = 0) \wedge \forall x\,(\exists w\,(w = x) \wedge F_1(x) \rightarrow \exists w\,(w = x') \wedge F_1(x'))$$
$$\rightarrow \forall x\,(\exists w\,(w = x) \wedge F_1(x)),$$

which is an instance of **Ind**. The proof of Lemma 3.8 therefore shows that if $N^* \vdash^0 \theta$, then $N^*-A3^* \vdash^0 \theta$; and the proof of Lemma 3.9 shows that $N \vdash_{PC_0} \theta$. Hence, $N''$ is a conservative extension of $N$.

**4.2.** The proof that **NBG** is a conservative extension of **ZF** is similar to the proof above. As axioms of **NBG** we may take the group of axioms $A \cup C$ together with the schema M4 (see GÖDEL [1940]). However, the specified formula $\varphi$ in M4 is required to contain no bound-class variables. We relax this condition by considering instead the system **NBG''**, namely,

$A \cup C \cup A3_n$, where the subscript $n$ is used both to emphasize the fact that instances of A3* are normal and to distinguish the schema $A3_n$ from the axiom A3 in the group of axioms $A$. We show that $\mathbf{NBG}''$ is a conservative extension of $\mathbf{ZF}$.

By interpreting $\mathfrak{Cls}(X)$ as $X = X$ and $\mathfrak{M}(X)$ as $\exists x\ (x = X)$, it is trivial to verify that the axioms A1–4, Cl–3 of $\mathbf{NBG}''$ hold in $\mathfrak{C}^*$ when $\mathfrak{C}$ is $\mathbf{ZF}$. The proofs are purely finitary. Thus, we only need to show that the Ersetzungs-axiom C4 "survives" the various replacement operations in Lemmas 3.7–3.9. Let C4* be the following schema:

$$\mathrm{Un}(T) \to \exists y\ \forall z\ (z\ \eta\ y \leftrightarrow \exists u\ (u\ \eta\ t\ \wedge\ \langle u,z\rangle\ \eta\ T))^1$$

and $\mathfrak{C}^{**}$ be $\mathfrak{C}^* \cup C4^*$.

Since every quantified formula which is specified in C4* is normal, C4* survives Lemma 3.7 intact. Furthermore, under the operations r1–r3 of Lemma 3.8 an instance of C4* either becomes another formula of the same form or a normal formula of the form

(1)
$$\forall u,z,z'(A(u,z) \wedge A(u,z') \to z = z') \to$$
$$\to \exists y\ \forall z\ (z\ \eta\ y \leftrightarrow \exists u(u\ \eta\ t\ \wedge\ A(u,z))),$$

and further applications of r1–r3 do not damage these. Let us denote by $\mathbf{Rep}_n$ the collection of formulas of the form (1) in which the quantified formulas which are specified are normal, and let us denote by $\mathbf{Rep}$ the collection of $\mathscr{L}$-formulas of the form (1). Then Lemmas 3.7 and 3.8 show that if $\mathfrak{C}^{**} \vdash^{r,T_r} \theta$, then $(\mathfrak{C}^{**}-A3^*) \cup \mathbf{Rep}_n \vdash^0 \theta$. Now the operations in Lemma 3.9 convert instances of C4* and $\mathbf{Rep}_n$ into instances of $\mathbf{Rep}$. Hence, Lemma 3.9 shows that if $(\mathfrak{C}^{**}-A3^*) \cup \mathbf{Rep}_n \vdash^0 \theta$, then $\mathfrak{C} \vdash_{PC_0} \theta$. Hence, $\mathbf{NBG}''$ is a conservative extension of $\mathbf{ZF}$.

An immediate corollary to the above is that $\mathbf{NBG}$ and $\mathbf{NBG}''$ are equivalent in the sense that they have the same theorems in the language of $\mathbf{ZF}$, but we get a stronger result than this in §3.

**4.3.** Finally, let $\mathfrak{C}$ be the theory of New Foundations ($\mathbf{NF}$) in QUINE [1957] and $\mathbf{ML}''$ be obtained from the Wang-Quine system $\mathbf{ML}$ in QUINE [1951] by allowing the comprehension axiom *202 to be normal in the sense that A3 is normal.

Note that $\mathbf{ML}$ can equivalently be written in a two-sorted language. Thus, $\mathbf{ML}''$ is $\mathfrak{C}''$ and Metatheorem 2.1 applies as it stands to show that $\mathbf{ML}''$ is a conservative extension of $\mathbf{NF}$.

---

$^1$ Here, $\mathrm{Un}(T)$ and $\langle u,z\rangle\eta T$ are abbreviations of the usual set-theoretic formulas, but written with $\eta$ instead of $\epsilon$ (the usual two-place predicate of Zermelo's set theory).

## 5. Other definitions of a normal formula

Throughout the proofs of Lemmas 3.7–3.9 we emphasized that instances of A3* were normal in the sense of p. 258. Since this requirement is weaker than the usual one, it might seem that the results in §2 are stronger than the corresponding results in SHOENFIELD [1954]. Indeed, since we did not require that instances of **Ind** contain no bound-class variables, our result that $N''$ is a conservative extension of $N$ certainly appears to be stronger than the corresponding result in SHOENFIELD [1954]. However, this is not so for the cases **NBG″** and **ML″**, for if **ML′** is like **ML″** except that it only contains instances of A3 whose specified formula $F(z)$ contains no bound-class variables, then since the ordered pair $\langle x,y \rangle$ is definable in **NBG** and **ML′**, one can easily show by induction on the length of formulas that $\textbf{NBG} \vdash A3_n^*$ and $\textbf{ML′} \vdash A3_n^*$.

Now, it is natural to ask if it is possible to obtain stronger results than those already obtained, by weakening still further the requirements of the normality of the schema A3*—for example, by

N1.     only requiring that there is no formula $QXB(X,z)$ in $F(z)$ which is *immediately* subordinate to $\forall z$ $(z \; \eta \; T^* \leftrightarrow F(z))$, $X$ being a class variable, not an individual variable; or

N2.     allowing instances of A3 to be impredicative, that is, allowing $F(z)$ to be any $\mathscr{L}''$-formula with one free individual variable.

Let $\mathfrak{C}_1''$ and $\mathfrak{C}_2''$ be the theories obtained from $\mathfrak{C}''$ by replacing our notion of normality by N1 and N2 respectively. $\mathfrak{C}_2''$ is what QUINE [1951], p. 316, calls an *impredicative enlargement* of $\mathfrak{C}$.

Quine pointed out that WANG [1949] showed that $\mathfrak{C}_2''$ (and hence $\mathfrak{C}_1''$) is a conservative extension of $\mathfrak{C}$, but the proof is non-finitary and we can see no way of adapting the proof of Metatheorem 2.1 so that $\mathfrak{C}_1''$ or $\mathfrak{C}_2''$ can be inserted in place of $\mathfrak{C}''$ in the statement of the Metatheorem. The reason for this is that the methods we used insist upon the elimination of (∗∗)-formulas, and there seems to be no way of doing this when instances of A3* are permitted to be (∗)-formulas. In fact, we suspect that if there is one, a finitary proof of Wang's theorem would use different methods altogether from those used here, but it would also use the result of Metatheorem 2.1.

We conclude with a question and some remarks.

Let **NBG₁** be like **NBG** except that instances of the class comprehension schema are only required to be normal in the sense of N1 above.

QUESTION.    Is there a finitary proof that **NBG** + **E** (resp. **NBG₁** + **E**) is a conservative extension of **NBG** + **AC** (resp. **NBG₁** + **AC**) with respect to

$ZF$-formulas, where $E$ is Gödel's axiom of choice and $AC$ is the $ZF$-form of the axiom of choice?

It is well known (see for example, FELGNER [1971], FLANNAGAN [1973], and GRIŠIN [1972]) that $NBG + E$ is a conservative extension of $NBG + AC$ with respect to $ZF$-formulas, but since a choice function in the sense of $E$ only makes selections from sets, there is no strong reason known to us as to why the axiom of foundation should be necessary in the statement of the theorem. Moreover, there is no known recursive proof of the result, let alone a primitive-recursive proof. If a primitive-recursive proof could be found, it might well make no use of the axiom of foundation in $NBG$ and hence might yield a proof that $NBG^0 + E$ is a conservative extension of $NBG^0 + AC$ with respect to $ZF$-formulas, where $^0$ denotes the absence of the axiom of foundation. The question of whether this result is true was raised in FLANNAGAN [1973] and independently in GRIŠEN [1972], but the question is still open. The nearest solution is the following (given by the author in a talk in Oberwolfach, April, 1974). If $Q$ is a $ZF$-type set theory, and $Q_\sigma$ is obtained from it by adjoining the one-place function symbol $\sigma$, adding the axiom $x \neq \emptyset \to \sigma(x) \in x$ and allowing $\sigma$ to figure in the schemata of $Q$, then every $\sigma$-free theorem of $S_\sigma^0 + CR_\sigma^S$ (and hence of $ZF_\sigma^0$) is a theorem of $S^0 + CR^S + AC$; and for $\Lambda \geq 1$, every $\sigma$-free theorem of $ZF_\sigma^0 + (N_\Lambda)_\sigma$ (and hence of $(ZM_\Lambda^0)_\sigma$) is a theorem of $ZF^0 + N_\Lambda + AC$. For notation, see FLANNAGAN [1974] or LÉVY [1960].

### References

ASSER, G. (1957) Theorie der logischen Auswahlfunktionen. *Zeitschr. f. Math. Logik* **3**, 30–68.

DOETS, H. C. (1969) Novak's result by Henkin's method. *Fund. Math.* **64**, 329–333.

FELGNER, U. (1971) Comparison of the axioms of local and universal choice. *Fund. Math.* **71**, 43–62.

FLANNAGAN, T. B. (1973) Ph.D. thesis. London.

FLANNAGAN, T. B. (1974) Set theories incorporating Hilbert's $\epsilon$-symbol. *Dissertationes Math.* **154**. Warszawa.

GÖDEL, K. (1940) *The consistency of the axiom of choice and of the generalized continuum hypothesis with the axioms of set theory.* Annals of Math. Studies, Vol. 3. Princeton. 66 pp. (2nd printing (1951), 74 pp.)

GRIŠIN, V. N. (1972) The theory of Zermelo–Fraenkel sets with Hilbert $\epsilon$-terms. *Math. Notes Acad. Sci. U.S.S.R.* **12**, 779–783.

HILBERT, D. and BERNAYS, P. (1934–1939) *Grundlagen der Mathematik* I (1934); II (1939). Springer, Berlin. 471; 498 pp. (2nd edition (1968); (1970), 488; 575 pp.)

LEISENRING, A. C. (1969) *Mathematical Logic and Hilbert's* $\epsilon$-symbol. Gordon and Breach, New York, 142 pp.

LÉVY, A. (1960) Axiom schemata of strong infinity in axiomatic set theory. *Pacific J. Math.* **10**, 223–238.

MOSTOWSKI, A. (1951) Some impredicative definitions in the axiomatic set theory. *Fund. Math.* **37**, 111–124. (Corrections, *ibid.* (1952) **38**, 238.)

NOVAK, I. L. (1948) A construction for models of consistent systems. Ph.D. thesis, Harvard.

NOVAK, I. L. (1951) A construction for models of consistent systems. *Fund. Math.* **37**, 87–110.

QUINE, W. V. (1937) New foundations for mathematical logic. *Am. Math. Monthly* **44**, 70–80. (A revised and expanded version is in QUINE (1953), pp. 80–101.)

QUINE, W. V. (1951) *Mathematical Logic* (revised edition) Harvard University Press, Cambridge, Mass., 346 pp. (First edition (1940).)

QUINE, W. V. (1953) *From a logical point of view.* Harvard University Press, Cambridge, Mass, 184 pp.

QUINE, W. V. (1963) *Set theory and its logic.* Belknap Press, Cambridge, Mass., 359 pp. (Revised ed. (1969), 361 pp.)

ROSSER, J. B. and WANG, H. (1950) Non-standard models for formal logics. *J.S.L.* **15**, 113–129. (Errata, *ibid.* p. iv.).

SHOENFIELD, J. R. (1954) A relative consistency proof. *J.S.L.* **19**, 21–28.

SHOENFIELD, J. R. (1967) *Mathematical logic.* Addison-Wesley, Reading, Mass. 344 pp.

WANG, H. (1949) On Zermelo's and von Neumann's axioms for set theory. *Acad. Sci. U.S.A.* **35**, 150–155.

WANG, H. (1950) A formal system of logic. *J.S.L.* **15**, 25–32.

SETS AND CLASSES; On the work by Paul Bernays
© North-Holland Publishing Company (1976) pp. 277–323.

# REFLECTION PRINCIPLES AND
# INDESCRIBABILITY

Klaus GLOEDE

*Heidelberg, West Germany*

## 0. Introduction

The aim of this paper is to present some results supplementary to P. Bernays' investigation of a second-order reflection principle (BERNAYS [1961]). This schema is classified within the hierarchy of reflection principles for various classes of formulas, beginning with the first-order language of Zermelo–Fraenkel set theory, which leads to the principles first introduced and studied by Lévy, and ending with the language of finite (or even transfinite) type theory, which is related to the notion of indescribability in the sense of Hanf and Scott. Taking this view, one is led in a natural way to take into account two aspects in the investigation of various set theories:

(i) the distinction between class terms (in the sense of Zermelo–Fraenkel set theory) and class variables (in the sense of Bernays and von Neumann–Bernays set theory) and

(ii) the classification of set-theoretical formulas according to their logical complexity.

Montague–Vaught's theorem is the most illuminating and striking illustration of (i), and we shall encounter a similar phenomenon at a higher level of type. (ii) Leads us to consider some subtheories of the Bernays–Lévy theory $\mathsf{BL}$, in particular the theory $\mathsf{BL}_1$ which corresponds to $\Pi_1^1$-indescribability.

A comprehensive treatment of the subject as indicated would require a whole monograph. Therefore, we restrict ourselves primarily to those results which have not yet been published in detail (although they seem to be well known to a large extent).

## 1. Reflection principles in set theory without class variables

*1.1. Reflection principles in the language of* $\mathsf{ZF}$ *set theory*

1.1.1. The language of $\mathsf{ZF}$ set theory, denoted by $\mathscr{L}_{\mathsf{ZF}}$, is the usual first-order language with (set) variables $v_0, v_1, \ldots$, atomic formulas $v_n = v_m$

277

and $v_n \in v_m$, and the logical symbols $\rightarrow$, $\wedge$, $\vee$, $\rightarrow$, $\leftrightarrow$, $\forall$ and $\exists$. We also use lowercase letters $a$, $b$, $c$,... for free, and $u$, $v$, $x$,... for bound variables (possibly with indices). Formulas of this language are denoted by $\varphi$, $\psi$,.... Some of the notation is self-explanatory.

1.1.2. Relativization.   If $\varphi$ is a formula of $\mathscr{L}_{ZF}$, the *relativization* of $\varphi$ to $a$, denoted by $\mathrm{Rel}\,(a,\varphi)$ or simply $\varphi^a$, is the formula obtained from $\varphi$ by replacing any quantifier $\forall x$ or $\exists x$ occurring in $\varphi$ by $\forall x \in a$ and $\exists x \in a$ respectively. Here, $\forall x \in a\,\psi$ and $\exists x \in a\,\psi$ are regarded as abbreviations of the formulas $\forall x\,(x \in a \rightarrow \psi)$ and $\exists x\,(x \in a \wedge \psi)$ resp.

Though the operation of relativizing is a purely syntactical notion (to be defined by recursion on the subformula relation), it has an obvious model-theoretic interpretation: Let $\mathsf{T}$ be a sufficiently strong set theory, e.g. Zermelo–Fraenkel set theory $\mathsf{ZF}$ or the Kripke–Platek theory $\mathsf{KP}$ of admissible sets (which we usually assume to include the axiom of infinity). One can define in $\mathsf{T}$ a set $\mathrm{Fml}_{ZF}$ which intuitively represents the set of all formulas of the language of $\mathsf{ZF}$. Every formula $\varphi$ of $\mathscr{L}_{ZF}$ corresponds to a suitably chosen term $\ulcorner \varphi \urcorner$ of $\mathsf{T}$ (the "Gödel number of $\varphi$" which may be a natural number or, more generally, a hereditarily finite set) such that $\mathsf{T} \vdash \ulcorner \varphi \urcorner \in \mathrm{Fml}_{ZF}$. Moreover, in the usual recursive manner one can define in $\mathsf{T}$ a formalized notion of *satisfaction in a structure* $\langle a, \in \rangle$ by a formula $\psi_0(v_0,v_1,v_2)$ of $\mathscr{L}_{ZF}$ such that

(a) in $\mathsf{T}$ $\psi_0(a,e,b)$ intuitively expresses the statement

> "*e is the Gödel number of a formula $\varphi$ of $\mathscr{L}_{ZF}$ with free variables among $v_0,\ldots, v_n$ for some natural number $n$, $b$ is a sequence of $n + 1$ elements of $a$ and $\varphi$ is true in the structure $\langle a, \in \rangle$ if $b(i)$ is assigned to $v_i$ for $i = 0,\ldots, n$*",

(b) one can prove in $\mathsf{T}$ the following schema:

$$\psi_0(a,e,b) \leftrightarrow \varphi^a(b(0),\ldots, b(n))$$

for any formula $\varphi$ with Gödel number $e$ and any assignment $b$ as in (a). (For more details see, e.g. JENSEN–KARP [1971], p. 147, or LÉVY [1965], §5, for formulas of rank $\leqslant j$, it is rather obvious how to remove this restriction.)

In order to remind the reader of the intuitive interpretation of the formula $\psi_0$ we write for $\psi_0(a,e,b)$,

$$\langle a, \in \rangle \models e\,[b]$$

or—somewhat imprecise—

$$\langle a, \in \rangle \models e \; [b(0), \ldots, b(n)]$$

(if $n$ is suitably chosen).

Thus, we may read $\varphi^a(a_0, \ldots, a_n)$ as "$\varphi$ *holds in* $a$" (under the obvious assignment and with the obvious interpretation of the membership relation). However, it should be kept in mind that $\varphi^a(a_0, \ldots, a_n)$ is a formula of $\mathscr{L}_{ZF}$ (in contradistinction to the metamathematical statement "$\varphi$ *holds in* $a$") and hence corresponds to a formalized notion of satisfaction.

1.1.3. Reflection principles (introduced into set theory by LÉVY [1958]). These are schemata of the following form:

$\text{PR}_\psi(\mathscr{L})$      $\varphi(a_0, \ldots, a_n) \to \exists u \; [\psi(u) \wedge a_0, \ldots, a_n \in u \wedge \varphi^u(a_0, \ldots, a_n)]$

$\hspace{10cm}$ (*partial reflection*)

or

$\text{CR}_\psi(\mathscr{L})$      $\exists u \; [a \in u \wedge \psi(u) \vee \forall x_0 \cdots x_n \in u(\varphi(x_0, \ldots, x_n)$

$\hspace{3cm} \leftrightarrow \varphi^u(x_0, \ldots, x_n))]$ $\hspace{3cm}$ (*complete reflection*)

where in both cases $\varphi$ is any formula of $\mathscr{L}$ with free variables among $v_0, \ldots, v_n$ and $\psi$ is some fixed formula (containing possibly free variables in addition to the indicated variable). If $\mathscr{L}$ contains formulas which are not in the basic language $\mathscr{L}_{ZF}$, the notion of relativization has to be extended in a suitable way to apply to all formulas of $\mathscr{L}$; examples of such extensions are discussed later.

In view of the model-theoretic interpretation of the notion of relativization (1.1.2) one can interpret these principles roughly as follows:

> *any property (not necessarily in the one-place sense) which is expressible by a formula of $\mathscr{L}$ and which is true in the universe (under some given assignment) is true (under the same assignment) in some set satisfying $\psi$ ($\text{PR}_\psi(\mathscr{L})$);*

or in the case of complete reflection ($\text{CR}_\psi(\mathscr{L})$):

> *for any property expressible by a formula $\varphi$ of $\mathscr{L}$ and any set $a$ there is a set $b$ which contains $a$ as an element, satisfies $\psi$ and is a complete "reflection" of the universe with respect to the property expressed by $\varphi$.*

It is shown in the sequel that reflection principles can conveniently be applied to yield the existence of sets satisfying certain closure properties.

In standard axiomatizations of set theory, the existence of such sets is proved by means of the axiom schema of replacement and certain types of the axiom of infinity. Conversely, the latter axioms, together with some basic axioms of set theory, imply certain types of reflection principles. (This fact should be rather obvious to anyone familiar with the Löwenheim–Skolem theorem.)

Axiomatizing set theory by means of reflection principles has several advantages. First, from the model-theoretic interpretation of these principles, one can easily deduce metamathematical properties of the corresponding systems (e.g. in the case of $CR_{Trans}(\mathcal{L}_{ZF})$: ZF is not finitely axiomatizable).[1] Second, the principles of partial and complete reflection for the language of ZF set theory admit straightforward generalization to richer languages (higher order, infinitary languages, etc.), thus yielding stronger axiom systems, or else can be weakened by restricting $\mathcal{L}$ to suitable classes of formulas.

1.1.4. For the sake of completeness and later reference, we indicate main steps for a proof of the well-known fact that the axioms of ZF can be derived from a principle of complete reflection together with some basic axioms.

The *axioms* of ZF are the following:[2]

Ext     $\forall x\,(x \in a \leftrightarrow x \in b) \to a = b$     (*Extensionality*)

Pair     $\exists x\,\forall y\,(y \in x \leftrightarrow y = a \lor y = b)$     (*Pairing*)

Sum     $\exists x\,\forall y\,(y \in x \leftrightarrow (\exists z \in a)y \in z)$     (*Sum set*)

Pow     $\exists x\,\forall y\,(y \in x \leftrightarrow y \subseteq a)$     (*Power set*)

Inf     $\exists x\,[\exists y\,(y \in x) \land \forall y \in x\,(\{y\}\forall x)]$     (*Infinity*)

ReplS     $\forall x, y, z\,(\varphi(x, y,\ldots) \land (x, z,\ldots) \to y = z) \to$     (*Axiom schema*
            $\exists z\,\forall y\,(y \in z \leftrightarrow \exists x \in a\,\varphi(x, y,\ldots)$    *of replacement*)

Fund     $\exists y\,(y \in a) \to \exists y \in a\,\forall z \in y\,z \notin a$     (*Axiom of foundation,*
                                          *Fundierung*)

Here and in the following we use the common set-theoretical notations: $\emptyset$ (empty set), $\{a,b\}$ (unordered pair), $\{a\} = \{a,a\}$, $\langle a,b \rangle = \{\{a\},\{a,b\}\}$ (ordered pair), $\subseteq$ (inclusion), $\mathscr{P}(a)$ (power set of $a$). A $\Delta_0$-formula $\varphi$ is a formula of $\mathcal{L}_{ZF}$ in which all quantifiers are restricted to sets, i.e. of the form $\forall v_n \in v_m$ or $\exists v_n \in v_m$ (LÉVY [1965]). For example $Rel(\varphi,a)$ is a $\Delta_0$-formula in which all quantifiers are restricted to the same set $a$; in

---

[1] A proof of this statement (due to R. Montague) can be found e.g. in FELGNER [1971a], p. 20 and KRIVINE (1971), p. 54. For a generalization, cf. LÉVY [1960].

[2] The symbol "=" is regarded as a logical symbol.

general, quantifiers may be restricted in $\Delta_0$-formulas to different set variables. Thus, the definition of a *transitive* (or *complete*) set may be given by the following $\Delta_0$-formula:

$$\text{Trans}(a): \leftrightarrow \forall x \in a \; \forall y \in x \; (y \in a).$$

We also need the following definition:

$$\text{Strans}(a): \leftrightarrow \text{Trans}(a) \wedge \forall x \in a \; \forall y \; (y \subseteq x \to y \in a)$$

("*a is supertransitive (supercomplete)*"; cf. BERNAYS [1961] and SHEPHERDSON [1952]).

We frequently make use of the fact that $\Delta_0$-formulas are "absolute" with respect to transitive sets, i.e. if $\varphi(a_0, \ldots, a_n)$ is a $\Delta_0$-formula with free variables as indicated then

$$\text{Trans}(a) \to \forall x_0 \cdots x_n \in a \; (\varphi(x_0, \ldots, x_n) \leftrightarrow \text{Rel}(a, \varphi(x_0, \ldots, x_n))).$$

*The Aussonderungsschema (schema of subsets)*

AusS          $\exists x \; \forall y \; (y \in x \leftrightarrow y \in a \wedge \varphi(y, \ldots))$

is provable in ZF. For our purposes, it is often sufficient to consider the weaker

$\Delta_0$-AusS          $\exists x \; \forall y \; (y \in x \leftrightarrow y \in a \wedge \varphi(y, \ldots))$

where $\varphi$ is any $\Delta_0$-formula.

We now turn to the principles $\text{PR}_\psi = \text{PR}_\psi(\mathscr{L}_{\text{ZF}})$ and $\text{CR}_\psi = \text{CR}_\psi(\mathscr{L}_{\text{ZF}})$:

PROPOSITION 1.1.

(a)          $\text{Ext} + \Delta_0\text{-AusS} + \text{PR}_\psi \vdash \text{Pair}$   (*for any formula* $\psi$),

(b)          $\text{Ext} + \Delta_0\text{-AusS} + \text{PR}_{\text{Trans}} \vdash \text{Pair} + \text{Sum} + \text{Inf}.$

PROOF.   Applying $\text{PR}_\psi$ to the formula

$$a_0 = a_0 \wedge a_1 = a_1$$

we obtain the formula

$$\exists x \; (a_0 \in x \wedge a_1 \in x)$$

and hence Pair by means of $\Delta_0$-AusS. This proves (a). The proof of (b) is similar and is given in BERNAYS [1961], pp. 127–128.

REMARK 1.1.   Let $\text{PR}'_\psi$ be the schema

$$\varphi(a_0, \ldots, a_n) \to \exists u \; (\psi(u) \wedge \varphi^u(a_0, \ldots, a_n))$$

($\varphi$ any formula of $\mathscr{L}_{\text{ZF}}$), as considered in BERNAYS [1961], p. 126. Though this is a weakening of $\text{PR}_\psi$, both schemata are in fact equivalent. (To deduce an instance of $\text{PR}_\psi$ from $\text{PR}'_\psi$, apply $\text{PR}'_\psi$ to the formula $\varphi(a_0, \ldots, a_n) \wedge \exists x \, (x = a_0) \wedge \cdots \wedge \exists x \, (x = a_n).$)

PROPOSITION 1.2.   $\text{Ext} + \Delta_0\text{-AusS} + \text{PR}_{\text{Strans}} \vdash \text{Pow}.$

PROOF (cf. BERNAYS [1961], p. 139). By $\text{PR}_{\text{Strans}}$ there is, for any set $a$ a set $b$ such that

$$a \in b \wedge \text{Strans}\,(b),$$

hence

$$a \in b \wedge \forall x \in b \,\, \forall y \, (y \subseteq x \to y \in b), \qquad \mathscr{P}(a) \subseteq b.$$

Hence $\mathscr{P}(a)$ is a set by $\Delta_0\text{-AusS}$.

Using the axiom of pairing, if $\psi(a) \to \text{Trans}\,(a)$, $\text{CR}_\psi$ implies $\text{PR}_\psi$. However, whereas the derivation of the axiom of pairing from $\text{PR}_\psi$ is obvious, we first need the axiom schema of replacement to derive Pair from $\text{CR}_\psi$. Without using Pair one can prove as in Propositions 1.1 and 1.2:

PROPOSITION 1.3.

(a)          $\text{Ext} + \Delta_0\text{-AusS} + \text{CR}_{\text{Trans}} \vdash \forall x \, \exists y \, (y = \{x\}) + \text{Sum} + \text{Inf},$

(b)          $\text{Ext} + \Delta_0\text{-AusS} + \text{CR}_{\text{Strans}} \vdash \text{Pow}.$

Before proving the axiom schema of replacement we need a lemma in which the iterated application of $\text{CR}_{\text{Trans}}$ can be replaced by a single one:

LEMMA 1.1 (Lévy).

$$\text{Ext} + \Delta_0\text{-AusS} + \text{CR}_{\text{Trans}} \vdash \exists u \, [\text{Trans}\,(u) \wedge \forall x_0 \cdots x_n \in u \bigwedge_{i=1}^{m} (\varphi_i \leftrightarrow \varphi_i^u)]$$

for any finite sequence of formulas $\varphi_1, \ldots, \varphi_m$ of $\mathscr{L}_{\text{ZF}}$ with free variables among $v_0, \ldots, v_n$.

PROOF (cf. LÉVY [1960], Theorem 2).   A proof can be found in FELGNER [1971a], pp. 18f and KRIVINE [1971]. It should be noted that having derived the axiom of pairing (Corollary 1.1), one can easily get Lemma 1.1 with the additional clause $a \in u$.

THEOREM 1.1 (Lévy).

$$\text{Ext} + \Delta_0\text{-AusS} + \text{CR}_{\text{Trans}} \vdash \text{ReplS}.$$

PROOF (outline).   Since we refer later to the proof of this theorem, we indicate the main steps of the proof which uses an argument taken from the proof of Theorem 3 of LÉVY [1960]:

Let $a_1, \ldots, a_n, a, b$ be all the free variables occurring in $\varphi(a,b)$ and let $\psi(d)$ be the formula we wish to prove:

$$\psi(d) := \forall x,y,z \; (\varphi(x,y) \wedge \varphi(x,z) \rightarrow y = z)$$
$$\rightarrow \exists u \; \forall v \; (v \in u \leftrightarrow \exists x \in d \; \varphi(x,v)).$$

Put

$$\varphi_1(x,y) = \varphi(x,y), \qquad \varphi_2(x,y) = \exists w \; \varphi(x,w),$$
$$\varphi_3(x) = \psi(x), \qquad \varphi_4 = \forall x_1 \cdots x_n x \; \psi(x).$$

Applying Lemma 1.1 to these four formulas we obtain the existence of a transitive set $c$ such that

(i)    $\forall x_1 \cdots x_n x, y \in c \qquad (\varphi(x,y) \leftrightarrow \varphi^c(x,y))$

(ii)   $\forall x_1 \cdots x_n, x \in c \qquad (\exists w \; \varphi(x,w) \leftrightarrow (\exists w \; \varphi(x,w))^c)$

(iii)  $\forall x_1 \cdots x_n, x \in c \qquad (\psi(x) \leftrightarrow \psi^c(x))$

(iv)   $\forall x_1, \ldots, x_n, x \; \psi(x) \leftrightarrow (\forall x_1, \ldots, x_n, x \; \psi(x))^c.$

The idea of the proof is as follows: Because of (iv), we need only show that the axiom of replacement (for $\varphi$ as above) holds when relativized to $c$. Hence we assume that $d$ and the parameters occurring in $\varphi$ are elements of $c$. Because of (iii), we need only show $\psi(d)$ (instead of $\psi^c(d)$). So we may assume $\forall x,y,z \; (\varphi(x,y) \wedge \varphi(x,z) \rightarrow y = z)$, i.e. $\varphi$ defines a function in the obvious sense. Since $c$ is transitive, $d \subseteq c$. (i) implies that $\varphi$ is absolute with respect to $c$, and together with (ii) we see that $c$ is closed under the function defined by $\varphi$. So we obtain:

$$\forall y \; (\exists x \in d \; \varphi(x,y) \leftrightarrow y \in c \wedge \exists x \in d \; \varphi^c(x,y)).$$

Hence by $\Delta_0$-AusS there is a set $d'$ such that

$$\forall y \; (y \in d' \leftrightarrow \exists x \in d \; \varphi(x,y)),$$

and this establishes our claim $\psi(d)$.

COROLLARY 1.1.   $\text{Ext} + \Delta_0\text{-AusS} + \text{CR}_{\text{Trans}} \vdash \text{Pair}.$

PROOF.   By Proposition 1.3(a) there is a set containing $\emptyset$ and $\{\emptyset\}$ as elements. By $\Delta_0$-AusS, $\{\emptyset, \{\emptyset\}\}$ is a set. Now apply the axiom of replacement to the formula

$$\varphi(c,d) := (c = \emptyset \wedge d = a) \vee (c = \{\emptyset\} \quad d = b).$$

The range of the function defined by this formula on the set $\{\emptyset, \{\emptyset\}\}$ is just $\{a,b\}$.

COROLLARY 1.2.   $\text{Ext} + \Delta_0\text{-AusS} + \text{CR}_\psi \vdash \text{PR}\psi$ *for any formula $\psi$ such that $\psi(a) \to \text{Trans}(a)$.*

We have not yet made any use of the axiom of foundation. As in BERNAYS [1961], p. 143 we can easily derive the *axiom schema of foundation*

FundS          $\varphi(a) \to \exists x\, (\varphi(x) \wedge \forall y \in x \to \varphi(y))$

from the axiom of foundation, Fund, by using $\text{PR}_{\text{Trans}}$. This is accomplished by a modification of Bernays' proof (note that we are not yet allowed to use class variables):

PROPOSITION 1.4.   $\text{Ext} + \Delta_0\text{-AusS} + \text{Fund} + \text{PR}_{\text{Trans}} \vdash \text{FundS}$.

PROOF.   Let $\psi$ denote the negation of the formula we wish to prove, i.e.

$$\varphi(a) \wedge \forall x\, [\varphi(x) \to \exists y\, (\varphi(y) \wedge y \in x)],$$

and let $a, a_1, \ldots, a_n$ be all the free variables occurring in $\psi$. Applying $\text{PR}_{\text{Trans}}$, we obtain

(i)          $\psi(a) \to \exists u\, [\text{Trans}(u) \wedge a, a_1, \ldots, a_n \in u \wedge \psi''(a)]$.

By the recursive definition of relativization, we have:

$$\psi^b(a) \leftrightarrow \varphi^b(a) \wedge \forall x \in b\, [\varphi^b(x) \to \exists y \in b(\varphi^b(y) \wedge y \in x)].$$

Using $\Delta_0\text{-AusS}$, there is a set $c$ such that

$$\forall x\, (x \in c \leftrightarrow x \in b \wedge \varphi^b(x)).$$

Then

$$a \in b \wedge \psi^b(a) \to a \in c \wedge \forall x \in c\, \exists y \in c\, y \in x,$$

(ii)          $\exists u\, (a \in u \wedge \psi''(a)) \to \exists u\, [a \in u \wedge \forall x \in u\, \exists y \in u\, y \in x]$.

But the conclusion of (ii) contradicts the axiom of foundation, hence by contraposition and using (ii), we obtain $\sim \psi$.

1.1.5.   We summarize these results as follows, considering the following theories:

$$T_1' = \text{Ext} + \Delta_0\text{-AusS} + \text{PR}_{\text{Trans}},$$
$$T_2' = \text{Ext} + \Delta_0\text{-AusS} + \text{PR}_{\text{Strans}},$$
$$T_3' = \text{Ext} + \Delta_0\text{-AusS} + \text{CR}_{\text{Trans}},$$
$$T_4' = \text{Ext} + \Delta_0\text{-AusS} + \text{CR}_{\text{Strans}},$$
$$T_i = T_i' + \text{Fund} \quad \text{for } i = 1, \ldots, 4.$$

Then we have the following results:

$$T_1' \vdash Pair + Sum + Inf, \qquad T_2' \vdash T_1' + Pow,$$
$$T_3' \vdash T_1' + ReplS, \qquad T_4' \vdash T_2' + Pow + ReplS,$$

in particular, $T_4 \vdash ZF$. (We shall see later that $ZF \vdash T_4$, too.) The relationship between these theories may be illustrated by the following diagram ($T_i \to T_j$ means: $T_j$ is an extension of $T_i$):

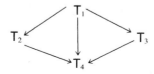

It can be shown that all these extensions are proper (assuming consistency, of course): LÉVY–VAUGHT [1961] proved that $T_4$ ($= ZF$) is "essentially reflexive" over $T_2$, in particular $T_4$ is properly stronger than $T_2$. Moreover, it can be proved (in ZFC or ZF + "The countable union of countable sets is countable") that $H(\omega_1)$, the set of hereditarily-countable sets, is a model of $T_3$ (cf. GLOEDE [1970], p. 31), but obviously it does not satisfy the axiom of power set. From these results it is immediate that all the extensions depicted in the above diagram are proper (and neither $T_2$ is an extension of $T_3$ nor conversely). In particular, the full axiom schema of replacement is not derivable in $T_2$ (assuming consistency). On the other hand, in $T_1$ with $PR_{Trans}$ restricted to $\Sigma$-formulas one obtains the axiom of replacement for $\Sigma$-functions.[1] Similarly, in $T_2$ (possibly with a restricted $PR_{Strans}$) one can prove the $\Sigma_1(\mathscr{P})$-replacement schema of KUNEN [1972], and hence $T_2$ is quite a strong set theory (KUNEN [1972], pp. 589ff and LÉVY–VAUGHT [1961], §2) provided the $\Delta_0$-Aussonderungsaxiom of $T_2$ is being replaced by a stronger schema (possibly the full schema of subsets). This suggests that the systems $T_1$ and $T_2$, with reflection restricted to suitable classes of formulas, may be more reasonable theories than $T_1$ and $T_2$.

Reflection principles in Ackermann's set theory have been investigated by LÉVY [1965] (Appendix C), LÉVY–VAUGHT [1961], and REINHARDT [1967], [1970].

### 1.2. Introducing class terms

The language $\mathscr{L}_{ZF}$ of set theory has been introduced as the usual first-order language with two binary-relation symbols denoting equality

---

[1] See, e.g. BARWISE [1969], Lemma 2.2. The Kripke–Platek theory KP of admissible sets is the theory obtained from $T_1$ by restricting the reflection schema to $\Sigma$-formulas and adding the axiom schema of foundation. The above mentioned result, however, does not require the latter schema.

and membership relation respectively. This is a particularly simple language as far as the metamathematics of set theory is concerned. On the other hand, for the development of set theory within this language, it is often more convenient to extend the basic language by introducing class terms (e.g. in the proof of Theorem 1.1 we already spoke of the "function" defined by a particular formula). This can be done in such a way that every formula of the extended language, possibly containing class terms, is equivalent to a formula of the basic language. As usual we proceed as follows: The basic language $\mathscr{L}_{ZF}$ is extended by adding *class terms* of the form $\{x \mid \cdots\}$ and adding the following formation rules for formulas:

If $\varphi(a,\ldots)$ *is a formula of the extended language then so is the formula* $a \in \{x \mid \varphi(x,\ldots)\}$.

Moreover, we add to the usual axioms and rules of the predicate calculus with equality the following schema:

CH $\qquad\qquad a \in \{x \mid \varphi(x,\ldots)\} \leftrightarrow \varphi(a,\ldots)$ $\qquad\qquad$ (Church)

by means of which class terms can be eliminated in an obvious way.[1] Following QUINE [1963] (cf. also JENSEN [1967]), we may even extend the logical frame further by introducing syntactical variables for class terms. In order to distinguish notationally from the class variables $A, B,\ldots$ to be introduced in the next chapter, we use $\boldsymbol{A}, \boldsymbol{B},\ldots$ to denote class terms in the above sense. Note that a formula containing such a syntactical variable $\boldsymbol{A}$ denotes a schema of formulas of the extended language, in contradistinction to a formula containing a (formal) class variable $A$.

With respect to these class terms, it is convenient to define equality and membership relation between class terms and (set) terms by the following schema of definitions:

$$t_1 = t_2 :\leftrightarrow \forall x\, (x \in t_1 \leftrightarrow x \in t_2), \qquad t_1 \in t_2 :\leftrightarrow \exists x\, (x = t_1 \wedge x \in t_2)$$

if $t_1$ and $t_2$ are class terms or set variables, but not both set variables.

It is now possible to rewrite the axiom schema of replacement in the following form (assuming the axiom of pairing):

$$\text{Ft}\,(\boldsymbol{F}) \wedge \exists x\, (x = \text{dom}\,(\boldsymbol{F})) \to \exists y\, (y = \text{rng}\,(\boldsymbol{F}))$$

where we have made use of the following definitions:

$$\text{Ft}\,(\boldsymbol{F}) :\leftrightarrow \forall z\, (z \in \boldsymbol{F} \to \exists x,y\, (z = \langle x,y \rangle)) \wedge$$
$$\forall x,y,z\, (\langle x,y \rangle \in \boldsymbol{F} \wedge \langle x,z \rangle \in \boldsymbol{F} \to y = z) \quad \text{``}\boldsymbol{F}\text{ is a function''},$$

---

[1] As long as we have not introduced class variables, we use the word "class term" for class abstracts of the form $\{x \mid \varphi(x,\ldots)\}$ whereas BERNAYS [1961] uses the word "class term" to denote either a class variable or a class term of the form $\{x \mid \varphi(x,\ldots)\}$ (in a somewhat extended sense insofar as $\varphi$ may contain class variables).

$$\text{dom}\,(F) := \{x \mid \exists y\,(\langle x,y\rangle \in F)\} \quad \text{\textit{"domain of F"}},$$
$$\text{rng}\,(F) := \{y \mid \exists x\,(\langle x,y\rangle \in F)\} \quad \text{\textit{"range of F"}}.$$

For the following discussion let us assume the following *convention*: By $\varphi(a_0,\ldots,a_m,A_0,\ldots,A_n)$ we denote the formula of the extended language obtained from the formula $\varphi(a_0,\ldots,a_m,b_0,\ldots,b_n)$ of the basic language $\mathscr{L}_{\text{ZF}}$ by substituting $A_i$ for $b_i$ for $i = 0,\ldots,n$. We now extend the notion of relativization to formulas of the extended language by requiring that for any formula $\varphi(a_0,\ldots,a_m,b_0,\ldots,b_n)$ of the basic language and any class terms $A_0,\ldots,A_m$

$$\text{Rel}\,(a,\varphi(a_0,\ldots,a_m,A_0,\ldots,A_n)) \quad \text{or} \quad (\psi(a_0,\ldots,a_m,A_0,\ldots,A_n)^a)$$

to be the formula $\text{Rel}\,(a,\psi)$ where $\psi$ is a formula of $\mathscr{L}_{\text{ZF}}$ obtained from $\varphi(a_0,\ldots,a_m,A_0,\ldots,A_n)$ by eliminating the class terms occurring in this formula in some canonical way. Alternatively, we may proceed as follows: We define by recursion the relativization of formulas and class terms of the extended language as follows:

$\text{Rel}\,(a,\varphi) = \varphi$ if $\varphi$ is atomic,

$\text{Rel}\,(a, \rightarrow \varphi) = \rightarrow \text{Rel}\,(a,\varphi)$, similarly for the propositional
$\qquad\qquad\qquad\qquad\qquad$ connectives $\wedge$, $\vee$, $\rightarrow$, and $\leftrightarrow$,

$\text{Rel}\,(a, \forall x\,\varphi) = \forall x \in a\,\text{Rel}\,(a,\varphi)$,

$\text{Rel}\,(a, \exists x\,\varphi) = \exists x \in a\,\text{Rel}\,(a,\varphi)$,

$\text{Rel}\,(a,b \in \{x \mid \varphi\}) = b \in \{x \mid \text{Rel}\,(a,\varphi)\}$,

$\text{Rel}\,(a,\{x \mid \varphi\}) = \{x \mid \varphi\}^a = \{x \mid \text{Rel}\,(a,\varphi)\}$.

Thus $\text{Rel}\,(a,\varphi(a_0,\ldots,a,A_0,\ldots,A_n))$ may also be defined by the formula $\varphi^a(a_0,\ldots,a_m,A_0^a,\ldots,A_n^a)$ which is obtained from $\varphi(a_0,\ldots,a_m,A_0,\ldots,A_n)$ by relativizing the quantifiers occurring in this formula to $a$ and substituting $A_i^a$ for $A_i$.

Now suppose again that $\varphi(a_0,\ldots,a_m,A_0,\ldots,A_n)$ is a formula of the extended language. Then the partial reflection principle $\text{PR}_\psi$ applied to such a formula and particular class terms (or, more exactly, to the equivalent formula of the basic language) yields

(+) $\qquad \varphi(a_0,\ldots,a_m,A_0,\ldots,A_n) \rightarrow \exists u\,[\psi(u)\wedge a_0,\ldots,a_m \in u$
$$\wedge\,\varphi^u(a_0,\ldots,a_m,A_0^u,\ldots,A_n^u)].$$

(We assume that the free variables of $\varphi(a_0,\ldots,a_m,A_0,\ldots,A_n)$ are among $a_0,\ldots,a_m$—note that the class terms may contain free variables.)

If $\psi(a) \rightarrow \text{Trans}\,(a)$, we may replace $A_i^u$ by $A_i^u \cap u$ in (+) (here we need the assumption on the free variables).[1] However, in general $A^a \cap a$ need not be equal to $A \cap a$ (even if $a$ is transitive); in fact, the principle

$$\exists u \; (\psi(u) \wedge A^u \cap u = A \cap u)$$

is a principle of complete reflection. Thus, in order to obtain the axiom of replacement, we either have to use a schema of complete reflection (cf. the proof of Theorem 1.1: we have made essential use of the fact that the formula defining a function is absolute with respect to some appropriate set $c$), or as in BERNAYS [1961], use a schema of partial reflection for formulas containing class variables which remain unchanged under the process of relativization. (It follows from Theorem 1.2 below that the latter principle implies the schema of complete reflection $CR_{\text{Trans}}$.) However, even without introducing free class variables, within the logical frame of ZF set theory, modified by the use of syntactical variables for class terms, we can treat these variables like the free class variables in Bernays' schema and consider the following principle:

$$PR\Pi_\omega^0 \qquad \varphi(a_0,\dots,a_m,A_0,\dots,A_n) \to \exists u \; [\text{Trans}(u)$$
$$\wedge \; \varphi^u(a_0,\dots,a_m,A_0 \cap u,\dots,A_n \cap u)]$$

(where $\varphi(a_0,\dots,a_m,A_0,\dots,A_n)$ is a formula of the extended language in the sense explained above).

Using an argument from Remark 1.1 it can easily be seen that we may add the clause $a_0 \in u \wedge \cdots \wedge a_m \in u$ as a conjunctive member within the scope of $\exists u$ in the principle above, and in this form $A_i \cap u$ may be replaced by $A_i$.

LEMMA 1.2.    $\text{Ext} + \Delta_0\text{-AusS} + PR\Pi_\omega^0 \vdash \text{Pair}$.

PROOF.    Apply $PR\Pi_\omega^0$ to the formula $\exists x \; (x = a_0) \wedge \exists x \; (x = a_1)$.

One can now use the method of BERNAYS [1961], pp. 133ff. to show that $PR\Pi_\omega^0$ (together with the axioms mentioned in Lemma 1.10) implies the axiom schema of replacement (using a class term $F$ instead of a free class variable $F$ as in Bernays' paper). Alternatively, we can prove the following

THEOREM 1.2.    $\text{Ext} + \Delta_0\text{-AusS} + PR\Pi_\omega^0 \vdash CR_{\text{Trans}}$.

PROOF.    Let $\varphi(a_0,\dots,a_n)$ to be a formula of $\mathscr{L}_{ZF}$ with free variables as

---

[1] Thus, we could also define the relativization of a class term $\text{Rel}(a,\{x \mid \varphi\})$ to be $\{x \mid x \in a \wedge \text{Rel}(a,\varphi)\}$, provided $a$ is transitive and $a_0,\dots,a_k \in a$ where $a_0,\dots,a_k$ are the free variables of $\varphi$.

indicated and define

$$A := \{y \mid \exists x_0 \cdots x_n \ (y = \langle x_0, \ldots, x_n \rangle \wedge \varphi(x_0, \ldots, x_n))\},$$

$$\psi(A,a) := \exists x \ (a = x) \wedge \forall x,y \ \exists z \ (z = \langle x,y \rangle)$$
$$\wedge \ \forall x_0 \cdots x_n \ (\exists y \ (y = \langle x_0, \ldots, x_n \rangle \wedge y \in A)$$
$$\leftrightarrow \varphi(x_0, \ldots, x_n)).$$

By Lemma 1.2, $\psi(A,a)$ is provable in the theory considered, hence by $\mathrm{PRII}_\omega^0$ there is a transitive set $b$ such that

$$a \in b \wedge \forall x,y \in b \langle x,y \rangle \in b \wedge \forall x_0 \cdots x_n \in b \ (\exists y \in b \ (y = \langle x_0, \ldots, x_n \rangle$$
$$\wedge \ y \in A \cap b) \leftrightarrow \varphi^b(x_0, \ldots, x_n)),$$

therefore,

$$a \in b \wedge \forall x_0 \cdots x_n \in b \ (\varphi(x_0, \ldots, x_n) \leftrightarrow \varphi^b(x_0, \ldots, x_n)).$$

Let $\mathsf{T}_5$ denote the theory $\mathsf{Ext} + \Delta_0\text{-}\mathsf{AusS} + \mathsf{Fund} + \mathsf{Pow} + \mathrm{PRII}_\omega^0$. Then we have the following

COROLLARY 1.3. $\mathsf{T}_5 \vdash \mathsf{T}_4$ *and* $\mathsf{T}_5 \vdash \mathsf{ZF}$.

We shall see later that $\mathsf{ZF} \vdash \mathsf{T}_5$ and, moreover, $\mathrm{PRII}_\omega^0$ can be further strengthened to yield a principle of complete reflection which is related to $\mathrm{PRII}_\omega^0$ like $\mathsf{CR}_{\mathrm{Trans}}$ to $\mathsf{PR}_{\mathrm{Trans}}$.

1.3. *Derivation of reflection principles in* ZF *set theory*

In this section we shall make further use of class terms in deriving principles of reflection in ZF set theory. For this purpose it is convenient to use the concept of *normal functions*:

*Ordinals* are defined as usual in such a way that they are well ordered by the $\in$-relation:

$$\mathrm{ord}\,(a) :\leftrightarrow \mathrm{Trans}\,(a) \wedge \forall x,y \in a \ (x \in y \vee x = y \vee y \in x)$$
$$\wedge \ \forall z \ (z \subseteq a \rightarrow z = 0 \vee \exists x \in z \ \forall y \in x \ (y \notin z))$$
$$a \text{ is an ordinal}$$

$$\mathrm{On} := \{x \mid \mathrm{ord}\,(x)\} \text{ is the } \textit{class of ordinals},$$

$$a + 1 := a \cup \{a\}, \ \lim(a) :\leftrightarrow \mathrm{ord}\,(a) \wedge a \neq 0 \wedge \forall x \in a \ \exists y \in a \ (x \in y).$$

Assuming the axiom of foundation, the last conjunctive member in the definition of an ordinal is redundant, and in this case $\mathrm{ord}\,(a)$ is defined by a $\Delta_0$-formula. We use lowercase greek letters to denote ordinals.

A *normal function* is one defined on the class of all ordinals, with range included in the class of ordinals and which is strictly increasing and continuous:

$$\text{Nft}\,(F) :\leftrightarrow \text{Ft}\,(F) \wedge \text{dom}\,(F) = \text{On} \wedge \text{rng}\,(F) \subseteq \text{On}$$
$$\wedge\ \forall x,y \in \text{On}\,(x \in y \to F(x) \in F(y))$$
$$\wedge\ \forall x\ (\text{Lim}\,(x) \to F(x) = \cup\,\{F(y)\,|\,y \in x\}).$$

For the remaining part of this section we assume the usual axioms of ZF. It is easy to see that the composition of normal functions is again a normal function and that every normal function $F$ has arbitrary large critical points (i.e. ordinals $\alpha$ such that $\alpha = F(\alpha)$).

Using transfinite induction one can prove that there is a sequence of sets $\langle V_x\,|\,x \in \text{On}\rangle$ satisfying the recursive conditions

$$V_0 = \emptyset, \qquad V_{\alpha+1} = \mathscr{P}(V_\alpha), \qquad \text{Lim}\,(a) \to V_a = \cup\,\{V_x\,|\,x \in a\},$$

and $V = \cup\{V_x | x \in \text{On}\}$ by the axiom of foundation. ($V_\alpha$ is $\psi(\alpha)$ in BERNAYS [1961], p. 146.)

METATHEOREM 1.1 (Scott–Scarpellini).  *For every formula* $\varphi(v_0,\dots,v_n)$ *of* $\mathscr{L}_{\text{ZF}}$ *with free variables as indicated there is a normal function* $F$ *(depending on* $\varphi$*) such that*

$$F(\alpha) = \alpha \to \forall x_0 \cdots x_n \in V_\alpha\ (\varphi(x_0,\dots,x_n) \leftrightarrow \text{Rel}\,(V_\alpha,\varphi(x_0,\dots,x_n))).$$

PROOF.   A proof can be found e.g. in MOSTOWSKI [1969], p. 23 where the proof is given in Quine–Morse set theory. The above version, however, which uses the concept of relativization rather than a formalized version of satisfaction for classes (which is not definable in ZF) can be proved in ZF along the lines of Mostowski's proof. (See also KRIVINE [1971], Ch. IV.)

Since the $V_\alpha$'s are supertransitive, we obtain:

COROLLARY 1.4.   $\text{ZF} \vdash \text{CR}_{\text{Strans}}$, *and hence* $\text{ZF} \vdash \text{T}_4$.

Metatheorem 1.1 has a further corollary for class terms:

COROLLR 1.5.  *For every class term* $A$ *with free variables among* $v_0,\dots,v_n$ *there is a normal function* $F$ *such that*

$$F(\alpha) = \alpha \to \forall x_0 \cdots x_n \in V_\alpha\ (A \cap V_\alpha = \text{Rel}\,(V_\alpha,A) \cap V_\alpha).$$

Combining Metatheorem 1.1 and Corollary 1.4, and using the fact that the composition of finitely many normal functions $F_1,\dots,F_k$ is again a normal function whose critical points are critical points of each $F_i$ we obtain:

COROLLARY 1.6.  *For every formula* $\varphi(a_0,\dots,a_m,b_0,\dots,b_n)$ *of* $\mathscr{L}_{\text{ZF}}$ *and every class terms* $A_0,\dots,A_n$ *such that the free variables of*

$\varphi(a_0,\ldots,a_m,A_0,\ldots,A_n)$ *are among* $a_0,\ldots,a_m$ *there is a normal function* $F$ *such that*

$$F(\alpha) = \alpha \rightarrow \forall x_0 \cdots x_m \in V_\alpha [\varphi(x_0,\ldots,x_m,A_0,\ldots,A_n) \leftrightarrow \varphi V_\alpha(x_0,\ldots,x_m,A_0$$
$$\cap V_\alpha,\ldots,A_n \cap V_\alpha)].$$

COROLLARY 1.7.   $\mathsf{ZF} \vdash \mathrm{PR}\Pi_\omega^0$, *and hence* $\mathsf{ZF} \vdash \mathsf{T}_5$.

As a further consequence of Corollary 1.6, the principle $\mathrm{PR}\Pi_\omega^0$ of partial reflection can be strengthened in $\mathsf{ZF}$ to the following principle of complete reflection:

$\mathrm{CR}\Pi_\omega^0$   $\exists u [\mathrm{Trans}\,(u) \wedge \forall x_0 \cdots x_m \in u(\varphi(x_0,\ldots,x_m,A_0,\ldots,A_n)$

$\leftrightarrow \varphi^u(x_0,\ldots,x_m,A_0 \cap u,\ldots,A_n \cap u))]$

where $\varphi$ and $A_0,\ldots,A_n$ are as in Corollary 1.6. (In addition, $\mathrm{Trans}\,(u)$ may be replaced by $\mathrm{Strans}\,(u)$.)

This possibility of strengthening a principle of partial reflection to the corresponding principle of complete reflection is a peculiar feature of $\mathrm{PR}\Pi_\omega^0$ (possibly with $\mathrm{Strans}\,(u)$ in place of $\mathrm{Trans}\,(u)$) and the schema $\mathrm{PR}\Pi_0^1$ to be introduced later, since in general the principle of complete reflection $\mathrm{CR}(\Sigma)$ is stronger than the corresponding principle of partial reflection $\mathrm{PR}(\Sigma)$ for the same set of formulas $\Sigma$. For example cf. the end of §1.1, §2.1, and remark (2), p. 305.

## 2. From class terms to class variables

### 2.1. *Bernays' set theory* B

In the preceding chapter we introduced a version of $\mathsf{ZF}$ set theory which allows for the use of class terms and even has syntactical variables $A, B, \ldots$ for arbitrary class terms. Replacing these syntactical variables by formal class variables $A, B, \ldots$ we obtain Bernays' set theory B (as in his 1958 monograph).

The language $\mathscr{L}_\mathsf{B}$ of B is an extension of the basic language $\mathscr{L}_\mathsf{Z}\mathsf{F}$ of $\mathsf{ZF}$ which has in addition free-class variables $A, B, \ldots$, but no bound-class variables. The formulas of this language will be denoted by capital greek letters $\Phi, \Psi, \ldots$. For simplicity, we assume that the language of $B$ has atomic formulas only of the form $u \in v$, $u = v$, and $u \in A$. We use the same symbol of equality "$=$" in formulas of the form $t = s$ where $t$ and $s$ are set or class variables; in case at least one of $t, s$ is a class variable, $t = s$ is defined according to the principle of extensionality (cf. §1.2). Thus, we write $a = A$ for $\mathrm{Rep}\,(A,a)$ (BERNAYS [1958]) and $a \equiv A$ (BERNAYS [1961]). Similarly we define $A \in t :\leftrightarrow \exists x (x = A \wedge x \in t)$ if $t$ is a class or a set variable (cf. §1.2). We further assume that formulas of B do not contain any class terms (apart from class variables); formulas of the form $a \in \{x \mid \Phi(x,\ldots)\}$ are regarded as "abbreviations" of $\Phi(a,\ldots)$. (Alternatively we may assume that class terms of the above kind are eliminated from formulas of B by means of the (extended) Church schema.)

We assume a suitable system of logical axioms and rules including the schema of equality $a = b. \to .\Phi(a,\ldots) \to \Phi(b,\ldots)$. (In particular, we have

$$a = b. \to .a \in A \to b \in A.)$$

Axioms for B are A1–A8 of BERNAYS [1958]; we may also use the following axioms for B:

Ext, Pair, Sum, Pow, Inf, and Fund (as in the case of ZF),

and finally

Repl[1]        $Ft\,(F) \wedge \exists x\,(x = \mathrm{dom}\,(F)) \to \exists y\,(y = \mathrm{rng}\,(F))$,

which is obtained from the axiom schema of replacement of ZF (as defined in §1.2) by replacing the syntactical variable $F$ by a free-class variable $F$.

We might call a formula of $\mathscr{L}_B$ a $\Delta_0$-formula iff it is equivalent to a formula in which all quantifiers are restricted to set variables (as in the sense of §1.1) and consider the following schema:

$\Delta_0$-AusS[1]        $\exists x\, \forall y\,(y \in x \leftrightarrow y \in a \wedge \Phi(y,\ldots))$

where $\Phi$ is any $\Delta_0$-formula of $\mathscr{L}_B$. However, since $a \in A$ is a $\Delta_0$-formula, this schema immediately gives the full *Aussonderungsaxiom* (*axiom of subsets*) of B:

Aus[1]        $\exists x\, \forall y\,(y \in x \leftrightarrow y \in a \wedge y \in A)$

We have excluded class terms from our formal language in order to simplify the notion of relativization for formulas of B: If $\Phi$ is such a formula then $\Phi^a$ (or $\mathrm{Rel}\,(a,\Phi)$) is the formula obtained from $\Phi$ by restricting any quantifiers occurring in $\Phi$ (note that there are only quantifiers on set variables) to $a$ (as in the case of a formula of $\mathscr{L}_{ZF}$). Again, if $\Phi$ contains any defined symbol or class terms then $\mathrm{Rel}\,(a,\Phi)$ is defined to be $\mathrm{Rel}\,(a,\Psi)$ where $\Psi$ is obtained from $\Phi$, by eliminating the defined symbols and the class terms occurring in $\Phi$.

Let us now consider the schema of partial reflection for formulas of the language of B:

PRII$_0$[1]        $\Phi(a_0,\ldots, a_m, A_0,\ldots, A_n) \to \exists u\,[\mathrm{Trans}\,(u)$

        $\wedge\, \Phi^u(a_0,\ldots, a_m, A_0 \cap u,\ldots, A_n \cap u)]$

where $\Phi$ is any formula of $\mathscr{L}_B$ with free variables as indicated.

REMARK. As in the case of $\text{PRII}_\omega^0$, one may add in $\text{PRII}_0^1$ the clause $a_0 \in u \wedge \cdots \wedge a_m \in u$ as a conjunctive member within the scope of $\exists u$ and replace $A_i \cap u$ by $A_i$.

THEOREM 2.1.   $\text{Ext} + \text{Aus}^1 + \text{PRII}_0^1 \vdash \text{Pair} + \text{Sum} + \text{Inf} + \text{Repl}^1$.

The axiom of pairing is proved as in Lemma 1.2. The proof of the remaining axioms is given in Bernays [1961], pp. 127, 128, and 133ff.

REMARK. Thiele's version of the axiom of replacement (Formula (19), p. 133 of BERNAYS [1961]) is in fact equivalent to (18) in B using the von Neumann rank of a set in a manner due to SCOTT [1955].

COROLLARY 2.1.   $\text{Ext} + \text{Aus}^1 + \text{Pow} + \text{Fund} + \text{PRII}_0^1 \vdash \text{B}$.

Conversely, one can prove by the method of §1.3 (Metatheorem 1.1):

METATHEOREM 2.1.   *For every formula* $\Phi(a_0, \ldots, a_m, A_0, \ldots, A_n)$ *of* $\mathscr{L}_\text{B}$ *with free variables as indicated, there is a normal function* $F$ *(more precisely, a class term* $F$ *defined by a formula of* $\mathscr{L}_\text{B}$ *which depends on* $\Phi$ *such that* $\text{B} \models Nft\,(F))$ *such that one can prove in* $\text{B}$:

$$F(\alpha) = \alpha \to \forall x_0 \cdots x_m \in V_\alpha\ (\Phi(x_0, \ldots, x_m, A_0, \ldots, A_n) \leftrightarrow$$
$$\Phi^{V_\alpha}(x_0, \ldots, x_m, A_0 \cap V_\alpha, \ldots, A_n \cap V_\alpha)).$$

Thus again $\text{PRII}_0^1$ can be strengthened in B to give a schema of complete reflection $\text{CRII}_0^1$ as in the case of $\text{PRII}_\omega^0$; similarly, if in $\text{PRII}_0^1$ and $\text{CRII}_0^1$, we replace Trans $(u)$ by Strans $(u)$, in this case the stronger principles imply the axiom of power set (cf. Proposition 1.2). Note that the proof of Metatheorem 2.1 is similar to the proof of Metatheorem 1.1 rather than Corollary 1.6, since $a \in A$ is now an atomic formula (whereas $a \in A$ need not be equivalent to an atomic formula in ZF). In fact, Corollary 1.6 can be proved along the lines of the proof of Metatheorem 1.1 by treating $a \in A$ as an atomic formula.

Thus we have the following results (as usual we write $\text{T}_1 = \text{T}_2$ to mean that $\text{T}_1$ and $\text{T}_2$ have the same theorems):

$$\text{ZF} = \text{Ext} + \Delta_0\text{-AusS} + \text{Pow} + \text{Fund} + \text{PRII}_\omega^0,$$
$$\text{B} = \text{Ext} + \Delta_0\text{-AusS}^1 + \text{Pow} + \text{Fund} + \text{PRII}_0^1,$$

and we can delete the axioms of power set on the right-hand sides if the respective schemata of partial reflection assert the existence of a "reflecting" set $a$ such that Strans $(a)$ rather than Trans $(a)$.

## 2.2. *Montague–Vaught's theorem*

Before presenting various results from MONTAGUE–VAUGHT [1959], we recall some definitions (throughout this section we assume the axioms of ZF): $\omega$ is the least infinite ordinal (and the set of natural numbers),

$$\text{Osq}\,(f) :\leftrightarrow \text{Ft}\,(f) \wedge \text{dom}\,(f) \in \text{On} \wedge \text{rng}\,(f) \subseteq \text{On}$$

"$f$ is a sequence of ordinals",

$$\text{AOsq}\,(f) :\leftrightarrow \text{Osq}\,(f) \wedge \forall x,y \,(x \in y \wedge y \in \text{dom}\,(f) \rightarrow f(x) \in f(y))$$

"$f$ is an ascending sequence of ordinals".
  If $f$ is a function such that $a \subseteq \text{dom}\,(f)$, then

$$\sup_{x \in a} f(x) := \cup \{f(x) \mid x \in a\}, \qquad \sup_{x \in a}{}^{+} f(x) := \cup \{f(x)+1 \mid x \in a\}.$$

$$\text{Nft}\,(f,\alpha) :\leftrightarrow \text{AOsq}\,(f) \wedge \text{dom}\,(f) = \alpha \wedge \text{rng}\,(f) \subseteq \alpha \wedge \forall x \in \alpha \,(\lim\,(x) \rightarrow$$

$$f(x) = \sup_{y \in x} f(y))$$

"$f$ is a normal function on $\alpha$",

$$\text{conf}\,(\alpha,\beta) :\leftrightarrow \exists s \,(\text{AOsq}\,(s) \wedge \text{dom}\,(s) = \beta \wedge \alpha = \sup_{x \in \beta}{}^{+} s(x)),$$

$$\text{cf}\,(\alpha) := \mu x \,\text{conf}\,(\alpha,x)$$

($\mu x \,\varphi(x)$ denotes the least ordinal $x$ such that $\varphi(x)$ if there is such an $x$, 0 otherwise),

$$\text{reg}\,(\alpha) :\leftrightarrow \text{cf}\,(\alpha) = \alpha$$

"$\alpha$ is regular",

$$\text{sing}\,(\alpha) :\leftrightarrow \neg\, \text{reg}\,(\alpha)$$

"$\alpha$ is singular",

$$\text{in}\,(\alpha) :\leftrightarrow \alpha > \omega \wedge \forall f \,(\text{Ft}\,(f) \wedge \text{dom}\,(f) \in V_\alpha$$

$$\wedge \,\text{rng}\,(f) \subseteq V_\alpha \rightarrow \text{rng}\,(f) \in V_\alpha)$$

"$\alpha$ is (strongly) inaccessible".
  Any infinite regular ordinal is a limit number, an inaccessible ordinal is regular. Assuming the axiom of choice AC, inaccessibles can also be characterized as follows (MONTAGUE–VAUGHT [1959], Lemma 6.4):

(ZFC)      $\text{in}\,(\alpha) \leftrightarrow \alpha > \omega \wedge \text{reg}\,(\alpha) \wedge \forall x \in \alpha \,(|\mathscr{P}(x)| \in \alpha),$

where $|a|$ denotes the cardinal number of $a$ (assuming AC).
  The formal notion of satisfaction for first-order formulas in a structure which is a set can be extended for second-order formulas of set theory (which are obtained from the language of B by admitting even bound-

class variables $\forall X_i$ and $\exists X_i$) in several ways. Here we decide to reduce the notion of satisfaction for the latter class of formulas in a structure of the form $\langle a, \in \rangle$ to the satisfaction of first-order formulas in the structure $\langle \mathcal{P}(a), \in \rangle$ as follows: As in §1.1.2 one can assign to each second-order set-theoretical formula $\Phi$ a term $\ulcorner \Phi \urcorner$ (the Gödel number of $\Phi$) and define in ZF a set $\mathrm{Fml}^2$ which intuitively represents the set of all such Gödel numbers such that $\mathrm{ZF} \vdash \ulcorner \Phi \urcorner \in \mathrm{Fml}^2$ for each second-order formula $\Phi$. Moreover, one can define in ZF a function $*$ which assigns in a suitable way to each $e \in \mathrm{Fml}^2$ a set $e^* \in \mathrm{Fml}_{\mathrm{ZF}}$. Instead of giving a formal definition of $*$ (this would presuppose an explicit definition of $\mathrm{Fml}_{\mathrm{ZF}}$ and $\mathrm{Fml}^2$ as well as several syntactical concepts) we describe it informally. If $\Phi(v_0, \ldots, v_m, A_0, \ldots, A_n)$ is a second-order formula of set theory, $\Phi^*$ is the formula of $\mathcal{L}_{\mathrm{ZF}}$ obtained as follows: replace the second-order variables $A_0, \ldots, A_n$ by the first-order variables $v_{m+2}, \ldots, v_{m+n+2}$ (renaming bound variables in $\Phi$, if there are any among $v_{m+1}, \ldots, v_{m+n+2}$), replace any first-order quantifier $\forall x\ (\exists x)$ occurring in $\Phi$ by $\forall x \in v_{m+1}\ (\exists x \in v_{m+1}$ resp.) and any second-order quantifier $\forall X\ (\exists X)$ by a first-order quantifier $\forall x\ (\exists x$ resp.) for some suitably chosen set variable $x$. We then define

$$\langle a, \in \rangle \models \Phi[a; b]$$

for a formula $\Phi$ as above, and a sequence $a$ of $m + 1$ elements of $a$, and a sequence $b$ of $n + 1$ elements of $\mathcal{P}(a)$ by

$$\langle \mathcal{P}(a), \in \rangle \models \Phi^*[c]$$

where $c$ is the sequence of $n + m + 3$ elements

$$a(0), \ldots, a(m), a, b(0), \ldots, b(n)$$

This means that we interpret class variables in a structure $\langle a, \in \rangle$ as ranging over the set of subsets of $a$. We denote by

$$\langle a, \in \rangle \models^2 e[a; b],$$

or (though notationally not quite correct),

$$\langle a, \in \rangle \models^2 e[a(0), \ldots, a(m); b(0), \ldots, b(n)],$$

if $n$ and $m$ are suitably chosen, the satisfaction predicate for second-order formulas of set theory formalized within ZF set theory in a manner described above informally. (For more details the reader may consult MOSTOWSKI [1969] or BOWEN [1972]. In Mostowski's book, however, this notion of satisfaction is defined for structures $\langle A, \in \rangle$ (where $A$ may be a proper class) in Quine–Morse set theory; the same definition, restricted to structures which are sets, can be defined in ZF set theory).

As usual, we write

$$\langle a, \in \rangle \models^2 \ulcorner \Phi \urcorner \quad \text{for} \langle a, \in \rangle \models^2 \ulcorner \forall x_0 \cdots x_m \; \forall X_0 \cdots X_n \; \Phi \urcorner,$$

or, equivalently,

$$\forall x_0 \cdots x_m \in a \; \forall y_0 \cdots y_n \subseteq a \; (\langle a, \in \rangle \models^2 \ulcorner \Phi \urcorner [x_0, \ldots, x_m; y_0, \ldots, y_n])$$

if $\Phi$ is a second-order formula with free first-order variables among $v_0, \ldots, v_m$ and free second-order (class) variables among $A_0, \ldots, A_n$. Also

$$\langle a, \in \rangle \models^2 E \quad \text{and} \quad \langle a, \in \rangle \models^2 \ulcorner \Phi_1 + \Phi_2 \urcorner$$

for a schema or a set of second-order formulas $E$ and formulas $\Phi_1$, $\Phi_2$ is assumed to be defined as usual. Finally, $\langle a, \in \rangle < \langle b, \in \rangle$ is a formal version (definable in ZF) of the predicate "$\langle a, \in \rangle$ is an elementary subsystem (with respect to first-order formulas, i.e. with respect to formulas of $\mathcal{L}_{ZF}$) of $\langle b, \in \rangle$" in the sense of TARSKI–VAUGHT [1957].

In order to simplify notation, we often identify a formula with its Gödel number (similarly in the case of a set of formulas) and write e.g. $\langle a, \in \rangle \models \mathsf{Ext}$ or $\langle a, \in \rangle \models^2 \mathsf{B}$, since in these cases the use of the symbols $\models$ or $\models^2$ indicates that we are dealing with the formal counterparts of the respective (metamathematical) satisfaction relations.

Using these definitions it can be shown (cf. MONTAGUE–VAUGHT [1959], p. 234):

LEMMA 2.1. *If $a \neq 0$ and $\alpha \neq 0$, then*

(i) $\quad$ Trans $(a) \to \langle a, \in \rangle \models \mathsf{Ext} + \mathsf{Fund}$,

(ii) $\quad$ lim $(\alpha) \to \langle V_\alpha, \in \rangle \models \mathsf{Pair} + \mathsf{Sum} + \mathsf{Pow}$,

(iii) $\quad \omega \in \alpha \to \langle V_\alpha, \in \rangle \models \mathsf{Inf}$,

(iv) $\quad \langle V_\alpha, \in \rangle \models^2 \mathsf{B} \leftrightarrow \text{in} \, (\alpha)$,

(v) $\quad \langle V_\alpha, \in \rangle \models^2 \mathsf{B} \to \langle V_\alpha, \in \rangle \models \mathsf{ZF}$,

(vi) $\quad \text{in} \, (\alpha) \to \text{reg} \, (\alpha)$.

The converse of (v) is not true. This is a consequence of the following:

THEOREM 2.2 (Montague–Vaught).

$$\langle V_\alpha, \in \rangle \models^2 \mathsf{B} \to \exists \xi < \alpha \; \langle V_\xi, \in \rangle < \langle V_\alpha, \in \rangle.$$

PROOF. We indicate a proof of the informal version of this theorem using the method of MOSTOWSKI [1969], pp. 25f. Let $\langle \varphi_n | n < \omega \rangle$ be an enumeration of the formulas of $\mathcal{L}_{ZF}$ such that the free variables of $\varphi_n$ are among $v_0, \ldots, v_n$. Since $V_\alpha$ is a model of ZF, by Scott–Scarpellini's Metatheorem 1.1 there exists for each $n$ a function $f_n$ (definable in $V_\alpha$)

such that Nft $(f_n,\alpha)$ and

$$\forall \xi < \alpha \,[f_n(\xi) = \xi \to \forall x_0 \cdots x_n \in V_\xi \,(\mathrm{Rel}\,(V_\alpha, \varphi_n(x_0,\ldots,x_n))$$
$$\leftrightarrow \mathrm{Rel}\,(V_\xi, \varphi_n(x_0,\ldots,x_n)))].$$

Define a function $f$ on $\alpha$ by recursion on $\beta < \alpha$ such that $f(0) = 1$, $f(\beta + 1) = \max\,(f(\beta), \sup_{n<\omega} f_n(\beta)) + 1$,

$$\mathrm{Lim}\,(\lambda) \wedge \lambda < \alpha \to f(\lambda) = \sup_{\xi<\lambda} f(\xi).$$

(Note that $f$ and the sequence $\langle f_n | n < \omega \rangle$ are definable in ZF but not in $V_\alpha$.) Obviously, $f$ is strictly increasing and continuous. Any critical point of $f$ is a critical point of each $f_n$, hence if $f(\beta) = \beta$ then for all $n < \omega$:

$$\forall x_0,\ldots, x_n \in V_\beta \,(\mathrm{Rel}\,(V_\alpha, \varphi_n(x_0,\ldots,x_n)) \leftrightarrow \mathrm{Rel}\,(V_\beta, \varphi_n(x_0,\ldots,x_n))).$$

Finally, it remains to show that $f$ has a critical point. In fact, if reg $(\alpha) \wedge \alpha > \omega$ (in particular, if $V_\alpha$ is a model of B by Lemma 2.1 (iv)), then we have Nft $(f,\alpha)$ and even Nft $(g,\alpha)$ where $g$ is the function enumerating the critical points of $f$ in increasing order.

A subset $a \subseteq \alpha$ is called *closed unbounded* in $\alpha$ iff it is the range of a normal function on $\alpha$:

$$\text{clo unb}\,(a,\alpha) :\leftrightarrow \exists f\,(\mathrm{Nft}\,(f,\alpha) \wedge a = \mathrm{rng}\,(f)).$$

Incidentally, we have thus proved the following stronger result:

COROLLARY 2.2.

$$\text{reg}\,(\alpha) \wedge \langle V_\alpha, \in \rangle \models \mathrm{ZF} \to \exists x \subseteq \alpha\,(\text{clo unb}\,(x,\alpha) \wedge$$
$$x \subseteq \{\xi < \alpha \mid \langle V_\xi, \in \rangle < \langle V_\alpha, \in \rangle\}),$$

*in particular* (Montague–Vaught):

$$\text{in}\,(\alpha) \to \exists \xi < \alpha (\langle V_\xi, \in \rangle < \langle V_\alpha, \in \rangle \wedge \text{cf}\,(\xi) = \omega).$$

COROLLARY 2.3.   $\langle V_\alpha, \in \rangle \models^2 \mathrm{B} \to \exists \xi < \alpha \langle V_\xi, \in \rangle \models \mathrm{ZF}$.

The same result can be expressed as follows:

COROLLARY 2.4.   $\langle V_\alpha, \in \rangle \models^2 \mathrm{PR\Pi_0^1} \to \exists \xi < \alpha \langle V_\xi, \in \rangle \models \mathrm{PR\Pi_\omega^0}$.

We have seen in §2.1 (Metatheorem 2.1) that the principle $\mathrm{PR\Pi_0^1}$ can be strengthened in the theory B, in fact, if $\langle V_\alpha, \in \rangle$ is a model of B then for each formula $\Phi(a_0,\ldots, a_m, A_0,\ldots, A_n)$ of $\mathscr{L}_\mathrm{B}$ with free variables as indicated and any $b_0,\ldots, b_n \subseteq V_\alpha$, the set

$$\{\xi < \alpha \mid \forall x_0 \cdots x_m \in V_\xi \,(\mathrm{Rel}\,(V_\alpha, \Phi(x_0,\ldots, x_m, b_0,\ldots, b_n))$$
$$\leftrightarrow \mathrm{Rel}\,(V_\xi, \Phi(x_0,\ldots, x_m, b_0,\ldots, b_n)))\}$$

contains a set which is closed unbounded in $\alpha$. Combining this result with Corollary 2.2 and the fact that for any regular $\alpha > \omega$ the closed-unbounded subsets of $\alpha$ generate a filter in the power set of $\alpha$, we obtain the following result:

If $\langle V_\alpha, \in \rangle$ is a model of B then $\langle V_\alpha, \in \rangle$ satisfies the following principles:

$$(+) \quad \exists \xi \, [\langle V_\xi, \in \rangle \models \mathsf{ZF} \wedge \forall x_0 \cdots x_m \in V_\xi (\Phi(x_0, \ldots, x_m, A_0, \ldots, A_n)$$
$$\leftrightarrow \mathrm{Rel}\,(V_\xi, \Phi(x_0, \ldots, x_m, A_0, \ldots, A_n)))],$$

in particular,

$$(++) \quad \Phi(a_0, \ldots, a_m, A_0, \ldots, A_n) \to \exists u \, [\mathrm{Strans}\,(u) \wedge \langle u, \in \rangle \models \mathsf{ZF} \wedge$$
$$\wedge \mathrm{Rel}\,(u, \Phi(a_0, \ldots, a_m, A_0, \ldots, A_n))]$$

(where in both cases, $\Phi$ is any formula of $\mathscr{L}_\mathsf{B}$ with free variables as indicated). This result should be compared with schema (11g) of BERNAYS [1961], p. 141 and Lévy's principle ((I) of BERNAYS [1961], p. 122, cf. LÉVY [1960]). These latter principles have in place of the formula

$$\mathrm{Strans}\,(u) \wedge \langle u, \in \rangle \models \mathsf{ZF}$$

the formula $\mathrm{Strans}\,(u) \wedge \mathrm{Mod}\,(u)$ (Bernays), and $\mathrm{Scm}^{\mathsf{ZF}}(u)$ (Lévy), respectively. In ZF,

$$\mathrm{Strans}\,(a) \wedge \mathrm{Mod}\,(a) \leftrightarrow \mathrm{Strans}\,(a) \wedge \langle a, \in \rangle \models^2 \mathsf{B}$$
$$\leftrightarrow \mathrm{Strans}\,(a) \wedge \mathrm{Scm}^{\mathsf{ZF}}(a),$$

and Montague–Vaught's theorem shows that $\mathrm{Scm}^{\mathsf{ZF}}(a)$ and $\mathrm{Trans}\,(a) \wedge \mathrm{Mod}\,(a)$ both are stronger than $\mathrm{Trans}\,(a) \wedge \langle a, \in \rangle \models \mathsf{ZF}$ (even if we add "strans $(a)$" in both cases), and in fact the latter principles are stronger than $(++)$ and even $(+)$ (assuming consistency). On the other hand, $(++)$ is a schema which is derivable in Quine–Morse set theory (cf. p. 306) and can be used as a motivation for Lévy's principle.

Finally, as it is known that the theories B and ZF are equiconsistent, $(++)$ cannot be proved in B (again assuming that B is consistent).

### 3. Reflection principles for second-order languages

3.1. *Second-order set theory*

The language $\mathscr{L}^2$ of second-order set theory is obtained from the first-order language $\mathscr{L}_{\mathsf{ZF}}$ of ZF set theory by introducing second-order (class) variables $X_i$ $(i < \omega)$ (as in the case of set variables, we often use capital letters from the beginning of the alphabet for free variables and letters from the end for bound variables). Again, as in the case of Bernays' set theory B, we assume that we have only atomic formulas of the form $u = v$, $: \in v$ and $u \in X$ and that our formal language does not contain class terms (apart from class variables). $t = s :\leftrightarrow \forall x$ $(x \in t \leftrightarrow x \in s)$ (if $t$ and $s$ are variables, but not both set variables) and $X \in t :\leftrightarrow \exists x (x = X \wedge x \in t)$ (for a set or class variable $t$) is defined as in §4. In a suitably extended language, $\{x \mid \Phi(x)\}$ denotes the class of all sets $x$ such that $\Phi(x)$.

The axioms of von Neumann–Bernays' set theory VNB consist of the axioms of Bernays' set theory B: Ext, Pair, Sum, Pow, Inf, Fund and Repl', and the following *schema of* (*predicative*) *class formation*:

$\Pi_0^1$-Comp      $\exists X \,\forall y \,(y \in X \leftrightarrow \Phi(y, a_0, \ldots, a_m, A_0, \ldots, A_n))$,

where $\Phi$ is any formula of $\mathscr{L}^2$ containing no bound-class variables (i.e. any formula of $\mathscr{L}_B$). The language $\mathscr{L}^2$ of VNB will also be denoted by $\mathscr{L}_{VNB}$.

If we replace in VNB the $\Pi_0^1$-comprehension schema by the (*impredicative*) *schema of comprehension*

$\Pi_0^2$-Comp          $\exists X \,\forall y \,(y \in X \leftrightarrow \Phi(y, \ldots))$,

where $\Phi$ is any second-order formula, we obtain Quine–Morse set theory QM.

LEMMA 3.1 (ZF).  $\langle a, \in \rangle \models^2 \Pi_0^2$-Comp   *for any set* $a \neq \emptyset$.

PROOF.  This fact is due to the particular definition of satisfaction $\models^2$ which interprets classes in $\langle a, \in \rangle$ as subsets of $a$, and the fact that $\langle a, \in \rangle \models^2 e[x, \ldots]$ is a formula of ZF set theory.

COROLLARY 3.1 (ZF).
$$\langle V_\alpha, \in \rangle \models^2 B \leftrightarrow \langle V_\alpha, \in \rangle \models^2 \text{VNB}$$
$$\leftrightarrow \langle V_\alpha, \in \rangle \models^2 \text{QM}$$
$$\leftrightarrow \text{in}\,(\alpha).$$

From the results of the previous chapter, we obtain:

$$\text{VNB} = \text{Ext} + \text{Aus}^1 + \text{Pow} + \text{Fund} + \Pi_0^1\text{-Comp} + \text{PR}\Pi_0^1,$$
$$\text{QM} = \text{Ext} + \text{Aus}^1 + \text{Pow} + \text{Fund} + \Pi_0^2\text{-Comp} + \text{PR}\Pi_0^1.$$

Lévy's classification of the formulas of ZF set theory (LÉVY [1965]) can be extended to formulas of VNB and QM set theory as follows: A $\Pi_0^1$-formula $\Phi$ is a formula of $\mathscr{L}_{VNB}$ which does not contain any bound-class variable (i.e. a formula of $\mathscr{L}_B$), $\Sigma_0^1 = \Pi_0^1$. A $\Pi_{n+1}^1(\Sigma_{n+1}^1)$-formula $\Phi$ is a formula of $\mathscr{L}_{VNB}$ of the form $\forall X \Psi$ (or $\exists X \Psi$ resp.) for a $\Sigma_n^1(\Pi_n^1)$-formula $\Psi$. Formulas of $\mathscr{L}_{VNB}$ are also called $\Pi_0^2$-formulas.

Let $\Phi$ be any formula of $\mathscr{L}_{VNB}$. Then $\Phi$ has a prenex normal form

(1)                         $Q_1 t_1 \cdots Q_n t_n \Psi$

where each $t_i$ is a set or a class variable, $Q_i$ is $\forall$ or $\exists$ and $\Psi$ does not contain any quantifier. $Q_1 t_1 \cdots Q_n t_n$ is called the *prefix* of the formula (1). Clearly, (1) is equivalent to a $\Pi_m^1$-formula for some $m$. We can obtain another classification of the second-order formulas by "ignoring" the bounded-set variables even in front of bounded-class variables: The *reduced form* of (1) is obtained from (1) by deleting any set quantifier in the prefix of (1).

A $\tilde{\Pi}_n^1$-formula ($\tilde{\Sigma}_n^1$-formula) is a formula in prenex normal form such that the reduced form of it is a $\Pi_n^1$-formula ($\Sigma_n^1$-formula). A $\Delta_n^1$-formula is a formula which is equivalent to both a $\Pi_n^1$- and a $\Sigma_n^1$-formula, similarly for $\tilde{\Delta}_n^1$. We sometimes use the symbol Q to denote any of the symbols $\Pi$, $\Sigma$, $\Delta$, $\tilde{\Pi}$, $\tilde{\Sigma}$, $\tilde{\Delta}$.

We show that under suitable assumptions the $\Pi_n^1$- and the $\tilde{\Pi}_n^1$-classifications agree and hence obtain a simple method for classifying a formula of $\mathscr{L}_{\text{VNB}}$ according to its bound variables. For the remaining part of this section, if not mentioned otherwise, we assume the axioms of VNB.

First, note that any two (and hence any finite number of) adjacent quantifiers of the same kind can be reduced to a single one using ordered pairs; in the case of class quantifiers, one may use a coding of finitely many classes into a single class (cf. ROBINSON [1945]). For example we may define the ordered pair of two classes $A$, $B$ by $(\{\emptyset\} \times A) \cup (\{1\} \times B)$, hence we have in VNB:

$$\forall X \, \forall Y \, \Phi(X, Y, \ldots) \leftrightarrow \forall Z \, \Psi(Z, \ldots),$$

where $\Psi(Z, \ldots)$ is obtained from $\Phi(X, Y, \ldots)$ by replacing any occurrence of $X$ and $Y$ of the form $u \in X$ by $\langle 0, u \rangle \in Z$ and $u \in Y$ by $\langle 1, u \rangle \in Z$ resp. (where $Z$ is assumed to be a variable which does not occur in $\Phi$).

Now, let $\Phi$ again be any formula of $\mathscr{L}_{\text{VNB}}$ written in prenex normal form (1) with alternating quantifiers. Obviously, if $\Phi$ is a $\Pi_n^1$-formula, then it is a $\tilde{\Pi}_n^1$-formula. In order to prove the converse, we have to show that any set quantifier occurring in the prefix of (1) can be moved over a class quantifier from left to right without introducing new bound-class variables. We generalize the ordered pair of classes by introducing the following coding for sequences of classes:

DEFINITION.   $A_a := A''\{a\} = \{x \mid \langle a, x \rangle \in A\}$.

(Though this notation might conflict with the metamathematical use of indices for class variables (e.g. in the notation $\Phi(a_0, \ldots, a_n, A_0, \ldots, A_m)$) we hope that the reader will always discover the right meaning from this context.)

In order to advance a set quantifier over a class quantifier in a suitable way, it seems necessary to assume some kind of axiom of choice. We consider the following forms:

**AC**    $\forall x \in a (x \neq 0) \to \exists f \, [\mathrm{Ft} \, (f) \wedge \mathrm{dom} \, (f) = a \wedge \forall x \in a \, f(x) \in x]$

*(set form of the axiom of choice)*

**SAC**    $\exists F \, [\mathrm{Ft} \, (F) \wedge \mathrm{dom} \, (F) = V \wedge \forall x \, (x \neq 0 \to F(x) \in x)]$

*(strong axiom of choice)*

**$Q_n^1$-AC**        $\forall x \, \exists Y \, \Phi(x, Y, \ldots) \to \exists Y \, \forall x \, \Phi(x, Y_x, \ldots),$

where $\Phi$ is any $Q_n^1$-formula.

LEMMA 3.2.    (a) **VNB** $+ \Pi_0^1$-**AC** $\vdash$ **SAC**.

(b) *In* **VNB**, *the* $\Pi_n^1$-**AC** *is equivalent to each of the following schemata*:

(i)        $\Sigma_{n+1}^1$-**AC**,

(ii)        $\forall x \, \exists Y \, \Phi(x, Y, \ldots) \leftrightarrow \exists Y \, \forall x \, \Phi(x, Y_x, \ldots), \; \Phi a \; \Sigma_{n+1}^1$-*formula*,

(iii)        $\exists x \, \forall Y \, \Phi(x, Y, \ldots) \leftrightarrow \forall Y \, \exists x \, \Phi(x, Y_x, \ldots), \; \Phi a \; \Pi_{n+1}^1$-*formula*.

PROOF.    (a) Let $\Phi(a,A)$ be the $\Pi_0^1$-formula $a = \emptyset \vee A \in a$, i.e.

$$\to \exists x \, (x \in a) \vee \exists x \, (x \in a \wedge \forall y \, (y \in x \leftrightarrow y \in A)).$$

Applying the $\Pi_0^1$-**AC** to the formula $\forall x \, \exists Y \, \Phi(x,Y)$ which is derivable in **VNB**, we obtain the existence of a class $A$ such that

$$\forall x \, (x \neq 0 \to A_x \in x).$$

Then $F := \{x,z \,|\, x \neq \emptyset \wedge z = A_x\} \cup \{(\emptyset,\emptyset)\}$ is a function as required.

In order to prove (b) we have to show that $\Pi_n^1$-**AC** implies $\Sigma_{n+1}^1$-**AC**. Thus, assume the former and let

$$\Phi(a,A,\ldots) = \exists X \, \Psi(a, A, X, \ldots)$$

be a $\Sigma_{n+1}^1$-formula, i.e. $\Psi$ a $\Pi_n^1$-formula. Assume

$$\forall x \, \exists Y \, \exists X \, \Psi(x, Y, X, \ldots).$$

We have to show, $\exists Y \, \forall x \, \exists X \, \Psi(x, Y_x, X, \ldots)$. Contracting the existential quantifiers, we have

$$\forall x \, [\exists Y \, \exists X \, \Psi(x, Y, X, \ldots) \leftrightarrow \exists Z \, \Psi(x, Z_0, Z_1, \ldots)]$$

where $Z_0, Z_1$ are defined as on p. 300, and from $\forall x \, \exists Z \, \Psi(x, Z_0, Z_1, \ldots)$, we obtain by applying $\Pi_n^1$-**AC**:

$$\exists Z \, \forall x \, \Psi(x, (Z_0)_x, (Z_1)_x, \ldots)$$

$$\exists Y \, \exists X \, \forall x \, \Psi(x, Y_x, X_x, \ldots), \qquad \exists Y \, \forall x \, \exists X \, \Psi(x, Y_x, X, \ldots).$$

REMARK. Theorem 3c of MOSCHOVAKIS [1971] shows that in several cases the application of $\Pi_0^1$-**AC** can be eliminated.

With respect to structures which are sets we have the following

LEMMA 3.3 (**ZF** + **AC**). $\langle a, \in \rangle \models^2 \Pi_n^1$-**AC** *for each* $n < \omega$ *and any set* $a \neq 0$ *which is transitive and closed under pairs.*

PROOF. Let $\Phi(a_0, \ldots, a_k, a, A_0, \ldots, A_m, A)$ be any $\Pi_n^1$-formula with free variables as indicated and assume

$$\langle a, \in \rangle \models^2 \forall x_{k+1} \exists Y_{m+1} \Phi[a_0, \ldots, a_k; b_0, \ldots, b_m]$$

for any $a_0, \ldots, a_k \in a$, $b_0, \ldots, b_m \subseteq a$. Then

$$\forall x \in a \exists y \subseteq a \langle a, \in \rangle \models^2 \Phi[a_0, \ldots, a_k, x; b_0, \ldots, b_m, y].$$

Since this is a formula of **ZF**, by **AC** there is a function $f$ such that dom $(f) = a$, rng $(f) \subseteq \mathscr{P}(a)$ and

$$\forall x \in a \langle a, \in \rangle \models^2 \Phi[a_0, \ldots, a_k, x; b_0, \ldots, b_m, f(x)].$$

Define $B := \{x, y \mid x \in a \land y \in f(x)\}$. Then $\forall x \in a B_x = f(x)$ and $B \subseteq a$ is a class as required.

THEOREM 3.1. *For any* $\tilde{\Pi}_{n+1}^1$-*formula* $\Phi$ *there is a* $\Pi_{n+1}^1$-*formula* $\Phi'$ *with the same free variables such that*

$$\textbf{VNB} + \Pi_n^1\text{-}\textbf{AC} \vdash \Phi \leftrightarrow \Phi'.$$

REMARK. $\Phi'$ can be obtained from $\Phi$ in a simple and uniform manner, e.g. there is a primitive recursive set function (in the sense of JENSEN–KARP [1971]) $F$ such that $F^\ulcorner \Phi^\urcorner = {}^\ulcorner \Phi'^\urcorner$. In fact, $\Phi'$ can be defined by recursion as follows:

$\Phi' = \Phi$ if $\Phi$ is a $\Pi_n^1$-formula for some $n$,

$$[\forall x \exists Y \Psi(x, Y, \ldots)]' = \exists Y \forall x \Psi'(x, Y_x, \ldots),$$

$$[\exists x \forall Y \Psi(x, Y, \ldots)]' = \forall Y \exists x \Psi'(x, Y_x, \ldots).$$

COROLLARY 3.2 (**ZF** + **AC**). *If* $\Phi$ *is a* $\tilde{\Pi}_n^1$-*formula, then there is a* $\Pi_n^1$-*formula* $\Phi'$ *with the same free variables such that for any transitive set* $a \neq 0$ *which is closed under pairs*:

$$\langle a, \in \rangle \models^2 \Phi \leftrightarrow \Phi'.$$

Finally, we extend the operation of relativizing a second-order formula of $\mathscr{L}_{\text{VBN}}$ to a set $a$ by defining Rel $(a, \Phi)$ (or $\Phi^a$) to be the formula obtained from $\Phi$ by replacing any quantifier of the form $\forall x$ ($\exists x$) by $\forall x \in a (\exists x \in a$ resp.) (as in the case of a first-order formula) and any quantifier of the form $\forall X$ ($\exists X$) by $\forall x \subseteq a$ ($\exists x \subseteq a$ resp.) for a suitably chosen variable $x$. Again it is tacitly understood that defined symbols (and possibly class terms other than class variables) have been eliminated from $\Phi$ before performing the process of relativizing. This definition is in agreement with our definition of satisfaction in a structure $\langle a, \in \rangle$ by the predicate $\models^2$; in fact one can prove in ZF:

$$\langle a, \in \rangle \models^2 e[a;b] \leftrightarrow \text{Rel}(a, \Phi(a(0), \ldots, a(m), b(0), \ldots, b(n)))$$

for any formula $\Phi$ of $\mathcal{L}_{\text{VNB}}$ with Gödel number $e$ such that the free variables of $\Phi$ are among $v_0, \ldots, v_m, A_0, \ldots, A_n$ and any sequences $a$ of $m + 1$ elements from $a$ and any sequence $b$ of $n + 1$ subsets of $a$ (cf. (b) of §1.1.2).

### 3.2. Second-order reflection principles

We now consider generalizations of the partial-reflection principles for second-order formulas:

$\text{PRQ}_n^1$
$$\Phi(a_0, \ldots, a_k, A_0, \ldots, A_m) \to \exists u (\text{Trans}(u) \wedge$$
$$\Phi^u(a_0, \ldots, a_k, A_0 \cap u, \ldots, A_m \cap u))$$

where $\Phi$ is any $Q_n^1$-formula with free variables as indicated. Similarly, $\text{PR}\Pi_0^2$ is the full second-order reflection principle of BERNAYS [1961].

REMARK 3.1. Using ordered $k$-tupels and a suitable coding of finite sequences of classes as in §3.1, and assuming some basic axioms (e.g. the axioms of pairing, union, Aus$^1$ and $\Pi_0^1$-Comp), the schema $\text{PRQ}_n^1$ can be replaced by the following schema:

$$\Phi(A) \to \exists u (\text{Trans}(u) \wedge \Phi^u(A \cap u))$$

where $\Phi(A)$ is any $Q_n^1$-formula with only $A$ as its free variable. Similarly, as in Ch. II, one may add in $\text{PRQ}_n^1$ the formula $a_0 \in u \wedge \cdots \wedge A_n \in u$ as a conjunction within the scope of "$\exists u$", and $A_i \cap u$ may be replaced by $A_i$.

LEMMA 3.4.  $\text{PR}\Pi_n^1 \vdash \text{PR} \Sigma_{n+1}^1$, and hence both schemata are equivalent.

PROOF.  Let $\exists X \Psi(X, \ldots)$ be a $\Sigma_{n+1}^1$-formula, i.e. $\Psi(A, \ldots)$ a $\Pi_n^1$-formula, and assume $\exists X \Psi(X, \ldots)$. Then there is a class $A$ such that $\Psi(A, \ldots)$. Applying $\text{PR}\Pi_n^1$, there is a transitive set $a$ such that $\Psi^a(A \cap a, \ldots)$, hence

$$(\exists X \Psi(X, \ldots))^a.$$

Let $\text{BL}_n$ be the theory $\text{Ext} + \text{Fund} + \text{Aus}^1 + \text{PR}\Pi_n^1$ (Bernays–Lévy). From §2.1 we recall that

$$\text{BL}_n \vdash \text{Pair} + \text{Sum} + \text{Inf} + \text{Repl}^1.$$

BERNAYS [1961], pp. 138ff proves: $BL_1 \vdash Pow$, hence $BL_1 \vdash B$, since $B = BL_0 + Pow$.

PROPOSITION 3.1.　$BL_{n+2} + AC \vdash \Pi_n^1\text{-}AC$.

PROOF.　Let $\Phi$ be a $\Pi_n^1$-formula and suppose that the instance of $\Pi_n^1\text{-}AC$ for such a $\Phi$ does not hold, i.e.

$$\forall x \, \exists Y \, \Phi(x, Y, \ldots) \wedge \forall Y \, \exists x \sim \Phi(x, Y_x, \ldots).$$

Obviously this formula is equivalent to a $\Pi_{n+2}^1$-formula $\Psi$. (For simplicity, we assume that $\Phi(a, A)$ has no free variables other than $a$ and $A$.) Applying $PR\Pi_{n+2}^1$ to $\Psi \wedge \forall x, y \, \exists z \, (z = \langle x, y \rangle)$ we obtain the existence of a transitive set $b$ which is closed under pairs such that

$$\langle b, \in \rangle \models^2 \ulcorner \psi \urcorner.$$

However, this contradicts Lemma 3.3.

COROLLARY 3.3.　$BL_{n+2} + AC \vdash SAC$.

PROOF.　Use Lemma 3.2(a).

In fact, Corollary 3.3 can be improved to

THEOREM 3.2.　$BL_1 + AC \vdash SAC$.

PROOF.　A proof is given in BERNAYS [1961], pp. 141ff.

Taking a closer look at the proofs given in BERNAYS [1961], one easily sees that all his results only require $BL_1$ rather than $BL = BL_0 + PR\Pi_0^2 = VNB + PR\Pi_0^2$ with one exception: Specker's result that the full impredicative schema of comprehension, $\Pi_0^2$-Comp, holds in BL.

If we introduce the following schemata:

$Q_n^1\text{-Comp}$　　　　　　$\exists Y \, \forall x \, (x \in Y \leftrightarrow \Phi(x, \ldots))$,

where $\Phi$ is any $Q_n^1$-formula (such that $Y$ is not bound in $\Phi$), Specker's method shows:

THEOREM 3.3.　(i) $BL_1 \vdash \Pi_0^1\text{-Comp}$, *hence* $BL_1 \vdash VNB$,

　　(ii)　　　　　$BL_{n+2} \vdash \Pi_n^1\text{-Comp}, \quad \Sigma_n^1\text{-Comp}$,

　　(iii)　　　　$BL_{n+1} \vdash \Delta_n^1\text{-Comp}$,

　　(iv)　　　　$BL_0 + PR\tilde{\Pi}_{n+1}^1 \vdash \tilde{\Pi}_n^1\text{-Comp}, \tilde{\Sigma}_n^1\text{-Comp}$,

　　(v)　　　　　$BL_0 + PR\tilde{\Pi}_n^1 \vdash \tilde{\Delta}_n^1\text{-Comp}$.

PROOF.　Suppose $Q_n^1$-Comp does not hold for some $Q_n^1$-formula $\Phi$, i.e.

$$\sim \exists Y \, \forall x \, (x \in Y \leftrightarrow \Phi(x, \ldots)).$$

Now, one only has to verify that in each of the cases (i)–(v) this formula is equivalent to a formula $\Psi$ to which the reflection principle of the respective theories applies. Hence there is a transitive set $a \neq 0$ such that $\Psi$ holds in $\langle a, \in \rangle$ (under some appropriate assignment of the free variables of $\Psi$ in (a) which contradicts the fact that $\langle a, \in \rangle \models^2 \Pi_0^2$-Comp (cf. Lemma 3.1). Parts (iv) and (v) are from BOWEN [1972], Lemma 2.1.5.

COROLLARY 3.4 (Specker). $\mathsf{BL} \vdash \Pi_0^2$-Comp, *and hence* $\mathsf{BL} \vdash \mathsf{QM}$.

*Remarks and additions.* (1) BOWEN [1972] denotes by $\mathsf{BL}_{n+1}$ the theory (which by Theorem 3.3 (i) and the Remark following below is equivalent to) $\mathsf{VNB} + \mathsf{PR}\Pi_{n+1}^1$, let us denote it by $\tilde{\mathsf{BL}}_{n+1}$; $\tilde{\mathsf{BL}}_0 = \mathsf{VNB} + \mathsf{PR}\tilde{\Pi}_0^1$. Then (in our notation) $\tilde{\mathsf{BL}}_n \vdash \mathsf{BL}_n$, and by Theorem 3.2: $\mathsf{BL}_{n+1} + \Pi_n^1\text{-}\mathsf{AC} \vdash \tilde{\mathsf{BL}}_{n+1}$. (Here $\Pi_n^1$-AC can also be replaced by $\Pi_{n+1}^1$-Comp + AC.) Therefore, assuming $\Pi_n^1$-AC, both theories are equivalent. Note that $\mathsf{BL}_{n+2} + \mathsf{AC} \vdash \Pi_n^1\text{-}\mathsf{AC}$ by Proposition 3.1. We do not know whether $\tilde{\mathsf{BL}}_{n+1}$ and $\mathsf{BL}_{n+1}$ are equivalent without assuming some kind of axiom of choice. Of course, assuming $\mathsf{ZF} + \mathsf{AC}$ (for the metatheory) by Lemma 3.3 and Theorem 3.1, both have the same transitive standard models (with respect to the satisfaction relation $\models^2$). In particular,

$$\langle V_\alpha, \in \rangle \models^2 \mathsf{PR}\tilde{\Pi}_n^1 \leftrightarrow \langle V_\alpha, \in \rangle \models^2 \mathsf{PR}\Pi_n^1.$$

In any case, even without the AC, we clearly have $\mathsf{BL} \vdash \tilde{\mathsf{BL}}_n$ for each $n$. Finally, it should be noted that BL is consistent iff the theories $\mathsf{BL}_n$ are consistent for each $n$.

(2) In BERNAYS [1961], pp. 138ff it is shown that in the theory $\mathsf{BL}_{n+1}$ the reflection principle $\mathsf{PR}\Pi_{n+1}^1$ can be strengthened to a schema which asserts the existence of a "reflecting" set of the form $V_\alpha$ for some inaccessible $\alpha$ (cf. Theorem 3.4). We cannot use this method in order to strengthen $\mathsf{PR}\Pi_0^1$, since by Lemma 2.1 (iv), and the fact that $\mathsf{B} = \mathsf{Ext} + \mathsf{Aus}^1 + \mathsf{Fund} + \mathsf{Pow} + \mathsf{PR}\Pi_0^1$ (§2.1), we have:

$$\text{in } (\alpha) \leftrightarrow \langle V_\alpha, \in \rangle \models^2 \mathsf{B} \leftrightarrow \langle V_\alpha, \in \rangle \models^2 \mathsf{PR}\Pi_0^1,$$

and therefore one cannot prove in B (nor in VNB) the existence of inaccessible cardinals (assuming consistency). So one has to use the method of §2.1, and in fact Metatheorem 2.1 shows that $\mathsf{PR}\Pi_0^1$, too, can be strengthened to assert the existence of a "reflecting" set of the form $V_\alpha$ (though $\alpha$ need not be inaccessible).

One can also use the method of §2.2 (which is an extension of the methods yielding Metatheorem 2.1) to obtain a strengthening of $\mathsf{PR}\Pi_0^1$ (and similarly for $\mathsf{PR}\Pi_{n+1}^1$) as follows:

Let T be the theory

$$\mathsf{VNB} + \Delta_1^1\text{-Comp, i.e. } \mathsf{BL}_0 + \mathsf{Pow} + \mathsf{Fund} + \Delta_1^1\text{-Comp}.$$

In T one can define a satisfaction relation $\text{Sat}_0\,(A,a)$ for the class $V$ of all sets with respect to formulas of $\mathscr{L}_B$ such that $\text{Sat}_0$ is a $\Delta_1{}^1$-formula and one can prove in T:

$$\text{Sat}_0\,(A \times \{j\}, \ulcorner \Phi(A_j)\urcorner) \leftrightarrow \Phi(A)$$

for any class $A$ and any $\Pi_0{}^1$-formula $\Phi(a_j)$ with $A_j$ as its free variable (cf. MOSTOWSKI [1969], BOWEN [1972], Lemma 2.1.14). This allows us to use the method of proof for Theorem 2.2 and Corollaries 2.2–2.4 replacing $V_\alpha$ by $V$ and deleting the assumption that $\langle V_\alpha, \in \rangle \models^2 B$ (which becomes redundant since $V$ is a "model" of T and $B \subseteq T$). Thus in T one can prove, e.g.

$$\exists \xi \langle V_\xi, \in \rangle < \langle V, \in \rangle,$$

and in T the schema $\text{PR}\Pi_0{}^1$ can be strengthened to yield the schemata (+) and (++) of §2.2.

Similarly, though by a somewhat different method, it is shown in BOWEN [1972], Corollary 2.1.19 that the following schema of complete reflection is provable in $\tilde{\text{B}}\text{L}_{n+1}$:

$$\text{CR}\tilde{\Pi}_n{}^1 \qquad \exists \xi\, [a \in V_\xi \wedge \forall x \in V_\xi(\Phi(x,A) \leftrightarrow \text{Rel}\,(V_\xi, \Phi(x,A \cap V_\xi)))]$$

where $\Phi(a,A)$ is any $\tilde{\Pi}_n{}^1$-formula with free variables as indicated (and similarly for formulas with finitely many free variables, cf. Remark 3.1). By the same method one can prove: $\text{BL}_{n+1} + \Delta_{n+1}^1\text{-Comp} \vdash \text{CR}\Pi_n{}^1$ (cf. also Theorem 4.6). This is the best possible result insofar as in $\text{BL}_1 + \Delta_1{}^1$-Comp ($\text{BL}_1$) one cannot prove $\text{CR}\Pi_1{}^1$ ($\text{CR}\tilde{\Pi}_1{}^1$ resp.) (assuming consistency; cf. GLOEDE [1970], p. 75). For a different situation in the case of $\text{PR}\Pi_\omega{}^0$ and $\text{PR}\Pi_0{}^1$ cf. the end of §1.3 and Metatheorem 2.1.

(3) One can easily prove that the theory BL is consistent with Gödel's axiom of constructibility $V = L$ (Gödel [1940]), (see BOWEN [1972], Theorem 3.1.2). This result has been extended to systems containing reflection principles of any finite or even transfinite-type theory by TAKEUTI [1965].

Let Ref' (BOWEN [1972]) be the (weak) second-order complete reflection principle

$$\exists \xi \, \forall x \in V_\xi [\Phi(x) \leftrightarrow \text{Rel}\,(V_\xi, \Phi(x))]$$

where $\Phi(a)$ is any $\Pi_0{}^2$-formula with $a$ as its only free variable (thus $\Phi$ may not contain any second-order free variable) and $\text{BL}' = \text{BL} + \text{Ref}'$. THARP [1967] has shown that

$$\text{BL}' + (V = L) \vdash \text{BL} \qquad \text{(cf. BOWEN [1972], Theorem 3.2.2)},$$

and by Bowen's result mentioned above, $\text{BL} \vdash \text{BL}'$. Therefore BL is consistent iff BL' is consistent.

(4) Finally, BOWEN [1972], Ch. III, has shown that the consistency of BL or even $BL_1$ implies the consistency of VNB with various axioms which imply $V \neq L$ (e.g.: for almost all regular cardinals $\alpha$, $\langle L_\alpha, \in \rangle$ is an elementary submodel of $\langle L, \in \rangle$) and which originally have only been obtained from axioms asserting the existence of certain large cardinals, the existence of which cannot be proved in BL.

### 3.3. *Mahlo's Principle*

In his 1961 paper, Bernays emphasizes the fact that the schemata of reflection for second-order languages are "self-strengthening" in a very strong way (the corresponding schemata of partial reflection for first-order formulas only partly partake of this property). In particular, the schema $PR\Pi_1^1$ can be strengthened to yield the existence of "reflecting" sets of the form $V_\alpha$, where $\alpha$ is a cardinal which is very large in the Mahlo hierarchy. In this section, we only discuss some of the results which are related to Mahlo's principle and to the problems which are relevant to the class terms and class variables distinction, as expressed by Montague–Vaught's theorem. For further results, we refer to GAIFMAN [1967] and GLOEDE [1971].

THEOREM 3.4.   *In the theory* $BL_{n+1} = Ext + Aus^1 + Fund + PR\Pi_{n+1}^1$, *the schema* $PR\Pi_{n+1}^1$ *can be strengthened to the following schema of partial reflection*:

$$\Phi(A_0, \ldots, A_m) \to \exists \xi \, [\text{in}\,(\xi) \wedge \Phi^{V_\xi}(A_0 \cap V_\xi, \ldots, A_m \cap V_\xi)],$$

*where* $\Phi$ *is any* $\Pi_{n+1}^1$-*formula with free variables as indicated.*

PROOF.   BERNAYS [1961], p. 141 shows that $PR\Pi_{n+1}^1$ can be strengthened to a schema which has in place of "Trans $(u)$" the stronger property

$$\text{Strans}\,(u) \wedge \text{Mod}\,(u).$$

As mentioned at the end of §2.2, one can prove in ZF:

$$\text{Strans}\,(a) \wedge \text{Mod}\,(a) \leftrightarrow \langle a, \in \rangle \models^2 B$$
$$\leftrightarrow \langle a, \in \rangle \models^2 VNB.$$

By a result of SHEPHERDSON [1952] (§3.14) (cf. MONTAGUE–VAUGHT [1959], p. 228), any super-complete model $\langle a, \in \rangle$ of VNB is of the form $V_\alpha$ for some $\alpha$: this follows from the absoluteness of the rank function and the axiom of Fundierung. Clearly, any such $\alpha$ must be inaccessible by Lemma 2.1(iv). Note that we have a corresponding result for $PR\Pi_0^1$, provided we drop the requirement "in $(\xi)$", cf. §3.2(2).

In particular, one can prove in $\mathsf{BL}_1$ that there is a "large" class of inaccessibles. There are several ways of interpreting the concept of a "large" class of ordinals, e.g. we might call a class $A$ of ordinals large, if it is unbounded or even closed unbounded (i.e. the range of a normal function defined for all the ordinals). Unfortunately, the class of inaccessibles is not closed, since the limit of an ascending sequence of inaccessibles need not be inaccessible (since it may be cofinal with $\omega$). A more suitable notion of a "large" class of ordinals is provided by the following definition:

DEFINITION 3.1.

$$\text{stationary}\,(A) :\leftrightarrow \forall F\,[\text{Nft}\,(F) \to \exists \xi \in A\; F(\xi) = \xi],$$
$$\text{stationary}\,(A,\alpha) :\leftrightarrow \forall f\,[\text{Nft}\,(f,\alpha) \to \exists \xi \in A\; f(\xi) = \xi].$$

Thus a class $A$ is *stationary* (sometimes also called *dense*) iff it intersects each closed unbounded class of ordinals; "$A$ is stationary in $\alpha$" is the corresponding concept relativized to $V_\alpha$.

LEMMA 3.5.

$$\lim\,(\alpha) \wedge A \subseteq \alpha. \to .\langle V_\alpha, \in\rangle \models^2 \text{stationary}\,(X_0)[A] \leftrightarrow \text{stationary}\,(A,\alpha).$$

A further strengthening of $\mathsf{PR\Pi}_{n+1}^1$ is provided by the following

THEOREM 3.5.

$\mathsf{BL}_{n+1} \vdash \Phi(A_0,\ldots,A_m) \to \text{stationary}\,(\{\xi \mid \text{in}\,(\xi) \wedge \Phi^{V_\xi}(A_0 \cap V_\xi,\ldots,A_m \cap V_\xi)\})$

*for any* $\Pi_{n+1}^1$-*formula* $\Phi$ *with free variables as indicated.*

PROOF.  Let $F$ be any normal function. Applying Theorem 3.15 to the $\Pi_{n+1}^1$-formula

$$\text{Nft}\,(F) \wedge \Phi(A_0,\ldots,A_m),$$

we obtain the existence of some ordinal $\alpha$ such that

$$\text{in}\,(\alpha) \wedge \text{Nft}\,(F \cap V_\alpha)^{V_\alpha} \wedge \Phi^{V_\alpha}(A_0 \cap V_\alpha,\ldots,A_m \cap V_\alpha).$$
$$\text{Clearly},\; \lim\,(\alpha) \to [\text{Nft}\,(F \cap V_\alpha)^{V_\alpha} \leftrightarrow \alpha = F(\alpha)],$$

and this proves the theorem.

Let us define the following versions of Mahlo's operation:

DEFINITION 3.2.

$$H(A) := \{\xi \mid \text{in}\,(\xi) \wedge \text{stationary}\,(A,\xi)\},$$
$$H_0(A) := \{\xi \mid \text{reg}\,(\xi) \wedge \text{stationary}\,(A,\xi)\}.$$

(These operations are roughly the duals of the operation $M$ of KEISLER–TARSKI [1964].)

In BERNAYS [1961], p. 41 it is shown that one can define in ZF a predicate Ma $(\alpha,\gamma)$ ("$\alpha$ is a Mahlo number of order $\gamma$") by a formula of $\mathscr{L}_{ZF}$ satisfying the following recursive conditions:

$$\text{Ma}\,(\alpha,0) \leftrightarrow \alpha \in H(\text{On}) \quad \text{(i.e. in }(\alpha)),$$
$$\text{Ma}\,(\alpha,\gamma + 1) \leftrightarrow \alpha \in H(\{\xi \mid \text{Ma}\,(\xi,\gamma)\}),$$
$$\text{Ma}\,(\alpha,\lambda) \leftrightarrow \forall \eta < \lambda \ \text{Ma}\,(\alpha,\eta) \quad \text{for } \lambda \text{ a limit number.}$$

(This definition agrees with the notion of a *hyper-inaccessible number of type $\gamma$* as defined in LÉVY [1960].) Replacing $H$ by $H_0$, we obtain Mahlo's original definition of the $\pi_{0\gamma}$ numbers ($\pi_{\alpha 0\gamma}$ is the $\alpha^{th}$ ordinal among the $\pi_{0\gamma}$ numbers, cf. MAHLO [1911–1913]).

COROLLARY 3.5.  $BL_1 \vdash M$, *where* $M$ *is the following formula* (*which might be called Mahlo's Principle*):

M              $stationary\ (A) \to stationary\ (H(A))$.

PROOF.  Apply Theorem 3.5 to the $\Pi_1^1$-formula *stationary* $(A)$ and use Lemma 3.5.

Although the intersection of two stationary classes may be empty, one can prove in $BL_1$ the following stronger Mahlo *diagonalization principle*:

M*       $\forall \eta\ (stationary\ (A_\eta)) \to stationary\ (\{\xi | in\ (\xi)$
$$\wedge\ \forall \eta < \xi\ stationary\ (A_\eta,\xi)\}):$$

COROLLARY 3.6.  $BL_1 \vdash M^*$.

PROOF.  Let $\Psi(A,\eta)$ be the $\Pi_1^1$-formula *stationary* $(A_\eta)$ (where $A_\eta = \{x \mid \langle \eta,x\rangle \in A\}$). Applying Theorem 3.5 to the formula $\forall \eta\ \Psi(A,\eta)$ which clearly is equivalent to a $\Pi_1^1$-formula, we have:

$$B = \{\xi \mid in\ (\xi) \wedge \forall \eta < \xi\ \Psi^{V_\xi}(A \cap V_\xi,\eta)\} \text{ is stationary.}$$

COROLLARY 3.7.  $BL_1 \vdash stationary\ (\{\xi \mid \text{Ma}\,(\xi,\gamma)\})$.

PROOF.  By induction on $\gamma$ using Corollary 3.5 for the case $\gamma = 0$ (On is stationary) and the successor stages, Corollary 3.6 for the limit stages.

We note that the result obtained in Corollary 3.7 can already be derived from the principle M* rather than $PR\Pi_1^1$, and in fact even from the principle $M^*$ obtained from M* by replacing the class variable $A$ by a syntactical variable $A$ ranging over class terms (of the language of ZF) only. While (the universal closure of) M* is a $\Pi_2^1$-statement, each instance of $M^*$ is a $\Sigma_2^1$-formula. Let $\alpha$ be an ordinal such that $\langle V_\alpha,\in\rangle \models^2 BL_1$. Then

$\langle V_\alpha, \in \rangle \models^2 \mathsf{PR} \, \Sigma_2^1$ by Lemma 3.4. Therefore, each instance of $M^*$ being satisfied in $V_\alpha$ is already satisfied in some $V_\beta$ for some $\beta < \alpha$. Moreover, since there are only countably, many formulas of $\mathscr{L}_{ZF}$ (and hence countably many instances of $M^*$), an argument due to LÉVY [1971] (Corollary 10b) shows that there is an inaccessible $\beta < \alpha$ such that $V_\beta$ satisfies each instance of $M^*$.

On the other hand, JENSEN [1972] (Theorem 6.1) has shown that

$$\langle V_\alpha, \in \rangle \models^2 \mathsf{PR\Pi_1}^1 \leftrightarrow \mathrm{reg}\,(\alpha) \wedge \forall x \subseteq \alpha \,[\mathrm{stationary}\,(x,\alpha) \to$$
$$\exists \xi < \alpha \; \mathrm{stationary}\,(x,\xi)]$$

assuming Gödel's axiom $V = L$. In particular (in $\mathsf{ZF} + (V = L)$):

$$\langle V_\alpha, \in \rangle \models^2 \mathsf{PR\Pi_1}^1 \leftrightarrow \langle V_\alpha, \in \rangle \models^2 \mathsf{B} + M^*,$$

whereas

$$\langle V_\alpha, \in \rangle \models^2 \mathsf{PR\Pi_1}^1 \to \exists \xi < \alpha \langle V_\xi, \in \rangle \models^2 \mathsf{B} + M^*,$$

hence

$$\langle V_\alpha, \in \rangle \models^2 \mathsf{B} + M^* \to \exists \xi < \alpha \langle V_\xi, \in \rangle \models^2 \mathsf{ZF} + M^*$$

as mentioned above. This result might be compared with Montague–Vaught's theorem, since $\mathsf{B}$ and $\mathsf{ZF}$ are related to each other like $M^*$ is related to $M^*$.

Some applications of the concept of Mahlo numbers can be found in SCHMERL [1972] and SCHMERL–SHELAH [1972]. For recursive analogues of Mahlo numbers cf. ACZEL–RICHTER [1970].

## 4. Indescribable cardinals

### 4.1. Higher-order languages

Having introduced class variables, which are called variables of type 2, whereas set variables are regarded as variables of type 1, it is natural to extend the language of $\mathscr{L}_{VNB}$ further by adding variables of any finite (and possibly even transfinite) type. Variables of type $n$ will also be denoted by $X^n, Y^n, \ldots$ . For formulas of this language (with atomic formulas of the form $s = t$ and $s \in t$ for any kind of variables $s$, $t$) we extend Lévy's classification of first-order formulas as follows (cf. HANF–SCOTT [1961]):[1]

---

[1] The definition that follows does not completely agree with the notation introduced in the previous sections since we have used $\Pi_0^2$ to denote the set of formulas of $\mathscr{L}_{VNB}$ which are not allowed to contain free variables of type 3, but only set and class variables. In most cases we consider only formulas which contain free variables of type at most 2 (i.e. class variables). Thus, if there is any risk of confusion, we give additional information on the free variables which are allowed to occur in the formulas under consideration.

A $\Pi_0^m$-*formula* is a formula in which every bounded variable is of type $\leq m$ and every free variable is of type $\leq m + 1$, $\Sigma_0^m = \Pi_0^m$. A $\Pi_{n+1}^m$-*formula* ($\Sigma_{n+1}^m$-*formula*) is a formula of the form $\forall X^{m+1} \Psi$ ($\exists X^{m+1} \Psi$ resp.) where $\Psi$ is a $\Sigma_n^m$-*formula* ($\Pi_n^m$-*formula* resp.). A $\Delta_n^m$-*formula* is a formula which (in some appropriate type theory) is equivalent to both a $\Pi_n^m$- and a $\Sigma_n^m$-*formula*. Thus the $\Pi_0^1$-formulas are just those of Bernays' set theory **B** (as in the 1958 monograph), and the $\Pi_0^2$-formulas containing free variables of type at most 2 are the formulas of **VNB** set theory (disregarding the fact that for some technical reasons, we have taken $u = v$, $u \in v$ and $u \in A$ as the only atomic formulas of these languages).

It is debatable whether the language of finite- or transfinite-type theory is more adequate for set theory than the languages considered in the previous chapter (for a discussion, cf. TAKEUTI [1965] and [1969]), in any case the idea of investigating the type-theoretical classification of various definitions and propositions with respect to a particular structure has turned out to be fundamental for a large number of results (cf. §1.3 for applications within the scope of this paper). Therefore, we do not introduce a logical system for type theory (this could be done along the lines sketched in §§3.1 and 3.2 for the second-order language), but consider only particular models for certain axioms in the language of type theory (like the reflection principles for this language). Taking this approach we avoid taking into account logical axioms for type theory like comprehension axioms and various kinds of choice principles (like those introduced in §3.1) since these are satisfied in any model under consideration (cf. Lemmas 3.1, 3.3 and Corollary 3.2 for the case of second-order language). Throughout this chapter we assume the axioms of **ZF + AC** for our metatheory (the use of the axiom of choice could be avoided in most cases by some simple modifications).

For the following we again require a suitable formalization of satisfaction in a structure of the form $\langle a, \in \rangle$ for formulas of finite-type theory. In particular, we assume that a set '$\Phi$' is assigned in a suitable manner to each formula $\Phi$ of finite-type theory. Then a formal satisfaction predicate $\models^{m+1}$ for $\Pi_0^{m+1}$-formulas can be defined in **ZF** set theory (e.g. by reduction to the case of satisfaction of a $\Pi_0^1$-formula in the structure $\langle \mathscr{P}^m(a), \in \rangle$ (where $\mathscr{P}^m(a)$ is the result of applying the power set operation to $a$ $m$-times, $\mathscr{P}^0(a) = a$) in a manner indicated in §2.2 for the case $m = 1$). We let

$$\langle a, \in \rangle \models^{m+1} e[\langle a_0, \ldots, a_k \rangle; \langle b_0, \ldots, b_n \rangle],$$

(though somewhat imprecise we also use the notation

$$\langle a, \in \rangle \models^{m+1} e[a_0, \ldots, a_k; b_0, \ldots, b_n])$$

be a suitable formalization in **ZF** set theory of the corresponding metamathematical statement

> "$e$ is the Gödel number of a $\Pi_0^{m+1}$-formula $\Phi$ with free set variables $v_0, \ldots, v_k$, free class variables $A_0, \ldots, A_n, a_0, \ldots, a_k \in a$, $b_0, \ldots, b_n \subseteq a$, and $\Phi$ is true in $\langle a, \in \rangle$ if $a_i(b_j)$ is assigned to $v_i$ ($A_j$ resp.) for $i \leq k$, $j \leq n$, and bound variables $X^{l+1}$ are interpreted to range over $\mathscr{P}^l(a)$".

($\models^1$ is $\models$ of §1.1.2, $\models^2$ is the same relation as defined in §2.2.)

A formal definition of satisfaction as required can also be given without referring to satisfaction for $\Pi_0^1$-formulas, details are given in BOWEN [1972], pp. 42ff, for the case $m = 1$ (and this definition can easily be generalized for any finite $m$). The requirements on the formal definition of satisfaction which we need in the sequel are the following:

**4.1.1. Uniform definability.** *For each $m > 0$, $n \geq 0$ there is a $\Delta_1^m$-formula $\Psi_m(v_0, X_0^{m+1}, \ldots, X_n^{m+1})$ with free variables as indicated such that for every $\Pi_0^m$-formula $\Phi(X_0^{m+1}, \ldots, X_n^{m+1})$ with free variables as indicated, for any inaccessible $\alpha$ and all $b_0, \ldots, b_n \in \mathscr{P}^m(V_\alpha)$:*

$$\langle V_\alpha, \in \rangle \models^{m+1} {}^\ulcorner\Phi{}^\urcorner[b_0, \ldots, b_n] \leftrightarrow \langle V_\alpha, \in \rangle \models^{m+1} {}^\ulcorner\Psi_m{}^\urcorner[{}^\ulcorner\Phi{}^\urcorner; b_0, \ldots, b_n].$$

($\Psi_m$ is just the formula defining satisfaction in $\langle V, \in \rangle$:

$$\langle V, \in \rangle \models^m {}^\ulcorner\Phi{}^\urcorner[A] \leftrightarrow \Psi_m({}^\ulcorner\Phi{}^\urcorner, A),$$

where $A$ is a class coding finitely many classes $A_0, \ldots, A_n$.)

As a consequence (cf. LÉVY [1971], Theorem 8):

**4.1.2. Absoluteness.** *For each $n, m > 0$ there is a $\Pi_n^m$-formula $\Psi(v_0, A_0)$ with the only free variables $v_0$ and $A_0$ which is universal for the set of $\Pi_n^m$-formulas $\Phi(A_0)$ which contain only the free class variable $A_0$, i.e. for any such formula $\Phi(A_0)$, every inaccessible $\alpha$ and every $A \subseteq V_\alpha$:*

$$\langle V_\alpha, \in \rangle \models^{m+1} {}^\ulcorner\Phi{}^\urcorner[A] \leftrightarrow \langle V_\alpha, \in \rangle \models^{m+1} {}^\ulcorner\Psi{}^\urcorner[{}^\ulcorner\Psi{}^\urcorner, A].$$

(To obtain $\Psi$ from the $\Delta_1^m$-formula $\Psi_m$ of §4.1.1 consider the formula

$$\forall X_1^m \cdots Q X_n^m \, \Psi_m^Q(v_0, A_0, X_1^m, \ldots, X_n^m)$$

where $\Psi_m^Q$ is the $\Pi_1^m$ ($\Sigma_1^m$)-formula which is equivalent to $\Psi_m$ if $Q$ is $\forall$ (or $\exists$ resp.). Now, contract the quantifiers $Q X_n^m$ and the first quantifier $Q Y^m$ of $\Psi_m^Q$ into a single quantifier $Q X_n^m$ (as described in §3.1 for the case $m = 1$) and substitute $g(v_0)$ for $v_0$ where $g({}^\ulcorner\forall X_1^m \cdots Q X_n^m \, \Phi{}^\urcorner) = {}^\ulcorner\Phi{}^\urcorner$ for any $\Pi_n^m$-formula $\forall X_1^m \cdots Q X_n^m \, \Phi(A_0, X_1^m, \ldots, X_n^m)$, $g(v_0) = 0$ otherwise.) (The requirement that $\alpha$ be inaccessible can be weakened in §§4.1.1 and 4.1.2.)

4.1.3. Adequacy. We extend the process of relativization to $\Pi_n^m$-formulas as follows: $\Phi^a$ is the formula obtained from $\Phi$ by replacing any quantifier of the form

$$\forall x \quad \text{by} \quad \forall x \in a,$$
$$\forall X \quad \text{by} \quad \forall x \in \mathcal{P}(a),$$
$$\forall X^{i+1} \quad \text{by} \quad \forall x \in \mathcal{P}^i(a),$$

and similarly for existential quantifiers (where in the last two cases $x$ is a suitably chosen first-order variable). Then we have, as in the case of a first-order formula, the following schema which expresses the material adequacy of the satisfaction relation:

*For any* $\Pi_n^m$-*formula* $\Phi(v_0,\ldots,v_k,A_0,\ldots,A_l)$ *with free variables as indicated and any elements* $a_0,\ldots,a_k \in a$, $b_0,\ldots,b_l \in \mathcal{P}(a)$:

$$\langle a,\in \rangle \models^{m+1} \ulcorner \Phi \urcorner [a_0,\ldots,a_k\,;\,b_0,\ldots,b_l] \leftrightarrow \Phi^a(a_0,\ldots,a_k,b_0,\ldots,b_l).$$

REMARK. Since we shall consider only structures of the form $\langle a,\in \rangle$ for transitive sets $a$, any free variable of type $i$ may also be considered as a variable of any higher type. Therefore, it is sufficient to define satisfaction for formulas which contain only free variables of the same (highest) type. We have separated the first-order free variables from the higher-order free variables only for technical reasons, in connection with the reflection principles which are considered later.

### 4.2. Indescribable cardinals

By PR$\Gamma$ we denote the *partial-reflection principle for formulas in* $\Gamma$ *which contain free variables of type at most* 2:

DEFINITION. Let $\Gamma$ be either $\Pi_n^m$, $\Sigma_n^m$, or $\Delta_n^m$. Then:

PR$\Gamma$ $\quad \Phi(a_0,\ldots,a_k,A_0,\ldots,A_l) \rightarrow \exists u\, [\text{Trans}\,(u)$
$$\wedge\, \Phi^u(a_0,\ldots,a_k,A_0 \cap u,\ldots,A_l \cap u)],$$

where $\Phi$ is any $\Gamma$-formula with free variables as indicated.

$\Gamma$-indesc $(\alpha) :\leftrightarrow \alpha > 0 \wedge \langle V_\alpha,\in \rangle \models^{m+1} \text{PR}\Gamma$ "$\alpha$ *is* $\Gamma$-*indescribable*",

$\Gamma$-desc $(\alpha) :\leftrightarrow \neg\, \Gamma$-indesc $(\alpha)$ "$\alpha$ *is* $\Gamma$-*describable*".

REMARK 4.1. (1) Note that for each set of formulas $\Gamma$ as considered above the predicate "$\alpha$ *is* $\Gamma$-*indescribable*" is defined by a formula of $\mathcal{L}_{\text{ZF}}$.

(2) If $m > 0$, we may also replace the principle PR$\Pi_n^m$ by the same principle restricted to $\Pi_n^m$-formulas $\Phi(A)$ with the free-class variable $A$ only (cf. Remark 3.1).

(3) Intuitively, "$\alpha$ *is* $\Pi_n^m$-*indescribable*" means that for each $\Pi_n^m$-

formula $\Phi(v_0,\ldots,v_k,A_0,\ldots,A_1)$ (with free variables as indicated) and any sets $a_0,\ldots,a_k \in V_\alpha$, $b_0,\ldots,b_1 \subseteq V_\alpha$, if

$$\langle V_\alpha,\in \rangle \models^{m+1} \Phi[a_0,\ldots,a_k\,;\,b_0,\ldots,b_1],$$

then there is a transitive set $a \in V_\alpha$ such that $a_0,\ldots,a_k \in a$ (if $m > 0$ *or* $n > 1$) and

$$\langle V_\alpha,\in \rangle \models^{m+1} \text{Rel }(v_{k+1},\Phi)[a_0,\ldots,a_k,a\,;\,b_0 \cap a,\ldots b_1 \cap a],$$

i.e. by §4.1.3

$$\text{Rel }(V_\alpha,\text{Rel }(a,\Phi(a,\ldots,a_k,b_0 \cap a,\ldots,b_1 \cap a)))$$

which again is equivalent to

$$\text{Rel }(a,\Phi(a_0,\ldots,a_k,b_0 \cap a,\ldots,b_1 \cap ))$$

(since $a \cap V_\alpha = a$), and again by 4.1.3 this is equivalent to

$$\langle a,\in \rangle \models^{m+1} \Phi[a_0,\ldots,a_k\,;\,b_0 \cap a,\ldots,b_1 \cap a].$$

Moreover, if $n > 0$ or $m > 0$ then, by Theorem 3.4 (and the remark at the end of the proof for the case of $\text{PR}\Pi_0{}^1$) $a$ can be assumed to be of the form $V_\beta$ for some $\beta < \alpha$, and $\beta$ can be assumed to be inaccessible if $n > 0$ and $m > 0$.

(Note that we not only identify a formula with its Gödel number, but also use the same letters to denote numerals (in the metamathematical sense) and natural numbers (in the formal sense). We hope that the reader will discover the right meaning from the context as a correct distinction will render the notation unnecessarily complicated.)

(4) Some authors define the notion of $\Gamma$-indescribability by using instead of $\Gamma$-formulas which contain free second-order variables $A_0,\ldots,A_k$, the corresponding formulas which have unary relation constants $\dot{A}_i$ in place of $A_i$ and replacing the structures $\langle V_\alpha,\in \rangle$ by structures $\langle V_\alpha,\in,b_0,\ldots,b_k \rangle$ where the $b_i$'s are subsets of $V_\alpha$ interpreting $\dot{A}_i$ (whereas $b_i$ is assigned to $A_i$ in our notation), and similarly for structures $\langle a,\in \rangle$ for arbitrary sets $a$ (cf. Lévy [1971]).

In this chapter we are only concerned with the case $m > 0$ which implies that every indescribable ordinal is a cardinal, in fact inaccessible:

PROPOSITION 4.1.  $\Pi_0{}^1$-indesc $(\alpha) \leftrightarrow \text{in }(\alpha) \leftrightarrow \langle V_\alpha,\in \rangle \models^2 \mathbf{B}$.

PROOF. Immediate from the fact that $\mathbf{B} = \mathbf{Ext} + \mathbf{Fund} + \mathbf{Aus}^1 + \mathbf{Pow} + \mathbf{PR}\Pi_0{}^1$ (§2.1), (§4) and Lemma 2.1(iv).

Similarly:

PROPOSITION 4.2.  $\Pi_0{}^2$-indesc $(\alpha) \leftrightarrow \langle V_\alpha,\in \rangle \models^2 \mathbf{BL}$.

PROPOSITION 4.3.    $\Pi_n^1$-indesc $(\alpha) \leftrightarrow \Sigma_{n+1}^1$-indesc $(\alpha)$.

PROOF.    Lemma 3.4.

DEFINITION 4.1.

$$\pi_n^m := \mu x (\Pi_n^m \text{-indesc } (x)),$$
$$\sigma_n^m := \mu x (\Sigma_n^m \text{-indesc } (x)),$$
$$\tau_n^m := \mu x (\Pi_n^m \text{-indesc } (x) \wedge \Sigma_n^m \text{-indesc } (x)).$$

Since the universal closure of each instance of $\mathsf{PR}\Pi_n^1$ is (equivalent to) a $\Pi_{n+1}^1$-sentence, it follows from 4.1.2 and the fact that the clause "*for all* $\Pi_n^1$-*formulas*" can be expressed by a universal quantifier ranging over the set of Gödel numbers of $\Pi_n^1$ formulas that for $n > 0$ there is a $\Pi_{n+1}^1$-sentence $\Psi$ such that

$$\langle V_\alpha, \in \rangle \models^2 \mathsf{PR}\Pi_n^1 \leftrightarrow \langle V_\alpha, \in \rangle \models^2 \Psi,$$

and hence $\pi_n^1$ is $\Pi_{n+1}^1$-describable (if it exists).[1] The last statement is true even for the case $n = 0$, for

$$\langle V_\alpha, \in \rangle \models^2 \mathsf{PR}\Pi_0^1 \leftrightarrow \langle V_\alpha, \in \rangle \models^2 \mathsf{VNB}$$

by Proposition 4.1, and the universal closure of the conjunction of the finitely many axioms, by means of which VNB is axiomatizable, is a $\Pi_1^1$-sentence. Alternatively, one may use the fact that there is a $\Pi_1^1$-sentence $\Psi$ such that in $(\alpha) \leftrightarrow \langle V_\alpha, \in \rangle \models^2 \Psi$. Therefore, we obtain:

THEOREM 4.1 (HANF–SCOTT [1961], LÉVY [1971], Corollary 17).

(i)    $\pi_n^1 = \sigma_{n+1}^1 = \tau_n^1$,

(ii)    $\pi_n^1 < \pi_{n+1}^1 < \pi_0^2$.

(*With the understanding that* $\mu x \varphi(x) < \mu x \psi(x)$ *is read as follows*: *if* $\exists \xi \, \psi(\xi)$, *then* $\exists \xi \, \varphi(\xi)$ *and* $\mu x \varphi(x) < \mu x \psi(x)$.)

We now turn to the case $m > 1$. The situation is completely different for this case for the following reason: In our definition of $\Pi_n^m$-indescribability, we have restricted the $\Pi_n^m$-formulas to those containing free variables of type at most 2, and for the case $m > 1$, this is a true restriction which, however, is necessary:

REMARK 4.2.    If in our definition of $\Pi_n^m$-indescribability, we allow any $\Pi_n^m$-formula $\Phi$ (containing variables of type $m + 1$) to occur in $\mathsf{PR}\Pi_n^m$, then we obtain (for $m > 0$) the following wider notion of indescribability: $\alpha$ is $\Pi_n^m$-*indescribable in the wider sense* iff for each $\Pi_n^m$-formula

---

[1] By "$\mu x \varphi(x)$ *exists*" we mean "$\exists \xi \, \varphi(\xi)$ *and* $\mu x \varphi(x)$ *is the least ordinal x such that* $\varphi(x)$".

$\Phi(A_0^{m+1},\ldots,A_k^{m+1})$ with free variables as indicated and any $b_0,\ldots,b_k \in \mathscr{P}^m(V_\alpha)$: if $\langle V_\alpha,\in\rangle \models^{m+1} \Phi[b_0,\ldots,b_k]$, then there is a transitive set $a \in V_\alpha$ such that

$$\langle a,\in\rangle \models^{m+1} \Phi[b_0 \cap \mathscr{P}^{m-1}(a),\ldots,b_k \cap \mathscr{P}^{m-1}(a)].$$

If $m = 1$, this agrees with our previous definition, however, if $m > 1$ then there are no $\Pi_n^m$-indescribable cardinals in the wider sense: Consider the $\Pi_0^2$-formula $\exists X\, (X = A_0^3)$. Then clearly for each $\alpha$:

$$\langle V_\alpha,\in\rangle \models^3 \exists X\,(X = A_0^3)[V_\alpha].$$

So, if there is a transitive $a \in V_\alpha$, such that

$$\langle a,\in\rangle \models^3 \exists X\,(X = A_0^3)[V_\alpha \cap \mathscr{P}(a)],$$

then there exists some $b \subseteq a$ such that

$$b = V_\alpha \cap \mathscr{P}(a).$$

On the other hand, $V_\alpha \cap \mathscr{P}(a) = \mathscr{P}(a)$ (since $a \subseteq V_\alpha$), hence $\mathscr{P}(a) \subseteq a$, a contradiction.

Now returning to our original definition of $\Pi_n^m$-indescribability, let us assume $m > 1$ and let us consider some instance of $\mathrm{PR}\Pi_n^m$ (corresponding to some $\Pi_n^m$-formula $\Phi$ with the free variable $A$ only). This is, in some suitable type theory, equivalent to a $\Sigma_n^m$-formula $\Psi(A)$, and its universal closure is of the form $\forall X\, \Psi(X)$. By the standard arguments of type theory the quantifier $\forall X$ can be moved across the quantifiers of higher type in the $\Sigma_n^m$-formula $\Psi$, and hence $\forall X\, \Psi(X)$ is equivalent to a $\Sigma_n^m$-formula. Now, as in the case $m = 1$, the statement $\langle V_\alpha,\in\rangle \models^{m+1} \mathrm{PR}\Pi_n^m$ introduces only an additional set quantifier ("*for all* $\Pi_n^m$-*formulas*"), and therefore we have a $\Sigma_n^m$-sentence $\Psi_0$ such that

$$\langle V_\alpha,\in\rangle \models^{m+1} \mathrm{PR}\Pi_n^m \leftrightarrow \langle V_\alpha,\in\rangle \models^{m+1} \Psi_0,$$

and hence $\pi_n^m$ is $\Sigma_n^m$-describable, if it exists. Similarly, $\sigma_n^m$ is also $\Pi_n^m$-describable, (if it exists). Thus we obtain:

THEOREM 4.2 (HANF–SCOTT [1961], LÉVY [1971], Corollary 17).

$$\pi_n^m, \sigma_n^m < \tau_n^m < \pi_{n+1}^m < \sigma_{n+1}^m < \pi_{n+1}^m < \pi_0^{m+1} \qquad (m > 0).$$

Therefore $\pi_n^{m+1} \neq \sigma_n^{m+1}$ for each $m,n$, but it is unknown whether

$$\pi_n^{m+1} < \sigma_n^{m+1} \quad \text{or} \quad \sigma_n^{m+1} < \pi_n^{m+1}.$$

However, Moschovakis has recently shown that the second alternative holds if one assumes $V = L$.

The inequalities of Theorems 4.1(ii) and 4.2 are very strong, e.g. one can prove:

THEOREM 4.3 (cf. BOWEN [1972], §2.1.15, THARP [1967], LÉVY [1971], Theorem 19h).

$$\Pi^1_{n+1}\text{-indesc}\,(\alpha) \to \text{stationary}\,(\{\xi \mid \Pi_n^1\text{-indesc}\,(\xi)\},\alpha).$$

PROOF. Let $\alpha$ be $\Pi^1_{n+1}$-indescribable, and let $\Psi$ be the $\Pi^1_{n+1}$-sentence (described in the proof of Theorem 4.1) such that for any inaccessible $\beta$:

$$\langle V_\beta,\in\rangle \models^2 \Psi \leftrightarrow \Pi_n^1\text{-indesc}\,(\beta).$$

In particular we have: $\langle V_\alpha,\in\rangle \models^2 \Psi$, since $\alpha$ is $\Pi_n^1$-indescribable and inaccessible. Hence by Theorem 3.5 and Lemma 3.5

$$\{\xi \mid \text{in}\,(\xi) \wedge \langle V_\xi,\in\rangle \models^2 \Psi\} \text{ is stationary in } \alpha,$$

whence the result follows.

Similarly:

THEOREM 4.4 (cf. LÉVY [1971], Theorem 19i).   For $m > 0$: if $\Pi^m_{n+1}$-indesc $(\alpha)$ or $\Sigma^m_{n+1}$-indesc $(\alpha)$, then

$$\text{stationary}\,(\{\xi \mid \Pi_n^m\text{-indesc}\,(\xi)\},\alpha),$$

and

$$\text{stationary}\,(\{\xi \mid \Sigma_n^m\text{-indesc}\,(\xi)\},\alpha).$$

*Additions.*   (1) LÉVY [1971] investigates the following weaker form of indescribability (where $\Gamma$ again denotes $\Pi_n^m$ or $\Sigma_n^m$):

$$w\text{-}\Gamma\text{-indesc}\,(\alpha) :\leftrightarrow \alpha > 0 \wedge \langle \alpha,< \rangle \models^{m+1} \mathsf{PR}\Gamma,$$

"$\alpha$ *is weakly* $\Gamma$-*indescribable*".

The main difference between both notions of indescribability results from a technical problem: If $\alpha$ is a limit ordinal, then $V_\alpha$ is closed under ordered pairs and these can be used, e.g. for contracting quantifiers of the same kind. In case of the structure $\langle \alpha,< \rangle$, however, one has to use an ordinal-pairing function (like Gödel's function $P$: On $\times$ On $\to$ On which is one-to-one and onto). If $\alpha$ is closed under $P$, e.g. if $\alpha$ is regular, $P$ can be used instead of the operation of ordered pairs. Second, whereas for limit ordinals $\alpha$, $V_\alpha$ is closed under the power-set operation this is not true for $\alpha$. Thus, one can only prove:

$$w\text{-}\Pi_0^1\text{-indesc}\,(\alpha) \leftrightarrow \text{reg}\,(\alpha) \wedge \alpha > \omega \quad \text{(compare with Proposition 4.1),}$$

and any weakly $\Pi_1^1$-indescribable cardinal is weakly inaccessible, but need not be (strongly) inaccessible. On the other hand, if $\alpha$ is strongly inaccessible then $|V_\alpha| = |\alpha|$ (by the AC). This implies that for inaccessible

$\alpha$ and any $m$, $n$ such that $m > 1$ or $m = 1$ and $n > 1$:

$$w\text{-}\Pi_n^m\text{-indesc}(\alpha) \leftrightarrow \Pi_n^m\text{-indesc}(\alpha) \quad (\text{LÉVY [1971] Theorem 2.1}).$$

Indescribability in the weak sense has also been investigated by KUNEN [1968], §16.

(2) Whereas Lévy's definition of $\Gamma$-indescribable ordinals is obtained from our definition by replacing the structures $\langle V_\alpha, \in \rangle$ by $\langle \alpha, < \rangle$, there is a recursive analogue of the $\Gamma$-indescribable cardinals which results from the former (roughly) by considering the structures $\langle L_\alpha, \in \rangle$ in place of $\langle V_\alpha, \in \rangle$. For more details we refer to ACZEL–RICHTER [1970].

## 4.3. *Large cardinals and indescribability*

In this section we review some indescribability results for large cardinals. We do not include proofs since in almost all cases a particular method of proof is required.

DEFINITION 4.2. A cardinal $\kappa > \omega$ is called *measurable* iff there is a $\kappa$-complete (which means closure under $< \kappa$ members) non-principal prime ideal $\mathcal{P}(\kappa)$; it is called $\omega$-*measurable* iff there is a non-principal $\aleph_1$-complete prime ideal in $\mathcal{P}(\kappa)$. The least $\omega$-measurable cardinal is measurable, and hence the least-measurable cardinal is $\Sigma_1^2$-describable, since it is the least $\omega$-measurable cardinal and is $> \aleph_1$). On the other hand:

*If $\kappa$ is measurable then $\kappa$ is $\Pi_1^2$-indescribable* (HANF–SCOTT [1961]). (The proof uses an ultrapower construction and an extension of Los' Theorem, cf. SILVER [1971], Theorem 1.10.)

VAUGHT [1963] has shown that the converse of the above is not true, this also follows from Silver's results described below.

DEFINITION 4.3. (ERDÖS–HAJNAL [1958]). If $f$ is a function and the domain of $f$ is $\kappa^{<\omega}(\kappa^{(n)})$, *the set of finite (n-element resp.) subsets of $\kappa$*, then a set $a \subseteq \kappa$ is called *homogeneous* for $f$ iff $f(x) = f(y)$ for all finite subsets $x, y \subseteq a$ of the same cardinality (of cardinality $n$ resp.).

$$\kappa \to (\alpha)^{<\omega} :\leftrightarrow \forall f \, [\text{Ft}(f) \wedge \text{dom}(f) = \kappa^{<\omega} \wedge \text{rng}(f) \subseteq 2 \to \exists x \, (x \subseteq a$$
$$\wedge \, x \text{ has order type } \alpha \wedge x \text{ is homogeneous for } f)],$$

$$\kappa \to (\alpha)^n :\leftrightarrow \forall f \, [\text{Ft}(f) \wedge \text{dom}(f) = \kappa^{(n)} \wedge \text{rng}(f) \subseteq 2 \to \exists x \, (x \subseteq a$$
$$\wedge \, x \text{ has order type } \alpha \wedge x \text{ is homogeneous for } f)].$$

If $\kappa$ is measurable, then $\kappa \to (\kappa)^{<\omega}$ (Erdös–Hajnal), and the least $\kappa$ such that $\kappa \to (\kappa)^{<\omega}$ is obviously $\Pi_2^1$-describable, hence by Hanf–Scott it is less than the first measurable cardinal (providing such a cardinal exists).

STATEMENT 4.1. $\kappa \to (\kappa)^2 \leftrightarrow \Pi_1^1\text{-indesc}(\kappa)$.

A proof of this statement and other properties equivalent to $\Pi_1^1$-indescribability can be found in SILVER [1971], Theorem 1.13 (cf. also BOWEN [1972], §2.2).

STATEMENT 4.2.  $\mu x(x \to (x)^2) < \mu x(x \to (\omega)^{<\omega}) < \mu x(x \to (x)^{<\omega})$; in fact, if $\kappa \to (\omega)^{<\omega}$, then there is a $\lambda < \kappa$ such that $\lambda$ is $\Pi_n^m$-indescribable for each $n, m < \omega$ (SILVER [1966], Corollary 4.4; see also REINHARDT–SILVER [1965] and §4.16 below). On the other hand, if $\kappa = \mu x(x \to (\alpha)^{<\omega})$ and $\alpha < \kappa$, then $\kappa$ is clearly $\Pi_1^1$-describable (assuming that $\alpha$ is a limit ordinal).

STATEMENT 4.3.  The notion of indescribability can be extended by using the language of transfinite type theory, viz. the partial-reflection principle $\mathrm{PR}\Pi_n^\gamma$ where $\Pi_n^\gamma$ is a straightforward generalization of $\Pi_n^m$ to transfinite-type theory. (Having gone so far, one could also allow $n$ to take transfinite values, i.e. introducing infinitary languages.) In order to define indescribability for transfinite-type theory in ZF set theory there are two approaches which are not equivalent since they are based on different formalizations of satisfaction for transfinite-type theory. For the case of finite $m$ one can reduce satisfaction of $\Pi_0^{m+1}$-statements in $\langle V_\alpha, \in \rangle$ to satisfaction of $\Pi_0^1$-formulas containing additional unary relation constants in the structure $\langle V_{\alpha+m}, \in, V_\alpha, V_{\alpha+1}, \ldots V_{\alpha+m-1} \rangle$, and since $V_\alpha, \ldots, V_{\alpha+m-1}$ are (first-order) definable in $\langle V_{\alpha+m}, \in \rangle$, again, this can be reduced to satisfaction of $\Pi_0^1$-statements in $\langle V_{\alpha+m}, \in \rangle$ (cf. §4.1). However, for transfinite $\gamma$, $V_{\alpha+\delta}$ need no longer be first-order definable in $V_{\alpha+\gamma}$ for $\delta < \gamma$, so the latter reduction is not possible in the case of transfinite-type theory. Of course, one could still generalize the first reduction for transfinite type theory; however, we shall take the following approach due to REINHARDT [1970], Definition 4.7 and JENSEN [1967a],

DEFINITION.  $\alpha$ is $\kappa$-*indescribable* iff for each $\Pi_0^1$-formula $\varphi(X_0, \ldots, X_n)$ with free variables as indicated and all $A_0, \ldots, A_n \subseteq V_\alpha$: if $\langle V_{\alpha+\kappa}, \in \rangle \models \varphi[A_0, \ldots, A_n]$ then there is a $\beta < \alpha$ such that,

$$\langle V_{\beta+\kappa}, \in \rangle \models \varphi[A_0 \cap V_\beta, \ldots, A_n \cap V_\beta].$$

We let $\kappa$-indesc $(\alpha)$ be the corresponding formal statement (expressible by a formula $\psi(\kappa, \alpha)$ of $\mathscr{L}_{ZF}$ using the formalized notion of satisfaction). Clearly we have (by the result of §4.1 to which we referred above):

$$\Pi_0^{m+1}\text{-indesc}\,(\alpha) \leftrightarrow m\text{-indesc}\,(\alpha)$$

for each finite $m$, in particular:

$$0\text{-indesc}\,(\alpha) \leftrightarrow \Pi_0^1\text{-indesc}\,(\alpha) \leftrightarrow \mathrm{in}\,(\alpha) \leftrightarrow \langle V_\alpha, \in \rangle \models^2 \mathsf{B},$$
$$1\text{-indesc}\,(\alpha) \leftrightarrow \Pi_0^2\text{-indesc}\,(\alpha) \leftrightarrow \langle V_\alpha, \in \rangle \models^2 \mathsf{BL}.$$

Then Silver's result mentioned in §4.2 can be strengthened as follows: If $\kappa$ is the least $\gamma$ such that $\gamma \to (\omega)^{<\omega}$ then

$$\{\xi < \kappa \mid \kappa\text{-indesc }(\xi)\} \text{ is stationary in } \kappa.$$

(Cf. JENSEN [1967a], Satz 4, p. 110, and GLOEDE [1972], Theorem 10.7.) If $\gamma < \alpha \leq \beta$ then we define (REINHARDT [1970], Definition 4.6) in ZF

$$\langle V_\alpha, \in \rangle \underset{\gamma}{\prec} \langle V_\beta, \in \rangle$$

to mean (informally)

$$\langle V_{\alpha+\gamma}, \in \rangle \models \varphi[a_0, \ldots, a_n] \leftrightarrow \langle V_{\beta+\gamma}, \in \rangle \models \varphi[a_0, \ldots, a_n]$$

for every $a_0, \ldots, a_n \in V_\alpha$ and every $\mathscr{L}_{ZF}$-formula $\varphi(v_0, \ldots, v_n)$ with free variables as indicated. Similarly, we define

$$\langle V_\alpha, \in, A \cap V_\alpha \rangle \underset{\gamma}{\prec} \langle V_\beta, \in, A \rangle \quad (\text{for } A \subseteq V_\beta).$$

Thus

$$\langle V_\alpha, \in \rangle \underset{0}{\prec} \langle V_\beta, \in \rangle \leftrightarrow \langle V_\alpha, \in \rangle \prec \langle V_\beta, \in \rangle,$$

and $\langle V_\alpha, \in \rangle \prec_1 \langle V_\beta, \in \rangle$ means that $\langle V_\beta, \in \rangle$ is a second-order elementary extension of $\langle V_\alpha, \in \rangle$.

THEOREM 4.5 (REINHARDT [1970], Theorem 4.8). *If $\kappa$ is $\gamma+1$-indescribable for some $\gamma < \kappa$, then there is some $\alpha < \kappa$ such that*

$$\langle V_\alpha, \in \rangle \underset{\gamma}{\prec} \langle V_\kappa, \in \rangle.$$

(Unfortunately, for $\gamma = 0$ this does not imply Montague–Vaught's Theorem 2.2.) In particular, if $\kappa$ is $\Pi_0^{m+2}$-indescribable, i.e. $(m+1)$-indescribable, then $\langle V_\kappa, \in \rangle$ satisfies the principle of complete reflection $\mathrm{CR}\Pi_0^{m+1}$ (which is defined in analogy to $\mathrm{CR}\Pi_n^1$ in §3.2. Using Reinhardt's method, this latter result can be improved as follows:

THEOREM 4.6 (GLOEDE [1970], Theorem 12.8). *Assuming* B+ $\mathrm{PR}\Pi_1^{m+1} + \Delta_1^{m+1}$-Comp, *there is some $\alpha$ such that*

$$\langle V_\alpha, \in, A \cap V_\alpha \rangle \underset{m}{\prec} \langle V, \in, A \rangle,$$

*in particular, if $\Pi_1^{m+1}$-indesc $(\kappa)$, then $\langle V_\kappa, \in \rangle \models^{m+1} \mathrm{PR}\Pi_0^{m+1}$.*

PROOF. By 4.1.1 there is a $\Delta_1^{m+1}$-formula $\Psi(v_0, X_0)$ such that for any given class $A$:

(i) $\forall x \, (\langle V, \in \rangle \models^{m+1} \Phi[x; A] \leftrightarrow \Psi(\langle \Phi, x \rangle, A))$,

for each $\Pi_0^{m+1}$-formula $\Phi(v_0, X_0)$ with free variables as indicated, and by

4.1.2, $\Psi$ is absolute with respect to $V_\beta$ if $\beta$ is inaccessible:

(ii) $\forall x \in V_\beta (\langle V_\beta, \in \rangle \models^{m+2} \Psi(v_0, A_0)[\langle \Phi, x \rangle; A \cap V_\beta]$
$\leftrightarrow \langle V_\beta, \in \rangle \models^{m+1} \Phi[x; A \cap V_\beta])$

for each $\Pi_0^{m+1}$-formula $\Phi(v_0, A_0)$. By $\Delta_1^{m+1}$-Comp there is some class $B$ such that $\forall y\ (y \in B \leftrightarrow \Psi(y, A))$, i.e.

$$B = \{\Phi, x \mid \Phi \text{ is a } \Pi_0^{m+1}\text{-formula} \wedge \langle V, \in \rangle \models^{m+1} \Phi[x; A]\}.$$

Define $\Phi_0(A_0, A_1) := \forall x\ (x \in A_0 \leftrightarrow \Psi(x, A_0))$. Obviously, $\Phi_0$ is a $\Pi_1^{m+1}$-formula. Hence by $P R \Pi_1^{m+1}$ there is some inaccessible $\alpha$ such that $\Phi_0^{V_\alpha}(B \cap V_\alpha, A \cap V_\alpha)$, i.e. by (ii)

(iii) $\forall x\ (x \in B \cap V_\alpha \leftrightarrow \langle V_\alpha, \in \rangle \models^{m+2} \Psi[x; A \cap V_\alpha])$.

Now let $\Phi(v_0, A_0)$ be any $\Pi_0^{m+1}$-formula and $a \in V_\alpha$. Then we obtain, using (i) and (iii):

$$\langle V, \in \rangle \models^{m+1} \Phi[a; A] \leftrightarrow \langle V_\alpha, \in \rangle \models^{m+1} \Phi[a; A \cap V_\alpha],$$

hence

$$\langle V_\alpha, \in, A \cap V_\alpha \rangle \underset{m}{\prec} \langle V, \in, A \rangle.$$

## References

ACZEL, P. and RICHTER, W. (1970) Inductive definitions and analogues of large cardinals. In *Conference in Math. Logic, London, '70*, W. Hodges (Ed.), pp. 1–9. Springer Lecture Notes in Mathematics, Vol. 255. Springer, Berlin. 351 pp.

BAR-HILLEL, Y., POZNANSKI, E. I. J., RABIN, M. O., and ROBINSON, A. (Eds.) (1961) *Essays on the foundations of mathematics.* (Dedicated to A. A. Fraenkel.) Magnes Press, Jerusalem. 351 pp.

BARWISE, J. (1969) Infinitary logic and admissible sets. *J.S.L.* **34**, 226–252.

BERNAYS, P. (1958) *Axiomatic set theory* (with a historical introduction by A. A. Fraenkel). North-Holland, Amsterdam. 226 pp. (2nd ed. (1968), 235 pp.)

BERNAYS, P. (1961) Zur Frage der Unendlichkeitsschemata in der axiomatischen Mengenlehre. In BAR-HILLEL et al. (1961), pp. 3–49. This volume. (English translation—revised version.)

BOWEN, K. A. (1972) The relative consistency of some consequences of the existence of measurable cardinal numbers. *Dissertationes Math.* Warszawa. 63 pp.

BULOFF, J. J., HOLYOKE, T. C., and HAHN, S. W. (Eds.). (1969) *Foundations of mathematics.* (Symposium papers commemorating the sixtieth birthday of Kurt Gödel.) Springer, Berlin. 195 p.

ERDÖS, P. and HAJNAL, A. (1958) On the structure of set mappings. *Acta Math. Acad. Sci. Hung.* **9**, 111–131.

ERDÖS, P. and HAJNAL, A. (1962) Some remarks concerning our paper "On the structure of set mappings". *Ibid.* **13**, 223–226.

FELGNER, U. (1971a) *Models of ZF-set theory.* Springer Lecture Notes in Mathematics, Vol. 223. Springer, Berlin. 173 pp.

GAIFMAN, H. (1967) A generalization of Mahlo's method for obtaining large cardinal numbers. *Israel J. Math.* **5**, 188–201.

GLOEDE, K. (1970) Reflection principles and large cardinals. Ph.D. thesis. Heidelberg. 129 pp.

GLOEDE, K. (1971) Filters closed under Mahlo's and Gaifman's operation. In *Proceedings of the Cambridge Summer School in Mathematical Logic,* August '71. A. R. D. Mathias and H. Rogers (Eds.), pp. 495–530. Springer Lecture Notes in Mathematics. Vol. 337. Springer, Berlin. 660 pp.

GLOEDE, K. (1972) Ordinals with partition properties and the constructible hierarchy. *Zeitschr. f. math. Logik* **18**, 135–164.

GÖDEL, K. (1940) *The consistency of the axiom of choice and of the generalized continuum hypothesis with the axioms of set theory.* Annals of Math. Studies, Vol. 3. Princeton University Press, Princeton, N.J., 66 pp. (7th printing (1966).)

HANF, W. and SCOTT, D. (1961) Classifying inaccessible cardinals (abstract). *Notices A.M.S.* **8**, 445.

JENSEN, R. B. (1967) *Modelle der Mengenlehre.* Springer Lecture Notes in Mathematics. Vol. 37. Berlin. 176 pp.

JENSEN, R. B. (1967a) Große Kardinalzahlen. Notes of lectures given at Oberwolfach (Germany). 121 pp.

JENSEN, R. B. (1972) The fine structure of the constructible hierarchy. *Annals of Math. Logic* **4**, 229–308.

JENSEN, R. B. and KARP, C. (1971) *Primitive recursive set functions.* In SCOTT (1971), pp. 143–176.

KEISLER, H. J. and ROWBOTTOM, F. (1965) Constructible sets and weakly compact cardinals (abstract). *Notices A.M.S.* **12**, 373–374.

KEISLER, H. J. and TARSKI, A. (1964) From accessible to inaccessible cardinals. *Fund. Math.* **53**, 225–308. (Corrections, *ibid.* **57**, 119 (1965).)

KRIVINE, J. L. (1971) *Introduction to axiomatic set theory.* Reidel, Dordrecht. 98 pp.

KUNEN, K. (1968) Inaccessibility properties of cardinals. Doctoral Dissertation. Stanford. 117 pp.

KUNEN, K. (1972) The Hanf number of second-order logic. *J.S.L.* **37**, 588–594.

LÉVY, A. (1958) Contributions to the metamathematics of set theory. Ph.D. thesis. Jerusalem.

LÉVY, A. (1960) Axiom schemata of strong infinity in axiomatic set theory. *Pacific J. Math.* **10**, 223–238.

LÉVY, A. (1965) A hierarchy of formulas in set theory. *Memoirs A.M.S.* **57**, 76 pp.

LÉVY, A. (1971) The size of the indescribable cardinals. In SCOTT (1971), pp. 205–218.

LÉVY, A. and VAUGHT, R. L. (1961) Principles of partial reflection in the set theories of Zermelo and Ackermann. *Pacific J. Math.* **11**, 1045–1062.

MAHLO, P. (1911) Über lineare transfinite Mengen. *Berichte über die Verhandlungen der Königlich Sächsischen Akademie der Wissenschaften zu Leipzig*, Math.-Phys. Klasse **63**, 187–225.

MAHLO, P. (1912–1913) Zur Theorie und Anwendung der $\rho_0$-Zahlen, *ibid.*, I: **64**, 108–112 (1912); II: **65**, 268–282 (1913).

MONTAGUE, R. and VAUGHT, R. L. (1959) Natural models of set theories. *Fund. Math.* **47**, 219–242.

MOSCHOVAKIS, Y. N. (1971) *Predicative classes.* In SCOTT (1971), pp. 247–264.

MOSTOWSKI, A. (1969) *Constructible sets with applications.* North-Holland, Amsterdam. 269 pp.

QUINE, W. V. (1963) *Set theory and its logic.* Belknap Press, Cambridge, Mass. 359 pp. (Revised ed., 361 pp.).

REINHARDT, W. N. (1967) Topics in the metamathematics of set theory, Doctoral Dissertation, 85 pp.

REINHARDT, W. N. (1970) Ackermann's set theory equals ZF. *Ann. Math. Logic* **2**, 189–249.

REINHARDT, W. N. and SILVER, J. (1965) On some problems of Erdös and Hajnal (abstract). *Notices A.M.S.* **12**, 723.

ROBINSON, R. M. (1945) On finite sequences of classes. *J.S.L.* **10**, 125–126.

SCHMERL, J. H. (1972) An elementary sentence which has ordered models. *J.S.L.* **37**, 521–530.

SCHMERL, J. H. and SHELAH, S. (1972) On power-like models for hyperinaccessible cardinals. *J.S.L.* **37**, 531–537.

SCOTT, D. (1955) Definitions by abstraction in axiomatic set theory (abstract), *Bull. A.M.S.* **61**, 442.

SCOTT, D. (Ed.) (1971) *Axiomatic set theory.* Proceedings of symposia in pure mathematics **13**. Am. Math. Soc., Providence, R.I.

SHEPHERDSON, J. C. (1952) Inner models for set theory—II. *J.S.L.* **17**, 225–237.

SILVER, J. (1966) Some applications of model theory in set theory. Doctoral Dissertation, Berkeley, 110 pp. (Published (with the deletion of §4) in SILVER (1971)).

SILVER, J. (1971) Some applications of model theory in set theory. *Ann. of Math. Logic* **3**, 45–110.

TAKEUTI, G. (1965) On the axiom of constructibility. Proceedings of Symposia of Logic, Computability and Automata at Rome. Mimeographed Notes, New York.

TAKEUTI, G. (1969) *The universe of set theory*, pp. 74–128. In BULOFF et al. (1969).

TARSKI, A. and VAUGHT, R. L. (1957) Arithmetical extensions of relational systems. *Compositio Math.* **18**, 81–102.

THARP, L. (1967) On a set theory of Bernays. *J.S.L.* **32**, 319–321.

VAUGHT, R. L. (1963) Indescribable cardinals (abstract). *Notices A.M.S.* **10**, 126.

SETS AND CLASSES; On the work by Paul Bernays
© North-Holland Publishing Company (1976) pp. 325-340.

# A REMARK ON MODELS OF THE GÖDEL-BERNAYS AXIOMS FOR SET THEORY

Andrzej MOSTOWSKI†

*Warzaw, Poland*

## 1. Notation

We denote the sets of axioms of Zermelo–Fraenkel and Gödel–Bernays by **ZF** and **GB** respectively. Both these systems are formulated in a first-order language L with identity (denoted by $\approx$) and with one binary predicate $\in$. Unlike GÖDEL [1940], we admit in **GB** only one primitive notion, viz. the binary relation $\in$ and define the predicates $\mathbf{Cls}(x)$ ($x$ is a class), $\mathbf{M}(x)$ ($x$ is a set) by formulas $x = x$, $(Ey)(x \in y)$ respectively. Axioms A1 and A2 of Gödel can then be omitted. A formula $\varphi$ is called predicative if all its quantifiers are limited to **M**. A system obtained from **ZF** by addition of the axiom of choice is called **ZFC**; similarly **GBC** denotes a system obtained from **GB** by adding to it the (set-form of the) axiom of choice.

All models for **ZF** or **GB** which we consider below have the form $(M, \in)$ where $M$ is a transitive set of sets. We write simply $M$ instead of $(M, \in)$. The extension of the predicate $M$ in a model $M$ is denoted by $V_M$. Thus, $V_M = M$ if $M \models \mathbf{ZF}$ but $V_M \subset M$ if $M \models \mathbf{GB}$. If $M_1$, $M_2$ are two families of sets such that $M_1 \subseteq M_2$ and $V_{M_1} = V_{M_2}$, then we call $M_2$ a *C-extension* of $M_1$ and write $M_1 \subseteq_C M_2$.

A language obtained from L by adding to it constants $c_m$ for each element $m$ of a set $M$ is denoted by $L_M$. We identify $c_m$ with a suitable element of $M$ which allows us to consider $L_M$ as a subset of $M$. All models for axioms formulated in $L_M$ always contain $M$, and $c_m$ is always interpreted as $m$.

$L(A)$ or $L_M(A)$ denotes a language obtained from L or $L_M$ by adding to it a new one-place predicate $A$. Models for axioms formulated in $L(A)$ or in $L_M(A)$ have the form $(N, X)$, where $N$ is a transitive family of sets and $X \subseteq N$; the interpretation of the new predicate $A$ is $X$ and the interpretation of $\in$ is the relation $\in$ of "being an element of".

For each family $M$ of sets we denote by $\mathrm{Def}_M$ the family of sets of the form $\{x \in V_M : M \models \varphi(c_x)\}$ where $\varphi$ is a predicative formula of $L_M$ with exactly one free variable and $\varphi(c_x)$ arises from $\varphi$ by replacing the free variable by $c_x$ wherever it occurs. Sets which belong to $\mathrm{Def}_M$ are said to be definable in $M$.

A slightly more general notion of definability is as follows: let $M$ be a transitive family of sets, $X \subseteq V_M$. A set $S$ is definable in $M$ with respect to $X$ if there is a predicative formula $\varphi$ of $L_M(A)$ with exactly one free variable such that $S = \{x \in V_M : (M,X) \models \varphi(c_x)\}$. We denote the family of all such sets by $\mathrm{Def}_M(X)$. It is easy to prove that if $M$ is transitive, then so is $\mathrm{Def}_M(X)$ for any $X \subseteq V_M$.

We intend to prove below the following theorem:

> For a given countable transitive model $M$ of ZFC there are $2^{\omega_1}$ models $L$ of GB such that $V_L = M$. Moreover these models form a full binary tree of height $\omega_1$ when ordered by inclusion; if two models $L_1, L_2$ do not lie on the same branch of the tree, then there is no transitive model $L$ of GB such that $V_L = M$ and $L \supseteq L_1 \cup L_2$.

A similar theorem is also valid for the "predicative extension" of Peano's arithmetic; an exact formulation of this theorem is given in §5.

## 2. Auxiliary theorems

LEMMA 2.1 (Marek). *If $M$ is a transitive model of GB and $C$ is the family of all transitive sets $K$ which satisfy the conditions*

$$M \subseteq K \subseteq P(V_M), \qquad V_K = V_M, \qquad K \models GB,$$

*then the union of any chain $L \subseteq C$ is an element of $C$.*

The proof of this lemma is very easy and we omit it. Marek deduced from this lemma the existence of maximal elements of $C$, and asked about their number. A partial answer to this question is given in Corollary 4.1 below.

LEMMA 2.2. *If $M$ is a transitive model of GB and $X \subseteq V_M$, then all the axioms of groups A and B of GB as well as the axioms C1–C3 and D are valid in the model $\mathrm{Def}_M(X)$. Moreover $\mathrm{Def}_M(X)$ is a C-extension of $M$.*

PROOF. The verification of Axioms A and B are left to the reader. In order to prove that $\mathrm{Def}_M(X)$ is a C-extension of $M$, let us assume that $x \in V_{\mathrm{Def}_m(X)}$, i.e. that there is a set $S$ such that $x \in S \in \mathrm{Def}_M(X)$. Hence, $S$ is a set definable in $M$ with respect to $X$ and therefore $S$ consists of elements of $V_M$ which proves that $x \in V_M$. Conversely, if $x \in V_M$, then the unit set $\{x\}$ is definable in $M$ with respect to $X$ whence $x \in \{x\} \in \mathrm{Def}_M (X)$ which proves that $x \in V_{\mathrm{Def}_M (X)}$.

Since Axioms C1–C3 deal exclusively with sets, it follows from their validity in $M$ that they are also valid in $\mathrm{Def}_M (X)$ since in both these models the interpretations of sets are identical. Lemma 2.2 is thus proved.

In connection with Lemma 2.2 it is necessary to point out that the statement "a sub-class of a set is a set" may (and generally does) fail in the family $\mathrm{Def}_M (X)$. Thus, if we agree to call elements of $V_M$ "sets of $M$", then $\mathrm{Def}_M (X)$ may, and generally does, contain "semi-sets", i.e. classes (elements of $\mathrm{Def}_M (X)$) which are contained in sets of $M$ (see VOPĚNKA and HÁJEK (1972)). The existence of semi-sets is due to the fact that the axiom of comprehension is, in general, false in $\mathrm{Def}_M (X)$.

In the case when $X$ is definable in $M$, the axiom of replacement and the axiom of comprehension are valid in $\mathrm{Def}_M (X)$ and thus, no semi-sets exist. We shall see below an example of $X$ when not definable in $M$ and yet no semi-sets exist because the axiom of comprehension is valid in $\mathrm{Def}_M (X)$.

The crux of the whole construction is a determination of a set $X \subseteq M$ such that $\mathrm{Def}_M (X)$ is a model for the axiom C4 of replacement. Unfortunately I do not know of any workable, necessary, and sufficient conditions for this to be the case and have to rely on results established by FELGNER [1971] in a special case of a denumerable model. In what follows, $M$ is a transitive denumerable model of GB.

Let $P \in \mathrm{Def}_M$ and $R \in \mathrm{Def}_M$ be a binary relation which partially orders $P$. Elements of $P$ are called conditions. We write $p \leqslant q$ instead of $pRq$ and read this formula: $p$ is an extension of $q$. We define by induction a binary relation $\Vdash$ (forcing), whose left domain is $P$ and right domain consists of all predicative sentences of $L_M(A)$:

$$(p \models c_m \approx c_n) \equiv (m = n), \qquad (p \models c_m \in c_n) \equiv (m \in n),$$
$$p \models A(c_m) \equiv (m \in P) \,\&\, (m \geqslant p),$$
$$(p \Vdash \to \varphi) \equiv (q)_{\leqslant p} \quad (q \text{ non} \models \varphi), \qquad (p \Vdash \varphi \vee \psi) \equiv (p \Vdash \varphi) \vee (p \Vdash \psi),$$
$$[p \Vdash (Ex)_M \varphi] \equiv (Em)_{V_M} (p \Vdash \varphi(c_m)) \quad \text{if } x \text{ is free in } \varphi,$$
$$[p \Vdash (Ex)_M \varphi] \equiv p \Vdash \varphi \quad \text{if } x \text{ is not free in } \varphi.$$

Whenever $\varphi$ is a formula, we denote by $\mathrm{Fr}(\varphi)$ the set of its free variables. For $\gamma \in M^{\mathrm{Fr}(\varphi)}$, we denote by $\varphi(\gamma)$ the sentence obtained from $\varphi$ by substituting $c_{\gamma(v)}$ for $v$ throughout $\varphi$ for each $v \in \mathrm{Fr}(\varphi)$. With this notation we have

LEMMA 2.3. *For each predicative formula $\varphi$ of $L_M(A)$ the set*

$$\{(p,\gamma)\in P \times M^{\mathrm{Fr}\,(\varphi)}: p \Vdash \varphi(\gamma)\}$$

*belongs to* $\mathrm{Def}_M$.

A set $G \subseteq P$ is *generic* (more exactly: generic in $P$ over $M$) if it has the properties:

  (i) If $p \in G$ and $p \leq q$, then $q \in G$;
  (ii) If $p$, $q \in G$, then $(Er)[(r \in G) \,\&\, (r \leq p) \,\&\, (r \leq q)]$;
  (iii) If $S \in \mathrm{Def}_M$ and $S$ is dense in $P$, then $G \cap S \neq \emptyset$.

LEMMA 2.4. *Each condition belongs to at least one generic set.*

LEMMA 2.5. *If $G$ is generic then $(M,G) \models \varphi \equiv (Ep)_G (p \Vdash \varphi)$ for each predicative sentence $\varphi$ of $L_M(A)$.*

In order to prove the next two lemmas we make the following assumption about $P$:

ASSUMPTION (A) Whenever $x \in V_M, \emptyset \neq x \subseteq P$ and $x$ is a chain with respect to $\leq$, then there is a condition $p$ such that $p \leq q$ for each $q$ in $x$.

LEMMA 2.6. *If $M \models \mathsf{GBC}$, $G$ is generic, $m \in V_M$ and $\varphi$ is a predicative formula of $L_M(A)$ with exactly one free variable $v$, then there is a set $n \in V_M$ such that*

$$(M,G) \models (v)\{(v \in c_n) \equiv [(v \in c_m) \,\&\, \varphi]\}.$$

PROOF. It is sufficient to show that the set

$$Q = \{p \in P: (x)_m [p \Vdash \varphi(c_x) \vee \rightarrow \varphi(c_x)]\}$$

is dense in $P$. Once this is shown the rest is easy: by Lemma 2.3 the set $Q$ belongs to $\mathrm{Def}_M$, hence there is a $p$ in $Q$ which belongs to $G$ and it is sufficient to take $n = \{x \in m: p \Vdash \varphi(c_x)\}$.

The proof that $Q$ is dense closely follows the construction used by FELGNER [1971]; it is therefore sufficient to indicate only the main steps of this proof. We can assume that $m$ is infinite. Let $q_0 \in P$. For arbitrary $(x,p)$ in $V_M \times P$ we denote by $Z(x,p)$ the set of elements $q$ in $P$ which have the following properties:

  (i) $q \leq p$ and $q \Vdash \varphi(c_x) \vee \rightarrow \varphi(c_x)$;
  (ii) whenever $r$ has the property (i), then $\mathrm{rk}\,(q) \leq \mathrm{rk}\,(r)$.

We easily see that $Z(x,p) \in V_M$. If $\emptyset \neq \alpha \in \mathrm{On} \cap V_M$ and $g \in V_M \cap P^\alpha$ then we denote by $W(g)$ the set of conditions $q$ which have the properties:

  (iii) $q \leq q_0$ and $q \leq r$ for each $r \in \mathrm{Rg}\,(g)$;
  (iv) whenever $s$ has the property (iii), then $\mathrm{rk}\,(q) \leq \mathrm{rk}\,(s)$.

For $\alpha = \emptyset$ we define additionally $W(g) = \emptyset$. We can show easily that $W(g) \in V_M$ for each $g \in V_M \cap P^\alpha$ and each $\alpha \in \mathrm{On} \cap V_M$.

Let $\mu$ be a cardinal of $V_M$ and let $f$ be a function such that $f \in V_M$ and $f$ is an injection of $\mu$ onto $m$. The existence of $\mu$ and $f$ follows from the assumption that $M \models \mathsf{GBC}$ and $m \in V_M$. Using transfinite induction we define two sequences $\{P_\xi\}, \{Q_\xi\}$ of type $\mu$ which are elements of $V_M$ and which satisfy the following equations for each $\xi < \mu$:

$$Q_\xi = \{g \in (\bigcup_{\alpha < \xi} P_\alpha \cup \{q_0\})^{1+\xi} : (g(0) = q_0) \,\&\, (\alpha)_\xi (g(1 + \alpha) \in P_\alpha) \,\&$$
$$(\gamma)_{1+\xi}(\delta)_{1+\xi}[\gamma < \delta \to g(\gamma) \geqslant g(\delta)]\},$$
$$P_\xi = \bigcup \{Z(f(\xi), y) : y \in \bigcup\{W(g) : g \in Q_\xi\}\}.$$

Using the axiom of choice in $M$ we can select functions $g, h$ in $V_M$ of type $\mu$ such that $g \restriction (1 + \xi) \in Q_\xi$, $h(\xi) \in W(g \restriction (1 + \xi))$ and $g(1 + \xi) \in Z(f(\xi), h(\xi))$ for each $\xi < \mu$. Thus $g$ is a decreasing function and by (A) the set $W(g)$ is non-void. For an arbitrary $p$ in $W(g)$ we have then $p \in Q$ and $p \leqslant q_0$ which proves the density of $Q$.

LEMMA 2.7.    *If $M$ is a transitive model of* $\mathsf{GBC}$, *$G$ is generic and $\gamma$ is a predicative formula of* $L_M(A)$ *with exactly two free variables $v$, $w$, then for each $m$ in $V_M$ there is a set $n$ in $V_M$ such that*

(∗)        $(M, G) \models (v)(w)\{[(v \in c_m) \,\&\, \varphi] \to (Ew)[(w \in c_n) \,\&\, \varphi]\}$.

PROOF.    This is again a repetition of the construction of Felgner and it is sufficient to indicate only its main steps. We put

$$R = \{p \in P : (En)_{V_M}(x)_m(y)_{V_M}(Ez)_n p \,\Vdash [\to \varphi(c_x, c_y) \vee \varphi(c_x, c_z)]\}$$

and claim that $R$ is dense in $P$. To show this we choose $q_0$ in $P$ and denote by $\mu$ and $f$ a cardinal and a bijection as in the previous proof. We can assume that $\mu$ is infinite. Let $Z(x, p)$ be a set defined as follows: if there are $q \leqslant p$ such that

(i) $q \Vdash \to (Ew)_M \varphi(c_x, w)$ then $Z(x, p)$ consists of all the conditions $q \leqslant p$ which have the property (i) and the following property:

(ii) whenever $r \leqslant p$ and $r$ has the property (i), then $\mathrm{rk}\,(q) \leqslant \mathrm{rk}\,(r)$.

If there are no $q$ with the property (i) then $(q)_{\leqslant p}(Er)_{\leqslant q} r \Vdash (Ew)_M \varphi(c_x, w)$ and hence there are $q \leqslant p$ such that

(iii) $q \Vdash (Ew)_M \varphi(c_x, w)$. In this case we let $Z(x, p)$ be the set of all conditions $q \leqslant p$ which have the property (iii) and are such that whenever $r \leqslant p$ has the property (iii), then $\mathrm{rk}\,(q) \leqslant \mathrm{rk}\,(r)$. It is easily seen that $Z(x, p) \in V_M$.

We define $S(x, q)$ as follows: if $q$ non $\Vdash (Ew)_M \varphi(c_x, w)$, then $S(x, q) = \emptyset$. Otherwise, let $S(x, q)$ be the set consisting of all the elements $y \in V_M$ with the following properties:

(v) $q \Vdash \varphi(c_x, c_y)$;
(vi) whenever $q \Vdash \varphi(c_x, c_z)$ then rk $(y) \leqslant$ rk $(z)$.

It is again easy to show that $S(x, q) \in V_M$.

Finally, let $W(g)$, $P_\xi$, $Q_\xi$, $g$, $h$ be defined as in the proof of Lemma 2.6. Using once more the axiom of choice, we obtain a function $k \in V_M$ with domain $V_M$ such that $k(\xi) \in S(f(\xi), g(1 + \xi))$ for each $\xi < \mu$. Then rg$(k)$ is a set $n \in V_M$ such that for any $p$ in $W(g)$ and arbitrary $x$ in $m$, $y$ in $V_M$ there is a $z$ in $n$ satisfying $p \Vdash \rightarrow \varphi(c_x, c_y) \vee \varphi(c_x, c_z)$; moreover $p \leqslant q_0$. The density of $R$ is thus proved.

If now, $p \in R \cap G$ and $n$ is a set whose existence is secured by the fact that $p \in R$, then formula (*) holds for this set $n$. This proves Lemma 2.7.

For the benefit of readers not acquainted with Felgner's paper [1971] we add below some comments about the intuitive meaning of constructions carried out in two proofs sketched above.

In order to prove the density of sets $Q$ and $R$ we have to show that each $q_0 \in P$ has an extension which belongs to both $Q$ and $R$. These extensions are obtained by constructing successive extensions of $q_0$ and repeating this process transfinitely many times.

In both proofs we represent the given set $m$ as the range of a one-to-one function $f$ whose domain is a cardinal $\mu$ and assume that $\mu$ is infinite. The sequence of successive extensions of $q_0$ is denoted in both proofs by $g$. Thus $g$ is a decreasing function with domain $\mu$ whose values are conditions. The initial term of $g$ is $g(0) = q_0$. If $\xi < \mu$ and $g(\alpha)$ is already defined for $\alpha < 1 + \xi$, then $g(1 + \xi)$ is an extension of all the $g(\alpha)$'s which satisfies an additional requirement. In Lemma 2.6 this additional requirement is: $g(1 + \xi)$ decides $\varphi(c_{f(\xi)})$, i.e. $g(1 + \xi)$ either forces this formula or its negation. In Lemma 2.7 the additional requirement is: $g(1 + \xi)$ forces $\rightarrow (Ew)_M \varphi(c_{f(\xi)}, w)$ if there are conditions which have this property and extend all the $g(\alpha)$'s; otherwise $g(1 + \xi)$ should force $(Ew)_M \varphi(c_{f(\xi)}, w)$.

To explain the notation previously used, we note that $g(1 + \xi)$ is constructed in two stages: first, we construct $h(\xi)$ which is an extension of all the $g(\alpha)$'s, $\alpha < 1 + \xi$ and then $g(1 + \xi)$ is selected from among such extensions of $h(\xi)$ as satisfy the additional requirements. The first fact is expressed by the formula $h(\xi) \in W(g \upharpoonright (1 + \xi))$ and the second by the formula $g(1 + \xi) \in Z(f(\xi), h(\xi))$. In case of Lemma 2.7 we construct still one additional function $k$ such that if $g(1 + \xi) \models (Ew)_M \varphi(c_{f(\xi)}, w)$ then $k(\xi)$ is an element of $V_M$ satisfying $g(1 + \xi) \Vdash \varphi(c_{f(\xi)}, c_{k(\xi)})$.

Once we have the functions $g$ and $k$ we can take as $p$ any condition which extends all the $g(\xi)$'s, $\xi < \mu$, and as $n$ the set rg $(k)$. The existence of $p$ is secured by assumption (A). In case of Lemma 2.6 we see immediately that $p$ decides $\varphi(c_x)$ for all $x$ in $m$ because each $x$ can be represented as $f(\xi)$ and $p$ is an extension of $g(1 + \xi)$ which decides $\varphi(c_{f(\xi)})$. Hence $p \in Q$. In case of Lemma 2.7 we see from the definitions of $g(1 + \xi)$ and $k(\xi)$ that if $p \Vdash (Ew)_M \varphi(c_x, w)$, then $p \Vdash \varphi(c_x, c_z)$ for a $z$ in $n$. Hence $p \in R$.

The essential point is that functions $g$ and $k$ are elements of $V_M$; otherwise we can neither claim that $n \in V_M$ nor that assumption (A) is applicable for obtaining $p$. In order to obtain $g$ and $k$ in $V_M$, we cannot proceed in a simple-minded way and for instance define $g$ as any extension of $q_0$ which decides $\varphi(c_{f(\xi)})$. The reason why this procedure is faulty, follows: the extensions of the $g(\alpha)$'s, $\alpha < 1 + \xi$, do not form, in general, a set which belongs to $V_M$; rather they form a "class", i.e. a definable subset of $V_M$. Thus we cannot use the set-form of the axiom of choice to select a particular extension. Yet we have only this form of the axiom at our disposal if we want to obtain in the end a function which belongs to $V_M$. To overcome this difficulty we consider not all the extensions of the $g(\alpha)$'s, but only those which possibly have a small rank. These extensions form a set $W(g \restriction (1 + \xi))$ which is an element of $V_M$. Also we select $g(1 + \xi)$ not from among all the conditions which satisfy the additional requirements because this would involve a choice from a "class", but from among those conditions which have possibly small ranks and which therefore form a set which belongs to $V_M$. Also $k(\xi)$ and $h(\xi)$ are selected from sets $S(f(\xi), g(1 + \xi))$ or $W(g \restriction (1 + \xi))$ which both belong to $V_M$. In this way we can obtain the required functions by applying the set-form of the axiom of choice which, according to our assumption, is valid in $M$ and so yields functions which belong to $V_M$.

Let us note that it is an open question whether Lemmas 2.6 and 2.7 remain valid if we replace the assumption $M \models \mathsf{GBC}$ by the weaker assumption $M \models \mathsf{GB}$.

From Lemmas 2.2 and 2.7 we obtain the following theorem which allows us to construct models of $\mathsf{GB}$:

THEOREM 2.1. *If $M$ is a denumerable transitive model of* $\mathsf{GBC}$, $P$, $R \in \mathrm{Def}_M$ *and $R$ is a partial ordering of $P$ such that $P$ satisfies* (A), *then* $\mathrm{Def}_M(G) \models \mathsf{GBC}$ *for every set $G$ which is generic in $P$ over $M$. Moreover,* $V_{\mathrm{Def}_M(G)} = V_M$, *i.e.* $\mathrm{Def}_M(G)$ *is a C-extension of $M$.*

PROOF. If $x \in y \in \mathrm{Def}_M(G)$, then $y \in V_M$ and hence $x \in V_M$. Conversely, if $x \in V_M$, then there are $y \in \mathrm{Def}_M(G)$ such that $x \in y$. Hence, the last equation stated in the theorem is proved. It follows in particular that the set-form of the axiom of choice is valid in $\mathrm{Def}_M(G)$. In view of Lemma 2.2 it remains for us to verify the validity of the axiom of substitution.

Thus, let $m \in V_M$ and $X \in \mathrm{Def}_M(G)$ and assume that $X$ is a function. Let $\varphi$ be a predicative formula with two free variables such that for all $u, v$ in $V_M$

$$\langle u,v \rangle \in X \equiv (M,G) \models \varphi(c_u,c_v).$$

In view of Lemma 2.7 there is $n_1 \in V_M$ such that whenever $u \in m$ and there is $y$ in $V_M$ satisfying $(M,G) \models \varphi(c_u,c_y)$, then there is a $y$ in $n_1$ satisfying the same formula. In view of our assumption $y$ is determined uniquely by $u$. Hence, all the values which the function $X$ takes for arguments in $m$ belong to $n_1$. Applying Lemma 2.6 we obtain a set $n \in V_M$ whose elements are exactly these values which proves the theorem.

## 3. A finite tree of C-extensions

Let $M \models \mathrm{GBC}$ be a transitive denumerable model and $N$ an integer. We consider subsets

$$S_0, S_1,\ldots, S_{k-1}, T_0, T_1,\ldots, T_{l-1}$$

of $\{0, 1,\ldots, N-1\}$ satisfying the conditions:

$$|T_h| \geqslant 2, \quad T_h - S_j \neq \emptyset \quad \text{for } j < k, \quad h < l.$$

LEMMA 3.1.  *There are $N$ transitive denumerable C-extensions $M_i$ of $M$ such that $M_i \models \mathrm{GBC}$ for $i < N$ with the following properties*:

(*)     *for each $j < k$ there is a transitive denumerable model $M'_j \models \mathrm{GBC}$ which is a C-extension of all the models $M_i$ with $i \in S_j$*;

(**)    *for no $h < l$ and no transitive model $M'' \models \mathrm{GBC}$, $M''$ is a C-extension of all the models $M_i$ with $i \in T_h$.*

PROOF.   Let $\mathrm{On}_M = \mathrm{On} \cap M$,

$$P = \{2^{\xi \times N} \in M : \xi \in \mathrm{On}_M\}, \quad \text{where } N = \{0, 1,\ldots, N-1\}.$$

We call elements of $P$ conditions and order them by inverse inclusion: $p \leqslant q \equiv p \supseteq q$. For $p$ in $P$ we put $\mathrm{dom}(p) = \mathrm{Dom}(\mathrm{Dom}(p))$; thus $\mathrm{dom}\, p$ is the ordinal $\xi$ such that $p \in 2^{\xi \times N}$. For each non-void set $X \subseteq N$ and each $p$ in $P$ we put $p[X] = p \restriction (\mathrm{dom}(p) \times X)$ and denote by $P[X]$ the set of all $p[X]$ where $p \in P$. For each $\emptyset \neq X \subseteq N$ and $p \in P[X]$ we put

$$\check{p} = \{\langle \alpha,i \rangle \in \mathrm{dom}(p) \times X : p(\langle \alpha,i \rangle) = 1\};$$

if $X \subseteq N$ and $G \subseteq P[X]$, then $\check{G}$ denotes the set $\mathrm{U}\{\check{p} : p \in G\}$. Let $D_n$ be a sequence of all dense subsets of $P$ which are definable in $M$. Similarly

$D_n[X]$ is a sequence of all dense subsets of $P[X]$ which are definable in $M$, the ordering of $P[X]$ being also the relation of inverse inclusion. If $p \leqslant q \in D_n$ then we say that $D_n$ covers $p$.

To simplify formulas we assume once and for all that the letter $i$ with or without subscripts denotes an integer $\leqslant N$, and the letters $j$ and $h$ denote integers less than $k$ and $l$ respectively.

Let $\{\alpha_n\}$ be a sequence (without repetitions) consisting of all the elements of $\mathrm{On}_M$.

We construct a sequence $p_n$ of elements of $P$ such that $p_n \geqslant p_{n+1}$ for each $n$ and a function $\varphi: \omega \to \omega$ such that the following conditions are satisfied:

(1)     $D_n[\{i\}]$ covers $p_n[\{i\}]$ for each $i$;
(2)     $D_n[S_j]$ covers $p_n[S_j]$ for each $j$;
(3)     $\alpha_m < \varphi(m) < \varphi(m+1)$ for each $m$;
(4)     $\underset{i \in T_h}{\cap} \mathrm{Dom}\,(\check{p}_n[\{i\}]) = \{\alpha_{\varphi(0)}, \alpha_{\varphi(1)}, \dots, \alpha_{\varphi(n-1)}\}.$

Before proving the existence of the sequences $p_n$ and $\varphi(n)$ we show that lemma 3.1 can be derived from (1)–(4).

Let

$$G_i = \{x \in P[\{i\}]: (En)(x \geqslant p_n[\{i\}])\},$$
$$H_j = \{x \in P[S_j]: (En)(x \geqslant p_n[S_j])\}.$$

In view of (1) and (2) these sets are generic respectively in $P[\{i\}]$ or $P[S_j]$ over $M$. By Theorem 2.1, the families $\mathrm{Def}_M(G_i)$ and $\mathrm{Def}_M(H_j)$ are transitive denumerable models of GBC and are $C$-extensions of $M$. Let $M_i = \mathrm{Def}_M(G_i)$, $M'_j = \mathrm{Def}_M(H_j)$.

We show that $M'_j$ is a $C$-extension of $M_i$ whenever $i \in S_j$. To prove this, it is sufficient to show that $G_i \in \mathrm{Def}_M(H_j)$ whenever $i \in S_j$ and this follows from the equivalence

$$x \in G_i \equiv (Ey)\{(y \in H_j) \,\&\, [x = y \restriction (\mathrm{dom}\,(y) \times \{i\})]\}.$$

To prove it we note that each $x \in G_i$ is obtained from a function $p_n[\{i\}]$ by restricting its arguments to $\alpha \times \{i\}$, where $\alpha$ is an ordinal $\leqslant \mathrm{dom}\,(p_n)$. If we restrict $p_n$ to $\alpha \times S_j$, we obtain a function $y \in H_j$ such that $x = y \restriction (\mathrm{dom}\,(y) \times \{i\})$. Similarly restricting the arguments of a function $y \in H_j$ to $\mathrm{dom}\,(y) \times \{i\}$, we obtain a function $x$ in $G_i$.

Now we prove (∗∗). Let us assume that $M''_i \models \mathsf{GBC}$ and $M''$ is a transitive $C$-extension of $M_i$ for each $i \in T_h$. It follows that $G_i \in M''$; hence, if we abbreviate $\cap_{i \in T_h} \mathrm{Dom}\,(\check{G}_i)$ by $X$ we obtain $X \in M''$. Each $G_i$ consists of pairs $\langle \alpha, i \rangle$ such that $x(\langle \alpha, i \rangle) = 1$ for some $x \in G_i$. Hence

$$\langle \alpha, i \rangle \in G_i \equiv (En)\{p_n[\{i\}](\langle \alpha, i \rangle) = 1\} \equiv (En)(\langle \alpha, i \rangle \in \check{p}_n[\{i\}]).$$

It follows that

$$\alpha \in \mathrm{Dom}\,(\check{G}_i) \equiv (En)\alpha \in \mathrm{Dom}\,(\check{p}_n[\{i\}]),$$

$$\alpha \in X \equiv (i)_{T_h}(En)(\alpha \in \mathrm{Dom}\,\check{p}_n[\{i\}]).$$

If $\alpha$ satisfies this condition then for each $i \in T_h$ there is an $n = n_i$ such that $\alpha \in \mathrm{Dom}\,(\check{p}_n[\{i\}])$. Selecting the largest of the $n_i$ and denoting it with $n$ we obtain (in view of the inclusions $\check{p}_n[\{i\}] \supseteq \check{p}_{n_i}[\{i\}]$) the result $\alpha \in \cap_{i \in T_h} \mathrm{Dom}\,(\check{p}_n[\{i\}])$. Conversely, if $\alpha$ belongs to this intersection, then it obviously belongs to $\mathrm{Dom}\,(\check{G}_i)$ for each $i \in T_h$. Thus

$$X = \underset{n}{\cup}\ \underset{i \in T_h}{\cap}\ \mathrm{Dom}\,(\check{p}_n[\{i\}]) = \underset{n}{\cup}\ \{\alpha_{\varphi(0)}, \alpha_{\varphi(1)}, \dots, \alpha_{\varphi(n-1)}\}$$

$$= \{\alpha_{\varphi(i)} : i \in \omega\}.$$

Since $X \in M''$ and the theorem on inductive definitions is valid in $M''$, we infer that there is a function $f$ in $M''$ with domain $\omega$ such that $f(0) = \alpha_{\varphi(0)}$, $f(k+1) = \min\,\{\xi \in X : \xi > f(k)\}$. Hence $f(k) = \alpha_{\varphi(k)}$. Since $\alpha_{\varphi(n)} > \alpha_n$, we obtain the result $(\xi)_{\mathrm{On}_M}(Ek)_\omega(f(k) > \xi)$ which clearly contradicts the assumption $M \models \mathsf{GBC}$. Thus, (∗∗) is proved.

We now indicate the construction of sequences $\{p_n\}$, $\{\varphi(n)\}$. We start with the void function $p_0$ and assume that $p_n$, satisfying (1)–(4), has already been constructed.

We first extend $p_n[\{0\}]$ to a condition $\bar{q}_0 \in D_{n+1}[\{0\}]$ and add to $p_n$ all the pairs $\langle\langle \xi, 0 \rangle, \in \rangle$ which belong to $\bar{q}_0 - p_n$ as well as pairs $\langle\langle \xi, i \rangle, 0 \rangle$ for $i \ne 0$, $\xi \in \mathrm{dom}\,(\bar{q}_0) - \mathrm{dom}\,(p_n)$. The resulting condition $p_{0n}$ has the properties:

$$p_{0n} \leqslant p_n, \qquad p_{0n}[\{0\}] = \bar{q}_0 \in D_{n+1}[\{0\}]$$

$$\underset{i \in T_h}{\cap} \mathrm{Dom}\,(\check{p}_{0n}[\{i\}]) = \{\alpha_{\varphi(0)}, \dots, \alpha_{\varphi(n-1)}\}$$

The first two properties are obvious. To prove the third we note that if $\alpha \in \mathrm{Dom}\,(\check{p}_{0n}[\{i\}])$ then $p_{0n}(\langle \alpha, i \rangle) = 1$ and this is possible only if either $\alpha \in \mathrm{Dom}\,(\check{p}_n[\{i\}])$ or $i = 0$. Since $|T_h| \geqslant 2$, the desired equation follows.

In the next step we extend $p_{0n}$. We start by selecting a $\bar{q}_1 \leqslant p_{0n}i$ such that $\bar{q}_1 \in D_{n+1}[\{1\}]$ and then extend $p_{0n}$ to $p_{1n}$ by adding to $p_{0n} \cup \bar{q}_1$ all the pairs $\langle\langle \xi, i \rangle, 0 \rangle$ where $i \ne 1$ and $\mathrm{dom}\,(p_{0n}) \leqslant \xi < \mathrm{dom}\,(\bar{q}_1)$. Again, we have

$$p_{1n} \leqslant p_{0n}, \qquad p_{1n}[\{1\}] \leqslant \bar{q}_1 \in D_{n+1}[\{1\}],$$

$$\underset{i \in T_h}{\cap} \mathrm{Dom}\,(\check{p}_{1n}[\{i\}]) = \{\alpha_{\varphi(0)}, \alpha_{\varphi(1)}, \dots, \alpha_{\varphi(n-1)}\}.$$

The condition $p_{1n}$ is extended next to $p_{2n}$ by adding to $p_{1n}$ a condition $\bar{q}_2 \leqslant p_{1n}[\{2\}]$ which belongs to $D_{n+1}[\{2\}]$ as well as pairs $\langle\langle \xi, i \rangle, 0 \rangle$ where $i \ne 2$ and $\mathrm{dom}\,(p_{1n}) \leqslant \xi < \mathrm{dom}\,(\bar{q}_2)$. Continuing in this way we finally obtain a condition $p_{N-1,n} = q_n$ satisfying the formulas:

$$q_n \leqslant p_n, \qquad q_n[\{i\}] \text{ is covered by } D_{n+1}[\{i\}],$$

$$\bigcap_{i \in T_h} \text{Dom}(\check{q}_n[\{i\}]) = \{\alpha_{\varphi(0)}, \alpha_{\varphi(1)}, \dots, \alpha_{\varphi(n-1)}\}.$$

In the next $k$-steps we extend $q_n$ so as to obtain conditions $q_{jn}$ such that $D_{n+1}[S_j]$ covers $q_{jn}[S_j]$ for each $j < k$. We start by extending $q_n[S_0]$ to $\bar{r}_0$ in $D_{n+1}[S_0]$, then add $\bar{r}_n$ to $q_n$ and also add to $q_n$ all the pairs $\langle\langle\xi,i\rangle,0\rangle$ where $i \notin S_0$ and $\text{dom}(q_n) \leqslant \xi < \text{dom}(\bar{r}_0)$. In the second step we extend the condition $q_{0n}$ just constructed as follows: let $\bar{r}_1 \in D_{n+1}[S_1]$ be an extension of $q_{0n}[S_1]$; we add to $q_{0n} \cup \bar{r}_1$ all the pairs $\langle\langle\xi,i\rangle,0\rangle$ where $i \neq 1$ and $\text{dom}(q_{0n}) \leqslant \xi < \text{dom}(\bar{r}_1)$. We continue in this way until we reach a condition $q_{N-1,n}$ which we abbreviate as $r_n$. It is easy to prove

$$q_n \geqslant r_n, \qquad r_n[S_j] \text{ is covered by } D_{n+1}[S_j] \text{ for each } j < k.$$

We show that

$$\bigcap_{i \in T_h} \text{Dom}(\check{r}_n[\{i\}]) = \{\alpha_{\varphi(0)}, \alpha_{\varphi(1)}, \dots, \alpha_{\varphi(n-1)}\}.$$

Assume that $\alpha$ belongs to the left-hand side, i.e. $r_n(\langle\alpha,i\rangle) = 1$ for each $i \in T_h$. If $\alpha \geqslant \text{dom}(p_n)$, then there exists a $j < k$ such that $q_{jn}(\langle\alpha,i\rangle) = 1$ and $\text{dom}(q_{j-1,n}) \leqslant \alpha < \text{dom}(q_{jn})$ (in case $j = 0$ we replace $q_{j-1,n}$ by $q_n$). This equation is possible only if $i \in S_j$. Hence if $\alpha$ belongs to the left-hand side of the above equation, then for each $i$ in $T_h$ there is a $j_i$ such that $i \in S_{j_i}$ and $\text{dom}(q_{j_i-1,n}) \leqslant \alpha < \text{dom}(q_{j_in})$. From these inequalities it follows that $j_i$ is independent of $i$ and can be denoted by $j$. But then $i \in S_j$ for each $i$ in $T_h$ which contradicts our assumption that $|T_h| \geqslant 2$ and $T_h - S_j \neq \emptyset$.

In the last step of our construction we define $\varphi(n)$. Let $\beta_n = \text{dom}(r_n)$. Hence $\beta_n \geqslant \alpha_{\varphi(n-1)}$. Let $\varphi(n)$ be the least integer such that $\alpha_{\varphi(n)} > \beta_n$ and $\alpha_{\varphi(n)} > \alpha_n$. We extend $r_n$ to $p_{n+1}$ by adding all the pairs $\langle\langle\xi,i\rangle,0\rangle$, where $i < N$, $\beta_n \leqslant \xi < \alpha_{\varphi(n)}$ and also the pairs $\langle\langle\alpha_{\varphi(n)},i\rangle,1\rangle$, where $i < N$. Formulas (1)–(4) are then clearly satisfied with $n$ replaced by $n + 1$. Lemma 3.1 is thus proved.

## 4. Models for the Gödel–Bernays set theory

In order to express the main results we now describe some special trees.

Let $N \in \omega$, and let the family of all non-void subsets of $\{0, 1, \dots, N - 1\}$ be partitioned into two families $A \cup B$ such that

(1) $A$ contains with any set $X$ all the non-void subsets of $X$, and $B$ contains with any set $Y$ all the non-void super-sets of $Y$;

(2) if $X \in A$ and $Y \in B$, then $Y - X \neq \emptyset$;

(3) if $Y \in B$, then $|Y| \geqslant 2$;

(4) $\cup A = \{0, 1, \dots, N - 1\}$.

We denote by $S_0, S_1, \ldots, S_{k-1}$ the maximal elements of $A$ with more than 1 element. Let $\Delta_N(A,B)$ be a tree with $N + k + 1$ nodes:

$$\{\omega, 0, 1, \ldots, N - 1, \sigma_0, \ldots, \sigma_{k-1}\}.$$

The initial node $\omega$ is connected with the $N$ nodes $0, 1, \ldots, N - 1$ which are said to lie below $\omega : i \leq \omega$. The node $\sigma_j$ is connected with the nodes $i$ such that $i \in S_j$ and lies below these nodes (i.e. $\sigma_j \leq i$ iff $i \in S_j$). Moreover, we assume that $\omega \geq \sigma_j$ for each $j$. No other pairs of nodes are connected. Nodes which lie below no other nodes are called the terminal nodes of $\Delta_N(A,B)$.

We also consider infinite trees of height $\omega_1$ which arise in the following way: there is just one node $\omega$ of height 0. If nodes of height $< \xi$ and edges connecting them are already defined then we correlate a tree $\Delta_g = \Delta_{Ng}(A_g, B_g)$ to each branch $g$ consisting of nodes already defined and place this tree below all nodes on the branch $g$. Thus, the initial node $\omega_g$ of $\Delta_g$ has height $\xi$ and nodes of $\Delta_g$ lying below $\omega_g$ have heights $\xi + 1$ or $\xi + 2$. Trees of this kind are called $\Delta_{\omega_1}$-trees.

THEOREM 4.1.   *For every denumerable transitive model* $M \models \mathsf{GBC}$ *and every tree* $\Delta = \Delta_N(A,B)$ *with the initial node* $\omega$ *there is a mapping* $\phi$ *of nodes of* $\Delta$ *into a family of transitive denumerable C-extensions of* $M$ *satisfying the following conditions*:

(1)  $\phi(\omega) = M$;

(2)  $\phi(w) \models \mathsf{GBC}$ *for each node* $w$;

(3)  *if* $w_1 \leq w_2$, *then* $\phi(w_1) \supseteq \phi(w_2)$;

(4)  $\phi(w_1)$ *and* $\phi(w_2)$ *have no joint C-extension* $M' \models \mathsf{GBC}$ *unless there is a* $w$ *such that* $w \leq w_1$ *and* $w \leq w_2$.

THEOREM 4.2.   *For every* $M$ *as in Theorem* 4.1 *and every* $\Delta_{\omega_1}$*-tree* $\Delta$ *there is a mapping* $\phi$ *of nodes of* $\Delta$ *into a family of transitive denumerable C-extensions of* $M$ *satisfying the same conditions* (1)–(4) *as in Theorem* 4.1.

Theorem 4.2 results immediately from Theorem 4.1 and Lemma 2.1.

To prove Theorem 4.1 we denote by $S_0, \ldots, S_{k-1}$, the maximal elements of $A$, and by $T_0, \ldots, T_{l-1}$, the minimal elements of $B$, construct models $M_0, M_1, \ldots, M_{N-1}, M'_0, \ldots, M'_{k-1}$ as in Lemma 3.1 and put $\phi(\omega) = M$, $\phi(i) = M_i$, $\phi(\sigma_j) = M'_j$. Conditions (1), (2), (3) of Theorem 4.1 are obviously satisfied. To prove (4) we note that if $w_1 = i_1$, $w_2 = i_2$ and there is a $w$ such that $w \leq w_1$, $w \leq w_2$ then $i_1, i_2 \in S_j$ for some $j$ and thus a common extension $\phi(w)$ exists. Otherwise $i_1, i_2$ must belong to a set $Y$ in $B$ and thus $i_1, i_2$ is one of the $T_h$ and therefore no common extension of $\phi(w_1)$, $\phi(w_2)$ exists. Now consider the case when one of the nodes $w_1, w_2$ is of the form $\sigma_j$, e.g. $w_1 = \sigma_j$. If $w_2 = i$ and $w_1$ non $\leqslant w_2$ then $i \not\in S_j$ and therefore $S_j \cup \{i\}$ contains one of the sets $T_h$. Thus no common extension of $M'_j$ and $M_i$ exists because otherwise there would exist an extension of all the $M_{i_1}$, $i_1 \in T_h$. Similarly if $w_2 = \sigma_{j'}$ there cannot be a joint extension of $M_j$ and $M_{j'}$ because $S_j \cup S_{j'}$ contains one of the sets $T_h$.

EXAMPLE. Let $N = 6$ and $A$ consist of the four sets

$$S_0 = \{0,1\}, \quad S_1 = \{1,2,3\}, \quad S_2 = \{2,3,4\}, \quad S_3 = \{5\}$$

and of their non-void subsets. The family $A$ has 14 sets. Let $B$ consist of the remaining 49 non-void subsets of 0, 1, 2, 3, 4, 5. The tree $\Delta_6(A,B)$ has the following form:

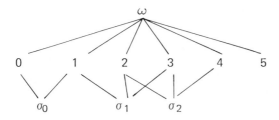

Theorems 4.1 and 4.2 show how complicated the family of transitive $C$-extensions $M \models \mathsf{GBC}$ of a given transitive denumerable model $M$ of GBC is.

From Theorem 4.2, we obtain

COROLLARY 4.1. *Given a transitive denumerable model $M \models \mathsf{GBC}$, there exists $2^{\omega_1}$ transitive $C$-extensions $M \models \mathsf{GBC}$ of power $\omega_1$.*

PROOF. To prove this we consider the full binary tree of height $\omega_1$ and a function $\phi$ as described in Theorem 4.2 by Lemma 2.1 the union $\cup \phi(w)$ taken over nodes $w$ lying on a branch $g$ gives us a $C$-extension $M_g$ of $M$ of power $\omega_1$ such that $M_g \models \mathsf{GBC}$ and for different branches $g_1$, $g_2$, we obtain different models.

Observing that models $M_{g_1}$, $M_{g_2}$ corresponding to two different branches do not have a common transitive $C$-extension, we obtain furthermore

COROLLARY 4.2. *There are at least $2^{\omega_1}$ maximal-transitive models $M \models \mathsf{GBC}$ with a given denumerable $V_M$.*

Under the assumption of the continuum hypothesis, this estimate of the number of maximal-transitive models with a given denumerable $V_M$ is sharp. Without this assumption, no such sharp estimate exists but it seems probable that Martin's axiom implies that their number is $2^{2^{\aleph_0}}$.

## 5. Models for the predicative arithmetic of second order

A Gödel–Bernays-type extension of a theory is possible not only for the theory ZF but for arbitrary first-order theories. Let us consider briefly the Gödel–Bernays-type extension of Peano's arithmetic $\mathscr{P}$. A detailed description of $\mathscr{P}$ can be found, e.g. in KLEENE [1952], p. 82. We extend $\mathscr{P}$ by adding to it a new sort of variable $X, Y, Z, \ldots$ called set variables and a binary predicate $\in$. Formulas with no bound-set variables are called predicative. As axioms of the extended theory we take axioms of Peano's system (Kleene's axioms 14–21) as well as the following ones:

(A1)    $(x = y) \rightarrow [(x \in X) \equiv (y \in Y)]$,
(A2)    $(X = Y) \equiv (x)[(x \in X) \equiv (x \in Y)]$,
(A3)    $(EX)(x)[(x \in X) \equiv \varphi]$   (set existence scheme),
(A4)    $(0 \in X) \,\&\, (x)[x \in X \rightarrow (x' \in X)] \rightarrow (x \in X)$.

In the set-existence scheme, $\varphi$ can be any predicative formula in which $X$ does not occur. The resulting system will be called predicative arithmetic of second order and denoted by $A_{pr}$. It is possible to replace the predicative set-existence scheme by a finite number of axioms as it is done in the case of set theory.

Models of $A_{pr}$ can be assumed to have the form $(\Omega, S, 0, ', +, \cdot, \in)$ where $(\Omega, 0, ', +, \cdot)$ is a model of Peano arithmetic and $S \subseteq P(\Omega)$. Moreover, $\Omega$ can be assumed to have as its initial segment the set $\Omega_0$ of ordinary integers. The operations $', +, \cdot$ restricted to $\Omega_0$ coincide with the usual arithmetical operations and 0 is the integer zero. If $\Omega = \Omega_0$ then the model $(\Omega, S, 0, ', +, \cdot, \in)$ is an $\omega$-model. If $M_i = (\Omega, S_i, 0, ', +, \cdot, \in)$ for $i = 1, 2$ and $S_1 \subseteq S_2$, then we say that $M_2$ is a $C$-extension of $M_1$. Later, we shall abbreviate our notation for models and write $(\Omega, S)$ instead of $(\Omega, S, ', 0, +, \cdot, \in)$.

LEMMA 5.1 *Lemma 2.1 (mutatis mutandis) holds for models of $A_{pr}$.*

We define the family $\text{Def}_M$ and $\text{Def}_M(X)$ similarly as on p. 326. If $\Omega \models \mathscr{P}$, then $(\Omega, \text{Def}_\Omega) \models A_{pr}$. Similarly, if $M = (\Omega, S) \models A_{pr}$, then $(\Omega, \text{Def}_M) \models A_{pr}$. Instead of Lemma 2.2, we have the following result: If $(\Omega, S) \models A_{pr}$ and $X \subseteq \Omega$, then all the axioms of $A_{pr}$ with the possible exception of (A4) hold in $(\Omega, \text{Def}_M(X))$.

The notion of a generic set is defined similarly as on p. 4 (cf. SIMPSON [∞]). We can prove easily (cf. SIMPSON [∞]) that if $(\Omega, M) \models A_{pr}$, $\Omega \cup M$ is denumerable and $P \in \text{Def}_M$ is a set partially ordered by a relation $R \in \text{Def}_M$ then generic sets $G \subseteq P$ exist. Moreover, $(\Omega, \text{Def}_M(G)) \models A_{pr}$.

Our main results are as follows:

THEOREM 5.1. *Given an integer N, a tree* $\Delta = \Delta_N(A,B)$ *and a model* $M = (\Omega,S) \models A_{\mathrm{pr}}$ *such that* $\overline{\Omega \cup S} = \omega$ *and* $\Omega \neq \Omega_0$, *then there exists a mapping $\phi$ of the nodes of $\Delta$ into denumerable C-extensions of M such that*
  (1) *the initial node of $\Delta$ is mapped onto M,*
  (2) *if $w_1$, $w_2$ are nodes of $\Delta$, then $\phi(w_1) \supseteq \phi(w_2)$ is equivalent to* $w_1 \leqslant w_2$;
  (3) *if $w_1$, $w_2$ are nodes of $\Delta$, then $\phi(w_1)$, $\phi(w_2)$ have a joint C-extension which is a model of $A_{\mathrm{pr}}$ iff there exists a w such that $w \leqslant w_1$ and $w \leqslant w_2$.*

THEOREM 5.2. *Theorem 5.1 holds if one replaces $\Delta_N(A,B)$ by a $\Delta_{\omega_1}$-tree.*

These theorems are proved essentially as Theorems 4.1 and 4.2. The crucial lemma corresponding to Lemma 3.1 is proved by considering conditions which are finite two-valued functions with domains of the form $\{x : x \leqslant n\} \times N$, where $n \in \Omega$ and $\leqslant$ is the "less-than" relation of the model $\Omega$. The word "finite" is meant here in the sense of $\Omega$ and the whole function has to be coded by a single element of $\Omega$.

We fix an increasing sequence $\{a_n\}$, $n \in \Omega_0$ of elements of $\Omega$ which is cofinal with $\Omega$. This sequence does not belong to the model. We arrange the construction of generic sets $G_i$, $i < N$, in such a way that the intersections $\cap_{i \in T_h} \mathrm{Dom}(\breve{G}_i)$ be equal to a set $X$ consisting of infinitely many $a_n$'s. This is possible because for each condition $p$ only finitely many $a_n$'s can belong to dom $(p)$.

We show that there is no model $(\Omega,S^*)$ of $A_{\mathrm{pr}}$ such that $S^* \supseteq \cup \{S_i : i \in T_h\}$. Otherwise, the set $X$ would be an element of $S^*$. Using the theorem on inductive definitions we could then find in $S^*$ a functional set $f$ whose domain is a segment of $\Omega$ such that $f(0) = a_0$, $f(x + 1) = $ the least element of $X$ greater than $f(x)$. Thus, the domain of $f$ would be the set of standard integers which is a contradiction because this set belongs to no model $(\Omega,S^*)$ of $A_{\mathrm{pr}}$.

It is rather remarkable that we have here a complete analogy between models of GBC and models of $A_{\mathrm{pr}}$ with non-standard integers. For models of $A_{\mathrm{pr}}$ with standard integers Theorems 5.1 and 5.2 are false because any two such models have a joint C-extension.

### References

FELGNER, U. (1971) Comparison of the axioms of local and universal choice. *Fundamenta Mathematicae* 71, 43–62.

GÖDEL, K. (1940) *The consistency of the axiom of choice and of the generalized continuum hypothesis with the axioms of set theory.* Annals of Math. Studies. Vol. 3. Princeton University Press, Princeton, N.J., 66 pp. (7th printing (1966).)

KLEENE, S. C. (1952) *Introduction to metamathematics.* North-Holland, Amsterdam, 550 pp. (2nd printing (1957).)

SIMPSON, S. G. (∞) Forcing and models for arithmetic. *Proceedings of the American Mathematical Society.* (To appear.)

VOPĚNKA, P. and HÁJEK, P. (1972) *The Theory of Semisets.* North-Holland, Amsterdam, 332 pp.

SETS AND CLASSES; On the work by Paul Bernays
© North-Holland Publishing Company (1976) pp. 341–352.

# BIBLIOGRAPHY

ACKERMANN, W. (1937) Die Widerspruchsfreiheit der allgemeinen Mengenlehre. *Math. Annalen* **114**, 305–315.

ACKERMANN, W. (1956) Zur Axiomatik der Mengenlehre. *Math. Annalen* **131**, 336–345.

ACZEL, P. and RICHTER, W. (1970) Inductive definitions and analogues of large cardinals. In *Conference in Math. Logic, London '70*, W. Hodges (Ed.), pp. 1–9. Springer Lecture Notes in Mathematics, Vol. 255. Springer, Berlin. 351 pp.

ADDISON, J. W., HENKIN, L., and TARSKI, A. (Eds.) (1965) *The theory of models*. Proceedings of the 1963 international Symposium at Berkeley. North-Holland, Amsterdam. 494 pp. (2nd printing (1972), 509 pp.)

ASSER, G. (1957) Theorie der logischen Auswahlfunktionen. *Zeitschr. f. Math. Logik* **3**, 30–68.

BAR-HILLEL, Y., POZNANSKI, E. I. J., RABIN, M. O., and ROBINSON, A. (Eds.) (1961) *Essays on the foundations of mathematics*. (Dedicated to A. A. Fraenkel.) Magnes Press, Jerusalem. 351 pp.

BARWISE, J. (1969) Infinitary logic and admissible sets. *J.S.L.* **34**, 226–252.

BARWISE, J. (1971) *Infinitary methods in the model theory of set theory*, pp. 53–56. In GANDY and YATES (1971).

BELL, J. L. and SLOMSON, A. (1969) *Models and ultraproducts: An introduction*. North-Holland, Amsterdam, 322 pp. (1st revised reprint (1971).)

BERNAYS, P. (1937–1954) A system of axiomatic set theory; I–VII. *J.S.L.* I: **2**, 65–77 (1937); II: **6**, 1–17 (1941); III: **7**, 65–89 (1942); IV: **7**, 133–145 (1942); V: **8**, 89–106 (1943); VI: **13**, 65–79 (1948); VII: **19**, 81–96 (1954). This volume.

BERNAYS, P. (1958) *Axiomatic set theory* (with a historical introduction by A. A. Fraenkel). North-Holland, Amsterdam. 226 pp. (2nd ed. (1968), 235 pp.).

BERNAYS, P. (1961) Zur Frage der Unendlichkeitsschemata in der axiomatischen Mengenlehre. In BAR-HILLEL et al. (1961), pp. 3–49. This volume (English translation—revised version).

BOFFA, M. (1968) Les ensembles extraordinaire. *Bull. Soc. Math. Belgique* **20**, 3–15.

BOFFA, M. (1968a) Elimination de cycles d'appartenance par permutation de l'univers. *C.R. Acad. Sci. Paris* **266**, 545–546.

BOFFA, M. (1971) Forcing and reflection. *Bull. Acad. Polon. Sc.* **19**, 181–183.

BOREL, E. (1898) *Leçons sur la théorie des fonctions.* Gauthiers Villars, Paris (1898). 2nd ed. (1914), 260 pp.; 3rd [4th] ed. (1928) [1950]. (Cf. *Math. Annalen* **60**, 194–195 (1905), and *Rev. du Mois* **1**, 248–250 (1906).)

BOWEN, K. A. (1972) The relative consistency of some consequences of the existence of measurable cardinal numbers. *Dissertationes Math.* Warszawa. 63 pp.

BULOFF, J. J., HOLYOKE, T. C., and HAHN, S. W. (Eds.) (1969) *Foundations of mathematics.* (Symposium papers commemorating the sixtieth birthday of Kurt Gödel.) Springer, Berlin. 195 pp.

CHANG, C. C. and KEISLER, H. J. (1973) *Model theory.* North-Holland, Amsterdam, 550 pp.

CHUAQUI, R. (1972) Forcing for the impredicative theory of classes. *J.S.L.* **37**, 1–18.

CHURCH, A. (1927) Alternatives to Zermelo's assumption. *Trans. A.M.S.* **29**, 178–208.

CHURCH, A. (1956) *Introduction to mathematical logic*—I. Princeton University Press, Princeton, N.J., 376 pp.

COHEN, P. J. (1966) *Set theory and the continuum hypothesis.* Benjamin, New York, 160 pp.

COHEN, P. J. (1974). Models of set theory with more real numbers than ordinals. *J.S.L.* **39**, 579–583.

DEDEKIND, R. (1888) *Was sind und was sollen die Zahlen?* 6th ed.: F. Vieweg & Sohn, Braunschweig (1930), 58 pp.; also in DEDEKIND (1930–1932) III. English ed. by W. W. Beman, in: *Essays on the theory of numbers* by R. Dedekind. Chicago and London (1901).

DEDEKIND, R. (1930–1932) *Gesammelte mathematische Werke.* R. Fricke, E. Noether and O. Ore (Eds.). 3 vols. F. Vieweg & Sohn, Braunschweig.

DOETS, H. C. (1969) Novak's result by Henkin's method. *Fund. Math.* **64**, 329–333.

EASTON, W. B. (1964) Powers of regular cardinals. Ph.D. thesis. Princeton University. 66 pp.

EASTON, W. B. (1970) Powers of regular cardinals. *Ann. of Math. Logic* **1**, 139–178.

ERDÖS, P. and HAJNAL, A. (1958) On the structure of set mappings. *Acta Math. Acad. Sci. Hung.* **9**, 111–131.

ERDÖS, P. and HAJNAL, A. (1962) Some remarks concerning our paper "On the structure of set mappings". *Ibid.* **13**, 223–226.

FEFERMAN, S. (1965) Some applications of the notions of forcing and generic sets. *Fund. Math.* **56**, 325–345. (Summary in ADDISON et al. (1965), pp. 89–95.)

FELGNER, U. (1971) Comparison of the axioms of local and universal choice. *Fund. Math.* **71**, 43–62.

FELGNER, U. (1971a) *Models of* ZF-*set theory.* Springer Lecture Notes in Mathematics, Vol. 223. Springer, Berlin. 173 pp.

FELGNER, U. and JECH, Th. J. (1973) Variants of the axiom of choice in set theory with atoms. *Fund. Math.* **79**, 79–85.

FEYS, R. (1944) *Logistiek.* Philosophische Biblotheek N.V., Antwerpen and Nijmegen.

FINSLER, P. (1926) Über die Grundlegung der Mengenlehre—I. Teil. Die Mengen und ihre Axiome. *Math. Zeitschr.* **25**, 683–713.

FIRESTONE, C. D. (1948) Review of Bernays' article: A system of axiomatic set theory—Part VI. *J.S.L.* **13**, 220–221.

FLANNAGAN, T. B. (1973) Ph.D. thesis, London.

FLANNAGAN, T. B. (1974) Set theories incorporating Hilbert's ε-symbol. *Dissertationes Math.* **154**. Warszawa.

FLANNAGAN, T. B. (1976) A new finitary proof of a theorem of Mostowski. This volume.

FRAENKEL, A. A. (1922) Zu den Grundlagen der Cantor-Zermeloschen Mengenlehre. *Math. Annalen* **86**, 230–237. (Cf. already Jahresber. D.M.V. 30 p. 97 ital. (1921).)

FRAENKEL, A. A. (1922a) Über den Begriff "definit" und die Unabhängigkeit des Auswahlaxioms. *Sitzungsberichte der Preuss.*

*Akademie d. Wiss.*, Phys.–Math. Klasse, pp. 253–257. (English translation in VAN HEIJENOORD (1967), pp. 284–289.)

FRAENKEL, A. A. (1925) Untersuchungen über die Grundlagen der Mengenlehre. *Math. Zeitschr.* **22**, 250–273.

FRAENKEL, A. A. (1927) *Zehn Vorlesungen über die Grundlegung der Mengenlehre.* Springer, Berlin, 182 pp.

FRAENKEL, A. A. (1927a) Über die Gleichheitsbeziehung in der Mengenlehre. *J. f. Math.* **157**, 79–81.

FRAENKEL, A A. (1928) *Einleitung in die Mengenlehre*, 3rd ed. Springer, Berlin, 424 pp. Reprinted (1964).

FRAENKEL, A. A. (1937) Über eine abgeschwächte Fassung des Auswahlaxioms. *J.S.L.* **2**, 1–25.

FRAENKEL, A. A , BAR-HILLEL, Y., LÉVY, A. and DALEN, D. VAN (1973) *Foundations of set theory.* North-Holland, Amsterdam, 404 pp.

FRIEDMAN, H. ($\infty$) Large models with countable height. *J.S.L.*, to appear.

GAIFMAN, H. (1967) A generalization of Mahlo's method for obtaining large cardinal numbers. *Israel J. Math.* **5**, 188–201.

GAIFMAN, H. (1968) Two results concerning extensions of models of set theory (abstract). *Notices A.M.S.* **15**, 947 pp.

GANDY, R. O. and YATES, C. E. M. (Eds.) (1971) *Logic colloquium '69.* Proceedings of the summer school and colloquium in mathematical logic, Manchester, August 1969. North-Holland, Amsterdam. 451 pp.

GLOEDE, K. (1970) Reflection principles and large cardinals. Ph.D. thesis. Heidelberg. 129 pp.

GLOEDE, K. (1971) Filters closed under Mahlo's and Gaifman's operation. In *Proceedings of the Cambridge Summer School in Mathematical Logic*, August 1971. pp. 495–530. A. R. D. Mathias and H. Rogers (Eds.) Springer Lecture Notes in Mathematics, Vol. 337. Springer, Berlin. 660 pp.

GLOEDE, K. (1972) Ordinals with partition properties and the constructible hierarchy. *Zeitschr. f. math. Logik* **18**, 135–164.

GÖDEL, K. (1938) The consistency of the axiom of choice and of the generalized continuum hypothesis. *Acad. U.S.A.* **24**, 556–567.

GÖDEL, K. (1939) Consistency proof for the generalized continuum hypothesis. *Ibid.* **25**, 220–224.

Gödel, K. (1940) *The consistency of the axiom of choice and of the generalized continuum hypothesis with the axioms of set theory.* Annals of Math. Studies, Vol. 3. Princeton University Press, Princeton, N.J., 66 pp. (7th printing (1966).)

Grelling, K. (1910) Die Axiome der Arithmetik. (Dissertation, Göttingen.)

Grišin, V. N. (1972) The theory of Zermelo–Fraenkel sets with Hilbert $\epsilon$-terms. *Math. Notes Acad. Sci. U.S.S.R.* **12**, 779–783.

Hájek, P. (1965) Modelle der Mengenlehre in denen Mengen gegebener Gestalt existieren. *Zeitschr. f. math. Logik* **11**, 103–115.

Hartogs, F. (1915) Über das Problem der Wohlordnung. *Math. Annalen* **76**, 438–443.

Hasenjaeger, G. (1953) Eine Bemerkung zu Henkin's Beweis für die Vollständigkeit des Prädikatenkalküls der ersten Stufe. *J.S.L.* **18**, 42–48.

Hanf, W. and Scott, D. (1961) Classifying inaccessible cardinals (abstract). *Notices A.M.S.* **8**, 445.

Heijenoort, J. van (Ed.) (1967) *From Frege to Gödel—a source book in mathematical logic, 1879–1931.* Harvard University Press, Cambridge, Mass., 660 pp.

Henkin, L. (1949) The completeness of the first-order functional calculus. *J.S.L.* **14**, 159–166.

Hessenberg, G. (1906) *Grundbegriffe der Mengenlehre.* (Abh. der Friesschen Schule, N.S. [1] Heft 4.) Göttingen, 220 pp.

Hilbert, D. and Bernays, P. (1934–1939) *Grundlagen der Mathematik* I (1934); II (1939). Springer, Berlin. 471; 498 pp. (2nd edition (1968; 1970), 488; 575 pp.)

Isbell, J. R. (1963) Two set-theoretical theorems in categories. *Fund. Math.* **53**, 43–49.

Isbell, J. R. and Wright, F. B. (1966) Another equivalent form of the axiom of choice. *Proc. A.M.S.* **17**, 174.

Jech, Th. J. (1973) *The axiom of choice.* North-Holland, Amsterdam. 203 pp.

Jensen, R. B. (1967) *Modelle der Mengenlehre.* Springer Lecture Notes in Mathematics, Vol. 37. Springer, Berlin. 176 pp.

JENSEN, R. B. (1967a) Große Kardinalzahlen. (Notes of lectures given at Oberwolfach (Germany).) 121 pp.

JENSEN, R. B. (1972) The fine structure of the constructible hierarchy. *Annals of Math. Logic*, vol. 4, 229–308.

JENSEN, R. B. and KARP, C. (1971) *Primitive recursive set functions*, pp. 143–176. In SCOTT (1971).

KEISLER, H. J. and TARSKI, A. (1964) From accessible to inaccessible cardinals. *Fund. Math.* 53, 225–308. Corrections, *ibid.* (1965) 57, 119.

KEISLER, H. J. and ROWBOTTOM, F. (1965) Constructible sets and weakly compact cardinals (abstract). *Notices A.M.S.* 12, 373–374.

KELLEY, J. L. (1955) *General topology.* Van Nostrand, New York. 298 pp.

KLEENE, S. C. (1935) A theory of positive integers in formal logic. *American J. of Math.* 57, pp. 153–173 and pp. 219–244 (especially the passage from theorem 15-IV to 15-V, pp. 220–221).

KLEENE, S. C. (1952) *Introduction to metamathematics.* Amsterdam. 550 pp. (2nd printing (1957).)

KÖNIG, J. (1905) Zum Kontinuum-Problem, *Math. Annalen* 60.

KORSELT, A. (1911) Über einen Beweis des Äquivalenzsatzes. *Math. Annalen* 70, 294–296.

KREISEL, G. and LÉVY, A. (1968) Reflection principles and their use for establishing the complexity of axiomatic systems. *Zeitschr. f. math. Logik* 14, 97–191.

KRIVINE, J. L. (1971) *Introduction to axiomatic set theory.* Reidel, Dordrecht. 98 pp.

KRUSE, A. H. (1963) A method of modelling the formalism of set theory in axiomatic set theory. *J.S.L.* 28, 20–34.

KRUSE, A. H. (1966) Grothendieck universes and the super-complete models of Sheperdson. *Compositio Math.* 17, 96–101.

KÜHNRICH, M. (1966) Über den Begriff des Universums. *Zeitschr. f. math. Logik* 12, 37–50.

KUNEN, K. (1968) Inaccessibility properties of cardinals. Doctoral Dissertation. Stanford. 117 pp.

KUNEN, K. (1972) The Hanf number of second-order logic. *J.S.L.* 37, 588–594.

KURATA, R. (1964) On the existence of a proper complete model of set theory. *Comm. Math. Univ. Sancti Pauli* **13**, 35–43.

KURATOWSKI, K. (1921) Sur la notion d'ordre dans la théorie des ensembles. *Fund. Math.* **2**, 161–171.

LEISENRING, A. C. (1969) *Mathematical Logic and Hilbert's $\epsilon$-symbol.* Gordon and Breach, New York, 142 pp.

LÉVY, A. (1958) Contributions to the metamathematics of set theory. Ph.D. thesis. Jerusalem.

LÉVY, A. (1959) On Ackermann's set theory. *J.S.L.* **24**, 154–166.

LÉVY, A. (1960) Axiom schemata of strong infinity in axiomatic set theory. *Pacific J. Math.* **10**, 223–238.

LÉVY, A. (1960a) Principles of reflection in axiomatic set theory. *Fund. Math.* **49**, 1–10.

LÉVY, A. (1964) The interdependence of certain consequences of the axiom of choice. *Fund. Math.* **54**, 135–157.

LÉVY, A. (1965) A hierarchy of formulas in set theory. *Memoirs A.M.S.* **57**, 76 pp.

LÉVY, A. (1968) On von Neumann's axiom systems for set theory. *Am. Math. Monthly* **75**, 762–763.

LÉVY, A. (1971) The size of the indescribable cardinals. In SCOTT (1971), pp. 205–218.

LÉVY, A. and VAUGHT, R. L. (1961) Principles of partial reflection in the set theories of Zermelo and Ackermann. *Pacific J. Math.* **11**, 1045–1062.

MacLANE, S. (1961) Locally small categories and the foundations of set theory. *Infinitistic methods*, Warszaw, pp. 25–43.

MAHLO, P. (1911) Über lineare transfinite Mengen. *Berichte über die Verhandlungen der Königlich Sächsischen Akademie der Wissenschaften zu Leipzig.* Math.-Phys. Klasse, **63**, 187–225.

MAHLO, P. (1912–1913) Zur Theory und Anwendung der $\rho_0$-Zahlen, *ibid.*, I: **64**, 108–112 (1912); II: **65**, 268–282 (1913).

MAREK, W. (1973) On the metamathematics of impredicative set theory. *Dissertationes Math.* **98**, Warszaw.

MAREK, W. and ZBIERSKI, P. (1972) Axioms of choice in impredicative set theory. *Bull. Acad. Polon. Sci.* **20**, 255–258.

MARKOV, A. A. (1948) On the dependence of axiom B6 on the other axioms of the Bernays–Gödel system. *Izvéstiyá Akadémii Nauk. SSSR*, ser. mat. Vol. 12, 569–570.

MENDELSON, E. (1956) The independence of a weak axiom of choice. *J.S.L.* **21**, 350–366.

MENDELSON, E. (1964) *Introduction to mathematical logic.* Van Nostrand, New York, 300 pp.

MONTAGUE, R. (1961) Semantical closure and non-finite axiomatizability—I. *Infinitistic methods.* Warszaw, pp. 45–69.

MONTAGUE, R. and VAUGHT, R. L. (1959) Natural models of set theories. *Fund. Math.* **47**, 219–242.

MORRIS, D. B. (1970) Adding total indiscernibles to models of set theory. Dissertation, Wisconsin.

MORSE, A. P. (1965) *A theory of sets.* Academic Press, New York, 130 pp.

MOSCHOVAKIS, Y. N. (1971) *Predicative classes*, pp. 247–264. In SCOTT (1971).

MOSTOWSKI, A. (1939) Über die Unabhängigkeit des Wohlordnungssatzes vom Ordnungsprinzip. *Fund. Math.* **32**, 201–252.

MOSTOWSKI, A. (1949) An undecidable arithmetical statement. *Fund. Math.* **36**, 143–164.

MOSTOWSKI, A. (1951) Some impredicative definitions in the axiomatic set theory. *Fund. Math.* **37**, 111–124. (Corrections, *ibid.* (1952) **38**, 238.)

MOSTOWSKI, A. (1969) *Constructible sets with applications.* North-Holland, Amsterdam. 269 pp.

MYHILL, J. R. (1952) The hypothesis that all classes are nameable. *Acad. U.S.A.* **38**, 979–981.

MYHILL, J. R. (1963) Remark on a system of Bernays. *J.S.L.* **28**, 75–76.

NEUMANN, J. VON (1925) Eine Axiomatisierung der Mengenlehre. *J. f. Math.* **154**, 219–240. Corrections, *ibid.* **155**, 128 (1926). Also in VON NEUMANN (1961) pp. 34–56. (English translation in VAN HEIJENOORT (1967) pp. 393–413.)

NEUMANN, J. VON (1928) Die Axiomatisierung der Mengenlehre. *Math. Zeitschr.* **27**, 669–752. Also in VON NEUMANN (1961) pp. 339–422.

NEUMANN, J. VON (1928a) Über die Definition durch transfinite Induktion und verwandte Fragen der allgemeinen Mengenlehre. *Math. Annalen* **99**, 373–391. Also in VON NEUMANN (1961) pp. 320–338. (Cf. FRAENKEL (1928) pp. 392–393.)

NEUMANN, J. VON (1929) Über eine Widerspruchsfreiheitsfrage in der axiomatischen Mengenlehre. *J. f. Math.* **160**, 227–241; also in VON NEUMANN (1961) pp. 494–508.

NEUMANN, J. VON (1929–1930) Allgemeine Eigenwerttheorie Hermitescher Funktionaloperatoren. *Math. Annalen* **102**, 49–131, in particular Kap. I and Anhang I therein.

NEUMANN, J. VON (1961) *Collected works*. Vol. I. Pergamon, New York. 654 pp.

NOVAK, I. L. (1948) A construction for models of consistent systems. Ph.D. thesis. Harvard.

NOVAK, I. L. (1951) A construction for models of consistent systems. *Fund. Math.* **37**, 87–110.

OBERSCHELP, A. (1964) Eigentliche Klassen als Urelemente in der Mengenlehre. *Math. Annalen* **157**, 234–260.

PÉTER, R. (1941) Review of TEICHMÜLLER (1939), *J.S.L.* **6** (1941), 65–66.

QUINE, W. V. (1937) New foundations for mathematical logic. *Am. Math. Monthly* **44**, 70–80. (A revised and expanded version is in QUINE (1953), pp. 80–101).

QUINE, W. V. (1951) *Mathematical logic* (revised edition). Harvard University Press, Cambridge, Mass., 346 pp. (First edition (1940).)

QUINE, W. V. (1953) *From a logical point of view*. Harvard University Press, Cambridge, Mass., 184 pp.

QUINE, W. V. (1963) *Set theory and its logic*. Belknap Press, Cambridge, Mass., 359 pp. (Revised ed. (1969), 361 pp.)

REINHARDT, W. N. (1967) Topics in the metamathematics of set theory. Doctoral Dissertation, 85 pp.

REINHARDT, W. N. (1970) Ackermann's set theory equals ZF. *Ann. Math. Logic.* **2**, 189–249.

REINHARDT, W. N. and SILVER, J. (1965) On some problems of Erdös and Hajnal (abstract). *Notices A.M.S.* **12**, 723.

ROBINSON, R. M. (1937) The theory of classes—A modification of von Neumann's system. *J.S.L.* **2**, 69–72.

ROBINSON, R. M. (1945) On finite sequences of classes. *J.S.L.* **10**, 125–126.

ROSSER, J. B. and WANG, H. (1950) Non-standard models for formal logics. *J.S.L.* **15**, 113–129. (Errata, *ibid.* p. iv.)

RUBIN, H. and RUBIN, J. E. (1963) *Equivalents of the axiom of choice.* North-Holland, Amsterdam, 134 pp. (2nd ed. (1970).)

RUSSELL, B. (1906) On some difficulties in the theory of transfinite numbers and order types. *Proc. of the London Math. Soc.* **4** (2), 29–53.

SACKS, G. E. (1972) *Saturated model theory.* Benjamin, New York, 335 pp.

SCHMERL, J. H. (1972) An elementary sentence which has ordered models. *J.S.L.* **37**, 521–530.

SCHMERL, J. H. and SHELAH, S. (1972) On power-like models for hyperinaccessible cardinals. *J.S.L.* **37**, 531–537.

SCHÜTTE, K. (1950) Schlussweisen-Kalküle der Prädikatenlogik. *Math. Annalen* **122**, 47–65.

SCOTT, D. (1955) Definitions by abstraction in axiomatic set theory (abstract). *Bull. A.M.S.* **61**, 442.

SCOTT, D. (1961) Measurable cardinals and constructible sets. *Bull. Acad. Polon. Sc.* **9**, 521–524.

SCOTT, D. (Ed.) (1971) *Axiomatic set theory.* Proceedings of symposia in pure math. **13**, Am. Math. Soc., Providence, R.I.

SHEPHERDSON, J. C. (1951–1953) Inner models for set theory. *J.S.L.* **16**, 161–190 (1951); **17**, 225–237 (1952); **18**, 145–167 (1953).

SHOENFIELD, J. R. (1954) A relative consistency proof. *J.S.L.* **19**, 21–28.

SHOENFIELD, J. R. (1967) *Mathematical logic.* Addison-Wesley, Reading, Mass. 344 pp.

SIERPINSKI, W. (1921) Une remarque sur la notion de l'ordre. *Fund. Math.* **2**, 199–200.

SILVER, J. (1966) Some applications of model theory in set theory. Doctoral Dissertation, Berkeley, 110 pp. Published (with the deletion of §4) in SILVER (1971).

SILVER, J. (1971) Some applications of model theory in set theory. *Ann. of Math. Logic* **3**, 45–110.

SIMPSON, S. G. (∞) Forcing and models for arithmetic. *Proceedings of the A.M S.* (To appear.)

SKOLEM, TH. (1923) Einige Bemerkungen zur axiomatischen Begründung der Mengenlehre. Wiss. Vorträge gehalten auf dem 5. Kongress der Skandinav. Mathematiker in Helsingfors, 1922, pp. 217–232. (English translation in VAN HEIJENOORT (1967), pp. 290–301.)

SKOLEM, TH. (1929) Über einige Grundlagenfragen der Mathematik. *Skrifter utgit av det Norske Vid.-Akad. i Oslo* I (4), 1–49.

SOLOVAY, R. M. (1966) On the consistency of Takeuti's TT (abstract). *J.S.L.* **31**, 691.

SPECKER, E. (1952) Habilitationsschrift.

SPECKER, E. (1957) Zur Axiomatik der Mengenlehre (Fundierungs- und Auxwahlaxiom). *Zeitschr. f. math. Logik* **3**, 173–210.

STEGMÜLLER, W. (1962) Eine Axiomatisierung der Mengenlehre beruhend auf den Systemem von Bernays und Quine. In Käsbauer et al. (Eds.) *Logik und Logikkalkül*, pp. 57–103. K. Alber, Freiburg.

STENIUS, E. (1952) Das Interpretationsproblem der formalisierten Zahlentheorie und ihre formale Widerspruchsfreiheit. *Acta Academiae Aboensis* (*Math. et Phys.*) **18** (3), Åbo Akademi, Åbo, 102 pp.

TAKEUTI, G. (1961) Axioms of infinity of set theory. *J. Math. Soc. Japan* **13**, 220–233.

TAKEUTI, G. (1965) On the axiom of constructibility. Proceedings of Symposia of Logic, Computability, and Automata at Rome. Mimeographed Notes, New York.

TAKEUTI, G. (1969) *The universe of set theory*, pp. 74–128. In BULOFF et al. (1969).

TAKEUTI, G. and ZARING, W. M. (1973) *Axiomatic set theory.* Springer, Berlin. 238 pp.

TARSKI, A. (1930) Fundamentale Begriffe der Methodologie der deduktiven Wissenschaften I, *Monatshefte für Mathematik und Physik 37*, Satz I. 56, p. 394.

TARSKI, A. (1938) Über unerreichbare Kardinalzahlen. *Fund. Math.* **30**, 68–89.

TARSKI, A. (1948) Axiomatic and algebraic aspects of two theorems on sums of cardinals. *Fund. Math.* **35**, 79–104.

TARSKI, A. and VAUGHT, R. (1957) Arithmetical extensions of relational systems. *Compositio Math.* **18**, 81–102.

TEICHMÜLLER, O. (1939) Braucht der Algebraiker das Auswahlaxiom? *Deutsche Mathematik*, **4**, 567–577.

THARP, L. (1966) Bernays' set theory and the continuum hypothesis (abstract). *Notices A.M.S.* **13**, 138.

THARP, L. (1967) On a set theory of Bernays. *J.S.L.* **32**, 319–321.

THIELE, E. J. (1955) Ein axiomatisches System der Mengenlehre nach Zermelo und Fraenkel. *Zeitschr. f. math. Logik* **1**, 173–195.

VAUGHT, R. (1963) Indescribable cardinals (abstract). *Notices A.M.S.* **10**, 126.

VOPĚNKA, P. and HÁJEK, P. (1972) *The Theory of Semisets*. North-Holland, Amsterdam, 332 pp.

WANG, H. (1949) On Zermelo's and von Neumann's axioms for set theory. *Acad. Sci. U.S.A.* **35**, 150–155.

WANG, H. (1950) A formal system of logic. *J.S.L.* **15**, 25–32.

ZERMELO, E. (1904) Beweis dass jede Menge wohlgeordnet werden kann. *Math. Annalen* **59**, 514–516. (English translation in VAN HEIJENOORT (1967), pp. 139–141.) (Cf. A. Schoenflies, E. Borel, P. E. B. Jourdain (1905). *Math. Annalen* **60**, 181–186, 194–195, 465–470.)

ZERMELO, E. (1908) Neuer Beweis für die Wohlordnung. *Math. Annalen* **65**, 107–128. (English translation in VAN HEIJENOORT (1967), pp. 181–198.)

ZERMELO, E. (1908a) Untersuchungen über die Grundlagen der Mengenlehre—I. *Math. Annalen* **65**, 261–281. (English translation in VAN HEIJENOORT (1967), pp. 199–215.)

ZERMELO, E. (1909) Sur les ensembles finis et le principe de l'induction complète. *Acta Math.* **32**, 185–193.

ZERMELO, E. (1909a) Über die Grundlagen der Arithmetik. *Atti del IV Congresso Internationale del Matematici* (Roma, 6–11 aprile 1908). Vol. 2, pp. 8–11.

ZERMELO, E. (1930) Über Grenzzahlen und Mengenbereiche. *Fund. Math.* **16**, 29–47.

ZORN, M. (1935) A remark on methods in transfinite algebra. *Bulletin of the A.M.S.* **41**, 667–670.

# INDEX

353

CHAPTER 2. P. BERNAYS: ON THE PROBLEM OF SCHEMATA OF INFINITY IN AXIOMATIC SET THEORY

CHAPTER 3. A. Lévy: The role of classes in set theory

**Axioms**
(I)       (extensionality)   174
(II)      (pairing)   174
(III)     (union)   174
(IV)      (power set)   175
(V)       (schema of subsets)   175
(V^c)     (subsets)   184
(VI)      (infinity)   175
(VII)     (schema of replacement)   175
(VII^c)   (replacement)   185
(VIII)    (local choice)   175
(VIII_σ)  (global choice)   176
(VIII_σ^c) (global choice)   192
(IX)      (schema of foundation)   175
(IX^c)    (foundation)   185
(IX*)     186
(X)       (extensionality for classes)   179
(XI)      (predicative comprehension for classes)   181
(XI 1)    187, (XI 2–8)   188f
(XII)     (impredicative comprehension)   197
(α)–(ξ) (axioms for Ackermann's set theory)   208–210

**Theories**
A   207ff
G   195
QM   197
ST$_2$   201
VNB   176ff, 186f
VNBC   192
VNBC$_σ$   192
ZF, ZFC   174
ZF*   200
ZF$_σ$   176
ZM   200

**Definitions**
pure condition   178
selector   175f

**Symbols**
O   175
Λ   182
V   182

P   202
$R(α)$   202
𝔇, 𝔉nc, 𝔢l   185

CHAPTER 7. A. MOSTOWSKI: A REMARK ON MODELS OF THE GÖDEL–BERNAYS AXIOMS FOR SET THEORY